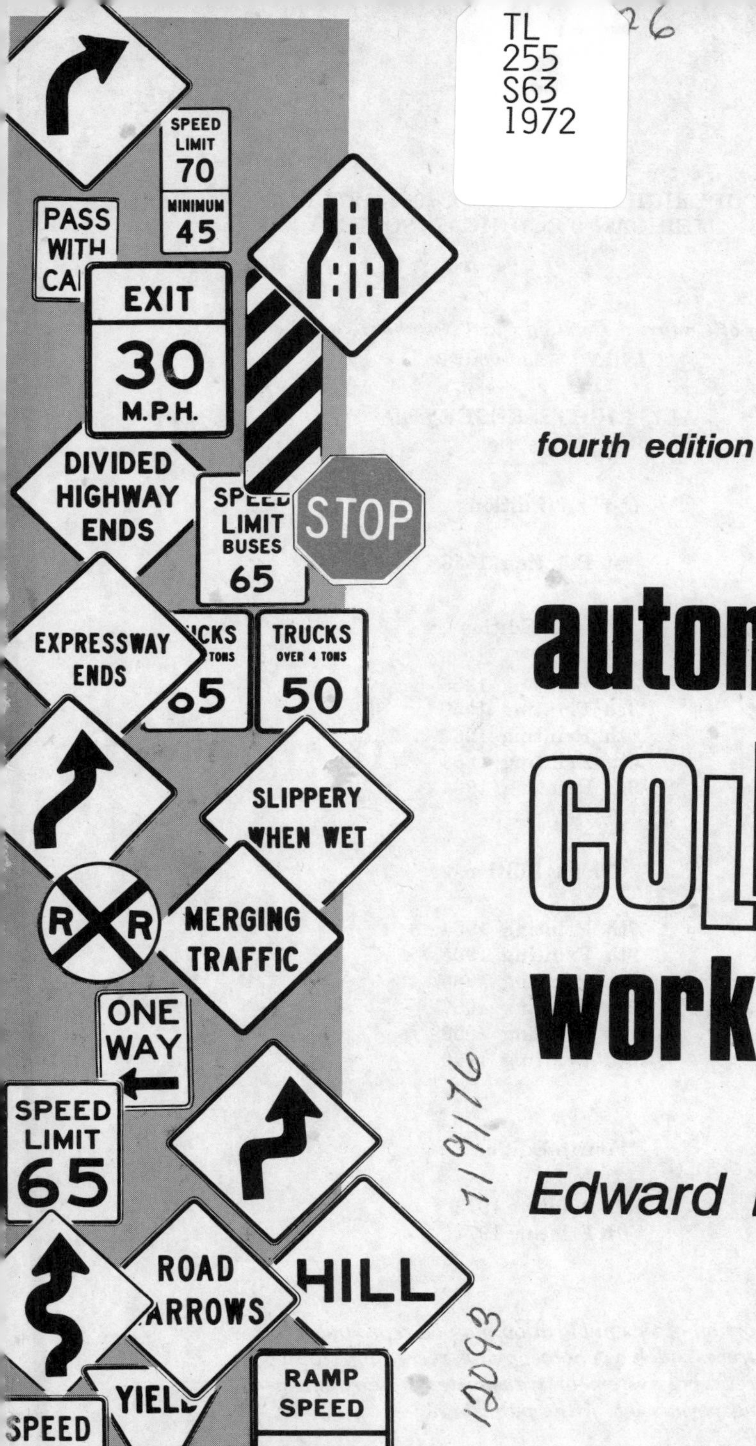

fourth edition

automotive COLLISION work

Edward D. Spicer

American Technical Society  Chicago 60637

Library of Congress Catalog Card Number: 76-175283
ISBN 0-8269-0022-4

First Edition

1st Printing 1953

Second Edition

2nd Printing 1955
3rd Printing 1959
4th Printing 1962
5th Printing 1963
6th Printing 1964

Third Edition

7th Printing 1964
8th Printing 1965
9th Printing 1966
10th Printing 1967
11th Printing 1969
12th Printing 1970

Fourth Edition

13th Printing 1972
14th Printing 1974

PRINTED IN THE UNITED STATES OF AMERICA

Preface

Fifteen and a half million accidents!

The National Safety Council estimates there will be fifteen and a half million accidents this year. The number is not surprising when you remember that there are almost 111,500,000 automobiles on the roads and highways of the United States.

The number of vehicles on the road is increasing at the rate of four to five million cars a year. Inevitably, the number of accidents will increase also. Whatever else accidents mean, they certainly mean crumpled fenders, misalignment of frames, damage to finishes, and the need for many forms of body repair.

Collision work has ballooned to proportions that offer body repairmen a large share in more than $2.5 billion dollars spent on repairs each year. That's $2,500,000,000.00! For the properly trained technician, good pay and steady employment are assured.

This newly revised edition of *Automotive Collision Work* covers collision work in all its aspects. Building from the basic concepts of frame and body construction in the first chapter, the book leads step-by-step through tools, types of welding, repair of doors, hoods, and deck lids, and even frame alignment.

New material has been added to this *4th edition* to keep pace with the fast moving automotive industry. The unitized body has been given new emphasis. New tools which speed up the job, new materials which the repairman must know, and the latest in plastics and wood grain finishes are now explained in detail.

Mr. Edward D. Spicer was asked by the publishers to revise this book because of the broadness and fullness of his experience. He has built on three previous editions put together by Ernest Venk, Ewart J. Davies, and Mr. Spicer.

Mr. Spicer has extensive experience in engineering and automotive work, and has as well a thorough knowledge of educational publications. As former Supervisor of Training and Publications, Lincoln-Mercury Division, Ford Motor Company, he was intimately concerned with directing a large educational enterprise.

Originally trained as an automotive and aircraft stress engineer, Mr. Spicer was formerly Vice President of the Nemathy Davis Company, a subsidiary of Western Publishing Company; and is currently President of Tra-Data Inc., a business communications and merchandising consulting firm. Author, lecturer, and educational advisor, Mr. Spicer has the ideal combination of backgrounds to enable him to carry on this revision of Automotive Collision Work.

A word of reminder, Mr. Venk, a co-author of the first three editions of Automotive Collision Work and other automotive texts, leaves as a memorial of his effort a substantial portion of the earlier work. Venk's background included a Master's degree in Vocational Education and thirty-six years of active teaching.

In the preparation of the first editions of Automotive Collision Work, Mr. Ewart Davies served as an Educational Consultant. His special knowledge and experience, both as educator and engineer, helped to build the qualities that have made this book a standard in its field.

Mr. Spicer's revision retains all the features which have long made Automotive Collision Work a must for apprentice and journeyman repairmen. Any one who wants to improve his knowledge and understanding of automotive collision work will profit by it. It will enable him to earn a better living and will assure his future employment. Keeping each automotive repairman up-to-date with new developments is a part of continuing education in the auto repair field.

The Publishers

Contents

Body and Frame Construction

Chapter 1

The many elements involved in the building of an automobile or truck such as design, engineering, manufacturing, and assembly plant operations are each focused on the production of vehicles which are functional, durable, and safe to operate. To be competitive in the marketplace attention must be given simultaneously to styling and comfort features.

In this chapter our primary concern will be the structural soundness or strength which must be built into the body and frame of a vehicle. It must survive the shock forces it is likely to encounter during its many thousands of miles of anticipated service life.

Two types of construction are used in automotive vehicles. One is the separate frame and body arrangement which has been used since auto building began. The other is *unit body construction* in which a stub frame and body combine to provide the necessary strength and rigidity.

The two types of construction including major body and frame parts are covered in later sections. Study them thoroughly. Detailed knowledge of auto construction is needed to become an expert body repairman.

The last section covers those principles of measurement which are necessary to determine whether or not a frame or body is misaligned.

Aside from the fact that damage to an automobile body is generally unsightly, anything which happens to loosen or distort the body or frame may affect the safety of the car.

How Metal Is Formed to Provide Strength

Where metal was used in early automobiles, strength was obtained by making the members of comparatively thick stock. An example of this practice was the heavy gage sheet metal from which fenders were constructed, encountered in vintage autos even today.

As the result of decades of continuing research, new methods were adopted to give strength to metal panels from light gage metal. However, when this light gage steel is shaped and assembled, strength and rigidity are added by the contours into which it is formed.

This section gives you a word picture of how metal is formed to obtain strength. Each type of forming is described under a heading indicating the method involved. Illustrations of each method of forming metal are also included.

Crowns. Probably the most common formation of metal in a body or fender is a curved surface. Curved surfaces are usually called *crowns*. An example of this type of surface is shown in Fig. 1-1.

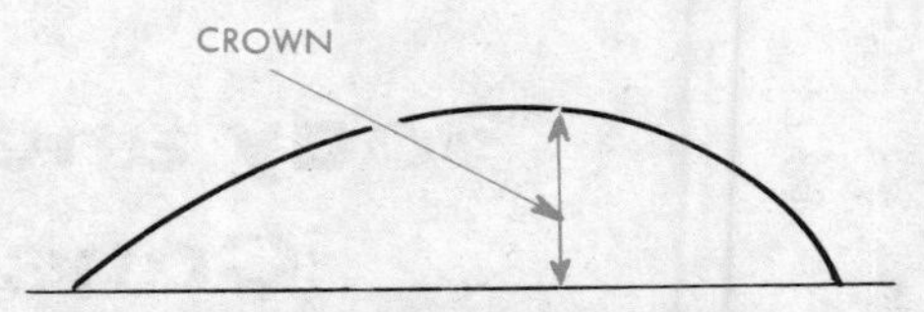

Fig. 1-1. Crowned surface from side.

A crowned surface may be shaped in one direction only, or in several directions from any given point on that surface.

A sheet of metal which has been crowned is much stronger than the same sheet would be if it were flat. The crowned sheet will resist any influence to change its shape. It will also have a permanent tendency to return to its original crowned shape, provided it is not distorted too far.

When the sheet has been formed into its original shape by a press, pressing gives the sheet a permanent shape. Each surface of the sheet is more dense than the metal at the center of the sheet.

When a sheet is formed, the last operation of the press squeezes the surfaces together. This causes the molecules in the metal to be crowded closer together at the surface under more stress than they would normally have. For this reason, the stressed sheet will be stronger than it was before pressing. Stressed surfaces will better resist any force to move them out of position. The more a surface is crowned or stressed, therefore, the greater is its tendency to resist movement and to return to its original pressed shape if it is distorted.

When a surface has a small crown or is not curved very much, it is called a *low crown* surface. An example of a low crown surface with which you will be working is the almost flat portion of an all-steel top or hood.

When a surface has a lot of crown, or is rounded in all directions, it is called a *high crown* surface.

Contrary to a popular belief, a curved surface in an automobile body need not have a true radius. The designer can create a curved surface by laying out points which, when connected, form a smooth, curved line.

Angles and Flanges. Another method of shaping metal to gain strength is to form highly stressed *angles* or *flanges* along the edges of large sheets or panels.

Angular or *corrugated* type of construction cannot be used when a smooth surface is required, but it is widely employed in the inner construction of automobile bodies.

Every time a panel or bracket is given a right-angle bend, it becomes stronger. Figure 1-2 shows an inner door panel which has a right-angle bend all around the door. It is this bend and the width of the formed flange which provides the depth for the inner work-

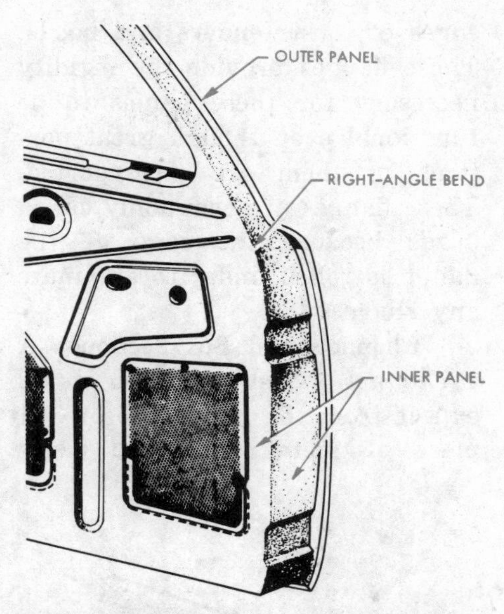

Fig. 1-2. Inner door panel showing right-angle bend and other formed surfaces.

ings of the door. However, an even more important function is that it supplies as much strength as would a frame of heavier metal.

You can acquaint yourself with the strength imparted by a right-angle bend in a piece of metal by the following experiment. Form a flange approximately one inch wide across one end of a piece of thin, flat, sheet metal, then try to bend the sheet crosswise to the angle. You will encounter difficulty in bending it after the flange is made.

Flanges are right-angle bends. Car panels require flanges to give stiffness to any unsupported edge. Flanges are found around the edges of most fenders and hoods. These flanges provide the rigidity necessary for these panels to be functional even though great portions of them are unsupported. These flanges are commonly called *beads* because the edge of the flange is rolled under to eliminate any sharp edge.

U-Channels and Box Sections—A *U-channel* is just what you would expect from the name. It is a flat piece of metal with two edges turned at right angles in the same direction, Fig. 1-3.

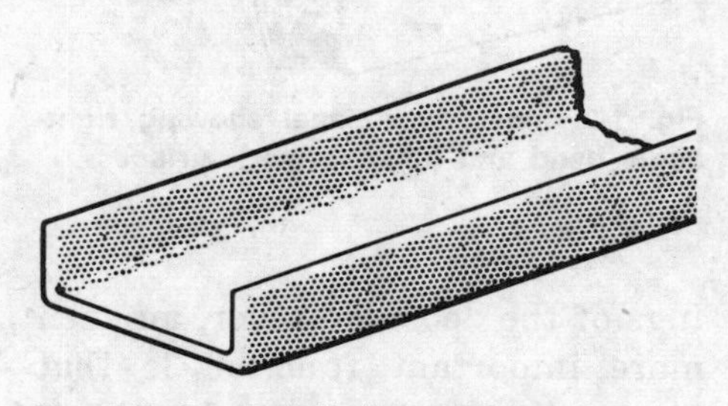

Fig. 1-3. Pressed U-channel form.

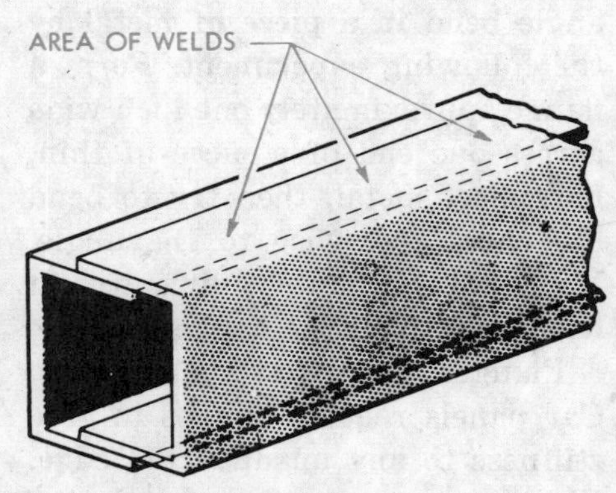

Fig. 1-4. Box formed with two U's.

U-channels are widely used in the inner construction of automobile bodies. More strength can be gained by making a U-channel section instead of a single-angle bend in a reinforcement bracket. The U-channel is also the most common type of construction found in automobile frames.

Another type of construction composed of two U-channel sections nested together, is called *box section construction,* Fig. 1-4. This more than doubles the strength of the individual sections, and will allow a certain amount of bending and shaping of the member.

Box section construction is obtained by overlapping the free edges of two U-channel sections and either welding, riveting, or bolting them together. Box section construction is used in conjunction with U-channel construction in the manufacture of automobile frames when great strength is necessary.

A close inspection of the body construction of an automobile will show that the panels, brackets, braces, etc., all have one or more of the types of construction mentioned in this section; that is, crowns, angles, flanges, U-channel, or box sections. You may also see many odd types of construction. However, they will be only a variation of one of these basic shapes.

Frame Construction

An understanding of the construction of the frame is extremely important because it is the foundation on which the car is built. Frames of all types to fit all conditions are described and illustrated in this section.

Frames can be constructed from U-channel, I-beam, box sections, angle, T-stock, Z-stock, tubing, flat plates, or combinations of these stocks. Frames are usually made wider at the rear than at the front. This permits a shorter turning radius by allowing more room for the front wheels. It also allows more space for supported load-carrying at the rear. The heaviest cross member is usually mounted somewhere under the front portion of the engine.

Passenger Car Frames. Several types of passenger car frames are shown in Fig. 1-5. One frame has an X-shaped member for added strength. You can also see from this

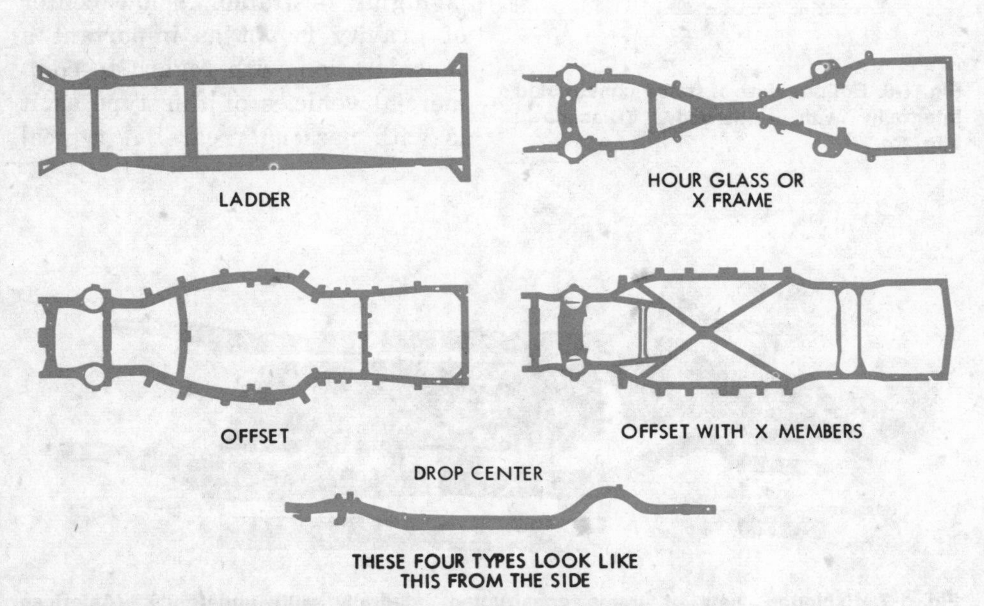

Fig. 1-5. Four types of passenger car frames (Blackhawk Mfg. Co.)

illustration what is meant by the term *drop center* used in connection with car frames. The main part or center of the frame is dropped down between the front and rear wheels to lower the vehicle for the increased safety of a low center of gravity.

In some automobiles, the frame is incorporated with the body. This is a form of unit body construction which is thoroughly discussed in another section of this chapter. Some feel that *integral frames* built in this manner are stronger and more durable than conventional type frames. Frames constructed integrally with the underbody are shown in Fig. 1-6 and Fig. 1-7.

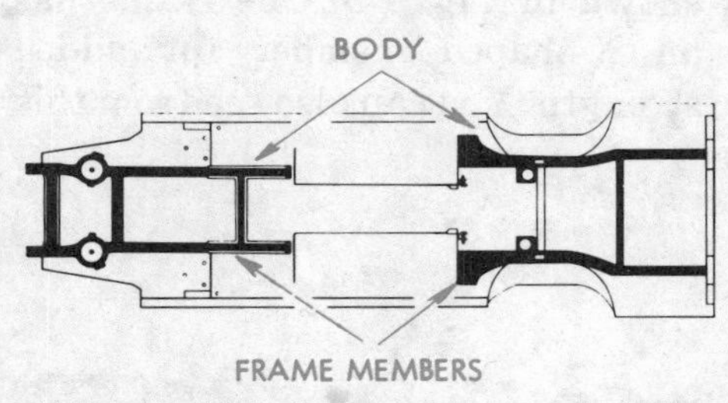

Fig. 1-6. Bottom view of frame constructed integrally with underbody. (Blackhawk Mfg. Co.)

Commercial Vehicle Frames. With the exception of the lighter vehicles, commercial vehicle frames are usually built flat. Light commercial vehicles are usually built on passenger car frames or on reinforced passenger car frames.

Large truck and bus frames are made flat without any drop in the center since a flat floor for the cargo or passenger carrying space is highly desirable. A low center of gravity is not as important a consideration with regard to commercial vehicles of this type as it is with passenger cars. A typical

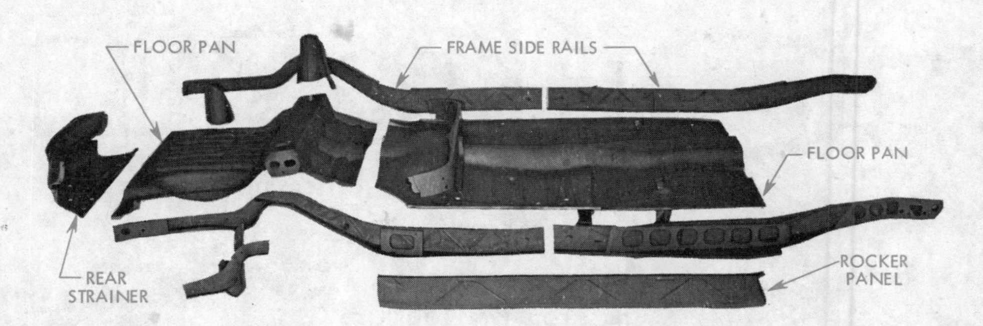

Fig. 1-7. Exploded view of frame constructed integrally with underbody. (American Motors Corp.)

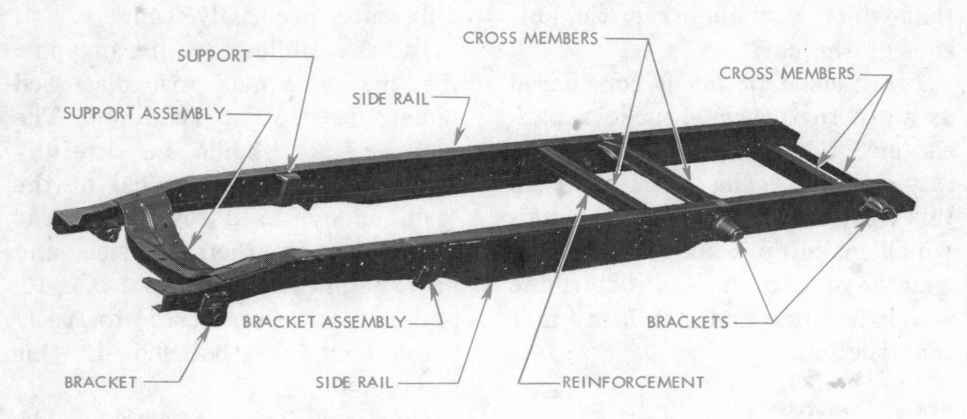

Fig. 1-8. Large truck frame differs from passenger car frame. (Dodge Div., Chrysler Corp.)

large truck frame is shown in Fig. 1-8. In this illustration, you can see that even though this frame has no drop, the side members are made wider where the load strain is greatest.

Conventional Bodies and Cabs

The passenger carrying compartment of a car is called the *body proper*. It is to the body that all of the doors and fenders or quarter panels attach to form a complete body assembly. In trucks, the passenger compartment body is called the *cab*. The cab is the nucleus around which the complete body is constructed.

Bodies and cabs differ a great deal in construction because of the different purposes for which they are intended. However, one factor is common to both. Each has outer and inner construction. These terms are used frequently in any discussion of automotive body construction.

Outer construction can be likened to the skin. In fact, some body experts use the term *skin* when referring to the outer surfaces of an automobile. Outer construction is usually considered as that which is visible from the outside of the car.

Inner construction is considered as all of the braces, brackets, panels, etc., that are used to give the car strength. The discussions in this section of the major panels which make up a body or cab will enable you to quickly determine which is outer and which is inner construction.

Body Construction

The body construction discussed here is the conventional type utilizing a full frame. Several types of bodies are available in most car lines. The most popular are the regular four-door sedan, of which the major panels are shown in Fig. 1-9, and the hardtop four-door shown in Fig. 1-10. The difference between these two styles is in the center pillar construction.

The center pillar is the vertical member between the rear and front doors. On the pillar sedan, the center pillar attaches to both the floor pan and the roof side rails. This gives great strength to the body sides.

In the hardtop sedan, the center pillar attaches to the floor pan only, and is only as high as the lower door panel reveal line, leaving an uninterrupted opening from front to rear when the windows are open. Station wagon construction is shown in Fig. 1-11. The differences are easily seen.

In the following paragraphs, the major panels are discussed under descriptive headings. The panel names should be carefully noted, as they are typical of the terminology used by most car companies in their service and parts publications. Figs. 1-9, 1-10, and 1-11 will be referred to freely throughout the balance of this discussion.

Cowl and Dash Assembly. The cowl or dash panel forms the front end of the body. This panel usually is formed by assembling several smaller panels. These are the *cowl upper panel* and the *cowl side panels,* which are joined by welds into one integral unit.

In some cars, the windshield frame is integral with the cowl panel. The cowl extends upward around the entire windshield opening so that the upper edge of the cowl panel forms the front edge of the roof panel. In this case, the windshield pillars are merely part of the cowl panel. The windshield pillars are the narrow sloping construction at either side of the windshield opening.

In some cars, only a portion of the windshield pillar is formed as part of the cowl.

The cowl is sometimes called the *fire wall* because it is the partition between the passenger compart-

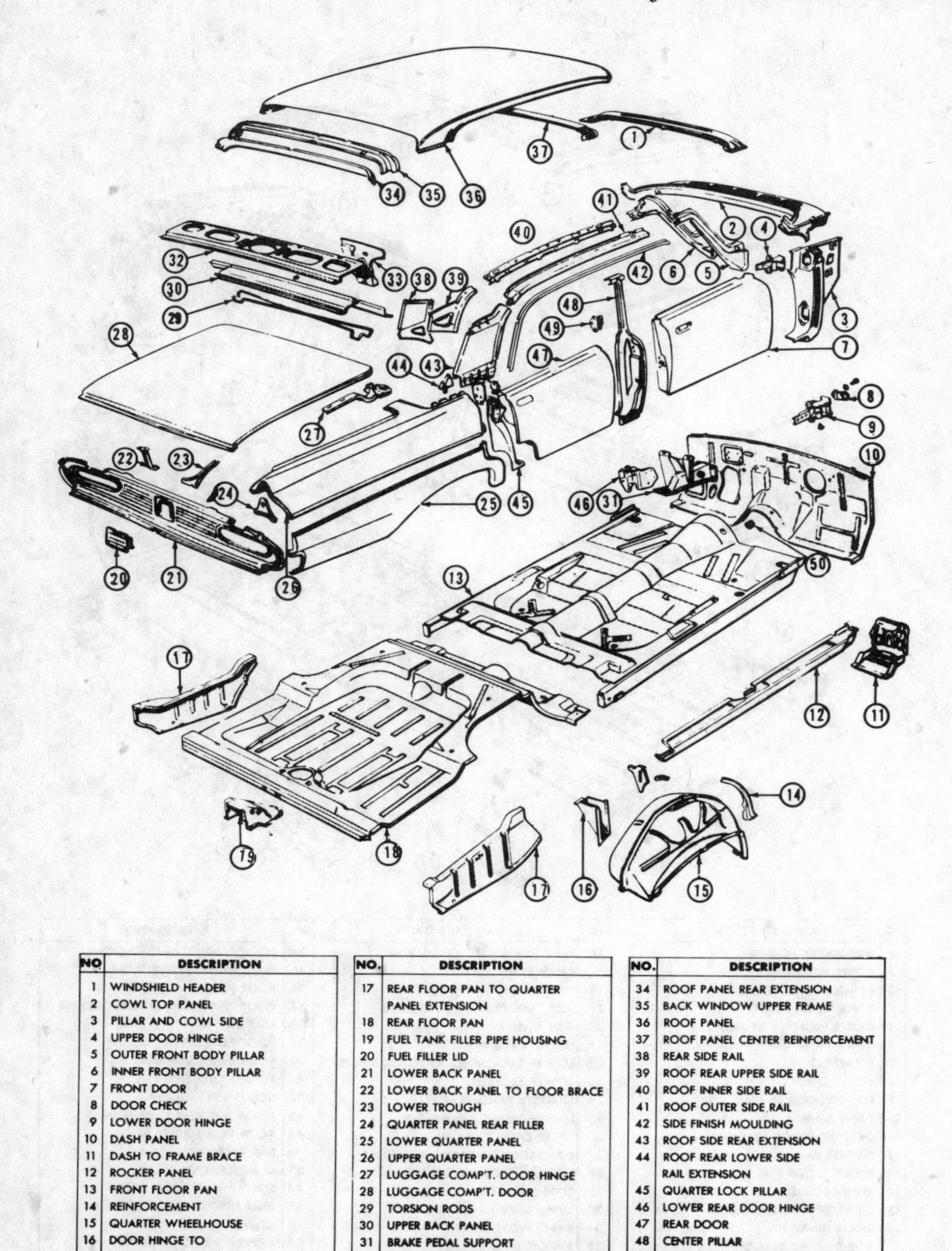

NO.	DESCRIPTION	NO.	DESCRIPTION	NO.	DESCRIPTION
1	WINDSHIELD HEADER	17	REAR FLOOR PAN TO QUARTER PANEL EXTENSION	34	ROOF PANEL REAR EXTENSION
2	COWL TOP PANEL	18	REAR FLOOR PAN	35	BACK WINDOW UPPER FRAME
3	PILLAR AND COWL SIDE	19	FUEL TANK FILLER PIPE HOUSING	36	ROOF PANEL
4	UPPER DOOR HINGE	20	FUEL FILLER LID	37	ROOF PANEL CENTER REINFORCEMENT
5	OUTER FRONT BODY PILLAR	21	LOWER BACK PANEL	38	REAR SIDE RAIL
6	INNER FRONT BODY PILLAR	22	LOWER BACK PANEL TO FLOOR BRACE	39	ROOF REAR UPPER SIDE RAIL
7	FRONT DOOR	23	LOWER TROUGH	40	ROOF INNER SIDE RAIL
8	DOOR CHECK	24	QUARTER PANEL REAR FILLER	41	ROOF OUTER SIDE RAIL
9	LOWER DOOR HINGE	25	LOWER QUARTER PANEL	42	SIDE FINISH MOULDING
10	DASH PANEL	26	UPPER QUARTER PANEL	43	ROOF SIDE REAR EXTENSION
11	DASH TO FRAME BRACE	27	LUGGAGE COMP'T. DOOR HINGE	44	ROOF REAR LOWER SIDE RAIL EXTENSION
12	ROCKER PANEL	28	LUGGAGE COMP'T. DOOR	45	QUARTER LOCK PILLAR
13	FRONT FLOOR PAN	29	TORSION RODS	46	LOWER REAR DOOR HINGE
14	REINFORCEMENT	30	UPPER BACK PANEL	47	REAR DOOR
15	QUARTER WHEELHOUSE	31	BRAKE PEDAL SUPPORT	48	CENTER PILLAR
16	DOOR HINGE TO WHEELHOUSE BRACKET	32	PACKAGE TRAY PANEL	49	UPPER REAR DOOR HINGE
		33	PACKAGE TRAY STRAINER	50	TRANSMISSION INSPECTION COVER

Fig. 1-9. Four-door pillar sedan body panels. (Lincoln-Mercury Div., Ford Motor Co.)

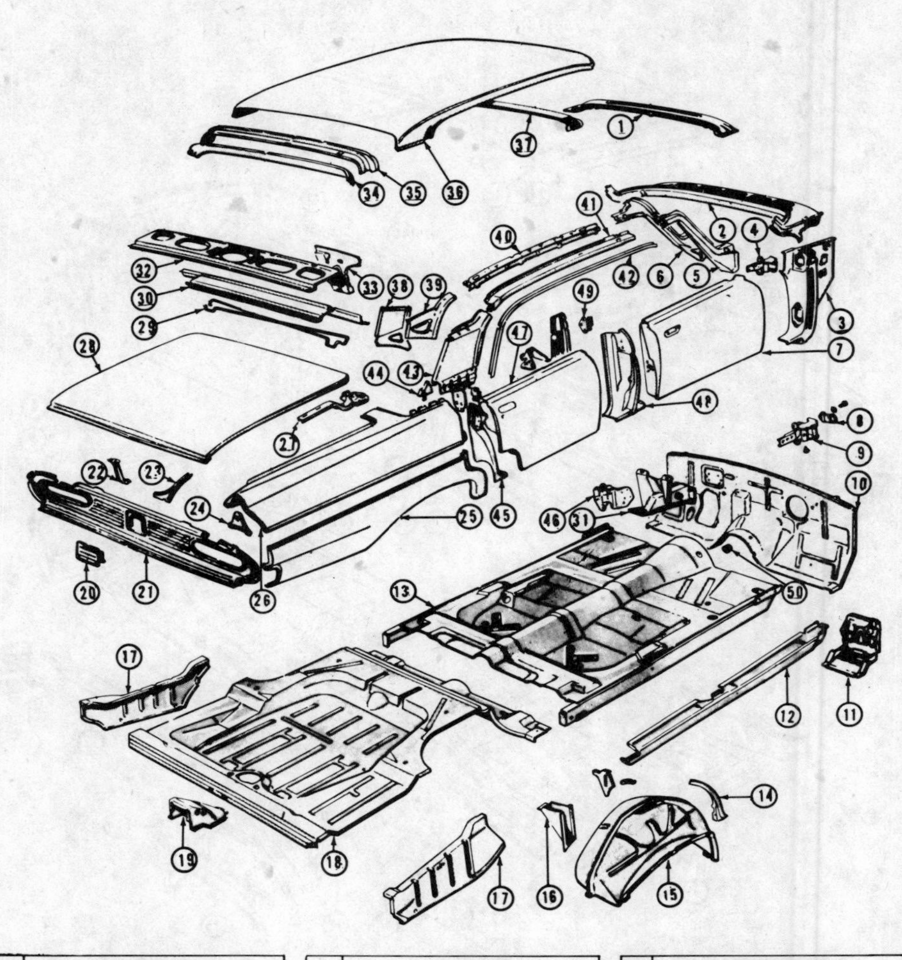

NO.	DESCRIPTION
1	WINDSHIELD HEADER
2	COWL TOP PANEL
3	PILLAR AND COWL SIDE
4	UPPER DOOR HINGE
5	OUTER FRONT BODY PILLAR
6	INNER FRONT BODY PILLAR
7	FRONT DOOR
8	DOOR CHECK
9	LOWER DOOR HINGE
10	DASH PANEL
11	DASH TO FRAME BRACE
12	ROCKER PANEL
13	FRONT FLOOR PAN
14	REINFORCEMENT
15	QUARTER WHEELHOUSE
16	DOOR HINGE TO WHEELHOUSE BRACKET
17	REAR FLOOR PAN TO QUARTER PANEL EXTENSION
18	REAR FLOOR PAN
19	FUEL TANK FILLER PIPE HOUSING
20	FUEL FILLER LID
21	LOWER BACK PANEL
22	LOWER BACK PANEL TO FLOOR BRACE
23	LOWER TROUGH
24	QUARTER PANEL REAR FILLER
25	LOWER QUARTER PANEL
26	UPPER QUARTER PANEL
27	LUGGAGE COMP'T. DOOR HINGE
28	LUGGAGE COMP'T. DOOR
29	TORSION RODS
30	UPPER BACK PANEL
31	BRAKE PEDAL SUPPORT
32	PACKAGE TRAY PANEL
33	PACKAGE TRAY STRAINER
34	ROOF PANEL REAR EXTENSION
35	BACK WINDOW UPPER FRAME
36	ROOF PANEL
37	ROOF PANEL CENTER REINFORCEMENT
38	REAR SIDE RAIL
39	ROOF REAR UPPER SIDE RAIL
40	ROOF INNER SIDE RAIL
41	ROOF OUTER SIDE RAIL
42	SIDE FINISH MOULDING
43	ROOF SIDE REAR EXTENSION
44	ROOF REAR LOWER SIDE RAIL EXTENSION
45	QUARTER LOCK PILLAR
46	LOWER REAR DOOR HINGE
47	REAR DOOR
48	CENTER PILLAR
49	UPPER REAR DOOR HINGE
50	TRANSMISSION INSPECTION COVER

Fig. 1-10. Hardtop four-door sedan body panels. (Lincoln-Mercury Div., Ford Motor Co.)

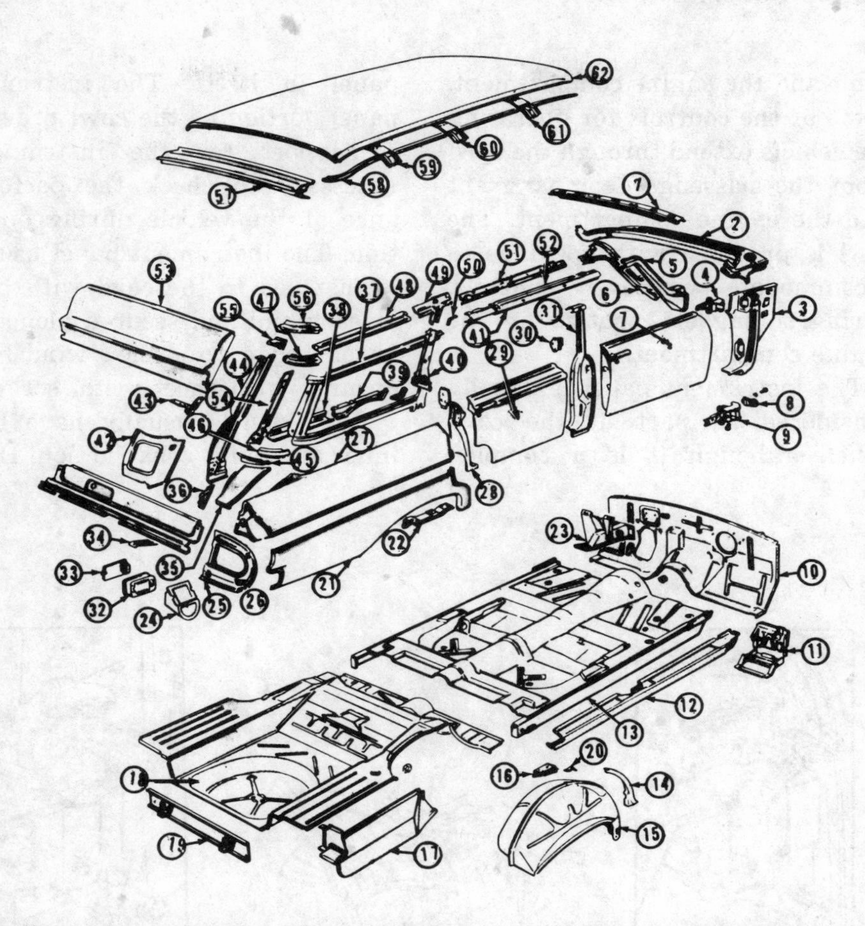

NO.	DESCRIPTION
1	WINDSHIELD HEADER
2	COWL TOP PANEL
3	PILLAR AND COWL SIDE
4	UPPER DOOR HINGE
5	OUTER FRONT BODY PILLAR
6	INNER FRONT BODY PILLAR
7	FRONT DOOR
8	FRONT DOOR CHECK
9	LOWER DOOR HINGE
10	DASH PANEL
11	DASH TO FRAME BRACKET
12	ROCKER PANEL
13	FRONT FLOOR PAN
14	QUARTER PANEL (LOCKSIDE) LOWER REINFORCEMENT
15	QUARTER WHEELHOUSE
16	REAR SEAT BACK STOP SUPPORT
17	REAR FLOOR PAN TO QUARTER PANEL EXTENSION
18	REAR FLOOR PAN
19	REAR FLOOR REAR SILL
20	REAR SEAT BACK STOP WHEELHOUSE BRACKET
21	LOWER REAR QUARTER PANEL
22	SEAT CUSHION SUPPORT RISER
23	BRAKE PEDAL SUPPORT
24	FUEL TANK FILLER PIPE HOUSING
25	LOWER REAR QUARTER PANEL EXTENSION
26	QUARTER PANEL REAR FILLER
27	UPPER REAR QUARTER PANEL
28	QUARTER LOCK PILLAR
29	REAR DOOR
30	REAR DOOR UPPER HINGE
31	CENTER PILLAR
32	FUEL FILLER OPENING COLLAR
33	FUEL FILLER LID
34	LOWER BACK PANEL BRACE
35	UPPER REAR QUARTER PANEL EXTENSION
36	FILLER (QUARTER PANEL) UPPER REAR TO LOWER REAR EXTENSION
37	QUARTER WINDOW FRAME
38	REAR QUARTER BELT RAIL
39	FRONT QUARTER BELT RAIL
40	CENTER LOWER INNER ROOF SIDE RAIL
41	FRONT ROOF RAIL OUTER EXTENSION
42	REAR QUARTER PANEL LOWER REINFORCEMENT
43	TAILGATE HINGE
44	OUTER REAR CORNER PILLAR
45	QUARTER PILLAR EXTENSION REINFORCEMENT
46	QUARTER PANEL REINFORCEMENT BRACKET
47	REAR ROOF RAIL OUTER EXTENSION
48	INNER REAR ROOF SIDE RAIL
49	CENTER, UPPER INNER ROOF SIDE RAIL
50	QUARTER WINDOW OPENING REAR CORNER UPPER FRONT FILLER
51	INNER FRONT ROOF SIDE RAIL
52	OUTER FRONT ROOF SIDE RAIL
53	TAILGATE ASSEMBLY
54	UPPER INNER REAR CORNER PILLAR
56	BACK WINDOW HEADER EXTENSION
56	INNER REAR ROOF SIDE RAIL EXTENSION
57	BACK WINDOW HEADER RAIL
58	ROOF DRIP SIDE MOULDING
59	ROOF PANEL REAR REINFORCEMENT
60	ROOF PANEL CENTER REINFORCEMENT
61	ROOF PANEL FRONT REINFORCEMENT
62	ROOF PANEL

Fig. 1-11. Four-door station wagon body panels. (Lincoln-Mercury Div., Ford Motor Co.)

ment and the engine compartment. Some of the controls for operating the vehicle extend through the cowl from the passenger compartment into the engine compartment. The cowl is provided with openings to accommodate whatever controls, wiring, tubing, etc., that go into the engine compartment.

The instrument panel is usually considered as part of the cowl panel, although it is a complex panel in itself. The instrument panel portion of the cowl provides a support for the instruments necessary to check the performance of the vehicle during operation. The instrument panel usually is fastened to the cowl with bolts at each end and secured along the lower edge of the windshield opening with sheet metal screws.

Cowl panels usually have both inner and outer construction. How-

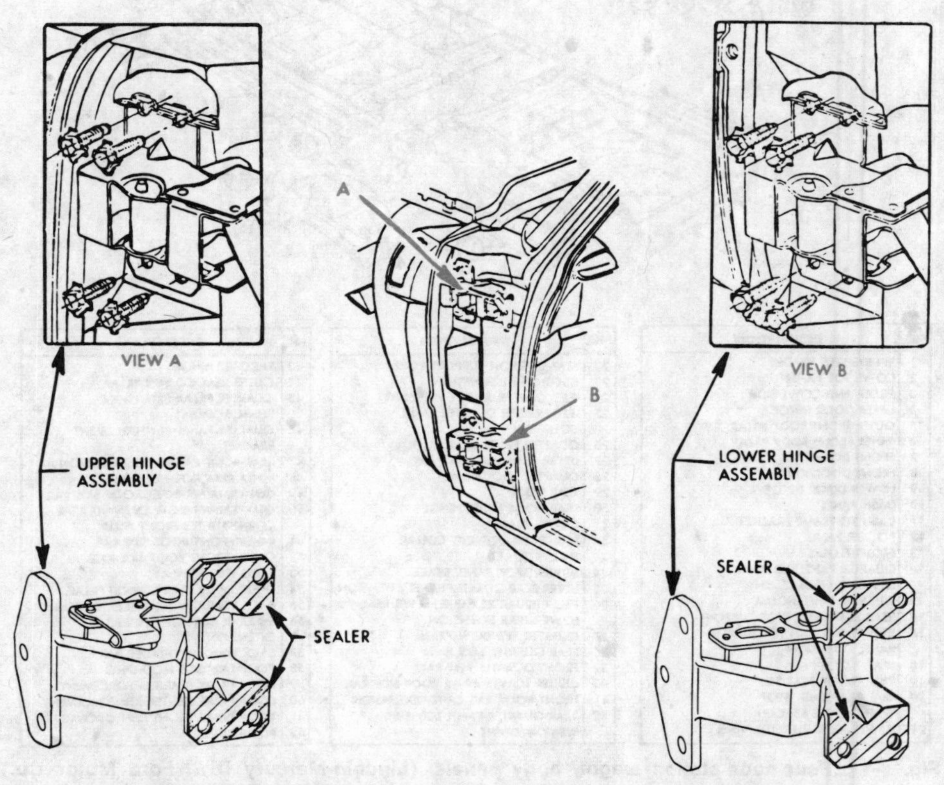

Fig. 1-12. Front door hinge assembly. (Lincoln-Mercury Div., Ford Motor Co.)

ever, on some cars only the upper portion of the cowl around the windshield is visible as an outer panel. On most cars, the front door hinge pillar is an integral part of the cowl as shown in Fig. 1-12.

Roof Panel or Assembly. The roof panel is one of the largest of all major body panels, but it is also one of the simplest in construction, Figs. 1-9, 1-10, and 1-11.

Usually, the roof is of all-steel, one-piece construction. The area which the roof encompasses varies between different makes and models of cars. On some cars the roof panel ends at the front at the windshield. On others, it extends downward around the windshield, so that the windshield opening is actually in the roof.

On some cars, the roof ends above the rear window at the rear. On others, it extends downward at the rear so that the rear window opening is in the lower rear roof. When this is the case, the roof forms the top panel around the rear deck opening.

Some special body designs incorporate different methods of rear window construction which affect the roof panel. This is particularly true of hard top convertibles. On these cars, the top is joined to the rear quarter panels by another smaller panel which is part of the roof assembly. In other special designs, the roof panel is completely covered with a waterproof vinyl plastic. This arrangement is merely for the sake of eye appeal.

Most roof panels have *stiffeners,* which are small metal strips, placed crosswise to the roof at intervals along the inside surface. These stiffeners are welded in place and provide the necessary tacking strips for securing the headlining and inside trim in place.

Underbody. The underbody, Fig. 1-13, is commonly called the *floor pan.* The floor pan is usually composed of several smaller panels which are either welded together or secured to one another by bolts to form one single unit. All floor pans are reinforced on the underside by floor pan cross bars, Fig. 1-14.

Most floor pans are irregularly shaped for several reasons. They are formed with indentations or *beads,* Fig. 1-13, to strengthen the pan. A floor pan must be shaped to fit around the chassis units and the frame. The passengers' feet are often accommodated by recessed areas in the floor. The most noticeable irregularities in floor pans are usually the transmission hump and the driveshaft tunnel, Fig. 1-14.

Rear Quarter Panel. The rear quarter panel is often integral with the rear fender on late model cars. An example of this type of arrangement is shown in Fig. 1-15. How-

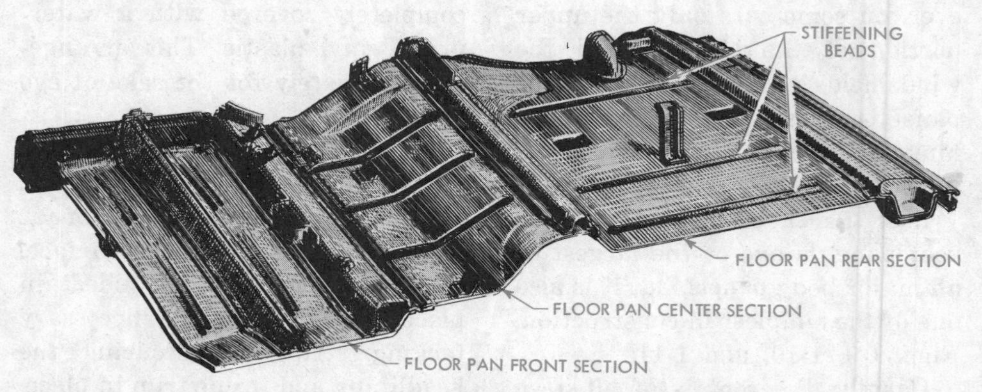

Fig. 1-13. Top view of floor pan showing reinforcements and bends.

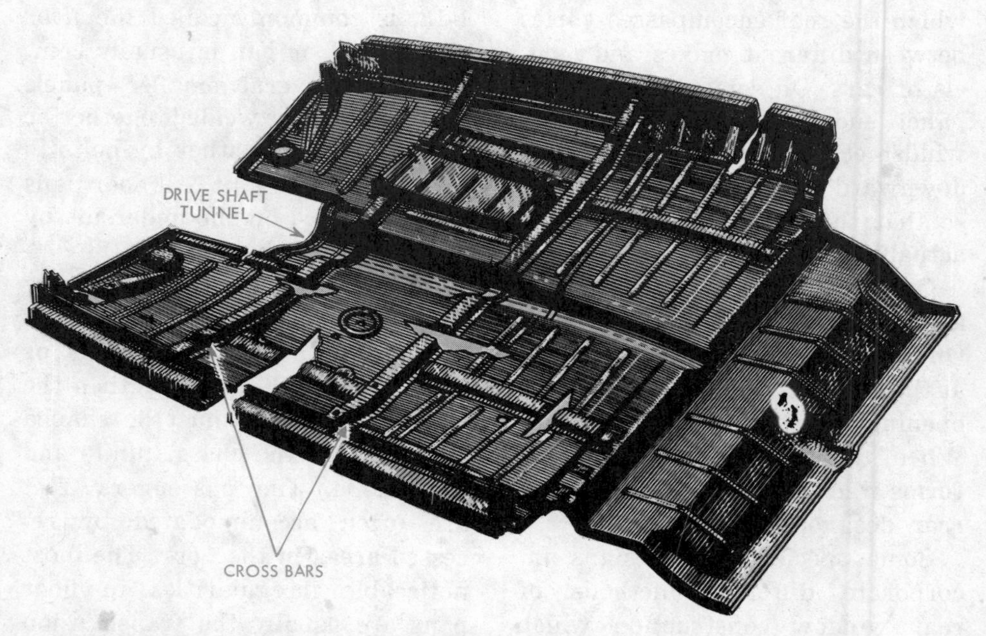

Fig. 1-14. Bottom view of floor pan showing floor pan cross bars.

ever, the common conception of what is meant by rear quarter panels is illustrated in Figs. 1-9, 1-10, and 1-11.

The quarter panel has both inner and outer construction. The outer construction or outer panel is, of course, smooth, except for the

Fig. 1-15. The rear quarter panel is integral with the rear fender on this car. (Lincoln-Mercury Div., Ford Motor Co.)

breaks caused by the design of the car. The outer panel wraps around the inner construction at the edges which are exposed at fender openings or door openings. Both welding, and bolts and screws are used to secure the outer panel to the inner construction.

The inner construction of a quarter panel is made up of many strong reinforcement brackets welded or bolted together to form a single unit.

The quarter panel inner construction usually extends across the vehicle at the rear of the passenger compartment. This provides a support for the rear seat back if the car is so equipped, or it provides a partition between the luggage compartment and the passenger compartment. The most important function of these reinforcements is to provide additional strength across the rear quarter panel area of the car. A typical quarter panel, lower section arrangement, forward of the rear wheel, is shown in Fig. 1-16.

Quarter Panel Wheelhouse. On some cars, the rear wheelhouse is constructed as an integral part of the inner construction of the rear quarter panel.

A sectional view of a typical quarter panel wheelhouse arrangement is shown in Fig. 1-17. As you can see from this illustration, the wheelhouse is usually of two-piece construction. The pieces comprising the wheelhouse are either welded or bolted together. The wheelhouse is then attached as an integral part of the quarter panel.

Center Body Pillar. The center pillar (Fig. 1-9) is a typical arrangement for a four-door sedan body. In this type of construction, the center pillar acts as the central roof and side support be-

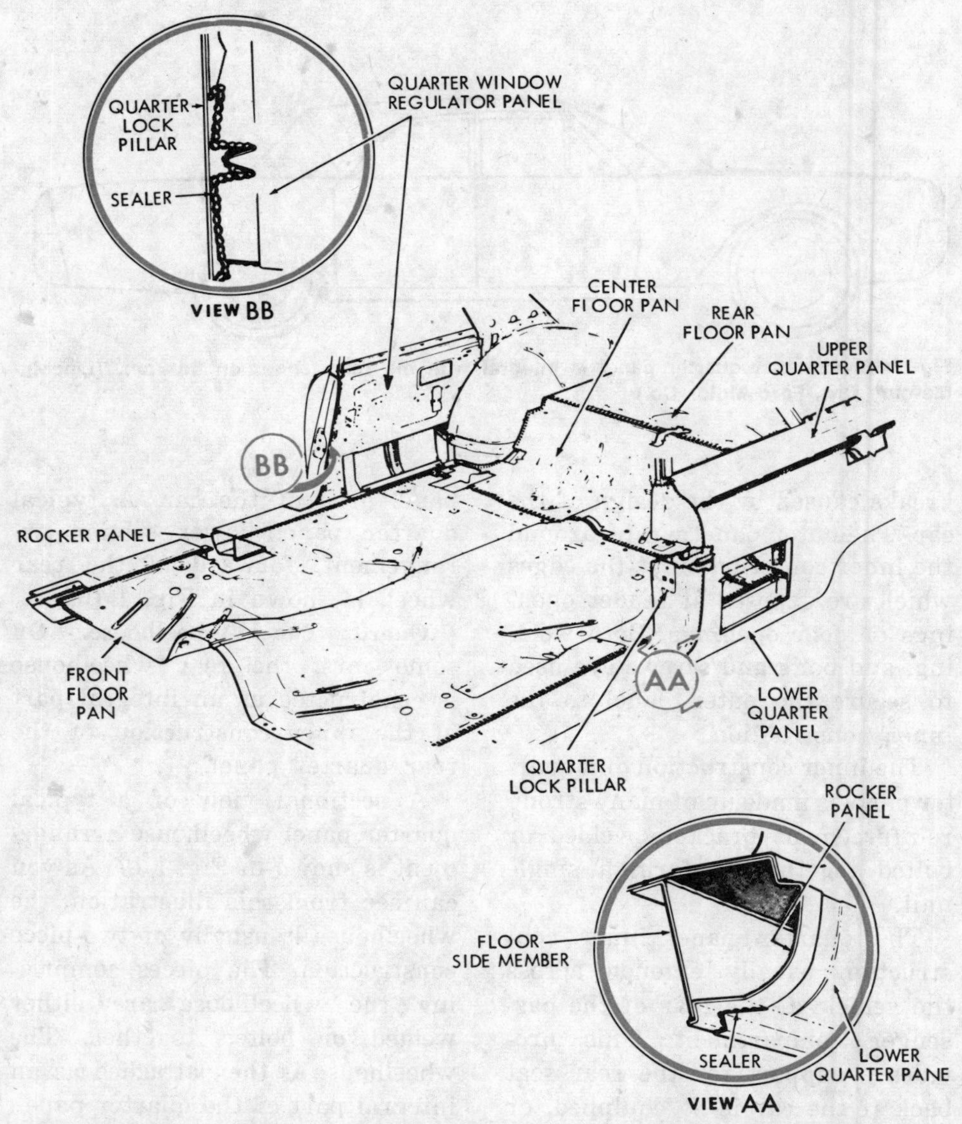

Fig. 1-16. Lower section of quarter panel forward of rear wheel. (Ford Motor Co.)

tween the rear and front of the car. For this reason, it is made from heavy stock and is constructed sturdily. In this type of arrangement, the center pillar acts as the hinge pillar for the rear doors and as the lock pillar for the front doors.

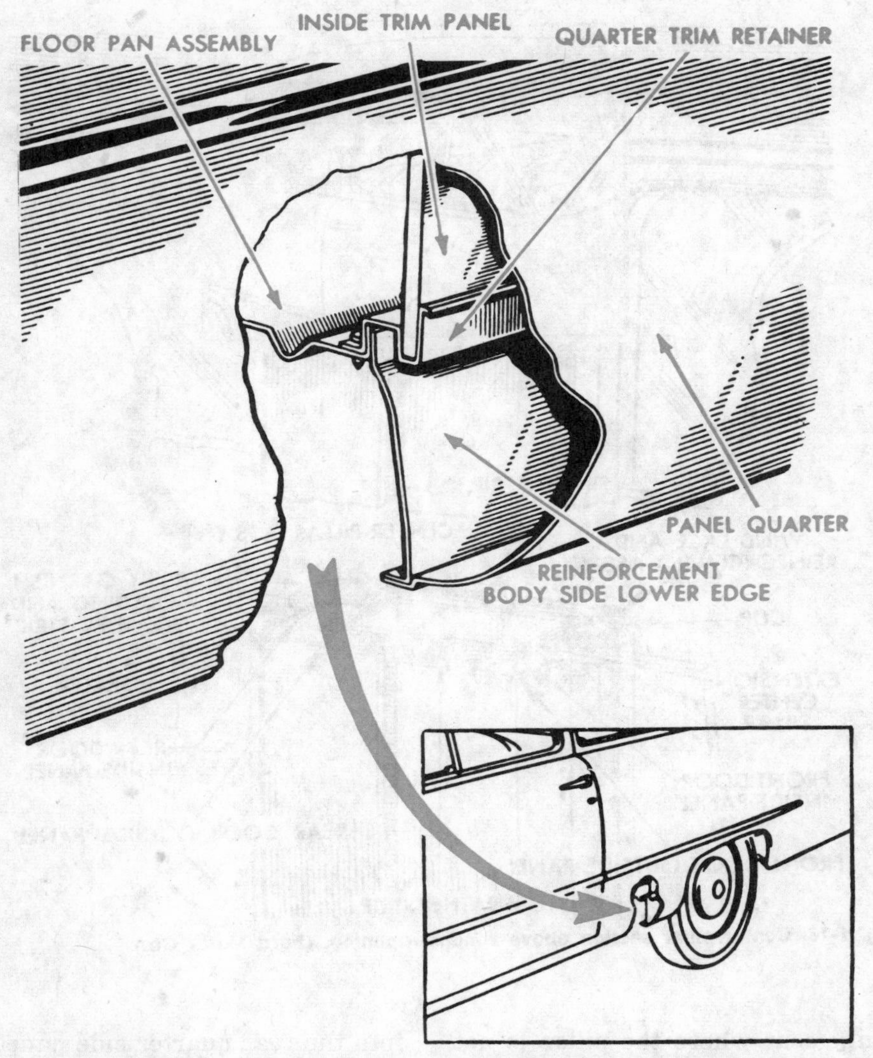

Fig. 1-17. Section through a rear quarter panel wheelhouse at center line of rear wheel. (Ford Motor Co.)

In some other makes of cars, the pillar is constructed similarly, but is visible from the outside when the doors are closed. In these cases, the pillar is wide with an outer panel surface.

The sectional views in Figs. 1-18 and 1-19 show a typical ar-

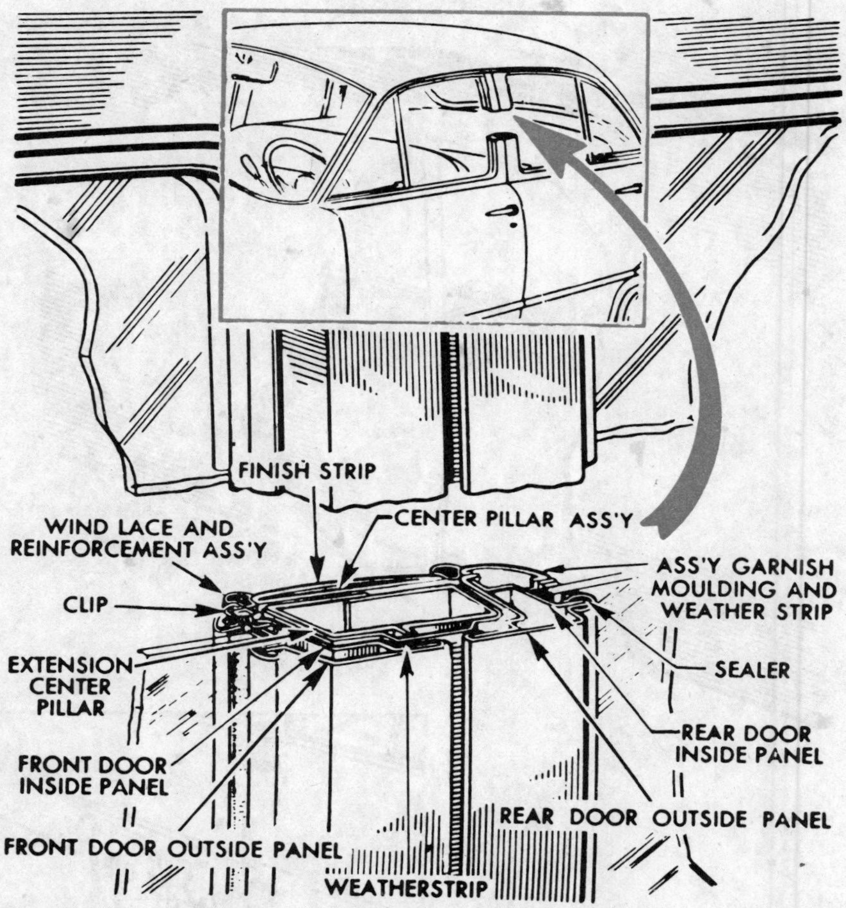

Fig. 1-18. Center pillar section above window opening. (Ford Motor Co.)

rangement where the pillar is not visible with the doors closed. The component parts of the pillar, including the trim parts and weather seals used around the center pillar, are also visible in these illustrations.

On two-door sedan type bodies, the center pillar is incorporated into the rear quarter side panel. It does, however, perform the same structural function on a two-door as on a four-door. The most common arrangement with two-door type cars is to have the center pillar act as the lock pillar for the door, and as the channel for the rear window.

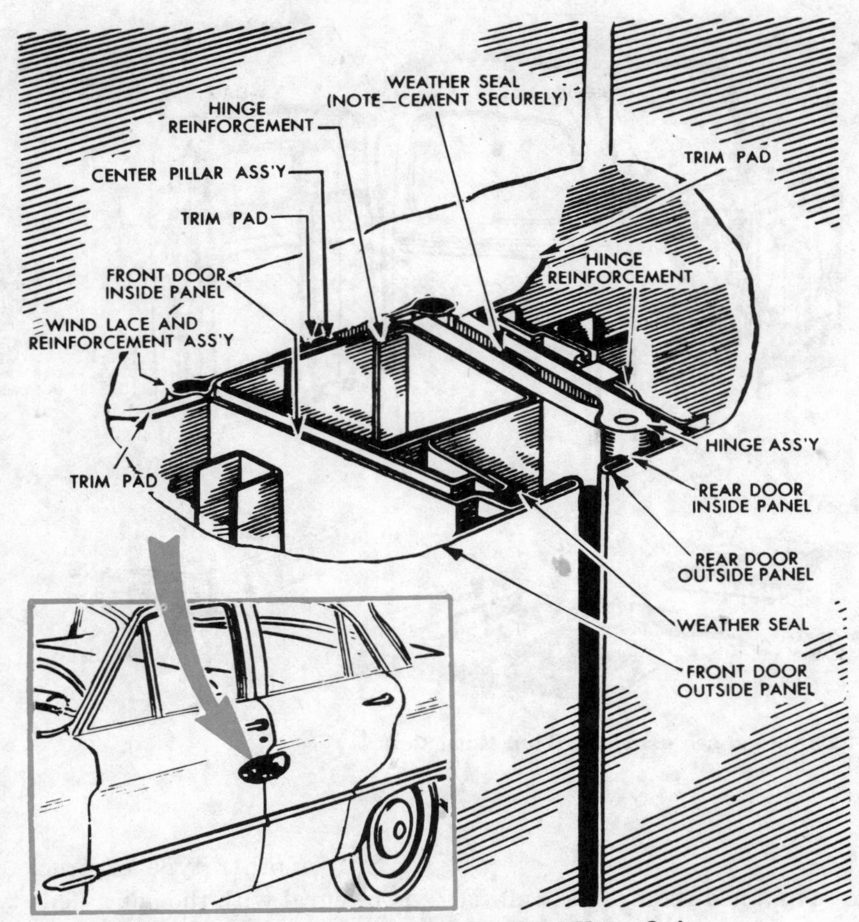

Fig. 1-19. Center pillar section below door handle. (Ford Motor Co.)

You can see from Figs. 1-18 and 1-19 that the center pillar is made from several pieces. These pieces are either welded or bolted together to form a single, strong unit.

The center pillar is usually irregular in shape. In fact, the center pillar design changes with each body style. The pillar must conform to the outside contour of the body as well as the contour of the door opening. Depressions are formed into the pillar at the time it is manufactured to accommodate the door lock striker plates and hinges, depending upon the body style.

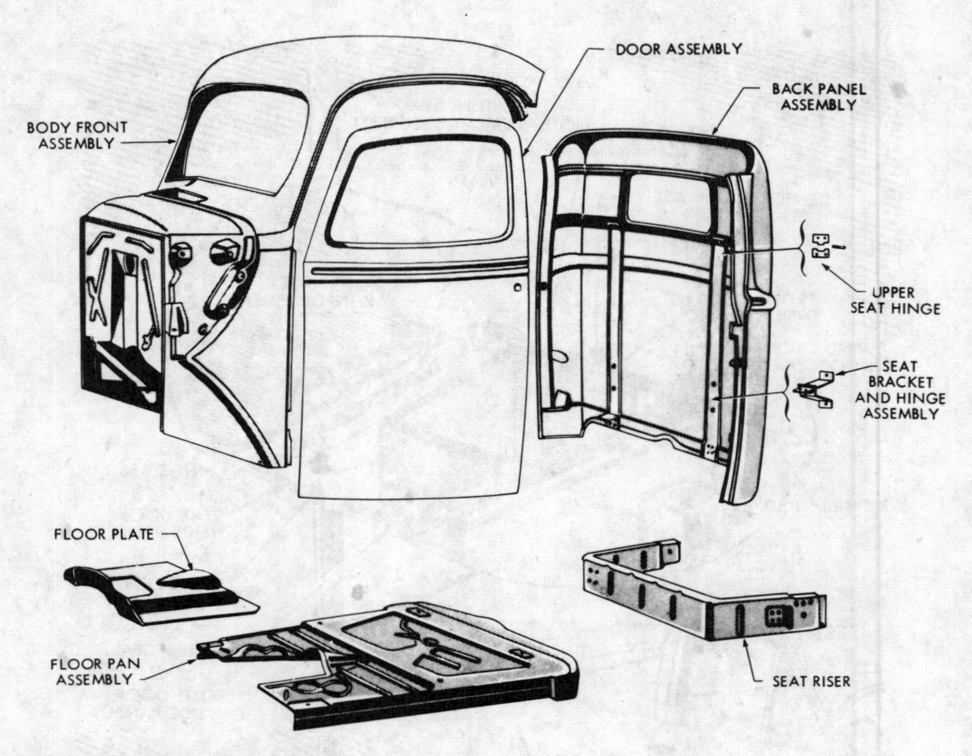

Fig. 1-20. Closed cab assembly. (Ford Motor Co.)

Cabs

As explained before, a cab is the passenger compartment of a truck. All cabs are not alike, however, but vary in size and arrangement according to the purpose for which the truck is intended.

A typical *closed cab* is shown in Fig. 1-20. All of the component parts of a closed cab are clearly labeled in this illustration.

A *cab-over-engine* type cab is shown in Fig. 1-21, with all the major panels labeled clearly.

Still another type of truck cab is integral with the body. This type of arrangement is called a *truck body* instead of a cab. This arrangement is popular for use in light delivery work. This type of truck usually is built on a passenger car chassis. A panel delivery truck body is shown in Fig. 1-22.

In Figs. 1-23, 1-24, and 1-25, several sections through different locations on truck cabs and bodies are shown which illustrate typical construction.

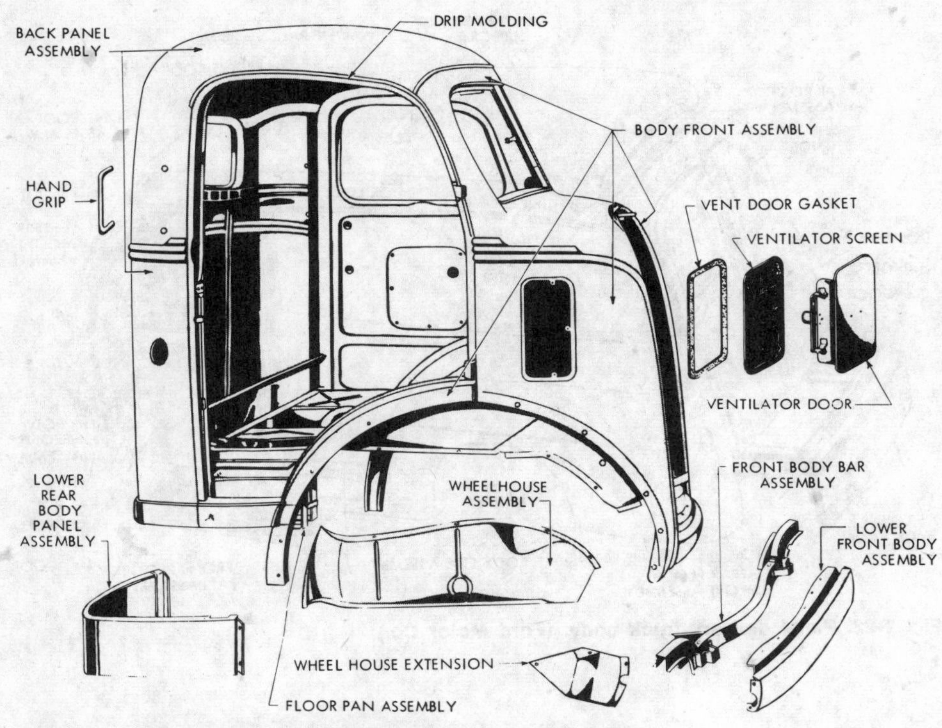

Fig. 1-21. Typical cab-over-engine assembly. (Ford Motor Co.)

You can easily see from these illustrations that the major panels of a truck cab, or body, and those of a passenger car body differ considerably. The same principles of construction are used in building truck cabs and bodies as passenger car bodies even though the panels differ in size and appearance.

You will undoubtedly encounter truck cabs and bodies which differ in appearance from those that have been shown. However, the construction in these instances will be similar to the cabs and bodies previously illustrated.

In some designs, the entire cab is hinged to the lower front body and can be unlatched at the lower rear edge and tilted forward. This arrangement is desirable in some instances because of the necessity of gaining access to otherwise inaccessible chassis components.

Body and Cab Assembly. At the time of original manufacture, the major panels of bodies and cabs are joined to one another in

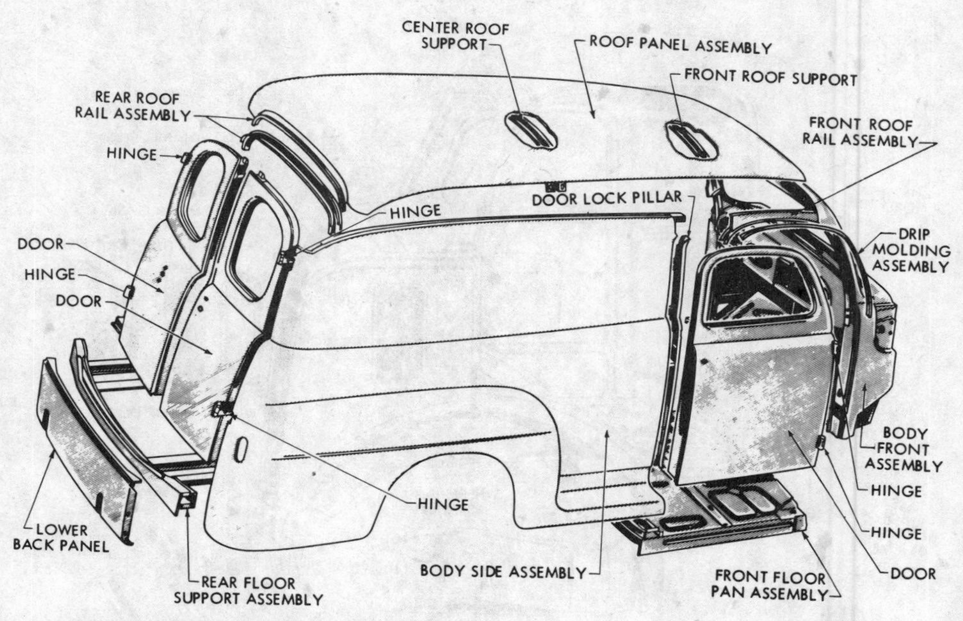

Fig. 1-22. Panel delivery truck body. (Ford Motor Co.)

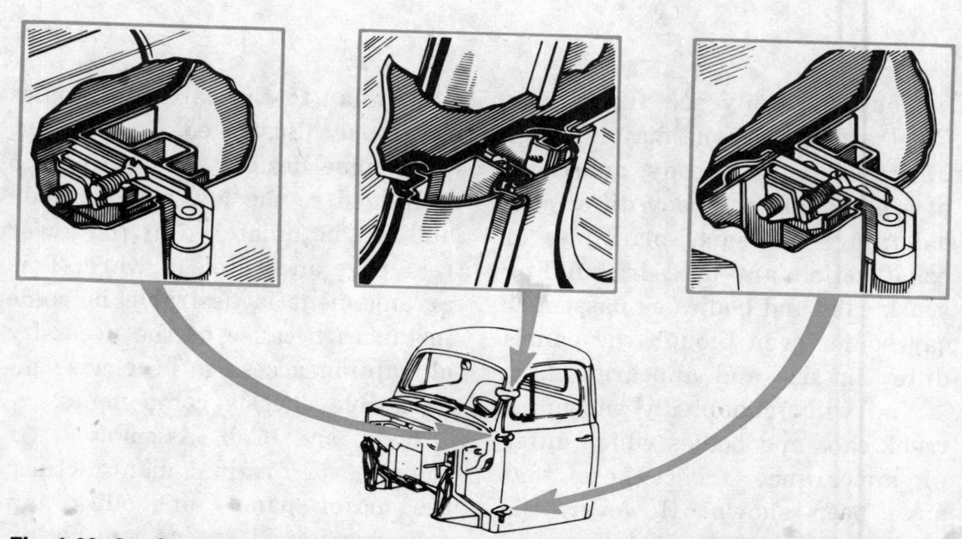

Fig. 1-23. Sectional view of front pillar and upper and lower door hinges. (Ford Motor Co.)

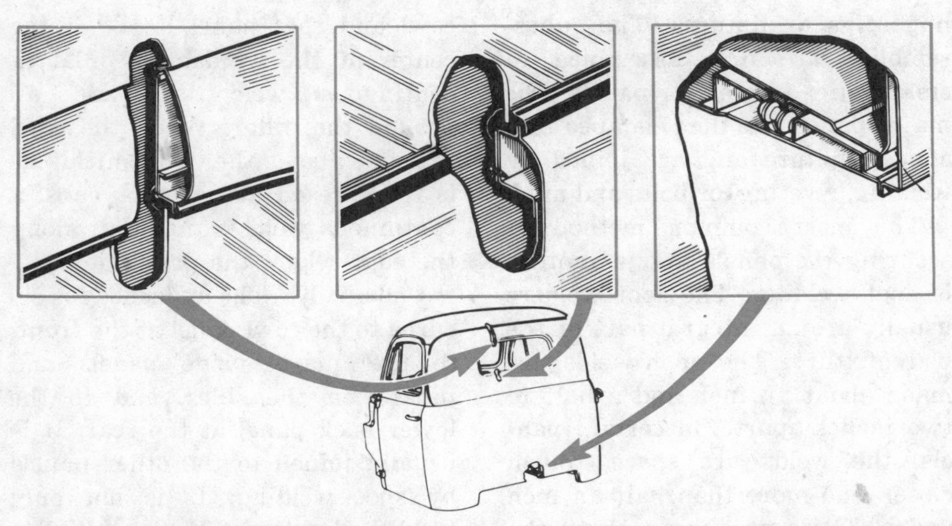

Fig. 1-24. Sectional view of top of rear window, bottom of rear window, and bottom of cab. (Ford Motor Co.)

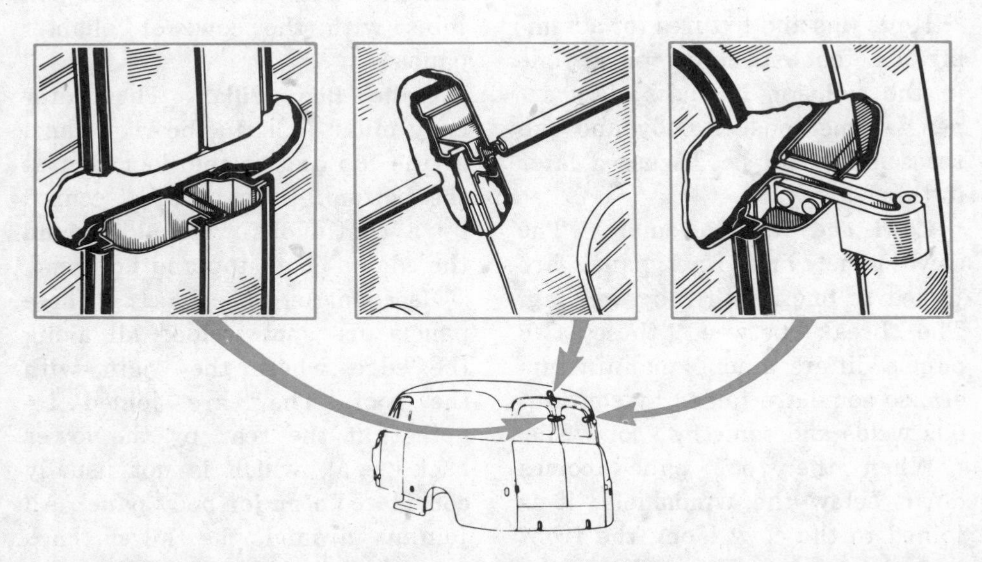

Fig. 1-25. Sectional view of rear door at drip rail and door latch, rear door at center, and door glass and upper hinge (panel delivery). (Ford Motor Co.)

huge jigs or fixtures. The subassemblies are first assembled in smaller jigs into major panels. The major panels are then clamped into a body fixture and are joined by welding, riveting, or bolts and nuts.

The most common method of securing the panels to one another is spot welding. The spot welders usually are an integral part of the body fixture. The spot welds are made about an inch and a half to two inches apart. On certain panels, the welds are spaced much closer—no more than half an inch apart. These are areas along the bottom of the body where the side panels are joined to the floor. The welds, being closer together, add strength to the structure and lessen the probability of dust and water leakage.

Huge jigs and fixtures for assembly are too expensive for anyone in the collision business; less expensive methods of body and cab reassembly will be discussed later in this book.

Cowl and Roof Assembly. The cowl panel and roof panel are joined to one another by welding. The break between these two panels differs among manufacturers, so some are joined by continuous welds and some by spot welds.

When the roof panel comes down below the windshield, it is joined to the cowl along the front edge by spot welding. When the cowl and roof panel break at the center of the windshield pillar, a continuous weld is made all around the pillar. When the cowl extends above the windshield, as is the case on many truck cabs, a continuous weld is made all along the edge where the panels join.

Underbody. The underbody is secured to the cowl panel at the front, to the quarter side panels and pillars on the sides, and to the lower back panel at the rear. It is usually joined to the other panels by spot welding. It is not only welded directly to the panels, but also to numerous brackets and braces which have previously been secured to the cowl or quarter panels. The welds are spaced approximately one-half inch apart along the seam where the floor pan joins with the cowl or quarter panels.

Center Body Pillar. The center body pillar joins to the roof panel at the top and to the floor pan at the bottom. It is usually secured by a continuous weld all around the edge at both top and bottom.

Rear Quarter Side Panels. These panels are spot welded all along the edge where they join with the roof. They are joined together at the rear by the lower back penal, which is not usually considered a major body panel. All joining around the lower back panel is done by spot welding.

When the rear fender is not integral with the rear quarter side panel, it is fastened to the quarter panel. The quarter panel in this case has holes punched around the edges of the fender opening for the screws which secure the fender to it.

Unit Body Construction

Unit, or *unitized* body construction is not a new engineering concept. Unitized body construction employs the same principles of design that have been used for years in the aircraft industry. The main goal has been strength and rigidity without unnecessary weight. Unit construction does not employ a conventional frame to which suspension, engine, and other chassis and power train components are attached.

Underbody

The major difference between a conventional body and a unitized body is in the design and construction of the floor pan, Fig. 1-26. In a unitized body, the floor pan area is generally called the *underbody*. The underbody is made up of formed

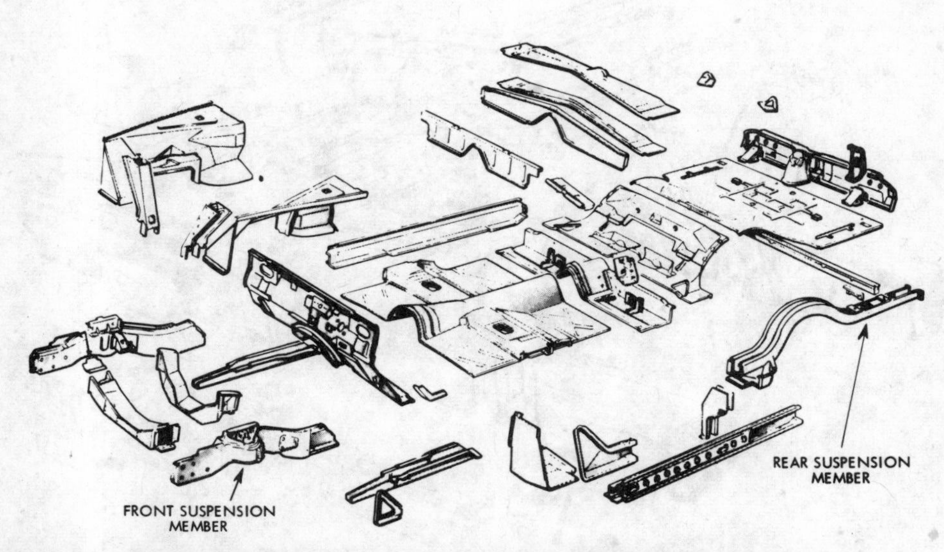

Fig. 1-26. Unitized underbody assembly. (Lincoln-Mercury Div., Ford Motor Co.)

floor pans, channels, box sections, formed rails, and numerous reinforcements.

In most unitized underbodies, a *suspension member* is incorporated at both the front and rear, Fig. 1-26. The suspension members have very much the same appearance as a conventional frame from the underside. However, the front suspension members terminate at the cowl and the rear suspension members terminate just forward of the rear kick-up. With the floor pans, side rails and reinforcements welded to them, the suspension members become an integral part of the underbody. The suspension members become the supports for engine, front and rear suspension and other chassis components.

There is a marked difference between the floor pan of a unitized body and the single thickness floor pan of a conventional body. In the unitized body the floor pan is usually of double thickness and has one or more box sections and several channel sections which may either run across the floor pan from side to side, or from front to rear. The major differences between underbody constructions are due to differences in wheelbase, length, and weight of the car.

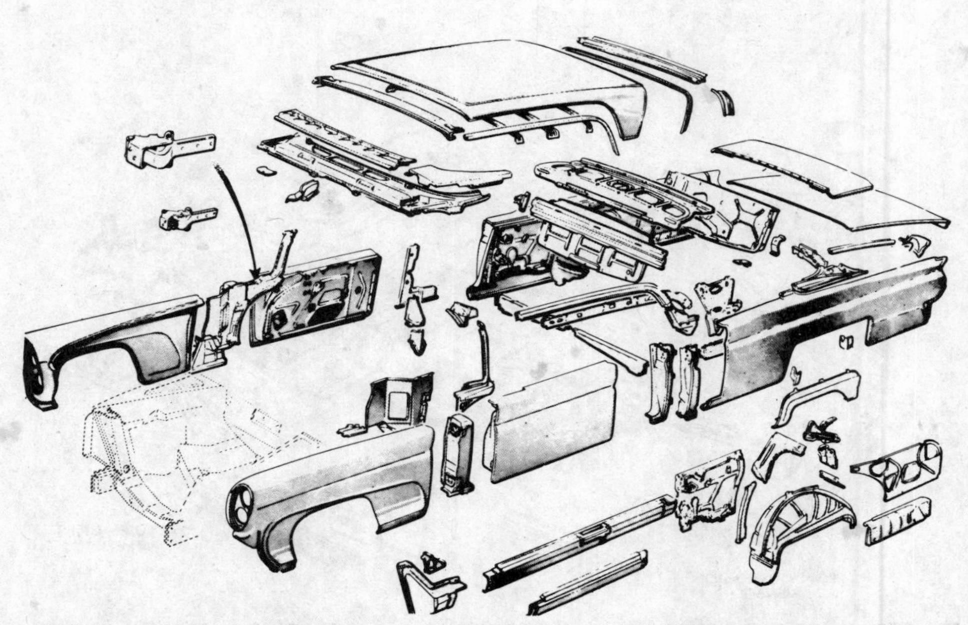

Fig. 1-27. Unitized upper body assembly. (Lincoln-Mercury Div., Ford Motor Co.)

Upper Body

A typical upper body for a unitized construction car is shown in Fig. 1-27. As you can see, the construction is very near the same as a conventional body. The major difference, however, lies in the package tray area in the rear and in the construction which joins the front fenders at the front. A typical front fender and the related supporting parts of wheel well and frame are shown in Fig. 1-28. Note that they would be welded or riveted together.

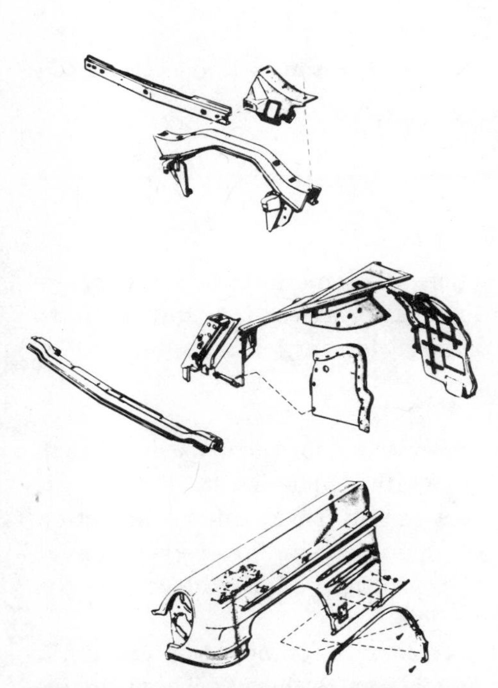

Fig. 1-28. Front fender and supporting construction of wheel well and frame. (Lincoln-Mercury Div., Ford Motor Co.)

The construction in the area to the rear of the back seat is much heavier in a unit construction body than in a conventional body. The same is true of the attaching members for the front fenders. Rigidity in the structure is necessary in these two areas to complement the cowl and floor pan construction and give strength and stability to the overall body structure across the width of the car.

Unitized Body Variations

As with any automotive components there are variations in construction methods among the various car makers. In some forms of unit construction, the entire front end area forward of the cowl is joined to the cowl with bolts. With this construction, the bolts at the cowl can be removed and the entire front end replaced as an assembly in the event of extensive damage to the underbody, or to the complex panels that make up the inner and outer construction.

In yet another and more recent development, the entire body side or door frame construction is of one piece, Fig. 1-29. Notice that there is both an inner panel and an outer panel which make up the total structure. These are welded together and are therefore very strong.

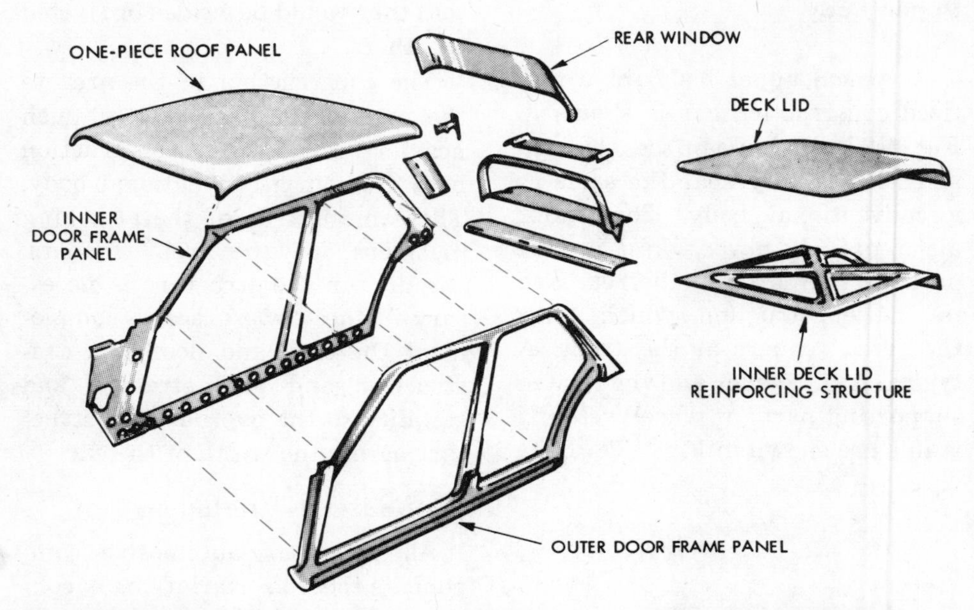

Fig. 1-29. Welded one-piece body side and door frame construction. (Lincoln-Mercury Div., Ford Motor Co.)

Doors and Deck Lids

The openings through which the passengers gain access to the body interiors are merely referred to as doors. The door through which access to the rear luggage compartment is obtained is called a *deck lid*.

In station wagon bodies, the opening into the passenger compartment through the rear of the body is generally termed a *tail gate*. Tail gates may be two-piece. The lower half is hinged at the bottom and swings outward and down to form a platform when open. On some models a side hinge may also allow the tail gate to swing sideways like a door.

Doors

Several doors are used on each type of vehicle built, whether it is a car or truck. The construction of doors is similar, regardless of the location of the door on the vehicle.

A door is composed of two main panels: an outer panel and an inner panel, Fig. 1-30. Both panels are of all-steel construction. The

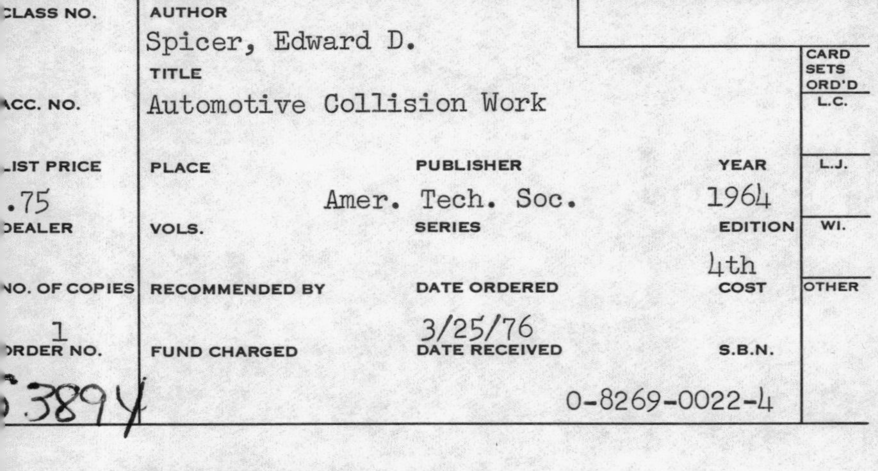

L. C. CARD NUMBER

CLASS NO.

AUTHOR
Spicer, Edward D.

TITLE
Automotive Collision Work

ACC. NO.

CARD SETS ORD'D

L.C.

LIST PRICE
.75

PLACE

PUBLISHER
Amer. Tech. Soc.

YEAR
1964

L.J.

DEALER

VOLS.

SERIES

EDITION
4th

WI.

NO. OF COPIES
1

RECOMMENDED BY

DATE ORDERED
3/25/76

COST

OTHER

ORDER NO.
5389

FUND CHARGED

DATE RECEIVED

S.B.N.
0-8269-0022-4

SAMPSON TECHNICAL INSTITUTE

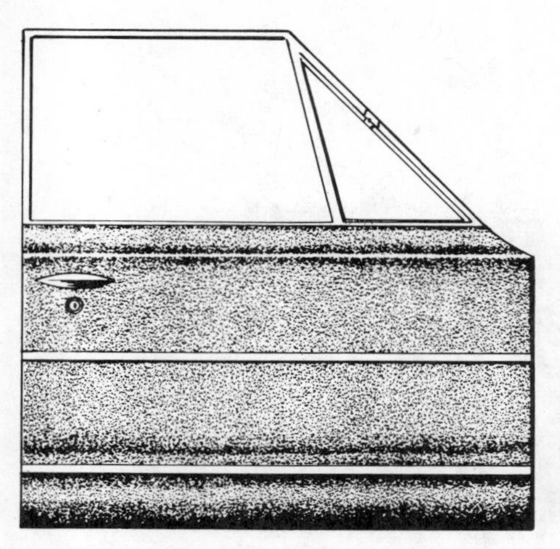
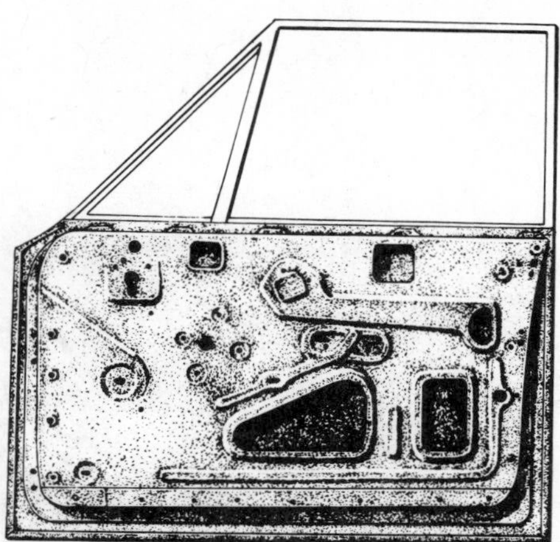

Fig. 1-30. Door outer panel and inner panel showing construction features.

door derives most of its strength from the inner panel, since the inner panel is constructed primarily to act as a frame for the door. The outer panel flanges over the inner panel around all edges to form a single unit.

The inner panel is made with offsets and holes for the attachment of door inner hardware. This hardware consists of the window regulator assembly and the door locking mechanism.

The installation of a door locking mechanism is shown in Fig. 1-31. these assemblies are installed through the large openings in the middle of the inner panel.

Much of the thickness of the door is due to the depth of the inner panel, which is necessary to accommodate the door latch and window mechanisms. The inner panel forms the lock pillar and also the hinge pillar sections of the door, Fig. 1-32. Small reinforcement angles are usually used between the outer and inner panels, both where the lock is inserted through the door and where the hinges attach to the door.

The outer panel is provided with an opening through which the outside door handle protrudes. In some instances, a separate opening is provided for the lock.

The upper portion of the door is a large opening which is closed by glass. The glass is held rigidly by the window regulator assembly. A channel is secured in the opening between the outer and inner panels in the upper portion of the door. When the window is raised, it slides in this channel. When it is fully closed, the window seats

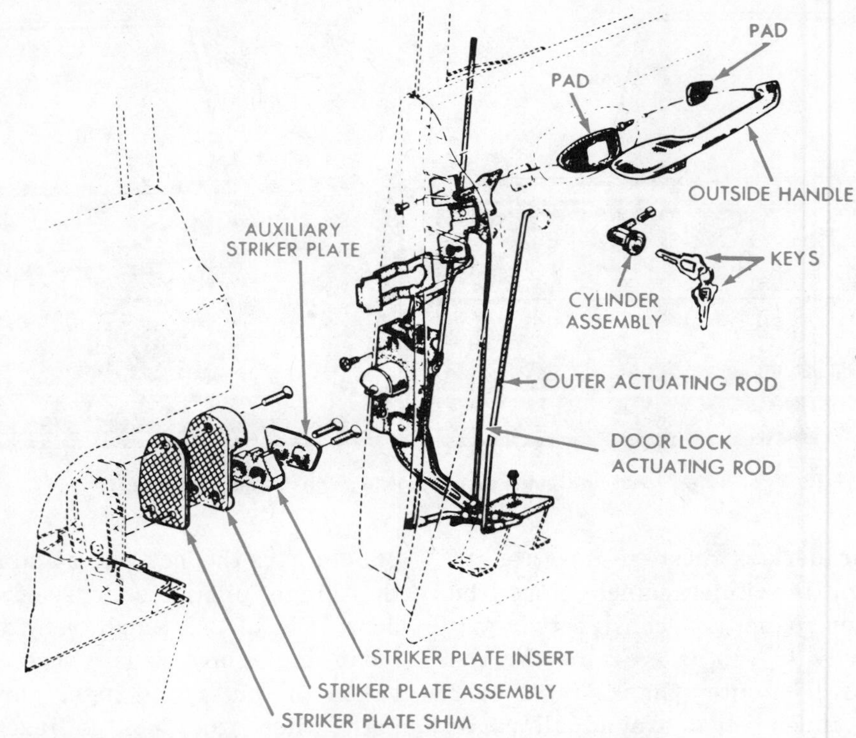

Fig. 1-31. Door locking mechanism before assembly. (Ford Motor Co.)

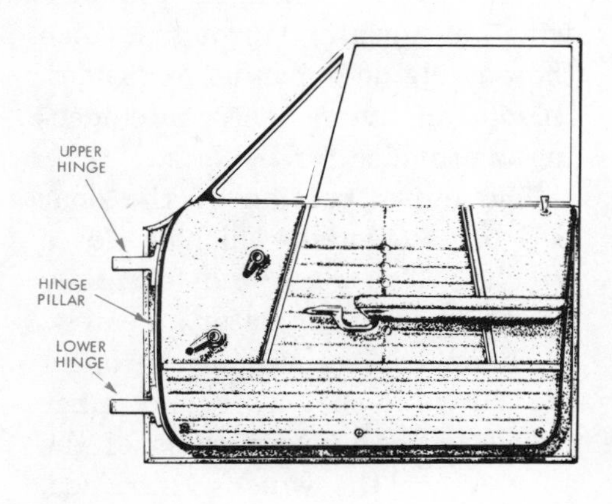

Fig. 1-32. Hinge pillar section of door panel.

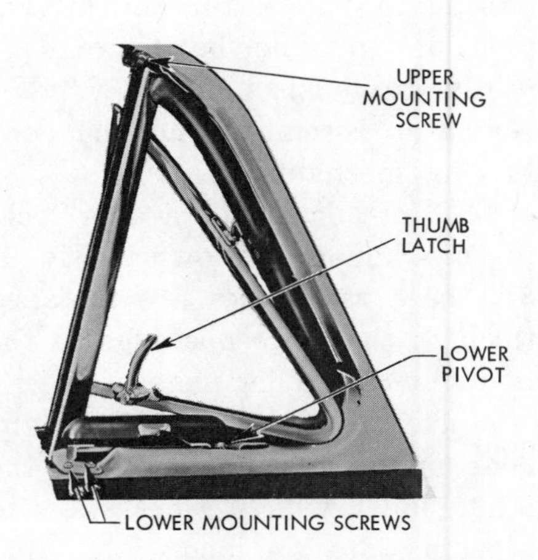

Fig. 1-33. Ventilator window with bar support for increased security.

tightly in this channel, effectively sealing out the weather. Some vehicles incorporate a ventilator window in front doors. A bar is placed upright in the door window opening, dividing it into a relatively large rectangular opening and a smaller triangular opening. Such an arrangement is shown in Fig. 1-33.

The smaller window is the vent window. The vent window is sealed by weather stripping so that it is weathertight. Different methods of control are used; some cars have a crank and gear arrangement for opening and closing the vent; others have a thumb latch next to the division bar.

When rear doors have a vent window, the construction is similar to that used for front doors. In some cases in two-door models, the rear quarter windows lower part way only. In others it cannot be lowered at all because of interference with the wheelhouse and rear quarter panel. Some two-door models are equipped with only a ventilator type quarter window. Some combine a fan shaped moveable window with a vent window.

Deck Lids

The deck lid is really another door which allows access to the luggage compartment in the rear of cars. A typical deck lid is shown in Fig. 1-34.

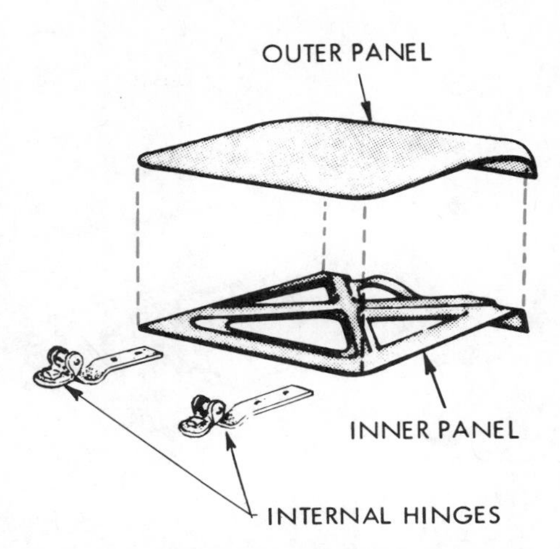

Fig. 1-34. Deck lid construction. (Lincoln-Mercury Div., Ford Motor Co.)

A deck lid is composed of an outer panel and an inner panel. These panels are spot welded together along their flanged edges to form a single unit in the same manner as in a regular door. The inner panel construction is shown in Fig. 1-35. This also shows one type of hinge arrangement (internal). Some cars use external hinges, while other cars have concealed hinges attached to the inner panel only, or to the sandwich of the margins of the inner and outer construction.

A latch is sometimes provided at the bottom rear of the deck lid and is controlled by an external handle. This external handle is sometimes concealed from the eye under a molding or some other type of trim.

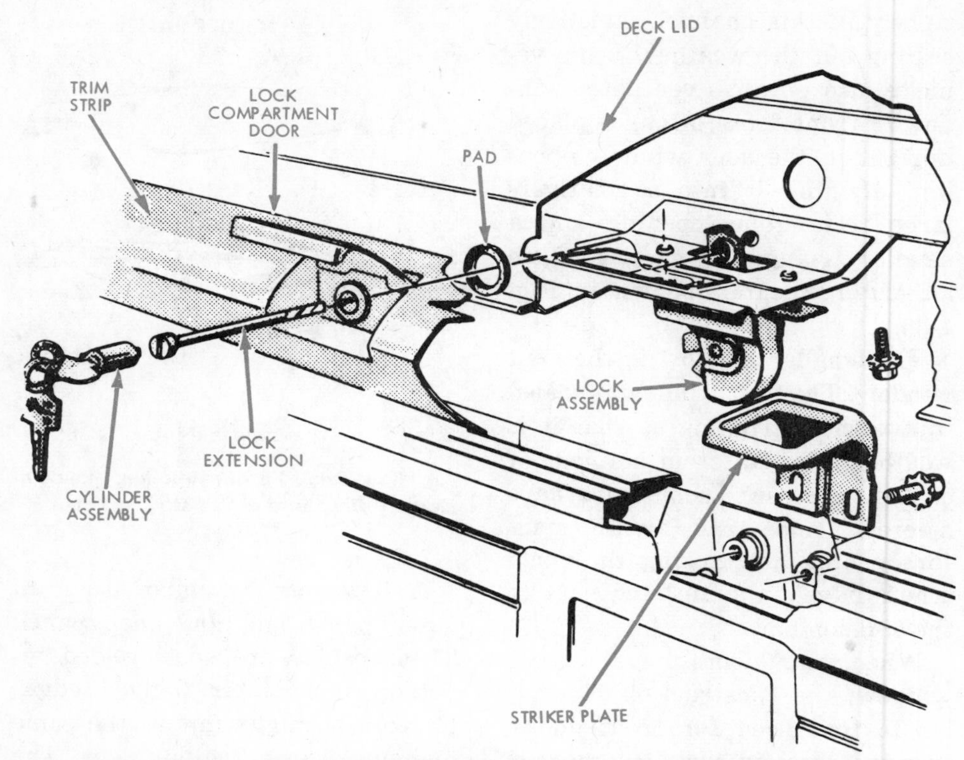

Fig. 1-35. Rear deck lid and latch mechanism without handle. (Lincoln-Mercury Div., Ford Motor Co.)

In some models, there is no handle on the rear deck lid, Fig. 1-34. Instead, the hinges are spring-loaded so that when the deck lid is unlocked, it automatically raises part way and is held in the open position by the springs in the hinge mechanism.

Installing Glass

Automotive glass, in terms of its installation, is either *stationary* (the windshield, some quarter windows, and the rear window or back light) or it is *moveable* (controlled vents, door windows, station wagon tailgate windows, and some quarter windows). In this section, our objective is to thoroughly describe the service procedures and techniques which apply to the replacement of each type.

In addition to the customary care one must take when handling glass, to protect it from impact, there are several general precautions which should be observed whenever a replacement is to be made.

Check Parts. Be certain that the replacement part is the correct part. The size and contour of the glass must be an exact fit in the opening into which it is to be installed. Thus, it pays to take the time to verify the piece before starting the job.

Use Protective Covers. Over all adjacent body surfaces, to minimize clean-up and avoid damage to paint finishes and fabrics, use a cover. These covers may also serve as a protection against chipping the glass or otherwise damaging the edges.

Inspect Hardware. Inspect for bends or obstructions the pinchweld flanges, glass run channels, frames, regulators, or whatever components may be involved in holding or moving the glass. Any indication of damage should be corrected before the replacement glass is installed, including dents in the body where the hardware fits.

Stationary Window Installations

Depending upon the manufacturer and model of car, windshields, and rear windows are installed either with butyl sealing tape, synthetic rubber adhesive caulking compound or pre-formed weatherstrip which has integral glass channeling and a peripheral slot which fits over the pinchweld flange. Fig. 1-36 is a composite which illustrates each of these methods of glass installation.

The factory recommended procedures for replacing glass installed by these methods follows.

Butyl Sealing Tape Installations. The first step in replacing a windshield or rear window is to remove all parts such as windshield wiper arms and blades, garnish moldings and reveal moldings, which might interfere with the job.

If the damaged glass incorporates a built-in radio antenna or a heating element, the electrical leads involved must be disconnected or cut depending upon the type of disconnect provisions supplied by the car manufacturer.

When automotive glass breaks rather than cracks, it has a tendency to pulverize. After cleaning up the loose pieces which have fallen out of the opening, remove any pieces which can be withdrawn by hand without force.

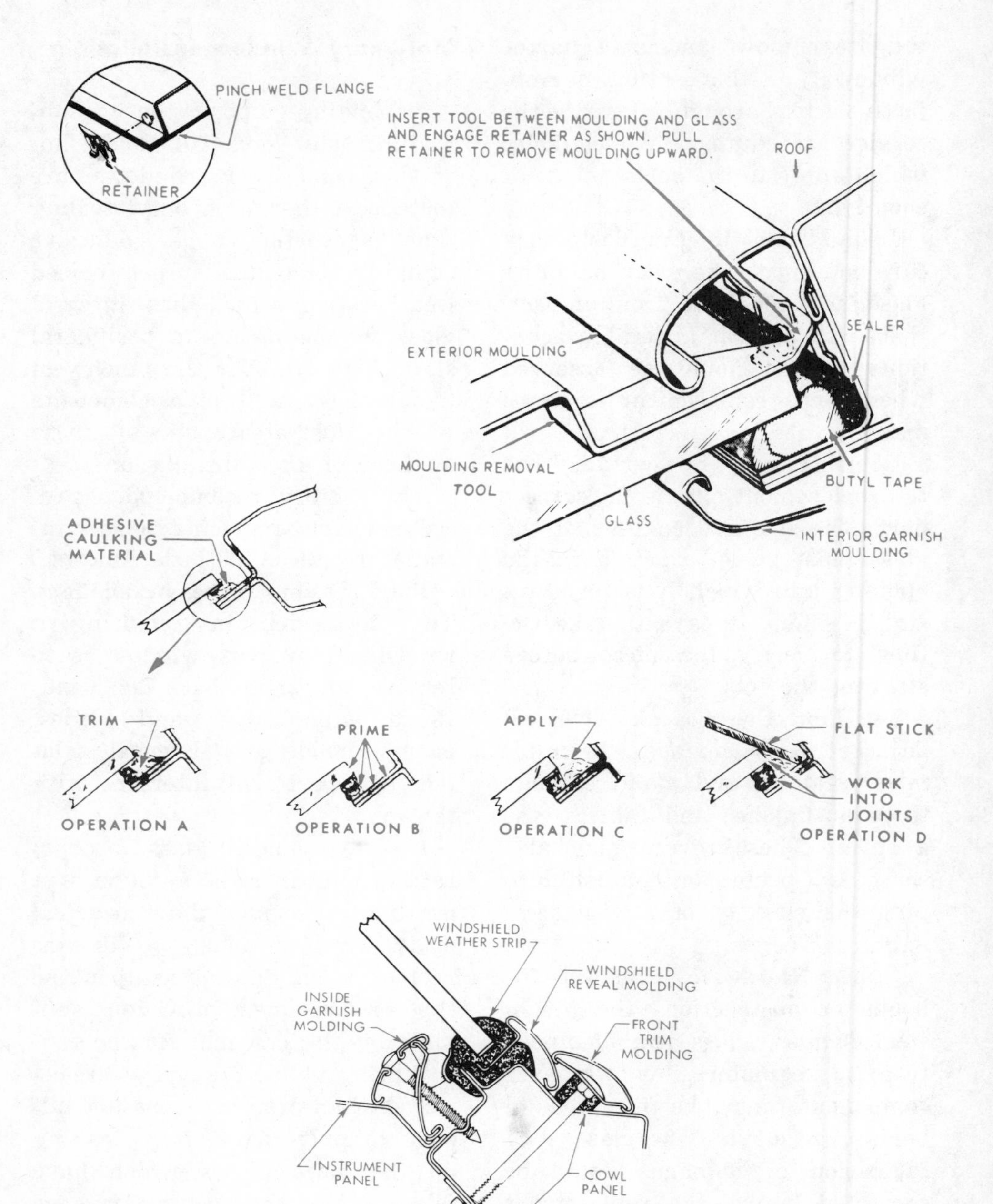

Fig. 1-36. Three types of stationary glass installation with some instructions.

The next step, if the glass is not pulverized to the point where the butyl tape is accessable, is to free the glass from adjacent surfaces. A tool is needed to accomplish this. The conventional devices used for stationary glass replacement are piano wire or an electric knife (hot knife method).

Piano Wire Removal. If piano wire is to be used, a piece should be cut to a length of approximately two feet. Then one end of the wire should be inserted between the edge of the glass and the surface of the pinchweld flange, Fig. 1-37.

When this is accomplished one end of the wire will be in the passenger compartment and the other will be protruding toward the hood. Wrap these loose ends around a piece of wooden dowel stock to form a handle at each end of the wire.

At this point, the aid of a second person will be needed to help pull the wire back and forth in a sawing motion which should proceed completely around the glass opening in the body. When this operation is finished, the glass can be lifted out of its opening.

The butyl tape is now exposed and ready to be removed. Using a wide-bladed screw driver or similar tool, pry the tape away from the pinchweld flange at any one of the corners in the glass opening. Then grasp the freed tape at a point close to the flange and pull it directly away from the flange. Most installations of this type have several spacers near the lower edge of the glass opening. These pieces should also be removed.

Fig. 1-37. Piano wire removal technique for removing stationary glass. (Fisher Body Div., General Motors Corp.)

The next step is to thoroughly clean the surfaces of body flanges in the opening. It is also the time to make any sheet metal molding retainer, or paint repairs which may be necessary.

Hot Knife Removal. Fig. 1-38 shows the method of removing glass with a hot knife. When a knife is used, the blade is inserted under the edge of the glass. Then, when the power is applied, the heated blade moves from side to side in an arc as it cuts the glass free from the tape.

Installation of replacement glass involves an important preliminary step. If the car being serviced is equipped with a vinyl roof, it is

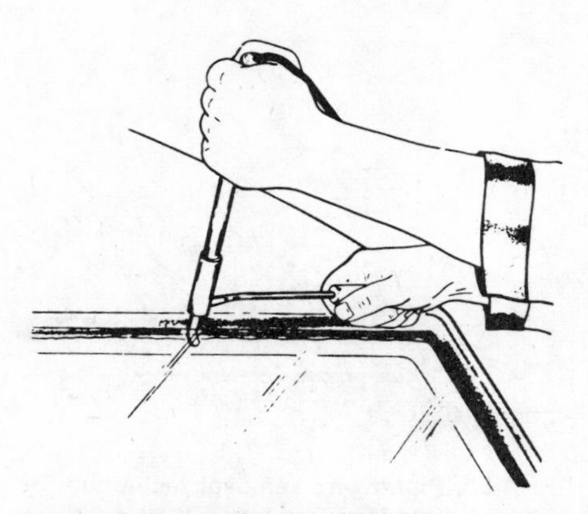

Fig. 1-38. Hot knife technique for removing stationary glass.

advisable to mask the vinyl in the area adjacent to the glass opening. It may also be advisable to mask the forward edge of the crash pad. Performing these precautionary steps will probably save time in clean-up as well as guard against accidental damage to the fabric.

When the masking operation is completed, install the spacers in their proper locations near the lower edge of the glass opening. Then temporarily install the replacement glass in the opening. Slide the glass to and fro in the opening as necessary to obtain the best glass-to-flange overlap condition. Then mark this location with a crayon.

Remove the glass and clean it thoroughly. Next, apply a coat of primer completely around the edge of the glass and inboard from the edge on the inner surface for a distance as specified by the manufacturer, approximately 3/8″.

While the primer is drying for its specified period of time, the self-adhering butyl tape may be installed in the glass opening. Tape installation should begin approximately mid-way up a side (vertical) flange. The tape should be positioned so that it doesn't overlap the edge of the pinchweld by more than 1/16″. It is important that the tape is not stretched at the corners of the glass opening. This will prevent leaks.

When the tape has been routed around the opening, cut off the excess in a manner which enables the making of a neat butt joint or seam. Fig. 1-39 shows a typical primer application to the glass and a butyl tape seam.

Now with the primer properly dried and the tape in position in the glass opening, install the glass in the opening using the previously made crayon mark to obtain proper alignment. Press the glass firmly against the tape, using hand pressure.

Visually check the quality of the seal. If there is a dull spot between the primed glass and the tape, the seal is poor at that point. Additional hand pressure at the dull area will usually correct the condition. Most manufacturers recommend a clearance between the glass and the pinchweld flange of approximately ¼″.

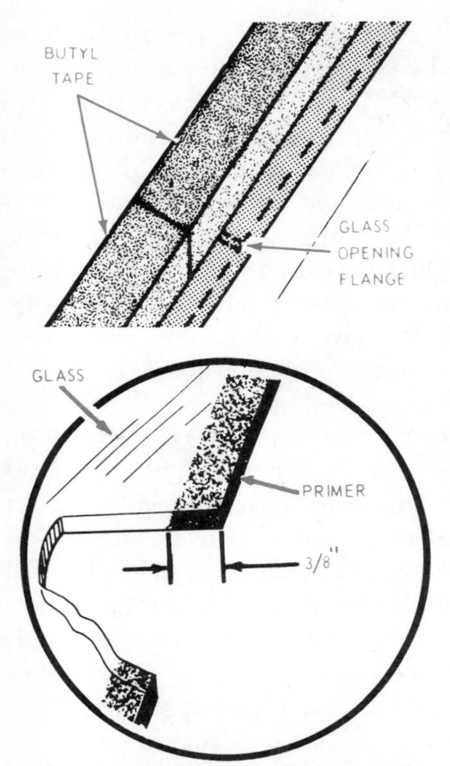

Fig. 1-39. Glass primer and tape installation. (Ford Motor Co.)

There will probably be some excess primer on the glass after the installation is completed. This may be removed with a razor blade and a cleaning cloth dipped in naphtha. Be careful that the naphtha does not get on the vinyl trim as naphtha may dissolve the vinyl.

The next step is to test the installation with water. A spray should be directed toward all points around the perimeter of the glass. If leaks are detected, they may be repaired by applying liquid butyl along the dry edges of the glass in the area where the leak occurs.

The final step is to remove any masking tape or other protective device used, install the garnish and reveal moldings, install the wiper arms and blades, connect any electrical circuits which were disconnected, and perform whatever clean-up may be necessary.

Adhesive Caulking Installations. Stationary glass which has been installed with adhesive caulking may be removed in the same manner as that previously described for butyl tape repairs, Fig. 1-37 and 1-38.

Manufacturers who use the adhesive caulking method of installation suggest that the extent of damage or other conditions which necessitate the removal of stationary glass open two avenues to repair . . . the *short* method and the *extended* method. The difference between the two is the extent to which the old caulking material is removed. If all caulking is removed down to the pinchweld flange, the extended method is being applied. If a smoothly trimmed bead of caulk is left in the flange area and new caulking material is added, the short method is being used.

Procedures related to preparations for replacement of glass, the removal of obstructing components, and masking of adjacent paint and vinyl are also similar to those outlined for butyl tape repairs. Masking is perhaps more critical inasmuch as a soft sealer is being used.

In describing the caulking procedure recommended by the manufacturer, we will begin with the extended method at the point where the glass has been removed from the opening.

The first step is to remove all of the old caulking from the pinchweld area. At this point it is advisable to check the flange for irregularities and the molding clips for any indication of damage and make whatever repairs and replacements may be necessary.

Spacers with this type of installations are required at specific locations around the glass opening. Fig. 1-40 illustrates a typical arrangement.

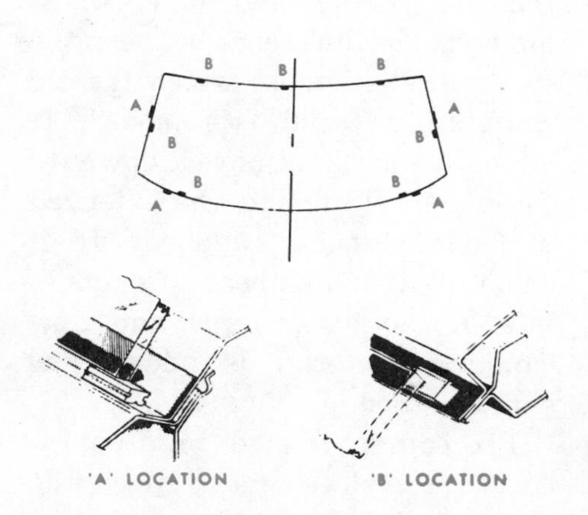

Fig. 1-40. Glass spacer installation. (Fisher Body Div., General Motors Corp.)

Notice in the illustration that the two spacers have different configurations. Both are installed in the approximate locations shown, using black weatherstrip adhesive or adhesive caulking material.

With the spacers in place, the glass is ready to be installed in the opening for a positioning fit. Fig. 1-41 shows a stationary window in position with masking tape being used to align the piece with the body. This is merely a variation of the crayon marking procedure mentioned in our description of glass installation over butyl tape. Either indexing method can be used with either type of installation.

When the glass has been positioned and marked, remove the glass and apply strips of masking tape so that a border of approximately ¼″ of glass is exposed completely around the window as in Fig. 1-41.

As shown in Fig. 1-42, the gun used for applying the caulking material is a standard tool. The nozzle and tube of caulking com-

Fig. 1-41. Indexing the glass to the body. (Fisher Body Div., General Motors Corp.)

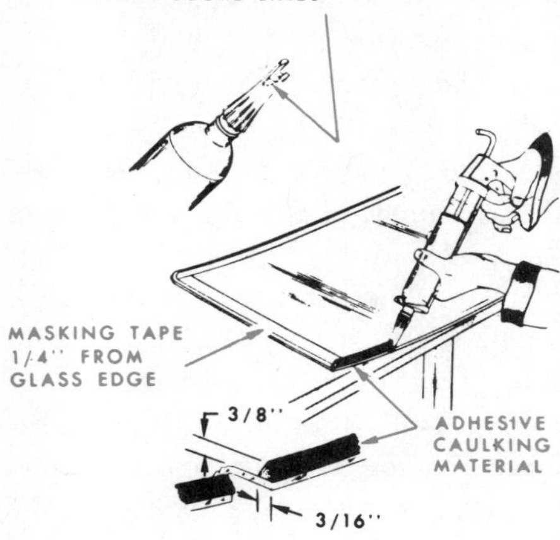

Fig. 1-42. Application of adhesive caulking. (Fisher Body Div., General Motors Corp.)

pound are usually bought as components of a repair kit. Fig. 1-42 also points out that the extended method of glass installation requires a simple adjustment of the nozzle to obtain the desired size of caulking bead.

Before applying the caulking, it is important that the border of glass between the tape and the edge be thoroughly cleaned with water and dried. Then a bead of the specified dimension should be run around this surface. Since curing time for most caulking compounds of this type is approximately 15 minutes, installation of the glass within this time limit is critical.

When the bead of caulking has been applied, place the glass in the opening and align it with the tape or crayon index marker. Then apply hand pressure around the edge to establish a smooth, even bond between the glass, caulking, and flange. Spray test the installation as soon as it is satisfactorily seated. If a leak is detected, use a flat-bladed tool to work in some additional caulking material at the point of defect.

The concluding steps, of course, are to remove the masking tape, perform the necessary clean-up, and install all parts which were removed.

With the short method of replacement, the steps involved are similar to those prescribed for the extended method. Inasmuch as a bead of cured caulking material remains in the flange area, spacer installation does not apply. Beyond that point in the extended method description, the steps to follow are the same.

Weatherstrip Type Seal. When pre-formed weatherstrip type of glass retention is involved, the removal of obstructing parts is again necessary. In recent production years, this method of installation has usually been confined to rear quarter and rear windows on passenger cars. Thus, the removal of garnish and reveal moldings should clear the obstructing components.

The methods used for reveal molding retention varies by vehicle manufacture, year, and model. In all cases the retainers are hidden and often require a special tool to free them.

Because of the many variations in molding installation techniques, it would be advisable to consult the appropriate vehicle shop manual for instructions regarding removal procedure.

When the moldings have been removed from a weatherstrip type of glass installation, the weatherstrip and glass can be pushed out of the opening. An assistant will most likely be required to perform this operation.

If either the weatherstrip or glass is to be reused, all old sealing material must be removed from the part. The old sealing material must also be removed from the glass opening in the body.

Replacement procedure begins with the application of sealer in the glass groove in the weatherstrip. The strip is then installed on the glass and positioned for uniformity. The next step is to install a draw cord in the pinchweld groove in the weatherstrip.

Fig. 1-43 illustrates this operation. The draw cord should overlap approximately 18 inches at the free ends after it has been passed through the pinchweld slot and then taped to the glass as shown.

The next step is to place the glass in its opening and, with the help of an assistant, apply hand pressure to the outside of the glass while the draw cord is being

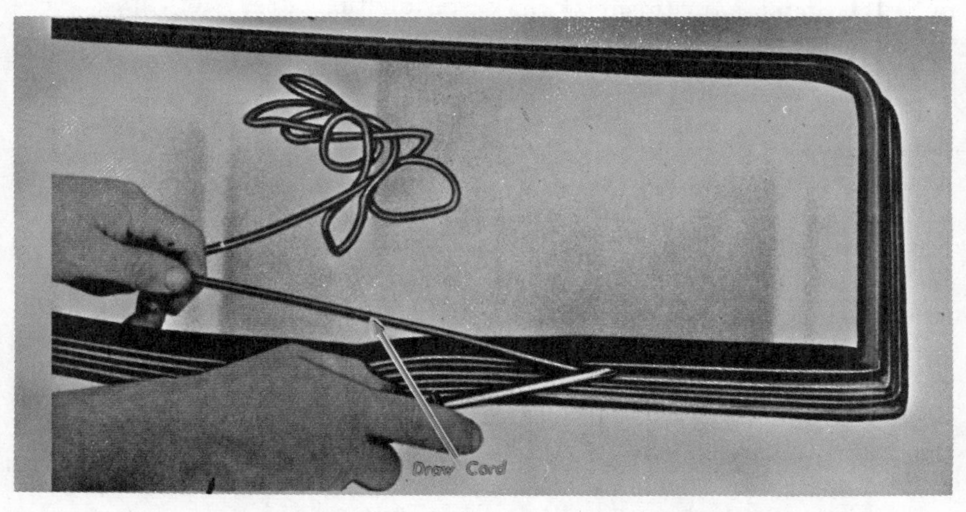

Fig. 1-43. Draw cord technique of glass installation. (Ford Motor Co.)

pulled to guide the lip of the weatherstrip over the flange.

In sequence, the strip should be fed onto the flange along the bottom, then up the sides, and finally across the top.

Finish the operation with a leak test, spot repairs if needed, installation of moldings, and general clean-up. If heated glass is involved, be sure that wiring is properly insulated at the flange, properly routed, and securely connected to its lead from the power source.

Movable Glass Installations

Movable glass on passenger cars is used in controlled ventilators, front and rear doors, some quarter windows, and back windows, primarily in station wagons. Each of these types of windows may either be power or manually operated. The text materials which follow describe these various types of movable glass.

Door Component Nomenclatures. Figs. 1-44 and 1-45 are provided as general reference pieces for those readers who may be unfamiliar with the construction of a door assembly. These figures illustrate two types of doors in common use in the industry. Fig. 1-46 shows a typical rear door glass installation and the mechanism used to operate the window. Some rear doors

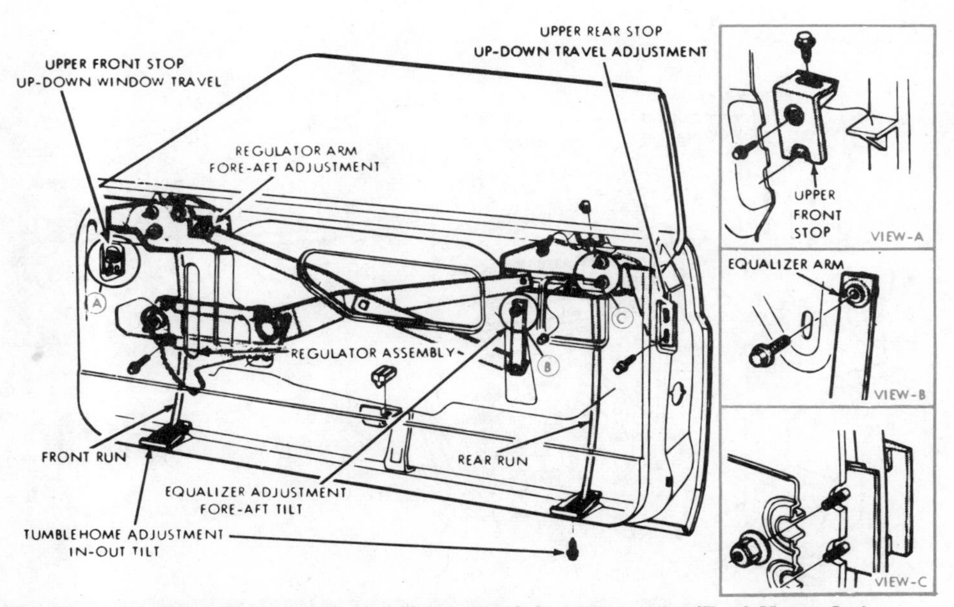

Fig. 1-44. Ventless window method and stages of door assembly. (Ford Motor Co.)

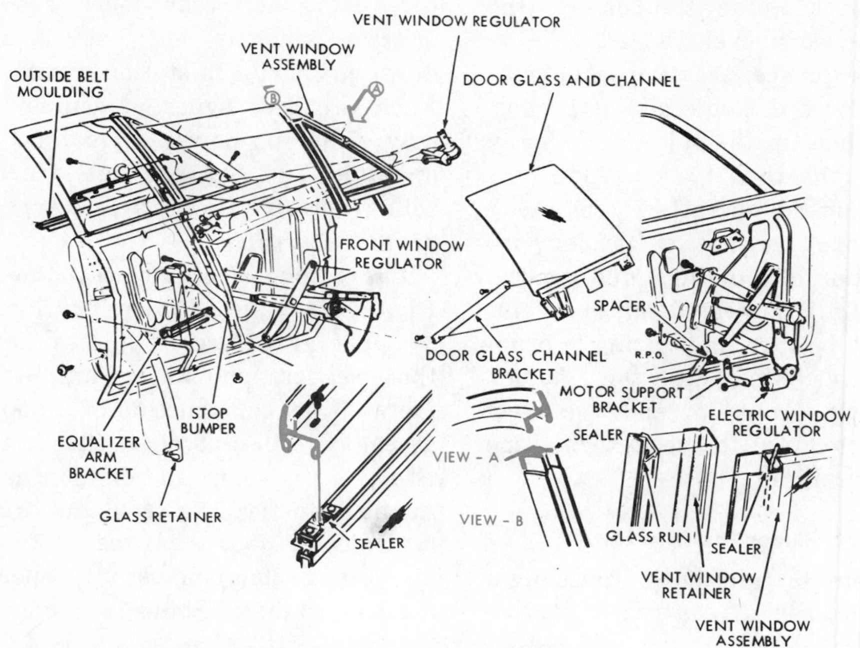

Fig. 1-45. Front door assembly with vent window assembly.

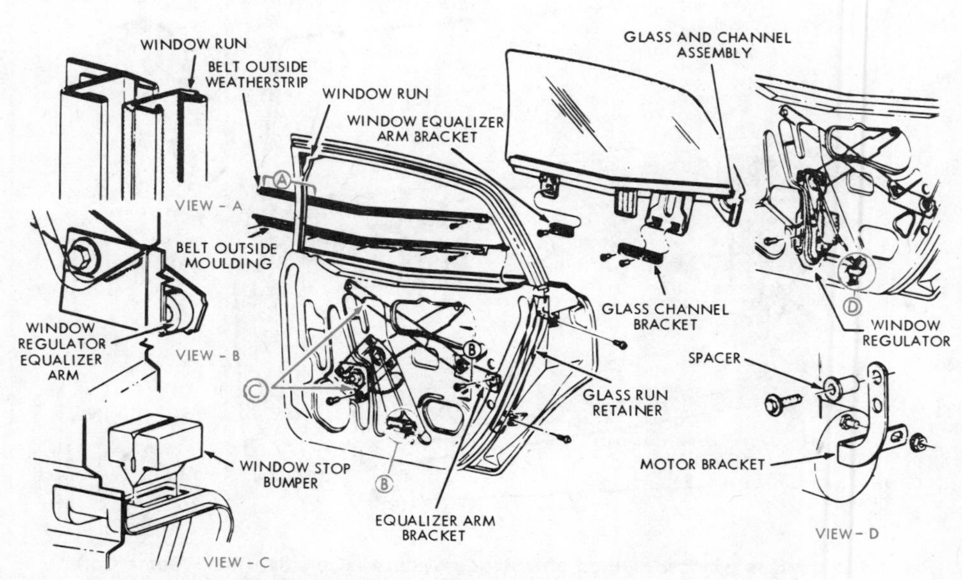

Fig. 1-46. Rear door window installation. (Ford Motor Co.)

incorporate a segment of stationary glass.

Front Door Window Ventilators. Access to ventilator attaching parts requires removal of the door trim panel and peeling back of all or a portion of the water resistant material which covers the door inner panel. When this is accomplished the attachments are cleared for removal.

In some cars, the vent window is an integral part of the window reveal or garnish molding. With this type of vent window arrangement, the vent window can be disassembled easily by removing the reveal or garnish molding.

A division bar is placed between the vent window opening and the large window opening. A weather strip is installed around the ventilator window, constructed in such a way that the vent window is sealed securely against the weather when closed, but is easily opened.

Another type of vent window arrangement is shown in Fig. 1-47. With this type of construction, the division bar and vent window are considered as a separate unit of the over-all door construction. The unit can be replaced without removing the large door glass.

Front and Rear Moveable Glass. Door window glass may be secured to it's holding brackets in one of several ways depending upon the vehicle manufacturer's preference. In current production, the most frequent methods used are bolting or riveting the base of the glass to the front and rear brackets. Some installations, however, use plain channel-type brackets with the glass being secured with a bonding tape or adhesive.

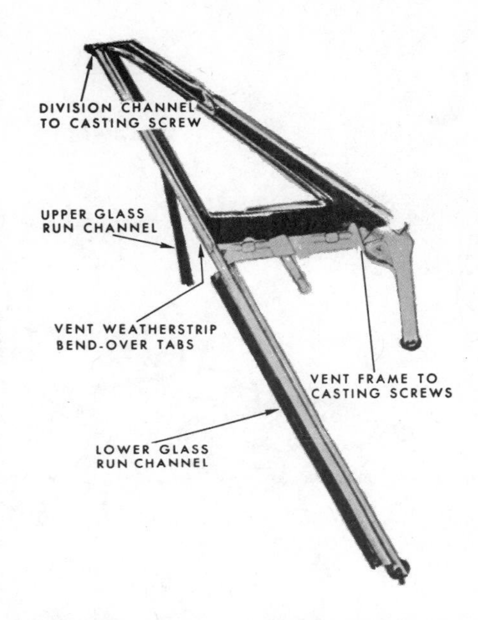

Fig. 1-47. Controlled ventilator glass installation. (Fisher Body Div., General Motors Corp.)

Fig. 1-48 illustrates a bolt-on type of front door glass. Notice that the glass configuration is designed for necessary clearance along the bottom edge and that the attaching holes are provided in the glass. When assembled, the glass is insulated from all metal parts by the neoprene bushings,

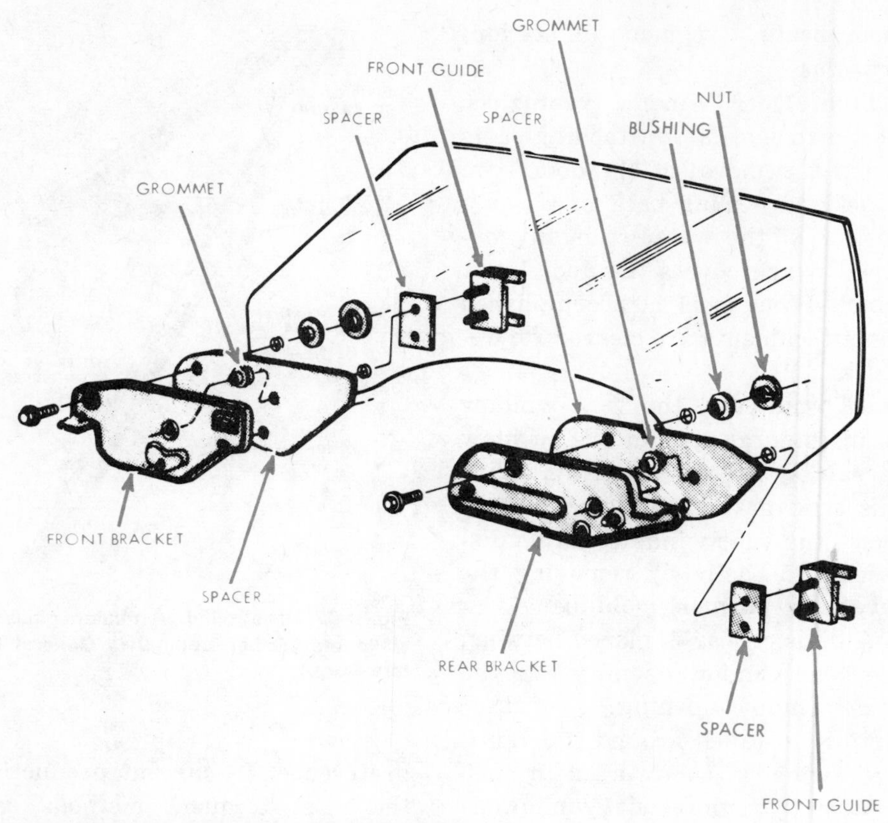

Fig. 1-48. Bolt-on front window glass. (Ford Motor Co.)

rubber spacers, and grommets.

A similar construction is used when the glass is assembled to its bracket(s) with rivets.

There are only minor variations in the overall design of door windows used by the various automobile manufacturers. Thus service procedures involving adjustment, removal, and installation are quite similar.

Fig. 1-49 is provided to give you the nomenclature of the components involved. The *tumblehome adjustment* in the figure refers to the inward and outward tilt of the glass at its upper edge. It is emphasized that adjustment and replacement procedures for moveable glass are similar for all cars. When actually performing a job, however, it is advisable to follow manufacturer's instructions for the specific installation.

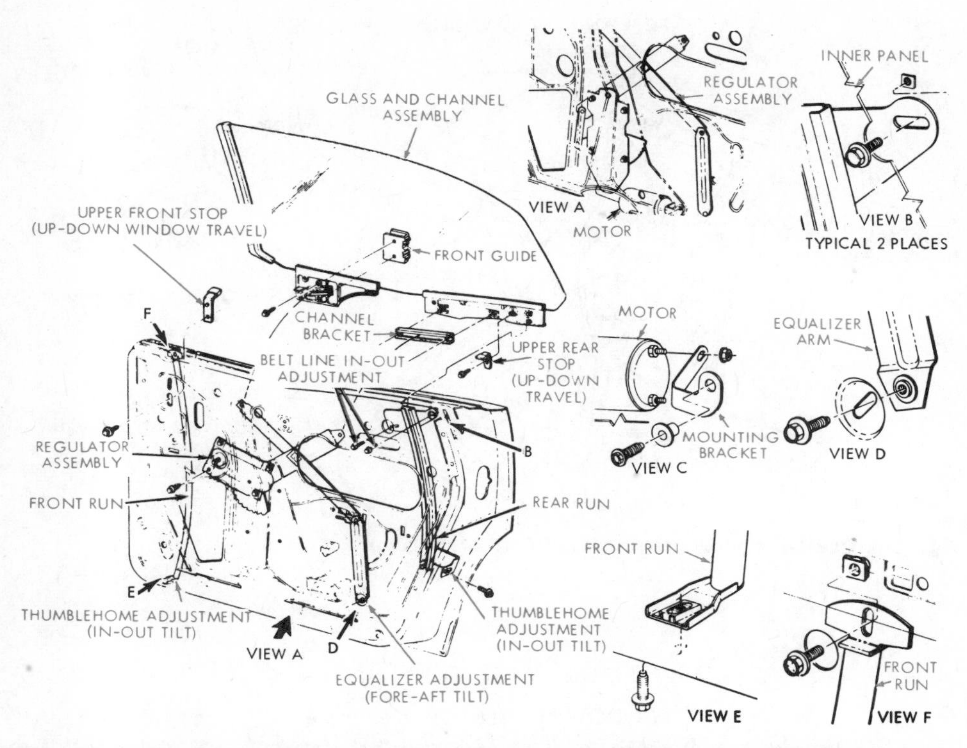

Fig. 1-49. Rear window attachments, with provisions for attaching and adjusting glass.

Quarter Window. The quarter window is the window in the rear quarter upper side panel. In some cars, the quarter window is a stationary installation and no provision is made for raising or lowering it. With this type of construction, the installation is similar to a windshield or rear window.

In other cars, the quarter window can be raised or lowered. A typical, movable quarter window arrangement is show in Fig. 1-50. In this case, the quarter window construction is similar to regular door window construction. Some quarter windows incorporate a small vent window. When this is the case, construction is similar to that of regular door vent windows.

In other cars, the quarter window is a vent window, similar in construction to front door vent windows, except that it is larger. These windows usually hinge at the top and the bottom near the front. Consequently, they pivot around a point forward of the center of the opening. In most cases, they are fastened in the closed po-

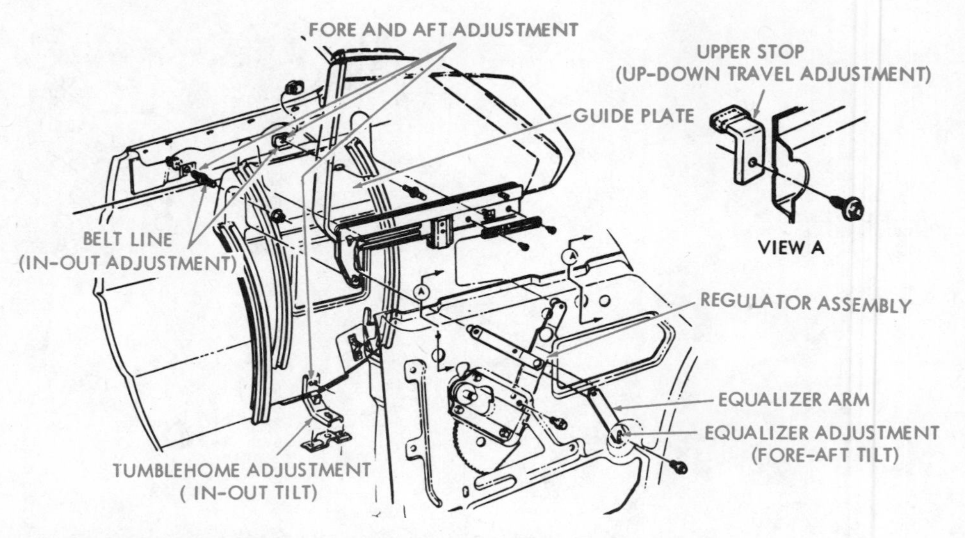

Fig. 1-50. Quarter window construction. (Ford Motor Co.)

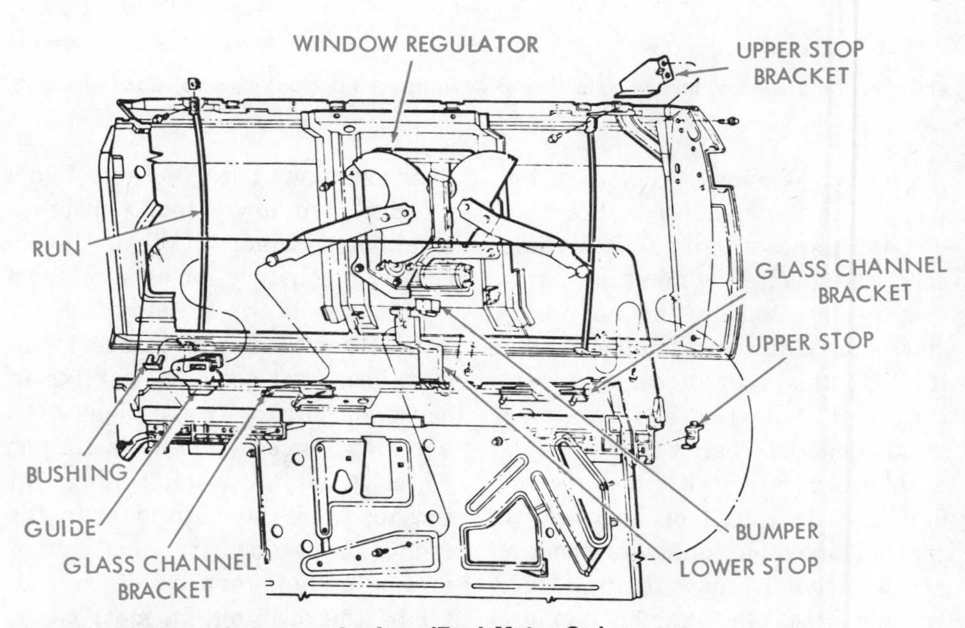

Fig. 1-51. Tailgate window mechanism. (Ford Motor Co.)

sition with thumb latches at the rear. They are also mounted in weatherstripping so that a tight weather seal is assured.

Tailgate Windows. All station wagons have a window in the upper portion of the tailgate. Fig. 1-51 shows a typical tailgate window arrangement. In this installation, the window is raised and lowered by means of an electric motor. In other arrangements, the window is hand operated by a crank.

Hardware and Trim

The preceding sections of this chapter have set forth in some detail the basic construction of automobile bodies and cabs. Bodies need hardware and trim to complete them and to conceal rough unfinished edges. In the automobile body the doors need handles and locks. The window openings are rough when viewed from the inside and require decorative trim to give them a finished appearance. On the car body the finishing touches, which are put on the outside as well as the inside, are called either *hardware* or *trim.*

The cars illustrated in Figs. 1-52 and 1-53 have all of the exterior hardware and trim parts labeled, and the method of attaching some of the items is shown.

In addition to providing eye appeal, some trim parts are functional as well as decorative. However, they all contribute to the comfort and convenience of the passenger. Door handles, window handles, locks, latches, etc., are all hardware parts. Trim parts, on the other hand, include moldings and some of the soft trim inside the car, and the bumpers, grille, and moldings on the outside of the car.

A car interior, with the hardware and trim parts labeled, is shown in Fig. 1-54.

The location of all hardware and trim parts is described in this section. How these parts are held in place is also described and illustrated. These discussions on trim and hardware are given under headings which are descriptive of the parts involved.

Standard methods for fastening trim parts in place are used throughout the automotive industry. The devices employed are designed for use in specific locations, and they are made so that hardware and trim parts can be easily and quickly removed. A variety of trim fasteners and retainers is shown, Fig. 1-55.

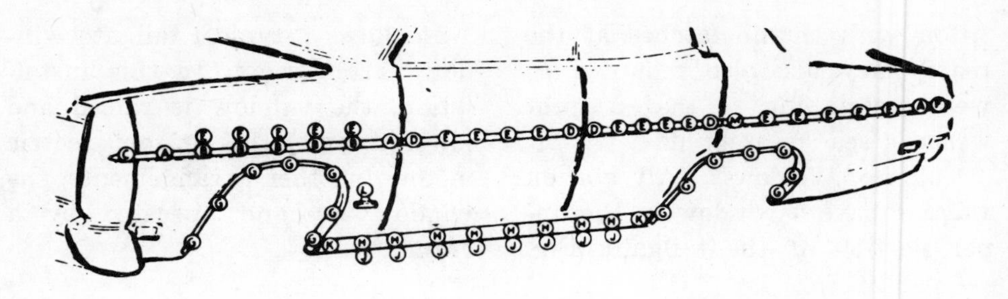

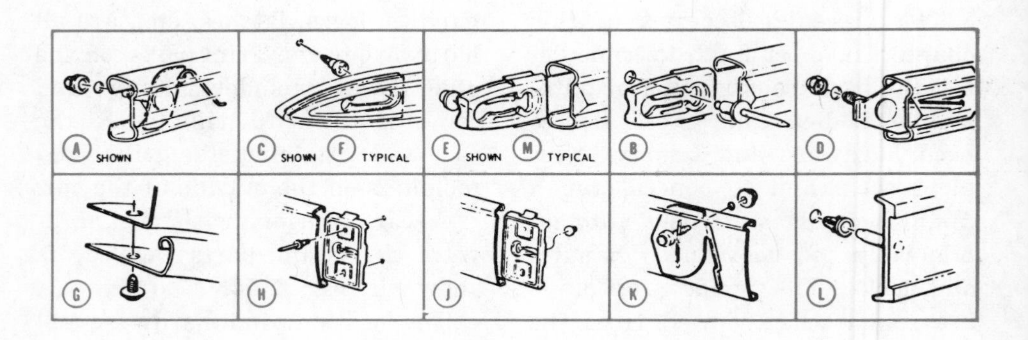

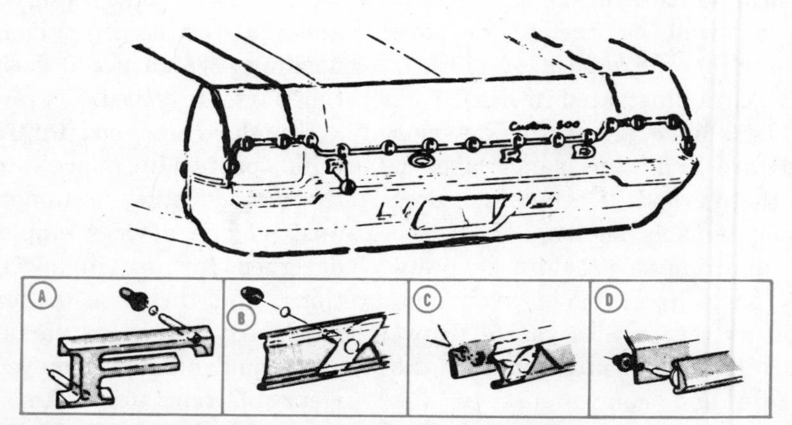

Fig. 1-52. Exterior hardware and trim locations. (Ford Motor Co.)

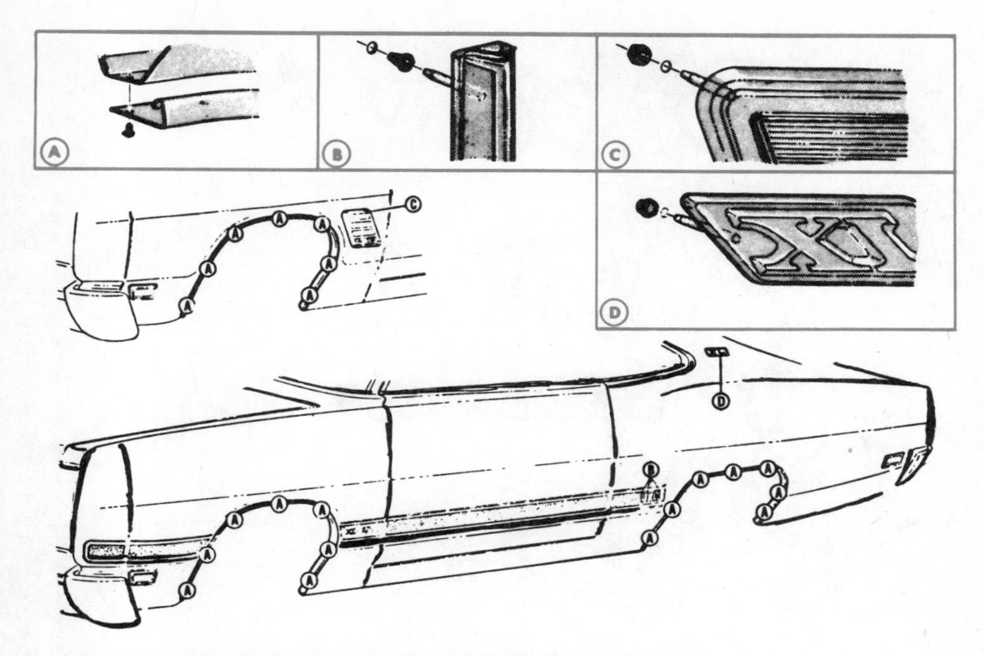

Fig. 1-53. Other trim and hardware locations. (Ford Motor Co.)

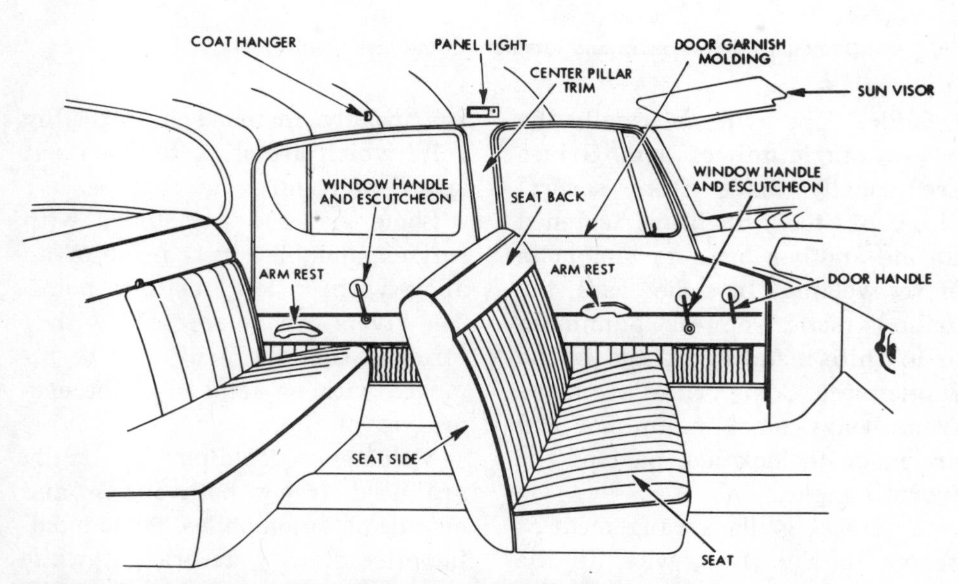

Fig. 1-54. Interior hardward and trim parts, an inside cutaway view.

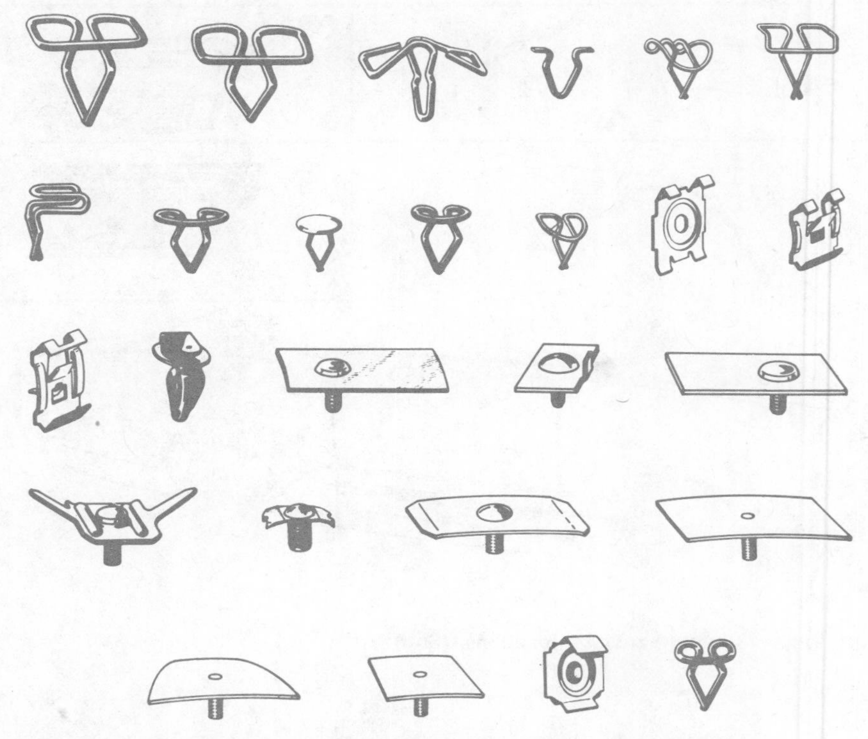

Fig. 1-55. Common trim fasteners and retainers of the last twenty years.

Grille. The grille is usually the largest single unit of trim. Grilles are usually made from several pieces of steel which are fastened to one another by nuts and bolts or by welding. In some cases, the grille is made from cast aluminum or a white metal alloy, and is one single piece. Some grilles are made from heavy steel stampings and are made to look like part of the front bumper.

A typical grille arrangement is shown in Fig. 1-56, with all the component parts labeled. Grilles are usually fastened in place by bolts which attach it to the front splash pan and front fenders.

Some grilles are fastened with soft expandable rivets made of an alloy with a low melting point. The rivets can be softened with a torch so that the grille can be removed without damage to the decorative plating.

Moldings. Moldings generally are used freely both inside and outside on automobiles. Some moldings are strictly decorative, while others are functional. Moldings dif-

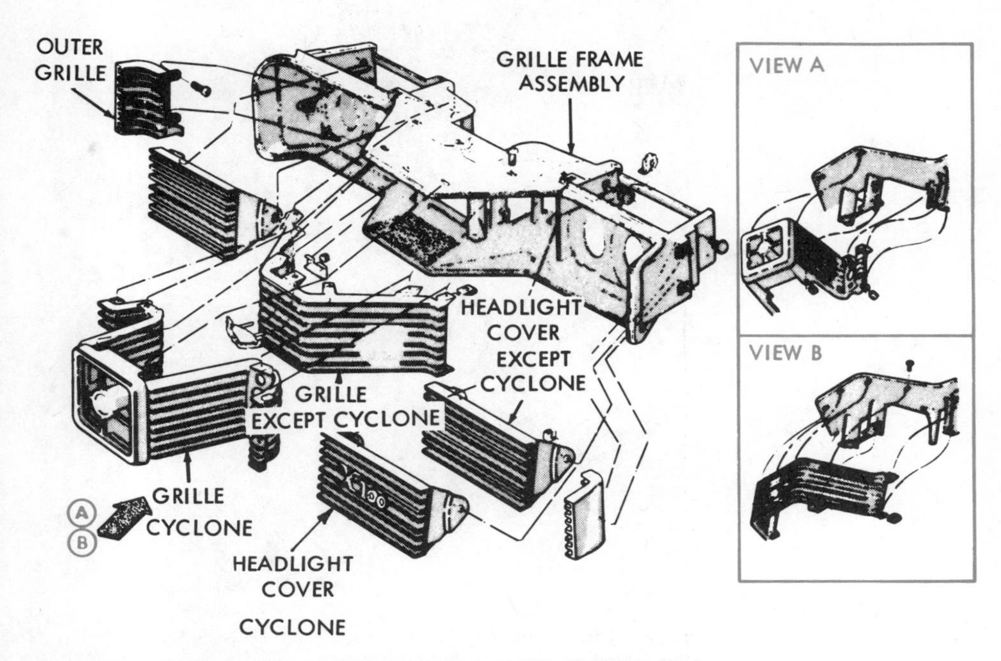

Fig. 1-56. Exploded view of grill arrangement. (Ford Motor Co.)

fer in type and style, depending on where they are used. The moldings shown in Fig. 1-57 are secured in place by retainers and by special clips designed for the particular model. The clips usually fasten to the molding and extend through the body to be secured on the inside by speed nuts which fit the clip studs.

The moldings used around the windshield and rear windows on most cars are held in place in an entirely different manner. The moldings generally used in a windshield installation are shown in Fig. 1-58.

The weather strip which is used to secure the windshield glass is also channeled to receive the outside reveal molding. The molding is held by its own spring action after it is inserted into the weather strip. The inside garnish molding which fits across the top of the instrument panel and around the windshield opening is fastened in place with sheet metal screws.

Sheet metal screws have bright metal on the heads so that they present an attractive appearance. Generally, the screws used are of the Phillips-head type (cross-slotted head) which requires a special screwdriver.

Another arrangement of windshield molding attachment is shown in Fig. 1-59.

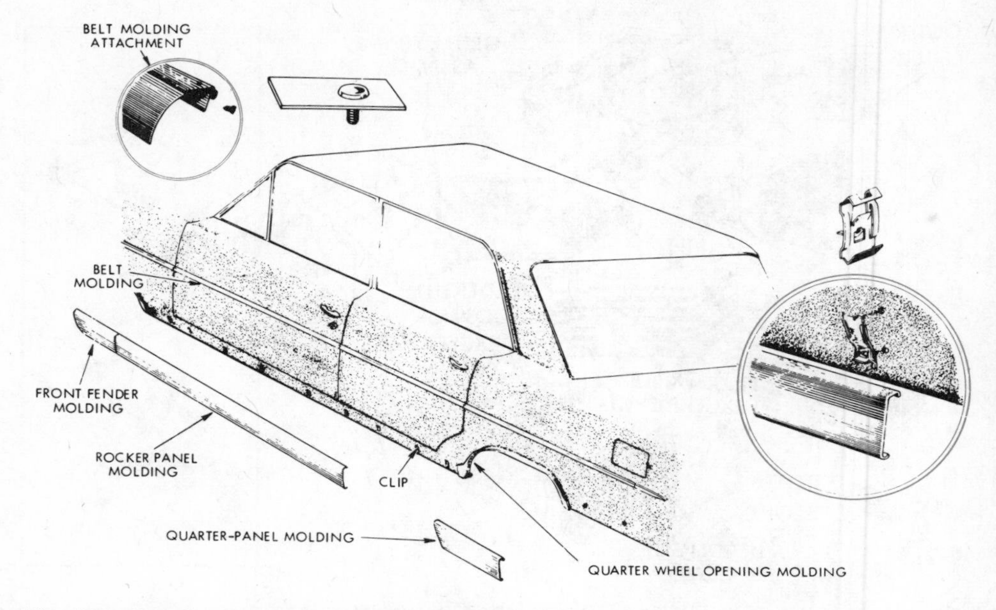

Fig. 1-57. Standard moldings and trim found on full line cars.

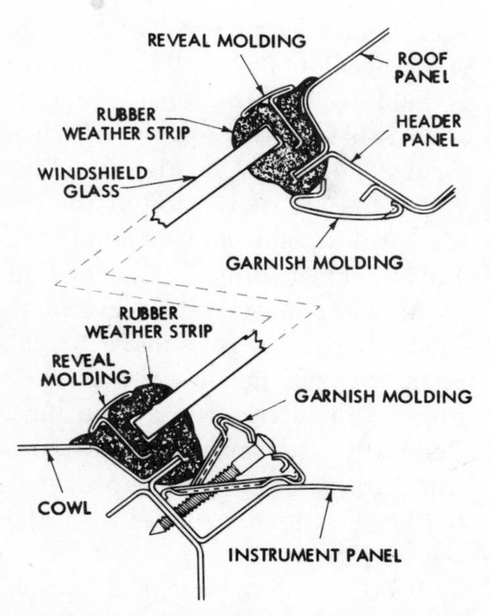

Fig. 1-58. Windshield installation showing moldings.

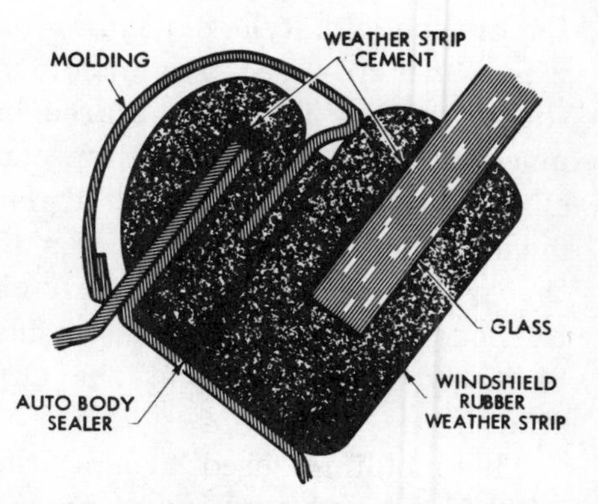

Fig. 1-59. Section through windshield weather strip and moldings.

The moldings used around rear windows usually are installed in the same manner as those around the windshield on the same model. Before such moldings can be removed, it is necessary to break the seal between the weather strip and the body. This can be done easily in most cases by inserting a thin knife blade between the weather strip and the body, then running it along the length of the molding.

A different type of molding is used around the window openings in the doors. This molding, called *door garnish molding,* is held in place by sheet metal screws. The screws may or may not be visible when the molding is in place with the door closed. If they do not show, it is because they are covered by the upholstery on the lower part of the door.

Most of the moldings are held in place by screws through the molding into the door inner panel. A spring clip is usually mounted on the door inner panel behind the lower portion of the molding. This engages the molding and holds it firmly against the door trim pad.

To remove a garnish molding, remove the screws and the door inside locking rod knob. Lift the molding out and upward to disengage it from the lower portion of the window opening and the spring retainer.

Bumpers. Bumpers may or may not be considered as trim. In any event, they are a necessary and functional part of the vehicle. Bumpers protect the car from damage due to minor collision.

Most bumpers are held in place by heavy steel strips which are bolted at one end to the bumper, the other end to the frame. Bumpers vary, of course, in size and shape depending on the make of car. Some bumpers are quite massive.

Handles. All of the doors on a vehicle have handles with which the latch is operated. Handles are used both inside and outside on the doors leading into the passenger compartment. A complete outside door handle assembly is shown in Fig. 1-60. Another type of outside door handle is shown in Fig. 1-61.

Only the front doors on a vehicle usually can be locked with a key, although some models have been produced with facilities for locking all four doors with a key.

In some cars, the lock on the front doors is constructed integrally with the door handle push button. In this case, the key opening is in the push button. On other cars, the locking mechanism is separate from the handle. A separate opening is provided in the door for the lock.

All outside door handles extend through the outer panel so that the necessary linkage can be connected to operate the latch mechanism. They are given ornate but functional designs to blend with the trim pattern of the vehicle.

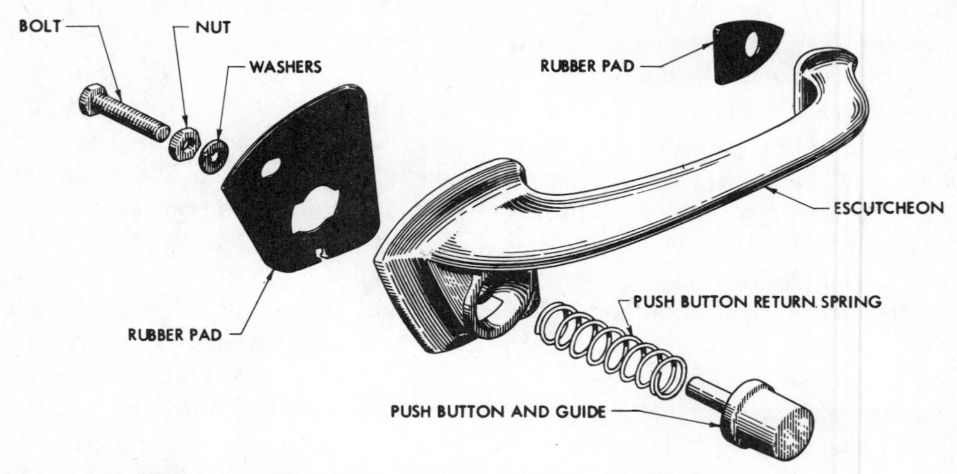

Fig. 1-60. Exploded view of door handle assembly for easy reference.

Fig. 1-61. Assembled and mounted door handle assembly. (Lincoln-Mercury Div., Ford Motor Co.)

Door handles are usually fastened in place by means of a machine screw through the door inner panel. This screw is accessible when the door is opened.

The deck lid door lock is usually an integral part of the handle. One type of deck lid handle and lock arrangement is shown in Fig. 1-62. With this arrangement, the handle is actually a decorative molding with a functional purpose.

Other arrangements have an integral deck lid handle and lock which is similar in appearance and operation to the passenger compartment door handle and lock. In some cars, the deck lid handle and lock are separate units, an opening being provided in the door for each.

All deck lid handles are secured from the inside with machine

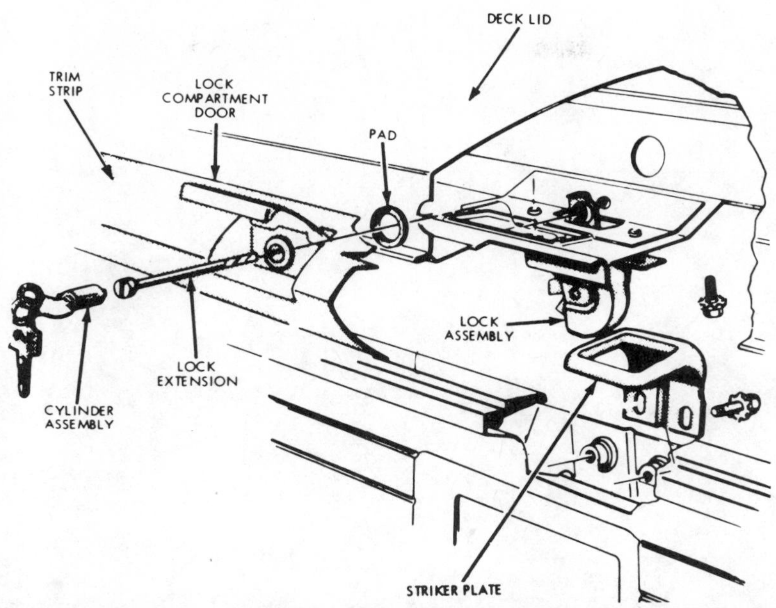

Fig. 1-62. Rear deck lid and latch mechanism without handle. (Lincoln-Mercury Div., Ford Motor Co.)

screws which are accessible when the deck lid is opened.

Inside door handles are used only on the doors which open into the passenger compartment. In most cases, an escutcheon plate, held in place by the handle, fits over the handle shaft and covers the hole where the handle comes through the door trim pad. This gives the handle a surface to ride on when the door or window is operated, Fig. 1-63.

The handle is held in place by a push fit pin which is concealed under the escutcheon when it is in place. A spring inside the escutcheon allows the escutcheon to be depressed for access to this retaining pin.

Another type of door handle which is used on some cars has an integral handle and escutcheon held in place by a spring retainer or *horseshoe clip,* as shown in Fig. 1-64. It is necessary to use a special pair of thin pliers to remove the spring retainer before the handle can be removed. When the retainer is removed, the handle can be pulled off the shaft easily.

Door Trim Pads. Door trim pads are the coverings used to conceal the lower portion of the inside panel of the doors. The pads are usually prefabricated and assem-

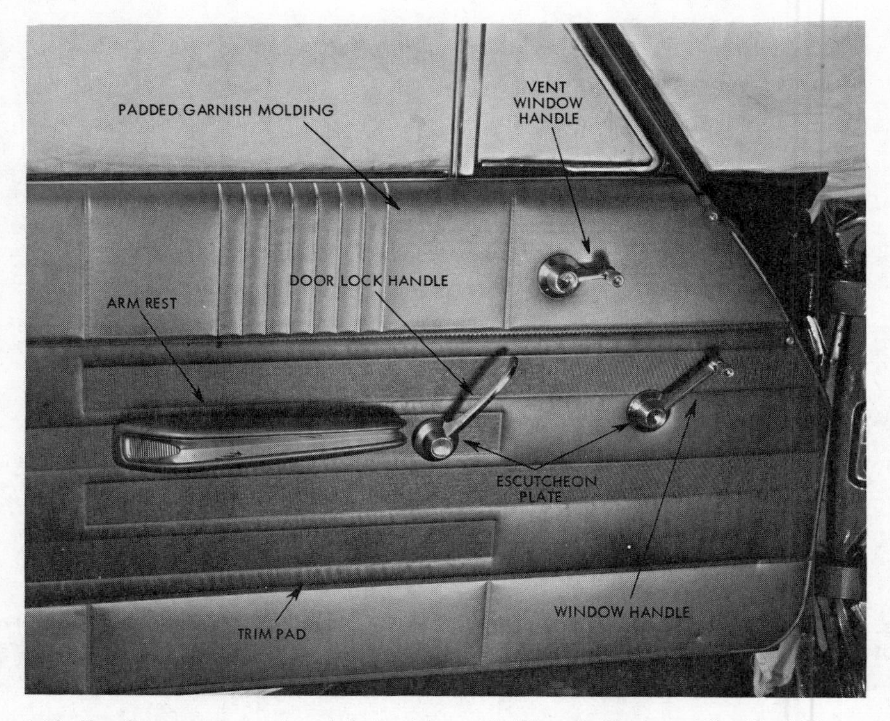

Fig. 1-63. Handle arrangement on interior trim pad. (Lincoln-Mercury Div., Ford Motor Co.)

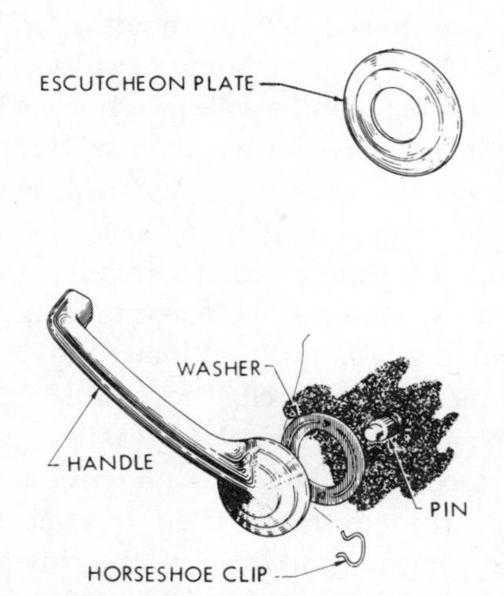

Fig. 1-64. Door handle and escutcheon, held by horseshoe clip. (Ford Motor Co.)

bled on the door as one unit. These pads are held in place by sheet metal screws and spring clips such as those illustrated previously (Fig. 1-55). A typical door trim pad is illustrated in Fig. 1-63. The pad is held firmly at each corner by sheet metal screws.

Door arm rests are provided on most cars, Fig. 1-63. They are sometimes considered as a part of the door trim pad. Arm rests are usually held in place by sheet metal screws which extend through the arm rest and trim into the inner metal.

Any trim or chrome which appears on the side of a fender is usually held in place by specially designed clips or fasteners which allow easy removal of the trim.

The unsupported edges of the fenders are formed into a bead to prevent cracks from developing in the edge of the fender due to vibration. Bending also provides a smooth finished appearance to the edge of the fender.

Rear Fenders. Rear fender construction differs greatly among the various makes of cars. In general, the rear fender is bolted to the body in the same manner as the front fender. However, many cars have no rear fender as such. Instead, the fender is an integral part of the rear quarter panel.

When the fender is bolted to the body proper, it is considered an *independent fender.*

Fender brackets are used as well as mudguards. These parts are easily recognized, and the method of removal is usually obvious.

When the fender is an integral part of the quarter panel, the inner construction is utilized to form part of a housing around the wheel called a wheelhouse.

The outer half of the wheelhouse is a separate panel which is welded to the underbody to complete the housing. This housing is totally concealed by the rear quarter panel, and damage done to it is sometimes difficult to detect. This wheel housing prevents road dirt from being thrown upward between the outer panel and inner body construction. The outer side of the wheelhouse usually is attached to the quarter panel around the wheel opening. The bottom edge of the quarter panel is flanged inward and upward around the lower edge of the outer wheelhouse.

Shields

Panels called *shields* or *stone deflectors* are mounted between the bumpers and the body proper, Fig. 1-69. The purpose of such a panel is to keep as much road dirt as possible from flying up between the bumpers and the body.

Sometimes fender skirts are used on the rear fenders of cars. These skirts cover the wheel opening and are attached to the fender by clamps. A shield of this type is used more for decorative purposes than any other reason.

Another type of shield is that used behind the front fender and under the grille assembly on some cars. The shield used behind the front fender, between the fender and the engine compartment, is called a *fender apron* or splash shield, Fig. 1-71.

The purpose of the fender apron is to keep road dirt and mud from entering the engine compartment. The apron is generally bolted into

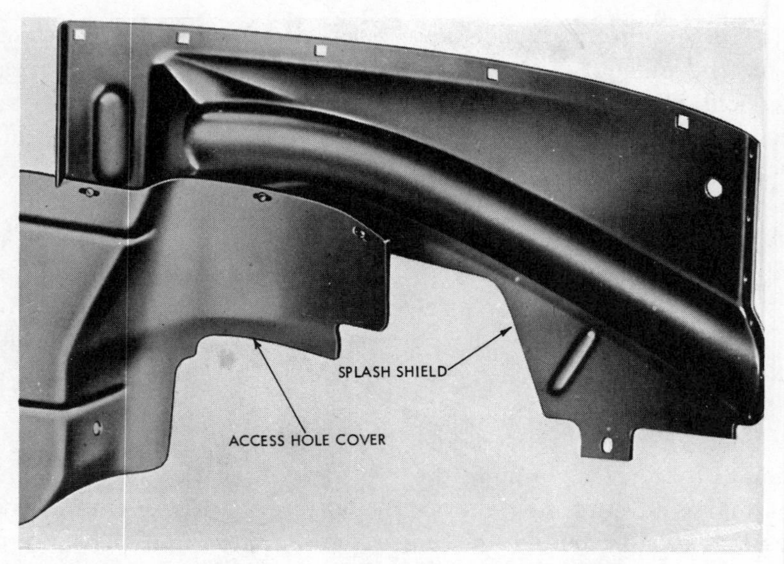

Fig. 1-71. Front fender apron showing construction and assembled form.

place with bolts through the frame and body cowl panel.

The shield which is used under the grille and radiator is called a *splash pan* or *lower shroud,* Fig. 1-69. The purpose of this panel is just as the name suggests; it keeps mud and water from splashing into the front of the engine compartment. In some cases, these shields have the function of directing air through the radiator core. Other shields are designed to prevent the recirculation of warm air from the engine compartment back through the radiator core.

Hoods

The hood is the panel which covers the engine compartment. Several kinds of hoods are in use on different makes of automobiles.

The most commonly used hood is the one-piece type, Fig. 1-69. A one-piece hood can be opened in different ways. On some cars, the hood is hinged at the front so that the rear end of the hood swings up when the hood is opened. Several makes of cars have the hood designed so that it opens toward the wind shield. Some one-piece type hoods, however, are of the alligator type. The hood is hinged at the rear. When opened, the front end swings up, Fig. 1-72.

The type of hood latching mechanism depends upon the type of hood. When a hood opens from the rear, it is latched at the rear. Alligator type hoods are latched at the front. In some cars, the latch

Fig. 1-72. Alligator type hood. (Ford Motor Co.)

mechanism is controlled remotely from the driver's seat. One good reason for this arrangement is because the battery is contained in the engine compartment. By having the hood latch control inside the car, theft of the battery can be made difficult.

One-piece hoods are quite large. To make opening the hood an easier task, the hinges are often counterbalanced. Adjustment of the hood position is possible by moving the hinges. Hood alignment and adjustment are discussed in a subsequent chapter of this volume.

Principles of Measurement

Damage to the body inner construction or to the frame of a car or truck might be quite severe and yet not be apparent. In some cases, the damage to the skin or sheet metal of the body can be repaired, and the original damage will appear to have been corrected. The job, however, is not done unless the frame or body inner construction is either known to have been undamaged or has been corrected.

Failure to check for and correct such damage can result in poor fitting doors, hood, or fenders; faulty steering control; and a multitude of other faults. The possibility of these faults makes necessary a number of measurements throughout the correction of collision damage. The measurements taken generally are not made in inches or feet as might be expected, but rather are comparative measurements in which one distance is compared by means of a trammel to another that should be equal.

This section gives the principles on which the standard for measurement in collision work is based. Methods of measuring specific units of bodies and frames are given in subsequent chapters of this volume where the correction of damage to those particular units is discussed. Comparative measurements are universally used by body and frame repairmen and are generally regarded as the simplest, speediest method for measurement in collision work.

Automobile bodies are generally regarded as having two sides which are exactly the same. Therefore, if one side only is damaged, it can be compared with measurements taken on the undamaged side. There is more to comparative measurement, however, than merely comparing a damaged panel with a similar but undamaged panel.

The occasion will arise when both sides of a vehicle are damaged so that it will be impossible to compare one side with the other. This is when the true meaning of comparative measurements comes to light. Fig. 1-73 shows a metal picture frame with sides *A* and *C*, and *B* and *D* of equal length respectively. Therefore, the diagonals *X* and *Y* are also equal. If the square is distorted the diagonals are no longer the same length. If you visualize this picture frame as being movable at the corners, you can readily see where pressure must be applied to make

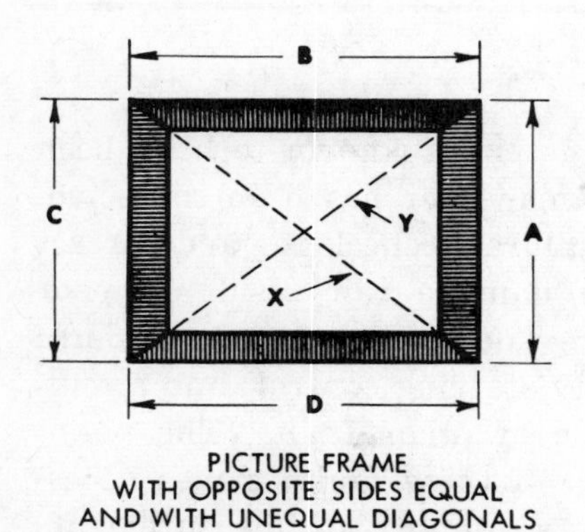

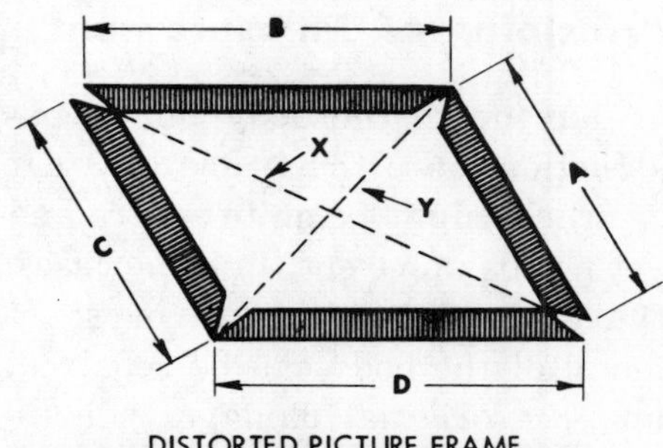

Fig. 1-73. Comparative measurement is an important technique to learn.

it square once more. You do not need to know the original length of either the sides or the diagonals. By making comparative measurements of the diagonals, you can tell when they are again equal.

If the frame is distorted, as in Fig. 1-74, it is possible for the diagonals to be the same if the distortion is exactly at the mid-point of side *A*. Therefore, a comparison of sides *C* and *A* will reveal the difference, and side *A* can be straightened until both side *C* and side *A* are the same length. A quick check will show that the diagonals are also the same length.

These illustrations show how it is possible to align a body or frame by measuring from nothing but the body or frame itself.

The comparison of diagonals is commonly called *X-checking*. Some occasions will arise, however, when it will be impossible to determine the original shape of a unit by *X*-checking or measuring the diagonals. An example of such a case is shown in Fig. 1-75.

In this case, the frame is bent up at one corner. The diagonals *X* and *Y* may be equal, although it is more likely they will not. However, a sure method of determining whether the frame has been restored to its original shape is to measure from a surface such as the table to each corner of the frame. When the frame is perfectly flat, the distance from each corner to the table will also be the same.

This type of measurement is used a great deal in frame straightening. When four points on a frame should be in the same plane, the four points, if placed on four

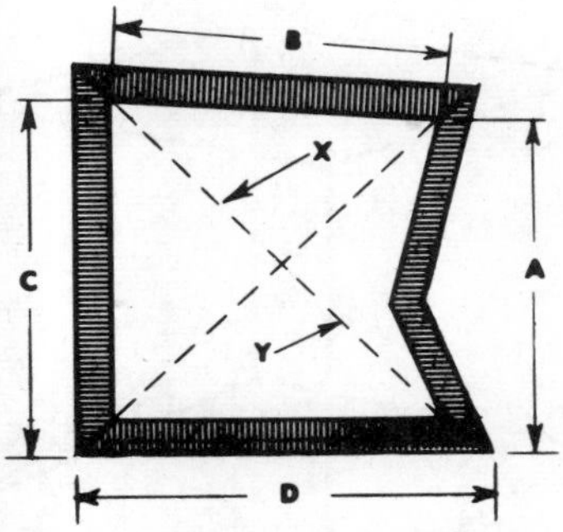

B
X
C
A
Y
D
DISTORTED SQUARE WITH UNEQUAL SIDES
DIAGONALS MAY OR MAY NOT BE EQUAL

Fig. 1-74. Comparative measurement errors.

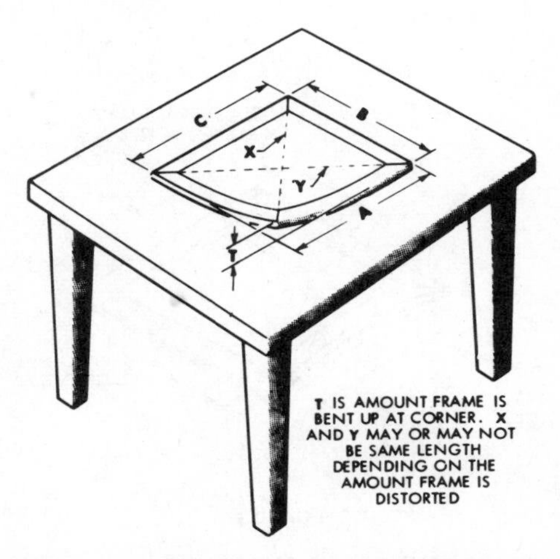

Fig. 1-75. Picture frame with corner bent out of line.

blocks of the same height, all should touch the blocks. If all do not, either the point that does not touch the block is bent up, or one of the points that does touch the block is bent down. The floor from which you make such a measurement must be flat and should be as near level as possible.

It is, of course, possible for four points to be in the same plane and yet have a member connecting these points bent up or down. An example of this is illustrated by the picture frame in Fig. 1-76.

By measuring first from the opposite, undamaged side of the frame to a surface, then from the bent portion to the same surface, you can determine how much and which way the frame is bent. By making these comparative measurements during the correction, you can determine when the frame is again flat.

When an entire section of the vehicle is knocked out of alignment, another aspect of X-checking measurement must be considered. The body proper can be considered as a cube. Any section of the body can also be considered as a cube. It is a simple matter to determine whether or not a cube is square by checking the diagonals from one corner of the box to another so that they cross in the exact center of the cube, Fig. 1-77.

This same principle can be applied to measuring the cubelike sections of an automobile body. It can also be applied to checking one section with another section. Examples of this type of measurement are explained and illustrated in subsequent chapters.

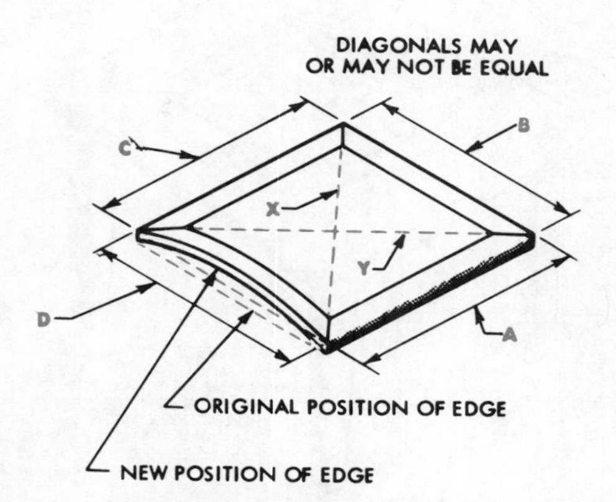

Fig. 1-76. Edge of picture frame bent up between corners.

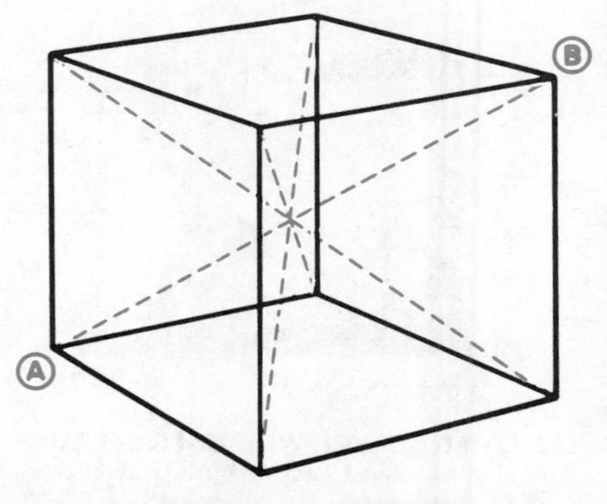

Fig. 1-77. Diagonals of cube from A to B are always of equal length.

Checking On Your Knowledge

The following questions give you the opportunity to check up on yourself. If you have read the chapter carefully, you should be able to answer the questions. If you have any difficulty, read the chapter over once more so that you have the information well in mind before you go on with your reading.

1. What is the term applied to the curved surface formation of metal in automobile bodies and fenders?
2. How is the strength of large metal sheets or panels affected by angles or flanges formed along their edges?
3. What is the construction of a U channel?
4. How are box sections for frame construction mode?
5. Where is the heaviest frame cross member mounted with regard to the chassis?
6. What quality is imparted to the vehicle by lowering the center of the frame between the wheels?
7. Why are heavy commercial vehicle frames made flat behind the cab?
8. Is it usually possible to see inner construction from outside a vehicle?
9. Does an automobile body derive most of its strength from the panel or the inner construction?
10. What major panel is the instrument panel considered part of?
11. Is the center body pillar always visible from the outside of the car?
12. How are major body panels held in place for assembly at the time of original manufacture?
13. What is the function of the weather strip on windshield and rear window glass other than to keep out the weather?
14. How is a door glass held in place so that it can be run up and down evenly?
15. What is the small triangular window incorporated in the front doors of some cars called?
16. How are bumpers held in place on automotive vehicles?
17. How are the steel strips attached which are used to hold bumpers in place?
18. What is an escutcheon plate? Where are they used?
19. How is an integral door handle and escutcheon assembly held in place?
20. What is the panel on which the rear of the hood rests? Do the front fenders connect to this panel?
21. What is the formed edge of a fender called?
22. What is the common name for the shield which goes between the bumper and the body proper?
23. What is the panel called which is used behind the front bumper and under the grille?
24. Is it necessary to know the original dimensions of a panel before it can be restored to its original shape?
25. What are the simplest, speediest measurements that can be made?

Chapter 2

Metal Bumping and Dinging

The restoring of body panels, such as fenders, hoods, doors to their normal contour after they have been damaged is referred to as metal *bumping* or *dinging*. Dinging is a highly skilled trade, and in areas where automobiles are manufactured, *dingmen* are in constant demand.

In retail establishments, the term dinging is rarely used. When it is used, it has a different meaning than it has in automotive manufacturing plants. In garages, car dealerships, and collision shops, dinging is accepted as meaning the same thing as bumping. In this field, the term bumping generally presumes that damage to the paint will result.

In automotive factories, however, dinging presumes that no damage to the paint will result and involves the highly skilled use of hand tools. These tools are the hammer, dolly, and the spoon, the employment of which, along with exercises that will help you develop skill in their use, is presented in this chapter. Generally these are the same tools used by the metal bumper in retail establishments.

The chief difference between dinging, as the term is understood in automotive factories, and metal bumping in the retail field is that the dingman must do his work without damaging the paint. The usual course of development for these men is from metal finishers to dingmen. Metal finishers in automotive plants bump, file, grind, and weld surfaces and build up contours with metal or plastic. It is generally felt that this background of experience is a necessary part of the development of a dingman.

Regardless of whether you want to become a collision expert, a metal finisher, a metal bumper in a retail establishment, or a dingman in an automotive plant, it will be necessary for you to learn all of the principles presented in this chapter and to acquire skill in the use of each of the hand tools.

Learning the proper use of these hand tools is the first and most important step in becoming a body repairman. Even though power tools (discussed in later chapters) are available for use in collision work today, hand tools are used exclusively for finishing work.

Collision work involves both metal bumping and straightening. Every job you encounter will require the fine handwork involved in metal bumping to finish the job. Much of the minor damage that you encounter will require dinging only. As a metal bumper, you will be able to restore the normal contour to most auto bodies and fenders with minor damage.

To become a metal bumper, you must apply yourself to the thorough mastery of each phase of the work. Practice is the only means by which the mastery of the necessary skills can be made possible.

Basic Requirements of Metal Bumper

Body bumping and dinging are highly paid trades which anyone with a mechanical aptitude can learn by practice.

Certain tools of the trade are required. You should obtain these tools before you start the exercises outlined in this chapter. However, before you invest in these tools, it may be advisable to evaluate your aptitude for this work.

In collision work, the use of the hammer is one of the most important factors. You must learn to strike an object squarely and to have complete control of the hammer at all times. If, from your past experience with a good hammer, you have found that you can drive nails without bending them, you can develop the skill necessary as a metal bumper and you can omit the following exercise.

If you have had trouble driving nails, the following exercise will permit you to judge whether or not you should attempt to master this trade.

Drive some ¾″-1″ nails in a board. Lath nails are a good size for this test. The board selected should be one without hard grain.

White pine is very good wood.

Place the board on a bench. Grasp a good hammer about three-fourths of the handle length from the hammer head. Hold the hammer so that the face of the hammer head rests squarely on the board and your forearm is parallel to it.

Using a wrist motion only, raise the hammer head about nine inches, then hit the board lightly. Remember to confine the movement to bending the wrist only. Do not bend your arm at the elbow. Increase the strength of your blows until the hammer head starts to mark the board.

If the marks indicate that you are hitting with one edge of the hammer face, either turn the hammer handle in your hand or raise or lower your elbow, whichever is required, until you hit the board squarely. Now, try driving the lath nails into the board, using the same arm and hammer movement just described. Hit the nail lightly at first, then gradually increase the strength of your blows until you drive a lath nail in with one blow.

Continue until you can drive ten nails without bending any of them. If you can do this, you have the co-ordination necessary to master this trade. If, however, after much practice you are still unable to control the hammer, examine it. If the hammer face is not parallel and square with the handle, get another and practice with it.

Anyone who can drive nails all the way into the board and have a evenly shaped hammer mark on the board should not experience any difficulty in achieving the co-ordination necessary.

As previously mentioned, a minimum number of tools will be required to start on minor repairs such as dings in fenders. It is necessary that you thoroughly understand just what these tools are and how to use them.

Ten separate tools are considered as the minimum number with which you should start. These ten tools are described and illustrated in the next section of this chapter. Later in the chapter, other tools and their use will be explained. However, you can develop the necessary skills with this minimum kit of tools. As you grow to be more and more proficient, you will gradually become aware of the need for additional tools.

Minimum Kit of Tools

A great variety of hand tools is available to the metal bumper, and you will no doubt acquire many of them eventually. The minimum kit of tools, however, takes into account a wide variation of forces.

Force, of course, is necessary to form metal. With a given hammer, you can vary the force of a blow. The difference between the strongest blow you can control and the lightest blow you can strike, however, is not great enough to do all the things you will have to do. For this reason, a vastly greater range is provided in these tools by differences in the areas through which the force is applied. An appreciation of this is a necessary part of learning the trade.

If a force of 100 lbs. is applied through the face of a hammer head 1¼″ in diameter (1.2284 sq. in.), the resultant force amounts to 80 psi (pounds per square inch). If the same 100 lbs. is applied through a hammer only $\frac{1}{16}$″ in diameter (0.0031 sq. in.), the resultant force amounts to 31,680 psi (nearly 16 tons). The $\frac{1}{16}$″ diameter approximates the size of the end of a *pick hammer* which is one of the ten tools in the minimum kit.

If a flat piece of steel having an area of 4 sq. in. is placed on the surface on which you are working, and is hit with a 100-lb. force, the effect of the blow will be distributed over the 4 sq. in. and the resultant pressure will amount to but 25 psi. Of course if your hammer blow only has a force of 4 lbs., the resultant force would be 1 psi.

A piece of steel to place between your hammer and the surface on which you are working is included in this minimum kit of tools and is called a *spoon*. Thus we see that not only is it necessary to apply force exactly where it is needed, but it is also necessary to vary the intensity of the force by having the right selection of tools.

With the tools just discussed, the force in the examples given varied from 25 to 31,680 psi with the same hammer blow.

With the ten tools in this minimum kit, you can do most of the minor repairs which you will encounter in body work. Each of these tools is described and illustrated in the following paragraphs.

Mallet. A mallet, Fig. 2-1, having a face diameter of about two inches permits a good distribution of force. The mallet head is of hard rubber or of *lignum vitae,* a hard, heavy wood from a tropical American tree found in the West Indies.

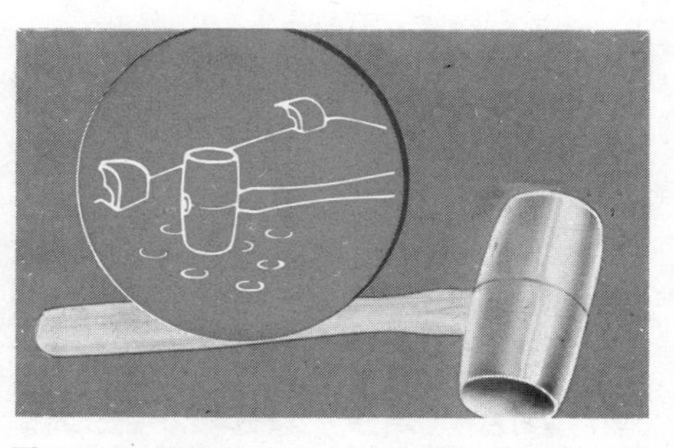

Fig. 2-1. Mallets avoid denting the metal.

Its light weight (as compared to metal hammers) permits soft blows. Since it is made of material softer than the metal being formed, hammer marks are not made on the surface. With such a mallet or with a hard rubber mallet, you will be able to correct some minor damage without injuring the paint.

Pick Hammer. As shown in Fig. 2-2, the pick hammer selected as a part of your minimum kit of tools has a round face which can be used for most hammering operations. The pick portion of the hammer is round for its entire length (about six inches) and tapered to a point. It should be noted that the pick is slightly curved so that, when properly held in your hand, the point of the pick is approximately the same distance from your wrist as the center of the face on the other end of the hammer. This assists you in hitting exactly where you want.

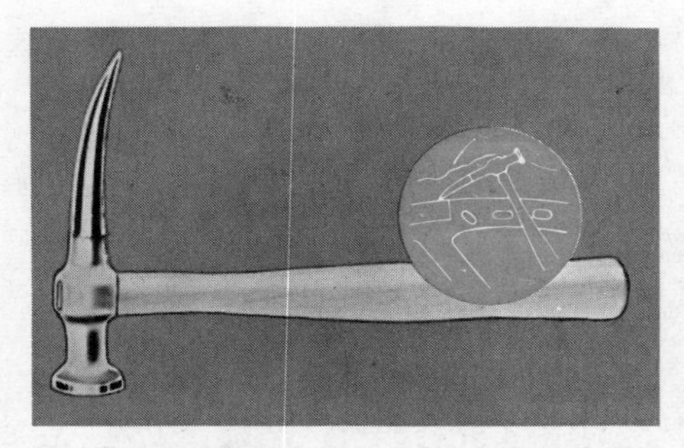

Fig. 2-2. Pick hammer for raising surfaces.

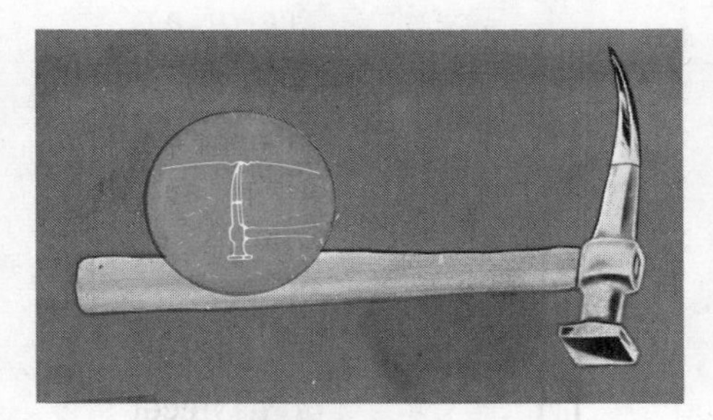

Fig. 2-3. Bead and molding hammer.

Square Face and Taper Shank Bead and Molding Hammer. The hammer shown in Fig. 2-3 will be required for those jobs where it is necessary to form the metal up to a corner. This hammer, under some circumstances, is used in the same way as the round shanked pick hammer.

In the various exercises described in the following pages, this hammer can be used for most of the exercises where a hammer is used in conjunction with a dolly. The sharp corners of the square head may result in marking the metal with the edge or corner of the hammer face if you do not hold the hammer properly.

Low Crown Dolly. As pointed out in Chapter 1, most surfaces on an automobile body are curved. Dollies are made to fit these contours to provide the necessary backing for the hammer. A low crown dolly, Fig. 2-4, is used in conjunction with bumping hammers primarily in places where a

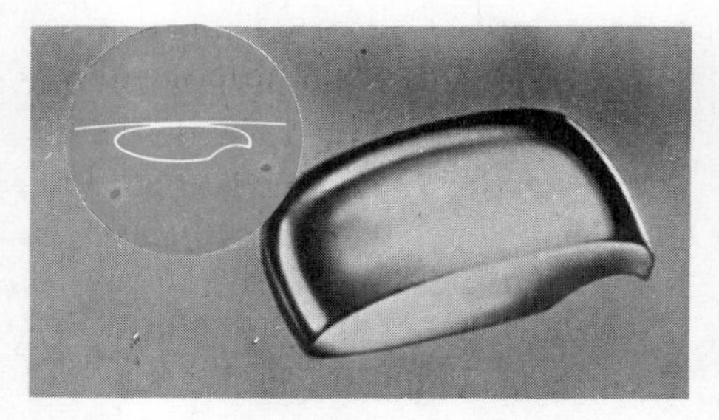

Fig. 2-4. Low crown dolly for bending slight contours.

slight contour is encountered, such as fender skirts, doors, tops of hoods, etc. It can also be used as a hammer for roughing out minor damage.

High Crown Dolly. A high crown dolly is also used in conjunction with bumping hammers. It is required for use whenever a high crown radius is encountered, Fig. 2-5. This dolly has a rounded

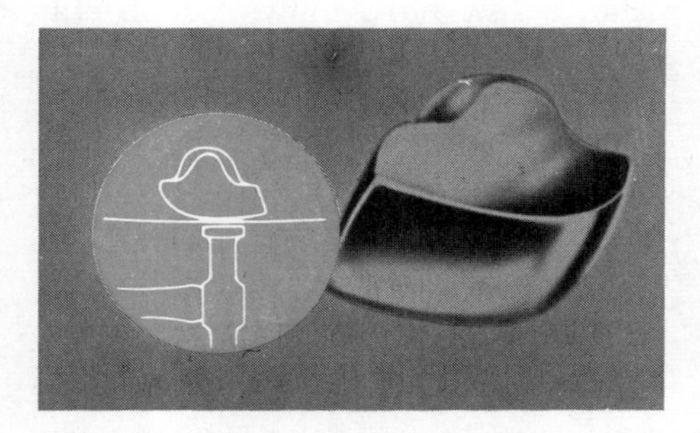

Fig. 2-5. High crown dolly for high radius.

corner which is useful for bringing up low spots as is done with a pick hammer.

Roughing Dolly. The roughing dolly, which is shown in Fig. 2-6, is one of the most versatile tools

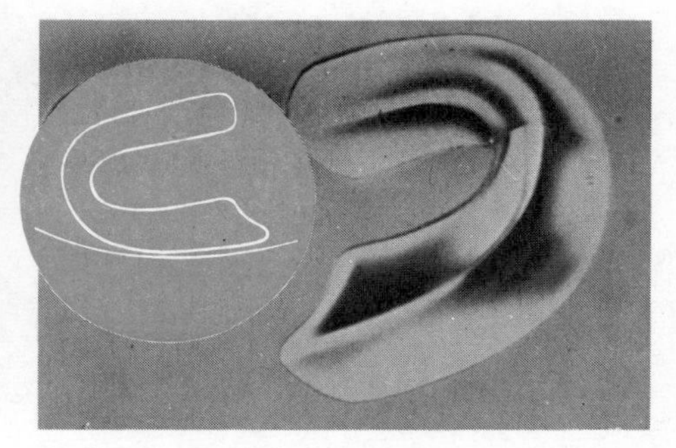

Fig. 2-6. Roughing dolly as light weight sledge.

in the group. This dolly weighs about four and one-half pounds and is heavy enough to force out a high percentage of the damage you will encounter when used as a hammer. Being formed in the shape of a U, it provides a variety of surfaces that can be used as either a dolly or as a hammer. One edge of the dolly is formed so it can be used for forming a bead on a fender.

Surfacing Spoon. The surfacing spoon shown in Fig. 2-7 is used with a bumping hammer. The main purpose is for driving high spots back to their normal posi-

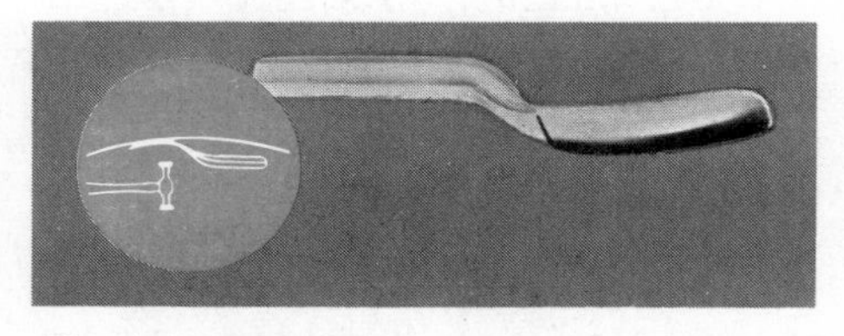

Fig. 2-7. Surfacing spoons reduce highs.

tions without disturbing or denting the surrounding surfaces. The broad face of the spoon distributes the force of the hammer blow over a larger area.

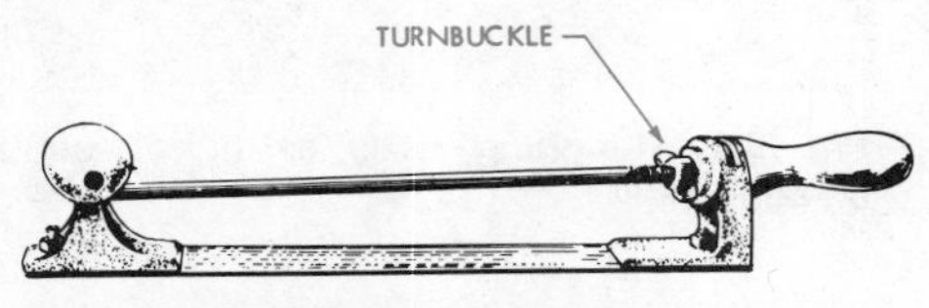

Fig. 2-8. Body file and holder for contour filling of rough finish work.

Body File and Holder. A body file and holder is necessary for smoothing the work after the hammering is finished. The body file is also used for other operations which will be explained in subsequent sections of this chapter. The file can be adjusted to fit the contour of the area being worked on by means of an adjustment screw or turnbuckle provided on the file holder, Fig. 2-8. Sometimes the blade is adjustable merely by turning the handle of the holder.

Skills of Metal Bumping

Constant practice is the only means of attaining skill in the use of the hand tools used in body repair work. Your degree of success depends upon your diligence in practicing with each tool and each piece of equipment until you have mastered them all.

This section presents a discussion of co-ordination and the care and maintenance of hand tools to get the best possible use from them.

Co-ordination. Perfect co-ordination between the hammer and dolly is necessary. The first step toward achieving this co-ordination is to become complete master of the hammer. To master the hammer, you have to be able to control the force as well as the accuracy of the blow. Many light blows with the hammer are better than a few hard blows which may look like they are doing the work, but which actually are stretching the metal, making your job much more difficult in the end.

How to handle the hammer is explained in the following paragraphs. As soon as you have become proficient in the use of the hammer alone, you can start practicing using the hammer and a dolly together.

Preliminary Hammer Exercises. Before you actually start to work on metal with the hammers used in body repair work, you should practice several different exercises to learn your hammering mannerisms and to acquire some new techniques.

In carpentry and in other trades employing a hammer, hammer blows are usually struck with a combination of wrist, elbow, and shoulder movement. In collision work, however, a much wider variation in the force of the blow to be struck is required, and additional ways should be learned.

What to you will probably be a new way of swinging a hammer is presented here and involves finger, or finger and wrist movement. This method of swinging the hammer is actually unnatural and will become normal to you only after much practice. This, however, should not discourage you inasmuch as most skills are not natural, but are learned only through much practice. The daily papers, for example, print columns on how to hold and swing a golf club and how to roll a bowling ball. These things do not come naturally, otherwise we would all bowl in the 200's and go around the golf course in the 70's. The same is true in the control of the bumping hammer.

Finger Movement. In most other trades involving the use of a hammer, very little use of the strength of the fingers is employed. In metal bumping, you often will be required to use finger strength. The ability to apply the hammer head by finger movement only at the surface on which you are working will be found to be of considerable advantage. When working on underneath surfaces, sometimes you can see neither the hammer nor the surface on which you are hammering.

In this exercise, you must remember that the hammer is held loosely in the hand. In fact, in the actual work with these hand tools, you will find that all such tools are held rather loosely. This makes the work less tiring and permits the achievement of a much higher degree of accuracy. Moreover, the loose holding of dollies and hammers permits them to bounce back naturally. This permits you to strike the next blow in the same place without conscious effort. Grasp the hammer as shown in Fig. 2-9, holding it loosely.

You will note that in this illus-

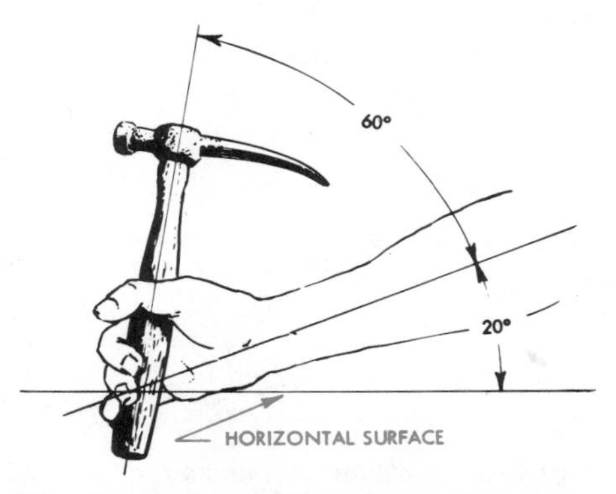

Fig. 2-9. Hammer at the top of the stroke.

tration the hammer handle is at about a 60° angle to the forearm, and that the forearm is about 20° out of parallel with the surface on which you will be hammering. The hammer handle is resting against the base of the thumb and is some distance from the heel of your palm. The fingers of your hand are hooked over the hammer handle as shown. With the hammer in this position, by merely closing the fingers you will be throwing the hammer head forward by finger strength.

With practice, a high degree of accuracy can be achieved by this method. Though it may be surprising to you at first, a considerable amount of force can be developed.

Practice this method of swinging the hammer without bending either the elbow or wrist. Generally, you will find that the hammer at the end of its movement will be in the attitude shown in Fig. 2-10, which shows the hammer about 20° out of parallel with the forearm. In other words, the hammer has moved about 100° by finger movement alone, neither the wrist nor the elbow contributing directly to length of movement.

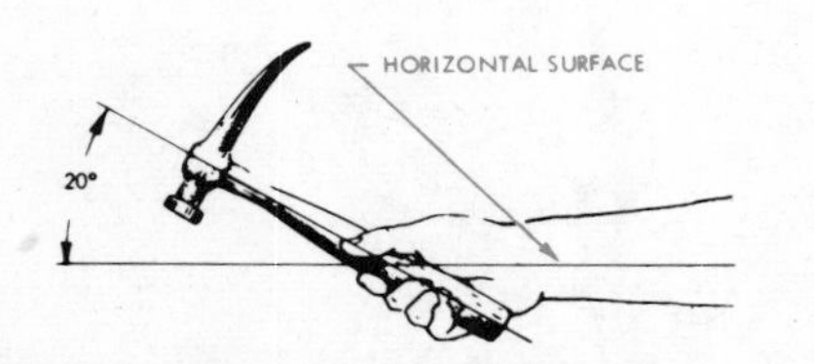

Fig. 2-10. Position of hammer at end of finger movement.

With no wrist movement practice the swinging of the hammer against the palm of your other hand until you have mastered the technique of throwing the hammer head by closing your fingers.

When you feel that you have mastered this method of throwing the hammer head at your other hand, try striking a board or some other surface with the hammer head. Hold the hammer as shown in Fig. 2-9, and position your arm at a 20° angle from the board. The bottom of your hand should be about three inches above the surface, as shown. Now raise the hammer until it assumes the attitude shown in Fig. 2-9. The fingers should be extended but hooked around the hammer handle. Strike the surface without moving your forearm. Continue to practice until you can hit the surface squarely.

The next step in this exercise involves the driving of lath nails into a soft board or plank. White pine is ideal. Drive the lath nails into the board using the hammer movement you have been practicing. Don't be concerned if you are unable to drive in the nail all the way at first. Just continue to hit each nail until it has been driven in all the way.

After you have driven a few nails into the board, examine the marks the hammer has left in the board. These marks left in the board by the hammer tell you a story. If you understand what they mean, you can easily correct any small errors which you are making before you actually start practicing on metal. For example, if the mark is heavy on the left side or the right side of the nail as you face the board, you are not holding the hammer straight in your hand. Turn the hammer slightly away from the side where it leaves the deepest mark.

If the mark in the board is deepest on the side of the nail which is farthest away from you as you face the board, you are holding your elbow too high. Lowering your elbow slightly will bring the hammer head so it strikes the board squarely.

If the hammer mark in the board is deepest on the side of the nail nearest to you as you face the board, you are holding your elbow too low. Raising your elbow slightly will square the hammer head with the board.

After you have closely examined your hammer marks and made the necessary corrections in the method of hammering, practice driving nails until you can leave the same kind of mark in the board every time.

In driving the nails all the way into the board with one blow, you may have the tendency to hit the nail too hard. After you have mastered the technique of leaving the same kind of mark in the board every time, try hitting the nail with lighter taps. By trial and error, you will find that you can drive the nail all the way into the board with a surprisingly light hammer blow. You will also find that the hammer will leave a mark which is barely discernible.

Finger and Wrist Movement. Once you have mastered the use of the hammer by finger movement, learn to complete the swing with a slight wrist movement. In this exercise, at the instant the hammer head strikes the surface on which you are hammering, the hammer handle and your forearm should be parallel as shown in Fig. 2-11.

Hold the hammer again as shown in Fig. 2-9. Your forearm, however, should be parallel to the surface you are to strike, as in Fig. 2-11. The hammer handle will be at about a 60° angle to the forearm. Close the fingers as you did

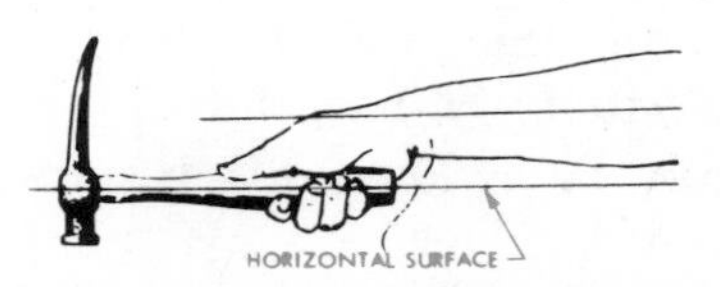

Fig. 2-11. Combination finger and wrist movement.

in the previous exercise. This time the hammer will not strike the surface, but will stop at about a 20° angle from the board. The blow is completed by a slight bending of the wrist so that the hammer strikes the surface on which you are working. The hammer, your hand, wrist, and forearm will be similar to the arrangement shown in Fig. 2-11.

Go through all of the exercises you performed with finger movement alone. The swing of the hammer is completed this time, however, by wrist movement. Drive nails and study the marks you make on the board. Continue these exercises until you feel that you have complete control of both the force and where you hit.

Exercises with Hammer and Dolly. Assuming that you have now mastered the basic principles of hammering by driving nails in a board, you are now ready for another exercise. Before you can actually start hammering on metal, you must further improve your control of the hammer, then learn to use the hammer in conjunction with the dolly block in perfect coordination.

Using the bumping hammer is like batting a baseball or driving a golf ball. The best results are obtained when you are perfectly at ease and as near as possible in a natural position. After you have faithfully practiced the finger and wrist movement in the use of the bumping hammer, you will find this method of swinging the hammer will come to you quite naturally and you will find you have a high degree of control of the force with which the hammer lands.

The force of the hammer blow is extremely important. In order to develop complete control of the force of the hammer blow, perfect finger and wrist action is necessary. As you develop this finger and wrist action, your accuracy with the hammer will improve.

You became familiar with the pick hammer while driving nails into a board, so you can again use it for the next exercise.

Grasp the pick hammer about three-quarters of the way down the handle from the head as shown in Fig. 2-10. Hold the hammer easily in your hand. Do not grip it tightly. By grasping the handle in this fashion, the hammer will assume an almost naturally balanced position when you swing it.

Practice different strokes with the hammer—both full swings, involving both finger and wrist movement, and short swings, using the power of your fingers only, allowing the flat side or face of the hammer head to land lightly in the palm of your free hand. Limit your movement to finger and wrist action. Allow your wrist to flex naturally. Wrist action multiplies the force of the hammer blow and permits hard blows with a short swing and a minimum of exertion on your part.

Now practice swinging the hammer with a medium stroke until the force of the blows seems to be the same on your free hand each time, and until the hammer feels as though it has assumed a natural position in your hand.

So far, you have merely been swinging the hammer into your free hand with your free hand always in the same relative position. It is now necessary to learn to swing the hammer and attain accuracy of the blows while moving your arm about. At the same time you are becoming proficient at this, you can also get the feel of using two tools at once.

For the next exercise you can again use the pick hammer. Instead of swinging against your hand, however, you can hold the high crown dolly in your free hand and practice hitting it with the face of the hammer, Fig. 2-12.

How you hold the dolly block for this exercise is important. It should lie naturally in your hand with the high crown side up. Different ways of holding the dolly blocks will be explained later in this chapter where different kinds of hammering are detailed.

The important thing to learn

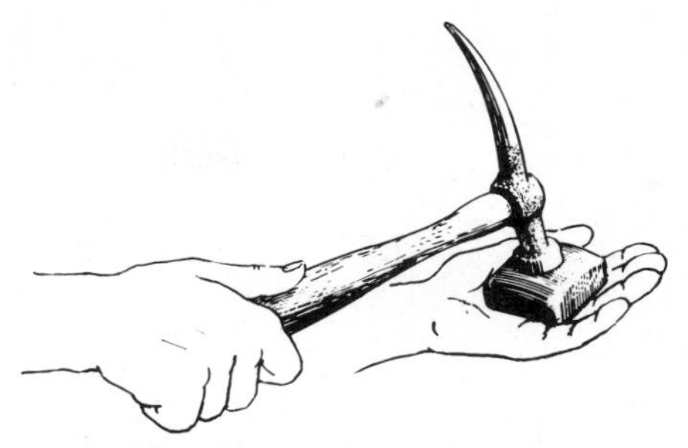

Fig. 2-12. Striking dolly block with pick hammer.

now is to strike the dolly squarely and with the same force with each blow of the hammer. Swing the hammer against the dolly block, moving both of your arms to different positions. Without changing the way you are facing, practice this exercise to the left so one arm passes in front of you, then to the right. Now hold the dolly at eye level and continue to exercise. Next, practice with the dolly on a level with your belt buckle.

Continue to practice in each position until the blows seem to fall against the dolly with no conscious effort. Don't grip either the hammer or the dolly tightly. Don't try to stop the hammer from bounding back, and don't let the hand holding the dolly become rigid. Let it move naturally as the hammer strikes it. This bounding back of the dolly is one of the important factors in straightening metal.

Each time the hammer strikes the dolly block it will have a certain metallic ring, and will impart an impact to the hand in which you are holding the dolly. Practice swinging the hammer against the dolly until the metallic ring is nearly the same with each impact and the shock to the hand holding the dolly feels the same with each hammer blow.

After you have practiced striking the dolly in different positions, move the hand holding the dolly after each two or three strokes. This exercise will help you to develop co-ordination of your two hands. Continue this exercise until you can bring the hammer and dolly together in any position.

After you have mastered the use of the hammer and dolly without actually hammering on anything, you are ready to start exercises with the hand tools on a metal body part.

Use of Hand Tools. The previous exercises have given you a good deal of practice with the hammer. You have been able during these exercises to get the *feel* of the basic hand tools while you can see both tools. In actual metal bumping, the metal to be worked will be between the hammer and the dolly, and you will be able to see only one of these tools at a time.

When a fender or body panel is formed, the shape of the die is imparted to the sheet metal. Later, if the panel becomes bent, creases in the panel hold it out of its acquired shape. Nevertheless, the stresses imparted to the metal when it was formed on the body die are mostly still in the panel, and when the stress of the crease is relieved, the panel will return to this original shape by itself.

Since the metal will try to return to its original contour of its own accord, the secret of dinging is to determine just what is preventing it from returning. It will be found that a *crease* has been formed by the impact causing the damage. This crease may exist either in the panel itself, or it may be a bend or a crease in the inner construction which is holding the panel from returning to its original contour. By undoing this crease, you will restore the original contour.

If, on the other hand, in trying to hammer or drive the damaged area back into shape the metal is hammered excessively, it will be stretched. The stretched portion of the metal will lose its tendency to return to the original contour. For these reasons, it is of the utmost importance that you approach each job with the object in mind of relieving the strain which is holding the damaged area out of position.

Since each hammer blow displaces some metal, it is important that you acquire skill in being able to hit exactly where you want to, and with exactly the right force. Light blows will not displace the metal as much as heavy blows, and several well-placed light blows are far more effective than one or two hard blows. Each well-directed blow of exactly the right force is a move toward permitting the metal to come back to its original contour. Each misplaced blow, and each blow that is harder than is required, may create additional damage which you will eventually have to correct.

You will have to acquire a high degree of skill in the use of each of the hand tools just described. Until such time as you have developed skill, it is not advisable to work on an automobile. As a means of acquiring these skills, obtain an old fender from a body shop, car dealership, or garage on which to practice.

During this part of your learning period, you are going to develop skills in doing a number of separate operations, all of which are used in restoring metal to its original contour. The exercises given will not represent any procedure that you will ever follow on any particular body or fender repair job. These exercises are merely intended to permit you to develop the skill you will need to use each of the tools. Don't be impatient to work on actual damage. Follow these exercises and you will be able to meet your first bumping job with confidence.

Body File and Holder. The body file is a simple tool. Being simple, however, does not mean that it is unimportant. Metal finishing with the file is one of the most important phases of sheet metal repair.

A body file is used for many things—to remove paint, to smooth metal, to find low spots, and to form the correct contour of areas that have been built up with solder. No doubt you have seen body men doing these same operations with a grinder, and you may wonder why you must learn the laborious method of hand filing. Several sound reasons exist which will become apparent to you as you master the separate techniques presented in this volume. By hammering alone, you will never make any surface perfectly smooth. However, you can achieve near perfection. Otherwise, in filing or grinding high spots, you will cut through or weaken the part.

The gage of metal on automobile bodies is as light as practical, and every precaution must be taken not to file (or grind) away any metal unnecessarily. Like all of the other hand tools used in bumping or dinging, you will have to develop skill in the use of the file. Many jobs do not lend themselves to grinding.

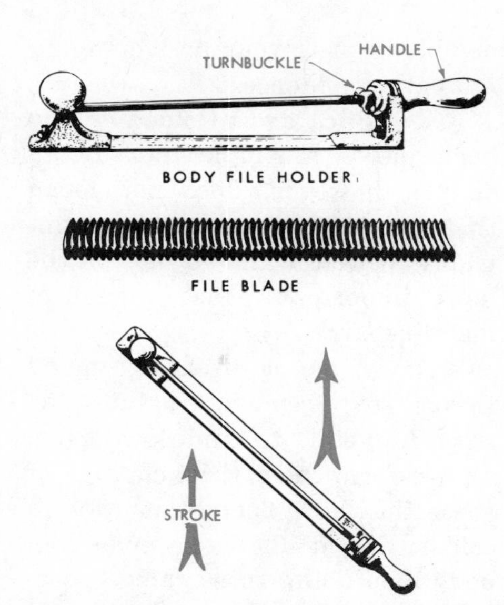

Fig. 2-13. Body file holder and file blade, and position of file to produce shearing action.

Construction of Body File Holder. The file blade is the most important part of this tool because it is the part that does the work. The file blade is detachable from the holder, Fig. 2-13, and is different from any other type of file. These blades are accurately machined with unbroken cutting edges about ⅛″ apart.

The holder is a flexible frame with some form of turnbuckle which makes it possible to adjust the blade to fit the different contours encountered. The blade fits into the holder snugly and positively, yet is quickly replaceable.

Examine the file blade closely and notice the curvature of the individual cutting edges. The curvature makes it possible to position the file as shown in Fig. 2-13 so that a larger area is covered with each stroke of the file. The file is pushed straight away from you, but the angle of the file produces a shearing action which produces a smoother surface.

Filing Metal. Fasten the file blade to the file holder with the cutting edges of the teeth facing away from the handle. Adjust the contour of the file holder so that it almost matches the contour of the surface, Fig. 2-14. One hand is used to hold the file handle. The other is used to grasp the file around the saddle at the opposite end.

For your first exercise, adjust the file blade so that it is concave, its center touching the surface on which you will be working and the ends clearing by $\frac{1}{16}$″ to ⅛″, Fig. 2-15. This illustration shows the file adjusted for use on a high crown surface. Secure the fender in some manner so that it will not move as you attempt to file it. Place the file on the fender. With a straight stroke, push the file away from you so that it is traveling in the same direction its length runs. If the file digs in, you are putting too much pressure on it. Lessen the pressure. At the end of the first stroke, raise the file and bring it back to where you started, and make a second stroke.

Repeat this until you have re-

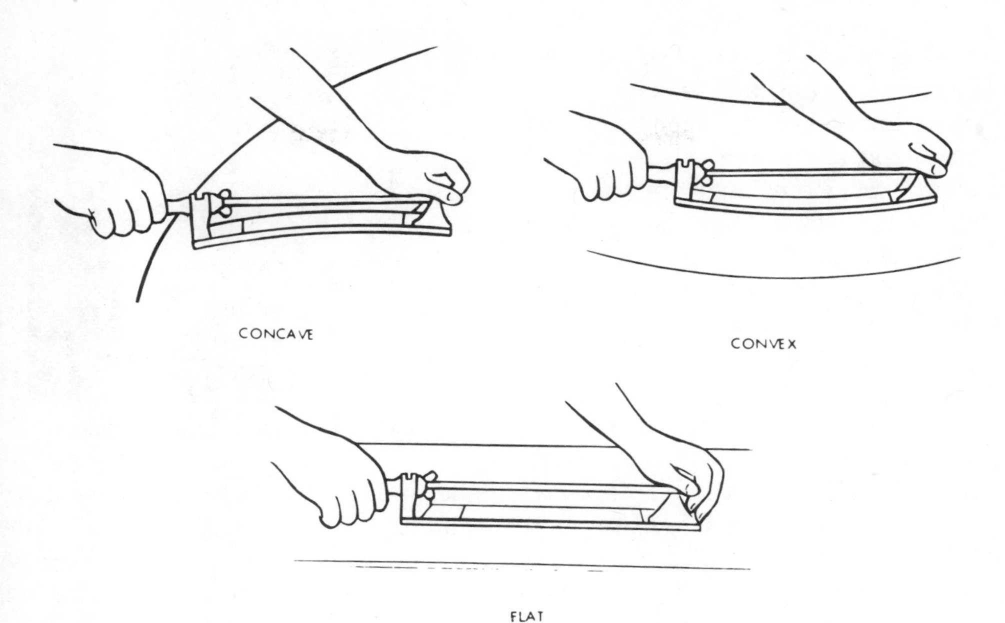

Fig. 2-14. The body file is adjustable to low and medium contours.

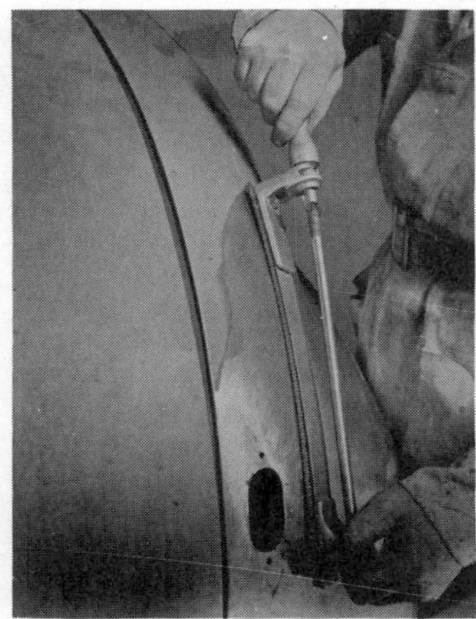

Fig. 2-15. File adjusted to slight contour and file adjusted for use on a high crown surface.

moved all of the paint from the area on which you are working, remembering to raise the file at the end of each stroke. It should not be dragged back over the metal. Dragging the file back over the metal will tend to dull the file blade, thereby shortening its life.

You will find that all of your file marks are parallel to each other and that you have removed all of the paint and probably some of the metal from the fender in the area on which you have been filing. This type of filing is referred to as *line filing*. The term merely means that the strokes and the file marks are in the same direction.

Now change the direction of your file strokes so that the file is moving at about a 45° angle from the previous direction. This is referred to in the trade as X-filing.

You may find that the contour of the area differs slightly when you change the file stroke 45°. If this is true, adjust the file holder again to nearly but not quite match the contour, then go over the entire area once lightly. You will now find that the new file marks cross the original file at a 45° angle, and that these two sets of file marks form a series of innumerable X's from which the term X-filing is derived. Continue to file in this direction until you have completely removed all of the original in-line file marks. You are now again filing in-line. In other words, all of your file marks are in one direction.

Now turn your file so that it is 90° from these file marks. You probably will again find that your file holder no longer matches the fender contour. As you proceed to file in this new direction, you will find that the new file marks imposed on the previous ones form crosses. This is referred to as *cross filing*, Fig. 2-16.

Fig. 2-16. File position for cross filing.

Of course, when cross filing or X-filing in actual practice, you make a few strokes in one direction, then a few strokes in the second direction, after which you go back to the first position, and so on to maintain the cross or X-pattern in the file marks. X-filing and cross filing are necessary to maintain or establish a contour which curves in more than one direction, whereas line filing is used on more simple surfaces. When filing, it is always a good plan to make a few cross or X strokes occasionally to make sure that you are not destroying a secondary contour in the metal. This is particularly important when filing areas that have been built up of solder or other soft material.

You should continue to practice on the fender until you have succeeded in setting up the various filing patterns over several differently crowned areas.

Pick Hammering. In the second hand-tool exercise you are going to create damage to the fender and at the same time gain valuable experience and practice. Using the pick hammer on an undamaged surface will create the damage. You will need this type of damage for a later exercise. While you are actually damaging the fender, you are at the same time developing skill in pick hammering. Pick hammering is difficult, and you will need a lot of practice before you can make competent use of this tool.

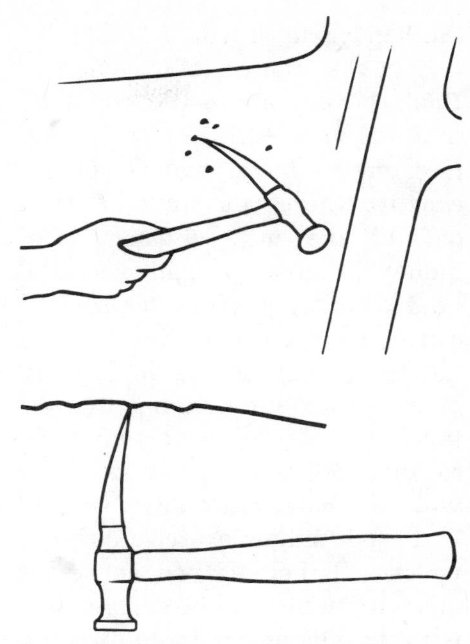

Fig. 2-17. Examples of pick hammering.

A pick hammer is used to bring up low spots, particularly in areas which have been badly creased or stretched and have lost their tendency to return to their normal contour. Fig. 2-17 illustrates examples of pick hammering employed to raise low spots. As a rule, the pick hammer, working from the underside of the metal, is used to hit the center of low spots 3/8″ or less in diameter. The pick, being sharp, stretches the metal, forming a pimple on the surface. At the same time this pimple is formed, the metal immediately surrounding it, while not displaced or stretched, is raised. From the foregoing, it is obvious that accuracy in the use of the pick is of the utmost importance.

Place a small cross on the outside surface of the practice fender skirt, and try to hit the center of this mark with the pick from underneath. Try a light blow, at the same time watching the surface of the fender to see if you are raising a pimple. If not, increase the force of the blow until you see a pimple raised by the pick.

Determine the distance and the direction that you will have to move the hammer in order to hit in the center of the cross mark, and continue to hit the underside of the fender until you actually hit under the center of the cross. Don't be discouraged if you find that you raise thirty or forty pimples on the metal before you hit exactly where you want. This is one of the most difficult techniques in dinging, and you will need a lot of practice before you can master it. Form the habit of noting quickly where a hammer blow strikes and judging the distance you have to move your hand so that following hammer blows will be where you want them.

A more simple exercise, but one which will help if you encounter difficulty in hitting the chalk marks with the hammer, is to practice hitting a point under your finger. Place the index finger of one hand against the outside surface of the fender, then try to hit the inside surface of the fender with the pick hammer so as to raise a pimple directly under the index finger.

It is usually easier to hit a point under your finger because your other hand will bring the hammer to your finger quite naturally. Practice doing this until you can raise a pimple directly under your finger every time. Then try hitting under the chalk marks again. Continue practicing with the pick until you can hit the mark every time. After you have become proficient in the use of the pick, you can move to the next exercise.

Direct Hammering. As a result of the exercise with the pick hammer, you will have an area of the fender skirt on which you have a number of small pimples. These can be removed by a method referred to as direct hammering. Fig. 2-18 shows how you should hold the dolly for this operation, as well as the relationship of the hammer to the dolly. As mentioned in the discussion of basic hand tools, you will find that you have a low crown dolly and a high crown dolly.

Before using the hammer and dolly together, it will be necessary to clean the underside of that portion of the fender on which you will be working. This will be true on all subsequent exercises and in actual practice when you are working on collision jobs. Body panels and some fenders will be

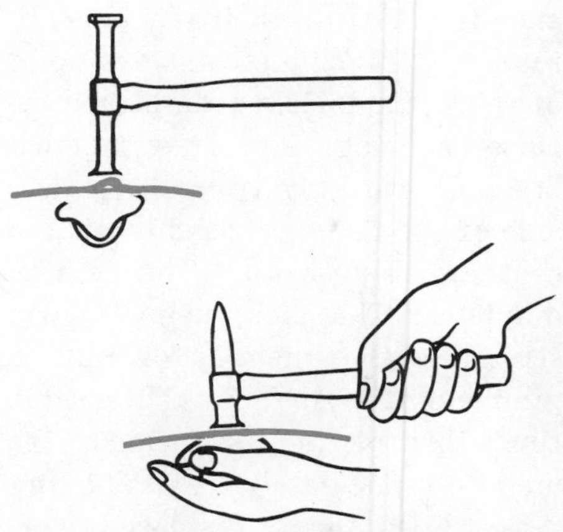

Fig. 2-18. How to hold the dolly in direct hammering.

covered with sound-deadening material which must be removed. Deadening material may be pads or mats of a felt-like material glued in place, or a heavy, tarlike, black material which has been applied in a semifluid state. In addition, the underside of fenders, hoods, and bodies may be undercoated.

Regardless of whether the panel to be reworked is covered with undercoating, tarlike, sound-deadening material, or a silencing pad, or is just dirty, it will have to be cleaned before you start with the hammer and dolly. Use a putty knife, wire brush, or whatever it takes to remove this material. Steam cleaning equipment is often used for this purpose.

If you fail to clean the surface, deadening material or road tar will not only gum up your dolly but will, to a large degree, destroy its effectiveness. Sand and gravel embedded in the undercoating may nick your dolly block.

Dolly blocks are important tools in body and fender repairing. Regardless of what your first impression of these tools might be, they are precision instruments, each scientifically designed for a particular job. Later in this section you will learn how to care for these tools, and how to correct damage that may occur to them.

Of first importance is the selection of the correct dolly block for the job you are going to do. The different dolly blocks which were introduced to you in the minimum kit of tools represent the basic kinds of dollies. Eventually, you may accumulate a wider selection. The main difference in dolly blocks is in the radius or crown provided on the anvil side of the block, and in the weight of the block itself. In some of the dollies you may later acquire, further variations in shape might be practical. However, you will be able to follow each of the exercises presented here with the three dollies included with a minimum tool kit.

In repairing a high crown radius of a fender you will have to use a dolly block with a high crown radius. Fig. 2-19 illustrates how a high crown dolly is used in conjunction with a bumping hammer on a high crown radius.

In repairing larger body panels and on door panels, front parts of quarter panels, tops of hoods, and centers of metal tops, it is necessary to use a dolly block with a low crown radius. How the low crown dolly you will be using in your primary operations is used in conjunction with a bumping hammer is also illustrated, and another type of low crown dolly is shown. In all cases, a dolly should nearly but not quite match the original contour of the metal being straightened.

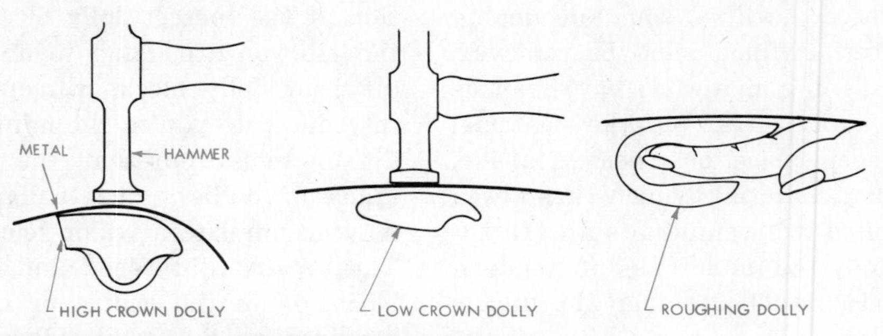

Fig. 2-19. Use of dollies for various surface conditions.

In direct hammering, by having a dolly that nearly matches the original contour under the damage and striking the damage with a hammer, you are pushing the displaced metal back to its original contour. The dolly provides support and prevents the undamaged areas (between the pimples) from being pushed out of place.

Here, again, accuracy is important. If you don't strike squarely over the dolly, you will be hitting an unsupported area of the sheet metal and will displace the metal, creating damage that you will later have to undo. Direct hammering requires skill in directing the hammer blow. It requires close observation of what you are doing so as not to hit the metal too hard, thereby displacing it. Perfect co-ordination between your two hands is necessary to enable you to move the dolly around under the damaged area and still continue to hit squarely over it with the hammer. If you have difficulty co-ordinating the hammer and dolly, practice hitting the dolly with the hammer as previously outlined.

Return to the damaged area of the fender, and hammer the pimples down. Start by using light blows that won't do the job but will show you whether or not you are hitting squarely over the dolly. Don't forget to let the dolly just lie in your hand and to grip the hammer loosely. Use the finger movement described in your first exercise.

With the dolly directly under the pimple to be flattened, using finger movement only, tap the top of the pimple. A true ring will be heard if you are directly over the dolly. Otherwise, the sound will be dull. When you are sure you are directly over the dolly, increase the force of the blow gradually until you have found just the right force to push the pimple back without flattening the surrounding metal.

When the first pimple has been eliminated, move to the next one, and so on, until all have been removed. You will find that, with each hammer blow, two additional things occur. The hammer bounds back of its own accord so that it is ready for the next stroke. Likewise, the dolly will spring away from the surface, and the normal resiliency of your arm will bring it back, striking a blow on the metal from underneath. These things will occur normally only if you hold both hammer and dolly loosely. The importance of this spring-back of the dolly becomes apparent as you practice indirect hammering.

Indirect Hammering. Metal that has not been excessively hammered, displaced, or stretched, will have a tendency to return to its original contour of its own accord. This is due to the internal strain imparted to the metal by the forming dies. If the metal is prevented from springing back by other strains imparted to it by additional bends or creases that have been formed through collision, the metal is restored to normal contour by relieving whatever new strain is holding it out of position.

In bumping or dinging, this is accomplished by indirect hammering. Fig. 2-20 represents a cross section of a damaged area in which sharp creases have been formed all around an area and another sharp crease has been formed in the low spot or center of the damaged area.

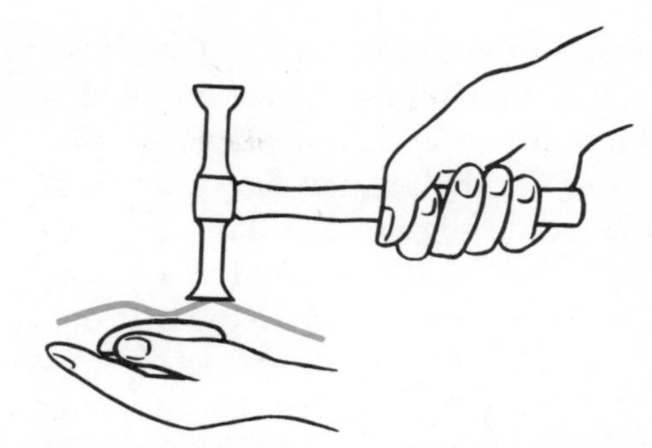

Fig. 2-20. How the dolly is held in indirect hammering.

The procedure employed in indirect hammering is to hold a dolly having the correct contour to match the original contour of the metal at the low spot and to strike a series of light blows around the outside crease. Fig. 2-20 also illustrates how the dolly is held and where to strike when you are doing indirect hammering.

The corrective action is as follows: A light blow will not displace the surrounding undamaged area, but the force of the blow will be transferred to the dolly block. In effect, this will be like pushing the bent portion downward to straighten it out.

As a result of receiving the hammer blow indirectly, the dolly will be pushed away from the low part of the damage. However, in doing this, it imparts a light push upward on this area. Being knocked away from the fender, your hand will automatically bring it back in place, imparting a second light blow to the area. As you progress, using light hammer blows around the outer edge of the damage, you will find that the center of the damaged area slowly rises until the original contour is restored.

To gain practice in this, use the roughing dolly to strike a sharp blow on the outside of a high crown area of the fender to create damage ranging from 1½″ to 3″ in diameter.

Select a dolly that matches the contour (high crown). Using the round head of the pick hammer, hold the matching contour of the dolly on the low spot of the damage (you can feel this with your fingers). Gently tap around the creased outside edge of the damaged area, going around and around progressively with light blows until the contour is restored. Don't strike hard blows, or you will create secondary damage which may be harder to correct than the original damage.

If, during this process, due to inaccuracy in handling the hammer, you have created indentations with the edge of the hammer head, repeat the first exercises (driving lath nails into a board) until you have perfected your control of the hammer. Whatever hammer marks you may have inadvertently created should be hammered smooth by direct hammering to complete this exercise.

Spring Hammering. When a crown is formed in metal, it becomes strong in that it resists any change to its shape. In one sense it can be compared to an arch used in the construction of a building or bridge. The strength of this arch or crown can, in many instances, be used to support the surface being hammered without the use of a dolly. This type of hammering is called *spring hammering.*

Creases in metal at points where it is impossible to back up the hammer often can be corrected by this method. To take advantage of a greater amount of the natural support provided by the crown of the metal, the force of the hammer blow is spread over a larger area through a spoon. The spoon is placed lengthwise over the ridge of the crease or other high spot and then struck a series of light blows with the hammer until the unwanted stress is relieved and the raised portion is back to its original shape or position.

In this method of hammering, no hammer marks are formed on the metal since all of the blows are on the spoon rather than on the metal. Once the metal is back to its original crown, additional hammering will cause the surface to sink and you will have to do more work to bring it up.

Always start with light blows, and as you near completion of the job, inspect the contour after each blow. This will reduce the possibility of sinking the hammered surface too low.

Keep the surface of your spoon clean and highly polished. Any irregularities in the surface of the spoon will be transferred to the surface of the metal on which you are working and will create additional work for you. Dingmen using a spoon to correct damage without injuring the paint often pass the surface of the spoon over their cheek before using it. This accomplishes several things. Any irregularities are felt by the sensitive skin of the face. At the same time, a light film of oil is spread over the surface of the spoon.

Strike your practice fender from underneath with the pick hammer to raise a pimple in a high crown area. Then without using a dolly, push back the raised metal by spring hammering with a hammer and spoon. Repeat this exercise. Spring hammering a crease in a door panel is illustrated in Fig. 2-21.

Delivering the hammer blow to the spoon when it is held directly over high spots drives the high spots back to their normal positions without disturbing or denting surrounding surfaces.

Next, strike several blows in a high crown area of your practice fender with a pick hammer from the outside. This will create depressions that can be brought back up by spring hammering from underneath.

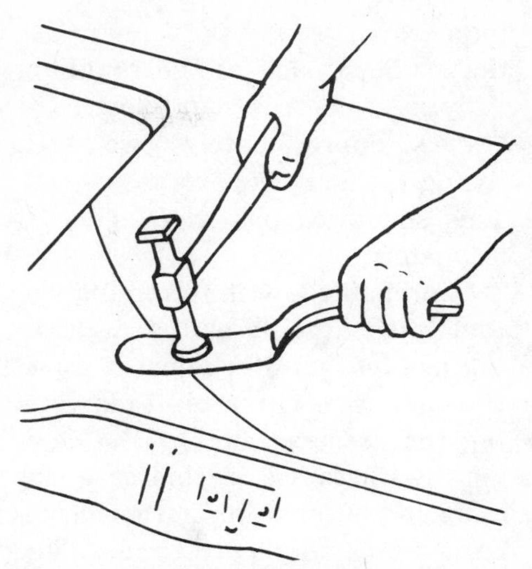

Fig. 2-21. Spring hammering, using a spoon.

In addition to fine finish work where the paint is to be preserved, spring hammering is effective in roughing out damaged areas, and is used in straightening high spots as they appear on either side of the metal.

Using a Roughing Dolly. In the previous exercises, damaged areas have been brought up to original contour by direct hammering, indirect hammering, and spring hammering. Again create damage in your discarded fender. Strike a sharp blow at a point where the fender skirt starts to blend into the high crown area of the fender. Use the rounded edge of the roughing dolly, and control your blow so it travels approximately two feet. Swing the dolly as hard as you can. This should cave in the fender at this point.

It probably is well to remind you that in all dinging and straightening methods used in collision work, the damage is corrected by reversing the process whereby the damage was created. In this case, the damage you have just created was caused by a single direct blow. The place where the blow was struck is now the lowest part of the damage.

To reverse the process whereby the damage occurred, you would hit the underside of the fender with approximately the same force directed against the low part of the damage, Fig. 2-22. If you can accurately hit this low spot with the roughing dolly with the same force that you hit it when you formed the damage, you will find that the fender will spring back almost to the contour it had prior to its damage.

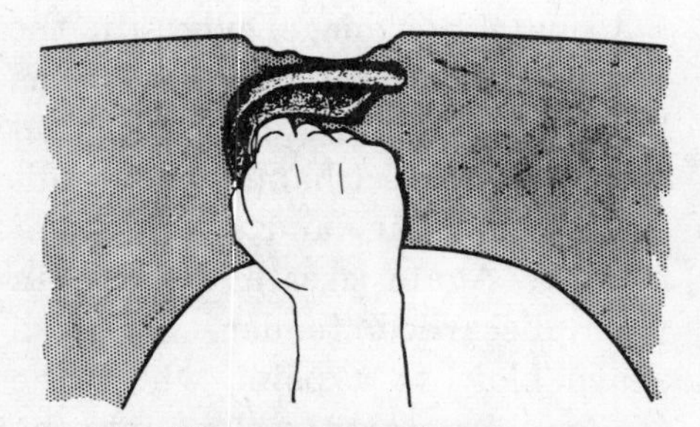

Fig. 2-22. How roughing dolly is used.

You will find that in many instances you will be able to correct fender damage with a single blow of a dolly in this manner. In most cases, however, the damaged area will not be completely restored to its original contour. However, it will be roughed out and the balance of the correction is easily accomplished by either direct or indirect hammering.

It will be noted that in the preceding exercise, and in previous exercises and discussions of hand tools, no mention has been made of a roughing hammer. This has been deliberate. While, in the hands of an accomplished metal bumper, a roughing hammer might be considered by some as an essential tool, it has no place in your tool kit at this time. Some doubt that roughing is ever advisable.

A roughing hammer permits heavy blows which are concentrated in a small area and invariably result in stretching or otherwise distorting the metal. In other words, a roughing hammer creates damage which you will later have to correct, and in thus stretching the metal, the metal involved loses its natural tendency to return to its original shape. A well-directed blow with a dolly that matches or nearly matches the original contour of the damaged material spreads the blow over a larger area and results in very little distortion or stretching of the metal.

A more difficult exercise with the roughing dolly is to create a more complex ding in the fender, then to rough it out with the roughing dolly. Then you can perform the necessary type of hammering in a logical sequence until the damaged area has been returned to its normal contour.

Use a sharp corner of the roughing dolly block and strike the fender hard enough to make a deep ding. Then strike the fender a second time adjacent to where you struck it the first time. This will give you a complex type of damage similar to that shown in Fig. 2-23. You now have damage that resulted from a series of events. You will first correct the damage that occurred last.

Strike the underside of the damaged area directly on the low spot that resulted from the second blow, trying to duplicate as nearly as possible the force with which the damage was created. Then strike a second blow on the low spot created by the first blow.

In a complex type of damage like this, you will have more than one low spot and more than one ridge and valley effect. Naturally, the more complex the damage, the more difficult it will be to straighten.

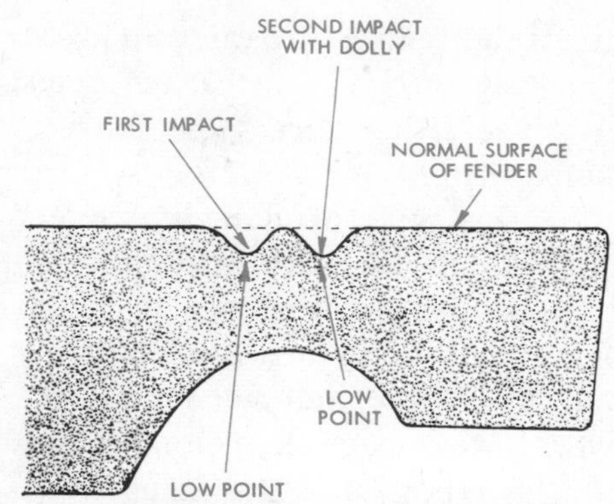

Fig. 2-23. Complex type of fender ding.

Again look at Fig. 2-23 and notice the two low points. The damage that occurred first caused the deeper ding.

Grasp the roughing dolly lightly in your hand, then strike the center of what appears to be the lowest point in the damaged area caused last. Strike the other low spot as near the center as you can. Then strike each low spot alternately with the roughing dolly until the low spots are pushed back to near normal. Be sure that you are using the crown of the roughing dolly that matches as nearly as possible the crown of the surface which you are trying to restore.

You may have noticed on your first exercise with the roughing dolly that when you had succeeded in forcing the damaged area back to normal, the surface was still not smooth. The roughing dolly is, of course, only to be used as a hammer for the first operation in straightening a damaged area. For the second operation, you may use either direct or indirect hammering.

In the type of damage which you set up from the example in Fig. 2-23, you will be able to finish bringing the surface back to normal by direct hammering. However, in this example, you only had two low spots, and the dings were not very deep. If you had a larger area of damage, you would still have ridges and valleys existing after you had used the roughing dolly to the limit of its efficiency. In this case, you would use indirect hammering to finish roughing out the damage.

Fig. 2-24 illustrates the conditions which may still exist after the damage has been roughed out with a roughing dolly. These small indentations will not be very deep, but they will be of such a nature that they will not easily lend themselves to straightening with a roughing dolly. An attempt to do more work with the roughing dolly than is possible will result in the metal becoming stretched. How to correct a stretched metal condition will be explained in later exercises.

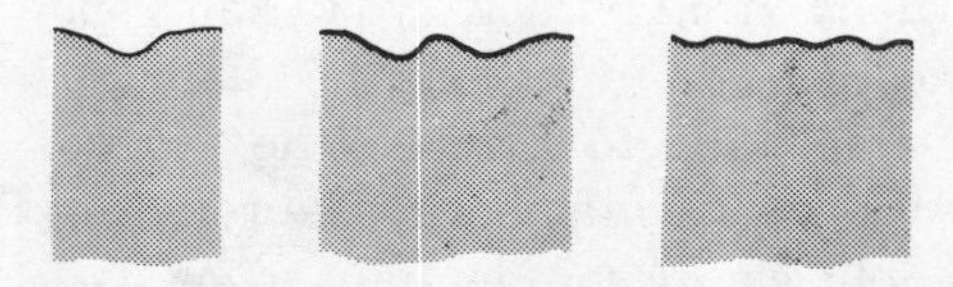

Fig. 2-24. Conditions after roughing dolly is used.

Locating Low Spots. Select one of the areas on the practice fender on which you have been working, and by means of direct hammering, go over the surface again and make it as smooth as you can. Don't hit the surface any harder than you have to or you will stretch the metal.

Either cross or X-file this surface just enough so that the tops of the high spots are removed by the filing. If, after a few file strokes in each direction, the high spots appear as little islands, you have not done a good enough job with your hammering. Continue with the direct hammering until a few strokes in each direction with the file make the low spots instead of the high ones appear as little islands on the surface.

These low spots are eliminated by pounding from underneath, which brings them up to the level of the surrounding surface. This can be accomplished in several ways. You will note that one corner of the high crown dolly is rounded, having a radius slightly smaller than that of a golf ball. Hold the dolly so that you can strike the underside of the fender with this rounded corner. Start with the low spot having the largest diameter, and hit it from underneath with the rounded corner of the dolly. It must be remembered that if you do not hit exactly in the center of the low spot, it will raise metal in some place where you do not want it to be raised. Accuracy in this can be accomplished by holding a finger in the low spot and lightly tapping the underside of the fender with the rounded corner of the dolly until you feel that it is exactly underneath your finger. Then strike a sharp blow to raise the metal at this point. Since the corner of the dolly represents a fairly large area, the low spot is raised with a minimum of distortion of the metal.

After you have raised each low spot in this manner, again cross or X-file the damaged area to again show up the low spots. You will now find that most of the low spots have been reduced in size. Continue to raise the low spots in this manner, concentrating on low spots of ⅜″ or more in diameter and again cross or X-file, repeating this process until all low spots have been reduced to ⅜″ or less.

After you have practiced with the dolly block for some time and have become successful at removing low spots with it, you are ready to try removing the smaller low spots with the pick hammer.

Relieving Low Spots With a Pick Hammer. Bringing up or *relieving* low spots by pick hammering is more difficult than by the use of the rounded corner of a dolly block. With the pick hammer, more accuracy in placing the blow will be required. Likewise, greater control of the force of the blow is necessary. However, many low spots can be brought up by pick only.

You can start using the pick hammer in a manner similar to the way you started with the dolly. Hold the end of your finger in the low spot. Tap the under surface of the fender lightly with the pick until you feel that the pick is directly below your fingers. Then strike a light blow from beneath the fender, of sufficient strength to form a pimple in the low spot. This pimple represents stretched metal, but, in being formed, the immediately surrounding metal was also raised.

When all of the low spots have been raised with the pick hammer in this manner, use a dolly that matches the contour of the fender, and hammer down these pimples by direct hammering. Here, extreme accuracy is required in hitting directly over the dolly block with each blow, as any blow that does not hit directly over the dolly will cause the surrounding surface to sink and this surface will have to be raised again.

After hammering down these pimples by direct hammering, again X-file or cross file the damaged area, repeating the raising of low spots until you have a smooth surface.

In the preceding exercise, it will be noted that the body file was used exclusively for revealing low spots. This was done deliberately to provide you with experience in the use of the file and to help you to develop skill in its use. It is suggested that this exercise be repeated a number of times. If necessary, obtain additional discarded fenders on which to practice. After you feel that you have acquired sufficient skill with the file, you will want to try several other methods for locating low spots.

Skill in the raising of the low spots will permit you to do this job in a mere fraction of the time you would use if you did not acquire mastery of the direction and force of the blows you strike, whether you use a hammer or dolly. To give yourself every advantage in locating these low spots, several things can be done.

Locating Low Spots with Chalk. During one of the exercises, substitute a piece of chalk for the file in detecting low spots.

Using the side of the chalk, draw it over the damaged area in several directions, Fig. 2-25. Form X's or crosses until you have gone over the entire damaged area at least twice. As you rub the chalk over the damaged area, it will rub off on the metal on the high spots only, and will leave the low spots clearly revealed to you. This means much less physical effort on your part as well as a great saving in time, as compared to locating the low spots by filing. It is, however, necessary to finish the job with the file, because only by filing on the last operation can the metal surface be made as smooth as it was originally.

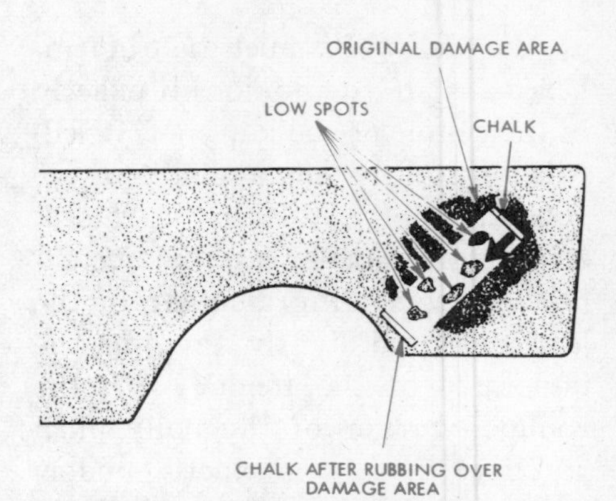

Fig. 2-25. Rubbing chalk on fender.

Locating Low Spots with Light. Another method for locating low spots is by the use of a bright light. A portable shop light which you can raise or lower and move around a vehicle is almost indispensable when doing body repair work. When working on fenders or other near vertical panels, you will find that a light on the floor will help you in locating low spots. Use a sheet of white paper for a reflector.

Hang the practice fender up so that it is in approximately the same position with relation to the

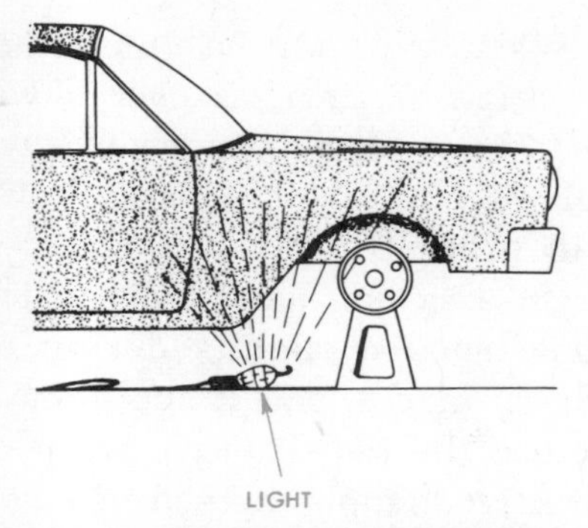

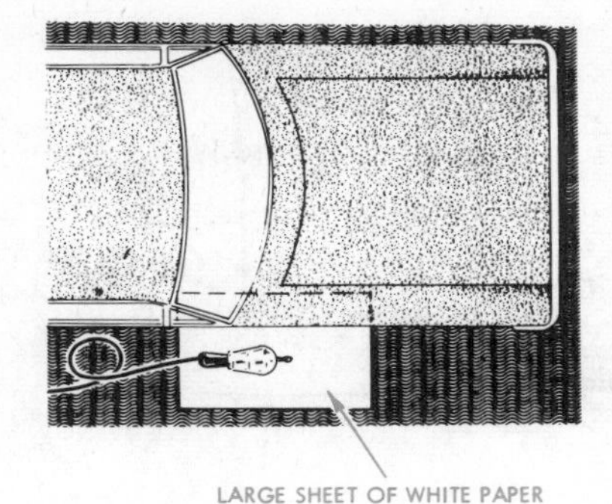

Fig. 2-26. Locating low spots with light reflections.

floor as it would be if it were on a car. Place a large sheet of white paper on the floor with one edge extending under the outside edge of the fender. Place a light on the white paper so that the reflection of the light is upward past the fender. Reflecting the light from a white sheet, a newspaper, or some other suitable dull reflecting surface will cause the shadows and the slight depressions to be on the same side of the high spots as your eyes, thereby making the low spots more readily seen.

Probably the most relaxing position for this operation will be for you to sit right on the floor in front of the fender. Move the light around until it is in the one best position to show up the imperfections in the surface of the work, Fig. 2-26. By sitting on the floor and manipulating the light, you will easily be able to reach up under or behind the fender surface on which you are working, once you get the light in the best position. As the low spots are shown up, you can remove them in the ways which have just been described.

You can easily see that there will be several areas of an automobile body that do not readily lend themselves to working with a light reflected from a paper. Whenever you encounter damage in any surface other than a vertical or near vertical plane, it will be necessary to suspend the light or otherwise locate it to get the best possible reflection.

Locating Low Spots with Gloves. You will notice that you can feel irregularities in the surface by rubbing your bare hand over it. However, you will notice immediately that by wearing an ordinary, loose-fitting cotton glove, your hands will be more sensitive, Fig. 2-27.

Without the glove, your hand is registering both the contour of the

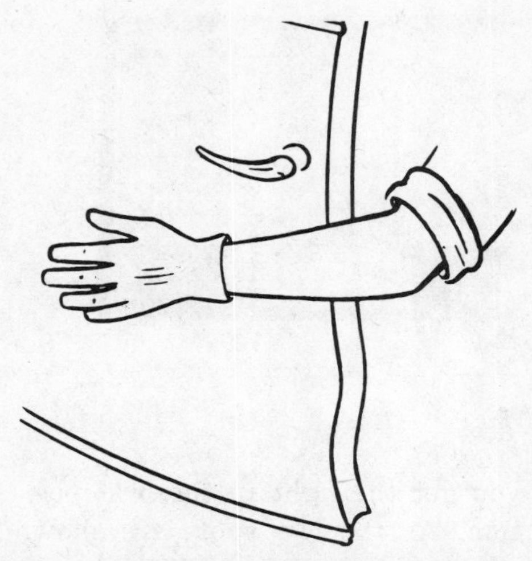

Fig. 2-27. Feeling irregularities in the metal with gloves.

metal and its temperature. With the glove, your hand is insulated from the metal, and needs to be sensitive only to the irregularities.

Care and Maintenance of Hand Tools. Quality work depends a great deal on the condition of the tools used to do the work. Any irregularities in the working surface of the hand tool will be imparted to the surface on which it is used. If your tools are allowed to become rusty, nicked, or dirty, it will also be assumed that you do sloppy work.

When tools are left unused for a period of time, as over a week end, they should be coated with a light film of oil. This film of oil will prevent rust formation.

On occasion, hand tools will become marred slightly during use. These marks should be removed before the tool is used again. An effective, simple method of removing such marks is by the use of emery cloth. Hold a piece of No. 100 emery cloth in the palm of one hand and stroke the working surface of the tool over it in one direction only. The emery cloth, when held in the hand, will conform to the surface of the tool and will not change its contour. Also, the edges of the emery cloth will have a tendency to curl around the edge of the tool, leaving a small radius instead of sharp edges.

Never allow a hammer head to remain loose on its handle. This will noticeably affect your control over the accuracy and force of hammer blows.

Remember the body file blade is an expensive tool. Avoid practices that will nick the cutting edges. Keep the file clean.

Forming Fender Flanges and Beads

Automobile fenders are constructed in such a way that one side is rigidly held in place while the other is virtually unsupported. One side, of course, is fastened to the body with either screws or bolts or by welding. The outside of the fender is supported mainly by the crown put in the fender itself. The metal all around the bottom edge of the outside of the fender is flanged, or formed into a bead, to give the fender more rigidity. In some cases, the bead is merely a flange with a small radius turned toward the inside of the fender, Fig. 2-28. In other cases, the bead is formed by turning the flange toward the inside of the fender, then turning it up. This forms a U-shaped section.

In any case where fender damage involves the bead, the bead will require re-forming after the fender is straightened. The bead is always formed last, because it would be impossible to reshape the edge of the fender before the fender has been drawn into shape.

In cases where the fender has been damaged so badly that the flange or bead has been torn, it will be necessary to repair the tear by welding, even though the tear might not show from the outside. The edges of fenders are subject to much vibration. For this reason, any small break in the edge would gradually grow larger.

The tools generally used to re-form flanges and beads are a dolly block and a bumping hammer.

With a dolly block, create damage to the flange or bead of the same practice fender you

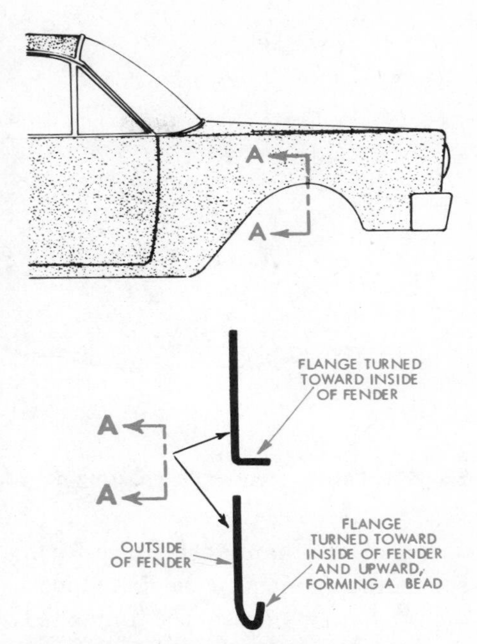

Fig. 2-28. Forming flanges and beads.

have been using. After you have smoothed the surface of the damaged area the way you have learned, find the surface of the low crown dolly that most nearly matches the contour of the fender just above the flange.

On one end or side of each dolly block there is an anvil which can be used to form the flange. Place the dolly block against the inside surface of the fender with the projecting anvil against the flange at the edge of the damaged area. The flange will be easier to re-form if you start at the edge of the damage area where the flange is undamaged.

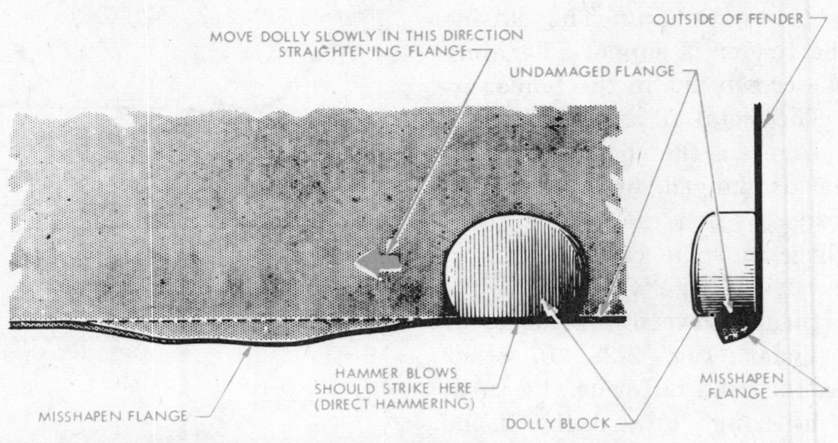

Fig. 2-29. Forming fender flange using dolly block and hammer.

By direct hammering, re-form the flange by moving the dolly block along slowly across the damaged area, forming the flange as you go, Fig. 2-29. The radius of the fender flange toward the outside surface of the fender will automatically be shaped by the radius on the anvil of the dolly block.

Use short, even strokes with the hammer, and do not strike the metal too hard, as there is danger that the flange might split. Also, be sure that the hammer blow falls squarely in the center of the anvil area of the dolly block. This will prevent the flange from being split over the edge of the dolly.

In cases of re-forming a U-shaped fender bead, make a second pass along the damaged area after the flange is turned toward the inside of the fender, and turn the edge up as required.

Practice forming the edge of your practice fender. It may have either a bead or just a plain flange turned toward the inside of the fender. Whichever it has, you can practice forming it until you are able to end up with a smooth contour on the edge that shows to the outside.

If the fender originally had a U-shaped bead, form a straight angle bead at one portion of the fender. If the fender originally had a straight flange, re-form it to a U-shape. Repeat this exercise until you feel that you will have no difficulty with it when you start working on an actual fender.

Whenever a flange or a fender bead is torn, it will be necessary to weld the two sides of the split metal together again. How this is done is explained in Chapter 3 of this volume.

Other Hand Tools

In preceding sections of this chapter, you learned of the basic hand tools required for body repair work and how they are used. However, there are many more hand tools used in body repair work than the ones which have been described to you so far.

In many instances, even though it is possible to do a job with the basic kit of tools, a tool developed especially for a particular job will do that job better. The tools which will be described and illustrated to you in the subsequent paragraphs of this section are variations of the basic kit of tools which have been designed for use with special contours, or which have been designed for reaching otherwise inaccessible places.

An example of an inaccessible place is the inside of a door panel when all of the inside trim has not been removed. Certain minor repair jobs on doors make it impractical to remove the inside trim. Consequently, if it is not desired to remove the trim, it is necessary to have the proper tools to do the job. These tools perform the same function as any of the tools in the basic kit; they are merely designed for special applications.

Two additional operations not practical with the basic kit of tools will be used in connection with welding and shrinking of metal as covered in Chapter 4. The two tools involved in these two operations, and a practice exercise whereby you can learn how to use them, are presented in the following paragraphs.

Tools for Shrinking Metal and Sinking Welds. The dolly block shown in Fig. 2-30 is called a *shrinking dolly*. This dolly is formed

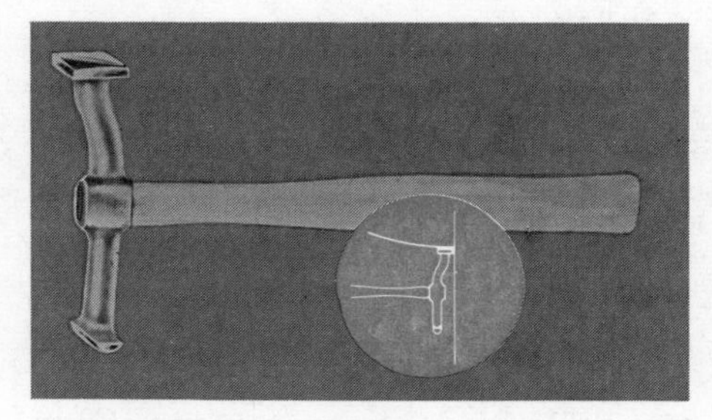

Fig. 2-30. Special dolly block and hammer for sinking welds.

so that two sides of it have a low crown radius, the two ends being concave.

The hammer is similar to other bumping hammers except that one end of the head is shaped to exactly fit the concave contour of the dolly block allowing for the thickness of body metal.

After a fender or panel is welded the dolly block is placed against the inside surface so that the concave portion of the dolly is directly under the seam of the weld, Fig. 2-30. A blow is then struck with the hammer directly against the seam. The seam, being unsupported, will be depressed in a neat fashion. This operation is continued for the full length of the weld, leaving what might be referred to as a *valley*. This depression is later filled with solder and smoothed off. How this is done is explained in a subsequent chapter.

The main benefit derived from this procedure is the strength that is achieved by not filing or grinding the weld smooth. The weld is further strengthened when the valley made by the hammer hand dolly is filled with solder.

In Chapter 4 you will learn how to shrink stretched metal with an acetylene torch and the shrinking dolly. Lacking a torch, the same effect can be accomplished with the dolly and hammer alone. This method is not too practical in actual collision work, but you can gain some experience in the use of these tools by performing this operation on your practice fender.

Whether the skirt of your practice fender is actually stretched or not makes little difference. For the purpose of this exercise, assume that the skirt of the fender bulges outward slightly.

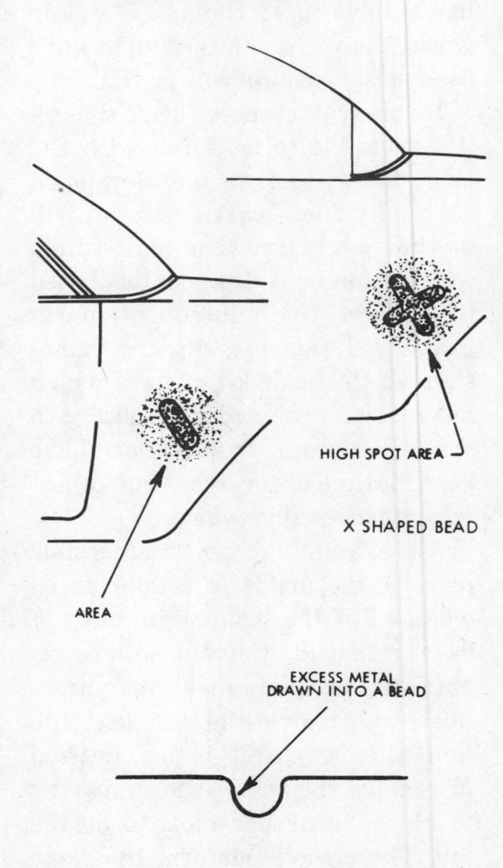

Fig. 2-31. Bead formed to remove a high spot.

Place the dolly under the high spot and form a concave bead or valley as shown in Fig. 2-31. Move the dolly along slowly in a straight line beneath the high spot and strike the outside surface with the hammer. Do not make the bead any longer or deeper than necessary to draw the stretched metal back to contour. It may be necessary to make an X-shaped bead as also shown in Fig. 2-31 if the metal is badly stretched.

An X-shaped valley is made in the same way as a single valley except that a second one is made at right angles to the first one. Form the second bead so that it intersects the other one near the center of the stretched area.

You will see that you have formed a rib that could be used to stiffen a panel to give it strength or to prevent *oil-canning* (the tendency of a panel to act like the bottom of an oil can).

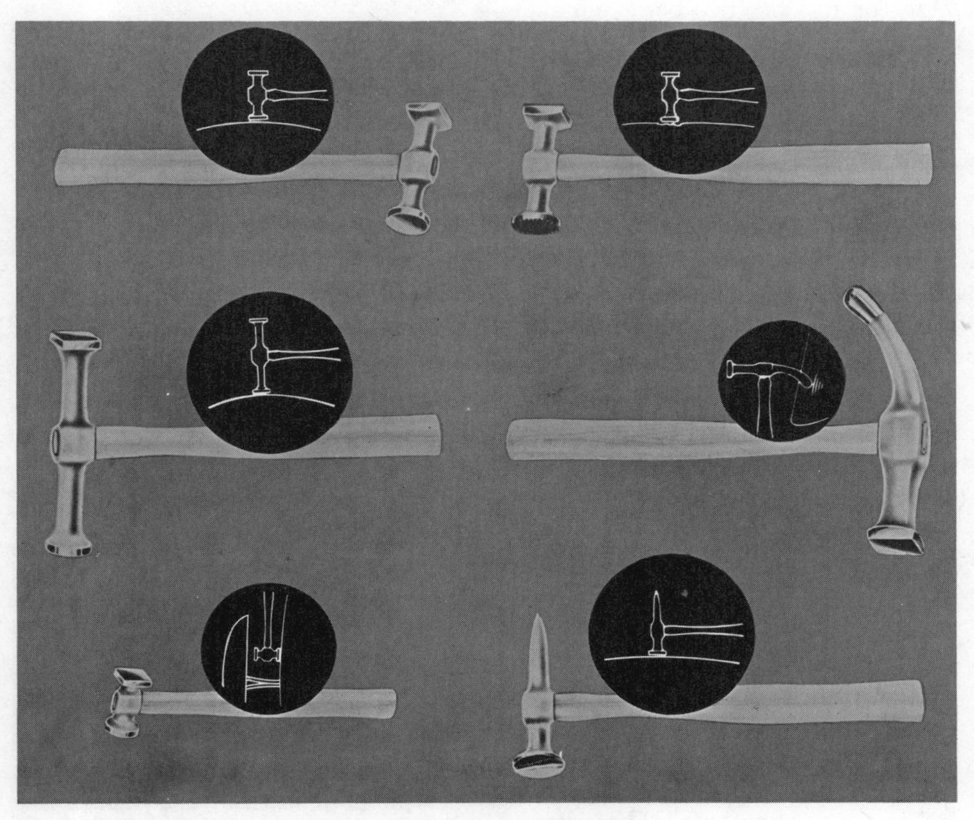

Fig. 2-32. Bumping hammers of many kinds for various jobs.

Do this operation several times until you can sink a neat valley in the metal each time.

Body and Fender Hammers. Eventually you will want to add tools to the basic kit described earlier in the chapter. Several different hammers and their use, therefore, are presented here. Don't be in too much of a hurry to buy these extra hammers; you may never really need some of them.

The hammer shown in Fig. 2-32, top left, is a general-purpose hammer for use on any body panel.

A serrated face hammer is also shown, top right. This type of hammer is preferred by some for roughing out either high or low crown surfaces where the metal has been badly creased. The two center hammers in Fig. 2-32 are other variations of bumping hammers. The heavy hammer with the long, curved end at bottom left is a roughing hammer. Don't use a roughing hammer until you have completely mastered your other tools. By that time you will probably find you don't need one. You cannot hammer out metal with a heavy hammer without stretching the metal.

A short-shanked, square and round face hammer is used when working where the space is restricted (such as between the bumper bar and the fender), lower left. The lower right hammer is a bullet-type, short pick hammer.

A hammer which is ideally suited for fine finishing work by dingmen who repair damage without injuring the paint is the high and low crown finishing hammer shown in Fig. 2-33. This hammer is used for fine finish hammering

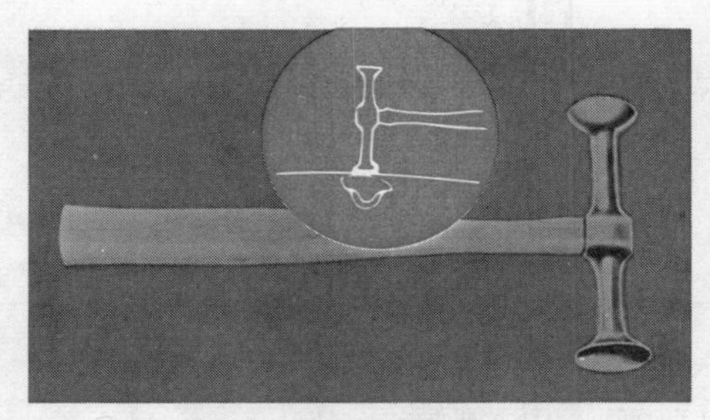

Fig. 2-33. High and low crown finishing hammer.

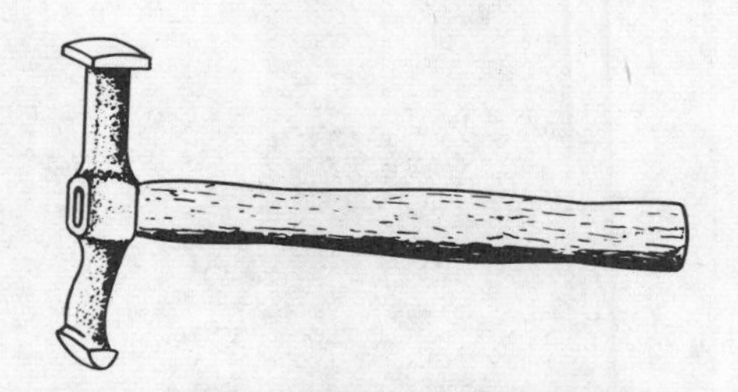

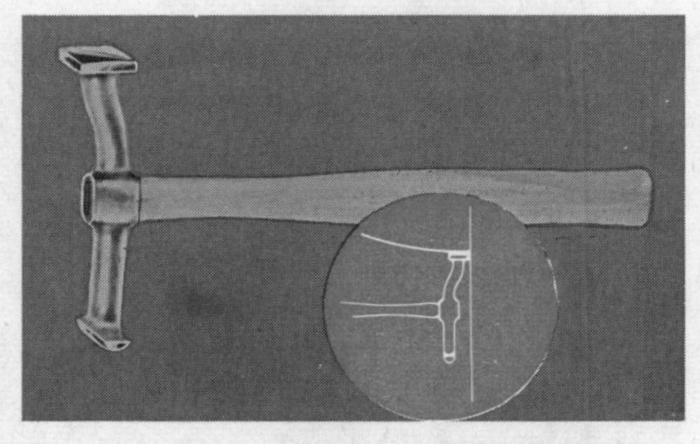

Fig. 2-34. Combination offset cross and straight peen hammer, and square face and cross peen bumping hammer.

on either low or high crown surfaces. Both ends of this hammer are crowned.

Two styles of offset hammers are shown in Fig. 2-34. The combination offset cross and straight peen hammer has a triple purpose; it has a high crown face for all narrow concave surfaces. The cross peen face has a high crown, and is used for wide concave surfaces. The hammer head, having one end offset from the other, not only gives this type of hammer its name, but also allows the user to work close to beads and seams without damaging the surrounding area.

The other offset hammer is a combination offset square face and cross peen bumping hammer. The offset square face is used for general work where an offset hammer is required. It affords ample clearance for adjoining panels. The high crown, cross peen face is designed for deep and narrow panel surfaces and return contours.

Spoons. You are acquainted with the surfacing spoon included in the minimum kit of tools. Many other spoons are available for use in body repair work. Each of these spoons is designed for some specific use on certain body panels or fenders.

The double end, lower back panel and quarter panel spoon, Fig. 2-35, upper left, is used for removing bumps on quarter panels around rear pillars. It is also used for getting behind inner construction and behind back panel strainers, center sills, and lower sills.

Another double end spoon is the heavy duty driving spoon, upper right. This is a general purpose utility spoon which has a variety of uses. It is employed for setting the inside seams of front fenders, bumping top rail moldings, calking quarter panel moldings, etc. It is also used extensively in beading work. It is sometimes used for raising low spots in fenders and around cowl ventilator openings.

Spoons have been developed especially for work on certain contours. One of them is the high crown, concave finishing spoon. This type of spoon is used for spring hammering with a mallet or bumping hammer on all concave surfaces. Another is the low crown, concave surfacing spoon which is used in the same way on low crown surfaces.

Two types of spoons designed especially for work on fenders are also shown. The fender and cowl bracket spoon is used to hook over a fender bracket. It may also be used as a dolly which sometimes makes unnecessary the removal of the wheels on jobs involving the fender brackets. It is also a handy tool when working over cowl strainers and cowl brackets from post to dash.

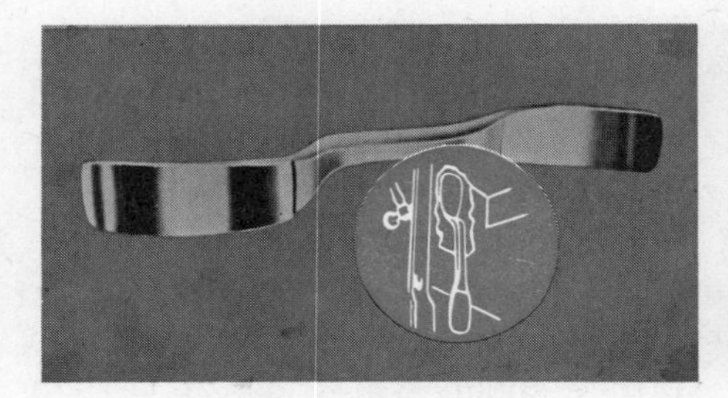

Double end, lower back panel and quarter-panel spoon

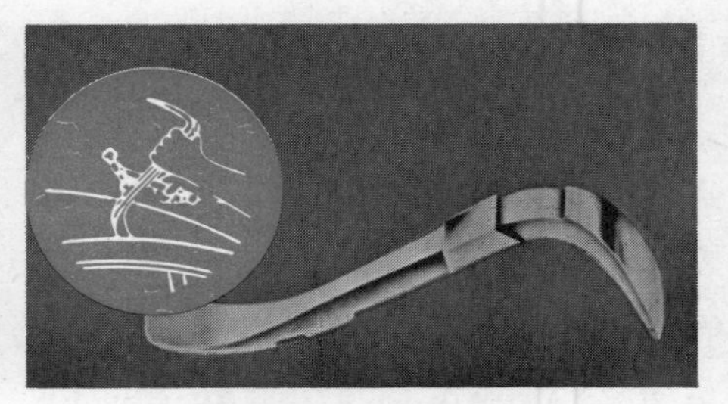

Heavy duty driving spoon

High crown, concave finishing spoon

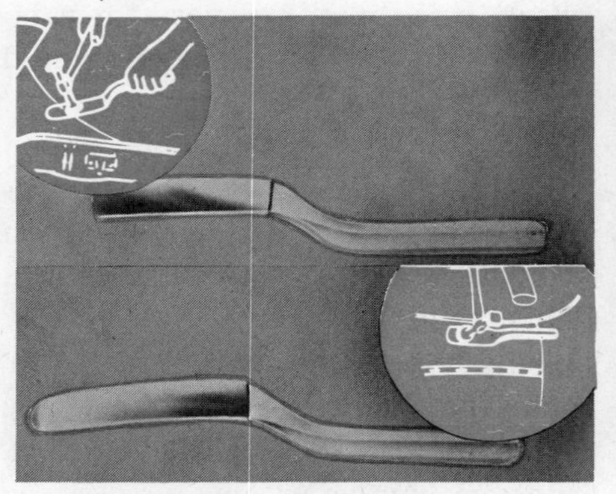

Low crown, concave surfacing spoon

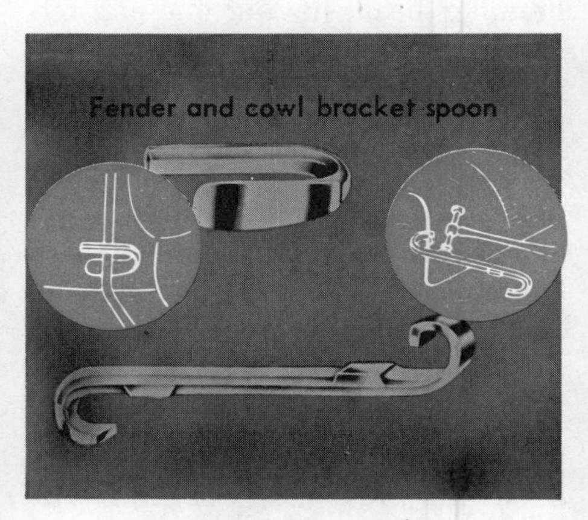

Fender and cowl bracket spoon

Fender beading tool

Special spoons for use on door and side panel inner construction.

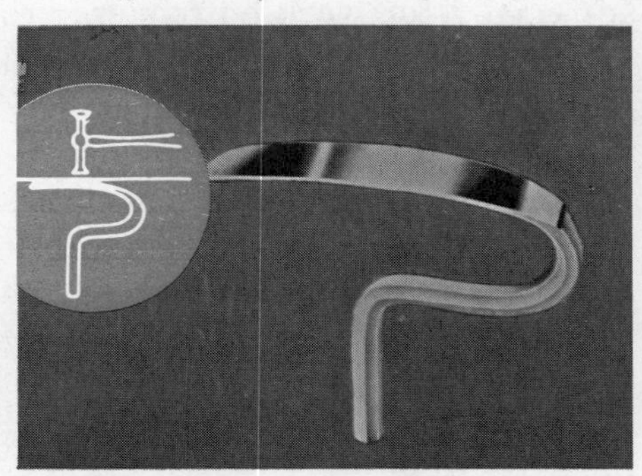

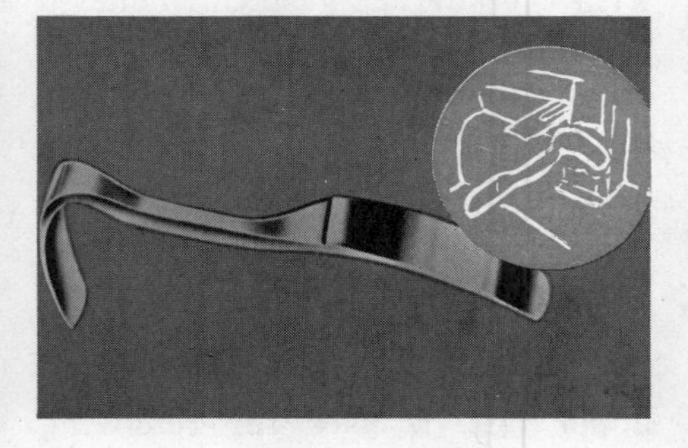

Fig. 2-35. Spoons are adapted to many conditions and take various shapes.

The especially designed fender beading tool is used with the latest style fenders. It may also be used for flanges on one-piece hoods and for aligning inner body panel construction. Some manufacturers provide hammer pads on this type of spoon for use in hammering operations. When hooked into the flange of the fender or hood, as shown in the insert of the illustration, the fender bending tool itself provides a surface on which you can pound with a hammer to bring the metal back in place.

In order to hold the amount of disassembly to a minimum, when you are working on door panels, it is necessary to have tools that you can use to reach far behind inner construction. The spoons shown at the bottom of Fig. 2-35 are designed for use especially on door and side panels. The function of these two spoons is very nearly the same, except that they are for use on slightly different contours and in slightly different cases.

Another tool which is usually considered to be of the spoon family is the wide caulking iron, Fig. 2-36. This tool is designed for use in caulking all straight-line surfaces along the center pillar door panels.

Dolly Blocks. Much money can be wasted in buying dolly blocks if you do not utilize each block you buy on all of the jobs for which it can be used. Besides the dollies with which you have already become familiar, there are other types, some of which you will want when you round out your kit of tools.

The finger dolly, Fig. 2-37, is especially useful because its unique shape allows it to be used for bump hammering where inner

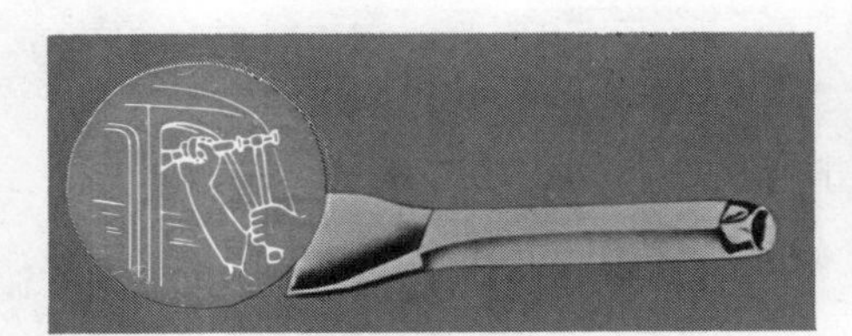

Fig. 2-36. Wide caulking iron.

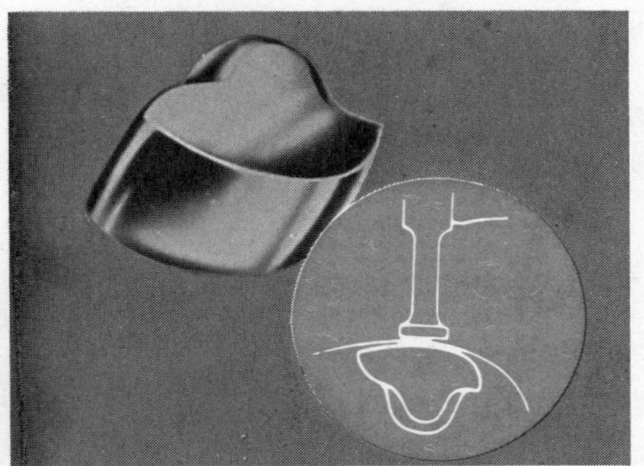

Fig. 2-37. Finger dolly block, and high crown dolly block.

construction or adjoining metal makes the use of the ordinary dolly difficult. Its design permits working in close quarters without danger of injury of the back of your hand on the back stroke.

You may want an additional high crown dolly heavier than the one included in the basic kit previously discussed. Such a dolly is shown to the right in Fig. 2-37.

Pick Tools. Pick tools have the same function as a pick hammer. However, many places are inaccessible with a pick hammer. For this reason, pick tools have been developed which can be used whenever it is found necessary to

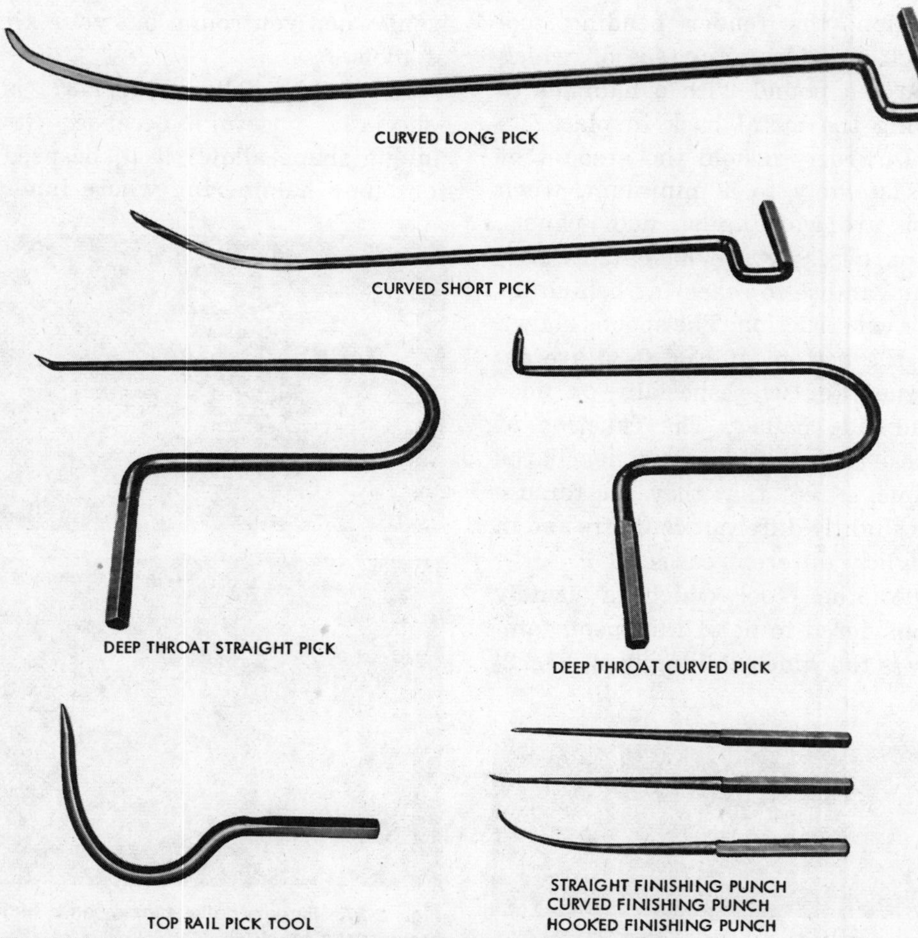

Fig. 2-38. Pick tools and punches for reaching inaccessible places.

work in one of these places. Two pick tools which have similar uses are the long curved pick and the short curved pick, Fig. 2-38. These pick tools are used where a long reach is required, either through inner construction or through the lower part of the frame. Both tools are curved so that when they are turned by the handle, when they are between an outside panel and the inner construction, small bumps in the metal will be forced back to its approximate original position. Pick tools designed especially for use around door panels and rear deck lids are also shown.

The deep throat straight pick is used for raising low spots in the center section of rear deck lids, or in the center sections of door panels, where it is necessary to get behind inner construction.

The deep throat curved pick is similar in design to the deep throat straight pick and it is used in a similar fashion. Where the straight throat is used for working on center sections of door panels, the curved pick is used for working around the edges of door panels, rear deck lids, and also around quarter panels where a tool is needed to reach around some inner construction.

Another type of pick tool shown is the top rail pick designed for fitting over the top rail inner construction so that fine finishing work may be done on the top rail panel above the drip molding.

The three other pick tools will round out the complete set of pick tools you may want eventually. These pick tools are really punches which, because of their design and intended use, are called pick tools.

These tools are particularly useful when you are working around

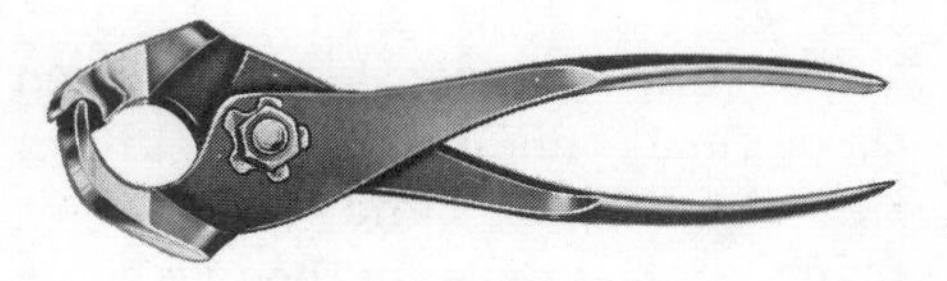

Fig. 2-39. Drip molding pliers.

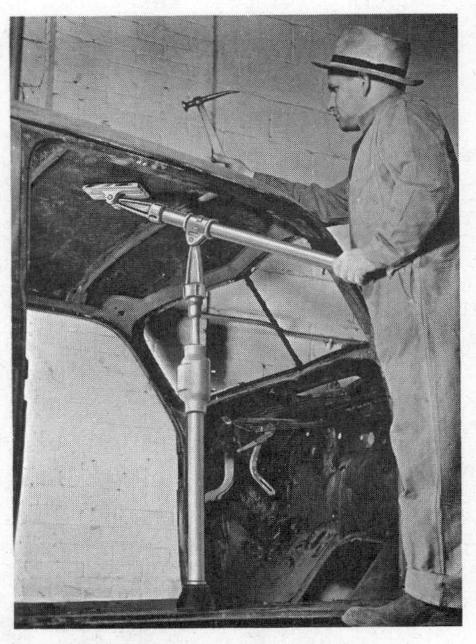

Fig. 2-40. Leverage dolly in action.

reveal moldings or where it is necessary to reach inside doors through door handle holes. They are also useful where offset blows are necessary, and when working around the rear deck lid. These are the ones which you will want to procure first.

Miscellaneous Tools. Several tools are available which will make certain jobs easier. One of these is a pair of drip molding pliers, Fig. 2-39, used for pulling out crushed drip moldings. Another tool which will be helpful to you is a leverage dolly, shown in Fig. 2-40.

A Typical Straightening Job

As has been emphasized throughout this discussion, skill in the use of the hand tools is of prime importance in body repair work. This skill can only be acquired through much practice. Of equal importance is the ability of the body repairman to apply his knowledge of the tools to the job at hand.

On any repair job, no matter how minor the damage might be, you should analyze the damage before you even consider starting to bump. By analyzing the damage, you can determine what it was caused by, the sequence in which it occurred, and what tools will be required to correct it. This should be the procedure on every repair job you encounter. When you actually become employed in a body shop, it will immediately come to your attention that analyzing the job has another value.

By analyzing the job, you can make an estimate of the cost of the repairs. Estimating is a subject in itself, and it will be covered in a subsequent chapter of this volume. For the present you are concerned with analyzing or studying the damage merely to determine what must be done to restore the damaged portions of the body.

Of the several reasons for studying the damage, the most important one is to determine the sequence in which the damage occurred. In complex types of damage (damage resulting from a series of events), it is necessary to reverse the process by which the damage occurred in order to straighten the damaged area with a minimum amount of effort. Another factor involved is the danger of stretching the metal or causing cracks or breaks where otherwise none would occur if the damage were removed in the reverse order of occurrence.

Straightening Metal Without Damaging Paint. In some simple types of damage, it is possible to remove the dent without damaging the paint. When the damage is slight and no sharp creases are involved, you should always consider the possibility of straightening the damage without damaging the paint.

Many fender repairs can be accomplished without disturbing the paint if the inside and outside surfaces have been thoroughly cleaned and properly prepared. A typical instance of straightening a minor damage without injuring the paint is illustrated in Fig. 2-41. In this example, a ding has occurred in the outside lower front corner of a front fender. The metal is merely caved in and is not torn or severely creased.

Hit the deepest portion of the dent from underneath with a heavy dolly such as the dolly shown. Use a surface of the dolly which conforms with the original contour of the metal. With practice, you will find that in many instances you can push the metal back with one blow. This is what you should strive for. However, if you need to, hit the number of blows necessary. Be careful not to hit the metal with the corner or edge of the dolly. If this happens, the metal will be stretched and the paint will become damaged.

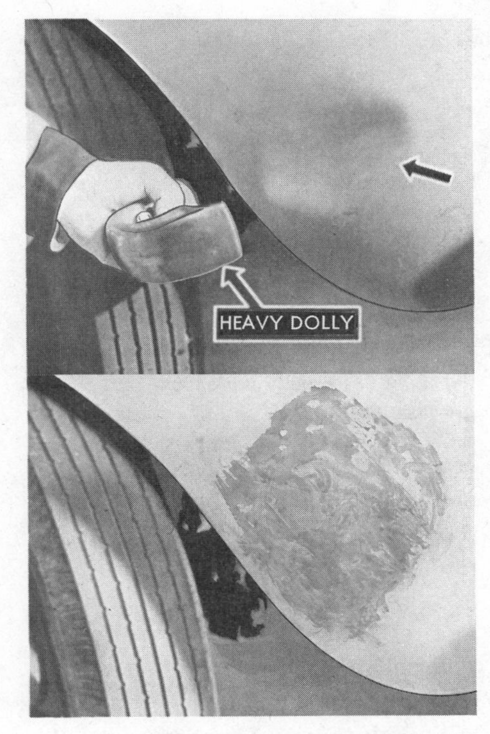

Fig. 2-41. Hammer from underneath with a heavy dolly, then cover the outside surface with oil.

After the dent has been pushed back, clean the outside surface, then cover it with oil. The oil will prevent the mallet from damaging the paint when you remove the small irregularities in the surface left by the dolly block.

Remove the irregularities or low spots by direct hammering with a wooden mallet and a dolly block of the proper contour. Hit the high spots, Fig. 2-42, with the mallet. At each blow, the dolly underneath leaves the fender. As it

Fig. 2-42. With dolly under low portion, hit the high spots.

comes back up, it will force up low spots, evening the surface.

If you exercise a reasonable amount of care in performing the straightening operations for damage of this type, you will save yourself and your customers much cost and inconvenience.

Straightening Damage by Reverse Process. The first step in straightening metal is to get it back as nearly as possible to its original shape or contour. Fig. 2-43 illustrates a fender which has been damaged by a series of events. In this fender, the corner of the skirt was hooked first, then pulled backward. Area *1* in the figure is pulled until the fender bracket bends, at which time the crown in area *2* reverses, leaving a concave surface.

To straighten the fender, this process must be reversed. First, loosen the fender bracket and push the metal in area *2* back to the original contour. Don't use a roughing hammer. Use a heavy dolly as shown in the figure. Be sure the contour of the dolly conforms with the original contour of the fender as nearly as possible. When using the dolly, be careful not to hit the metal with the corners of the dolly. To do so will stretch the metal.

After the low portion is removed, push the corner of the fender skirt back to its original position. You will notice that the dingman in the figure is using his hands and feet to push the fender skirt back into position. In a case such as this, where the damage is in an easily accessible portion of a panel, you can save much time by just pushing the damaged portion into place by hand. If you are able to do this, you accomplish the same result you would have achieved by indirect hammering.

It will be necessary for you to restore the original contour of the fender skirt by direct hammering, lower left. After the contour of the fender has been restored, it will be necessary to bring up the low spots, checking for low spots with chalk. If you do a thorough job of bringing up the low spots, it will save a lot of filing or grinding, making the job much easier.

As a final step, re-form the fender bead, lower right of Fig. 2-43. The fender bead stiffens the

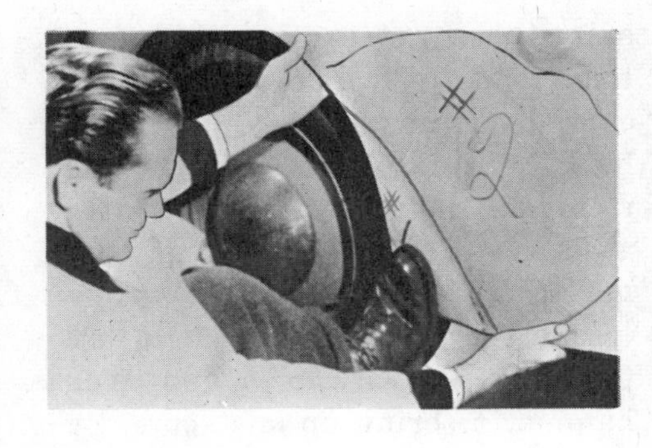

The lower left corner indicated as Area #1 is bent out and back under Area #2. By pushing it back in place you have restored it to its original shape.

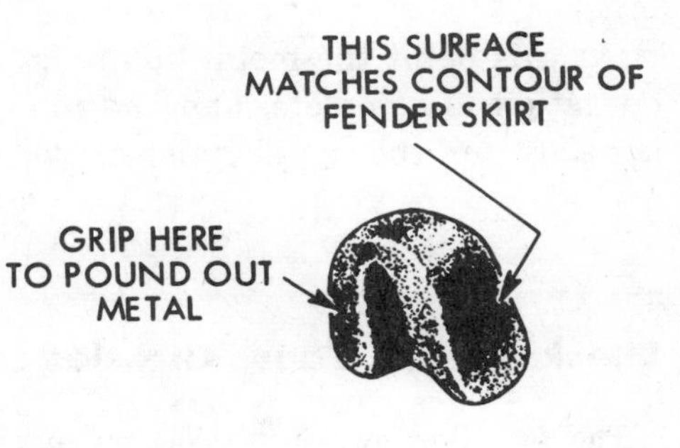

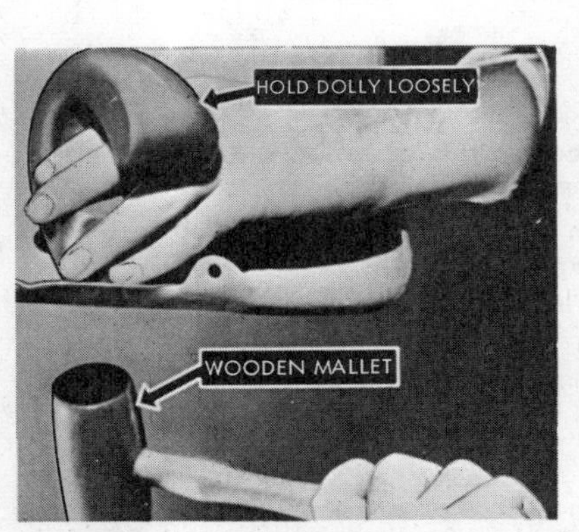

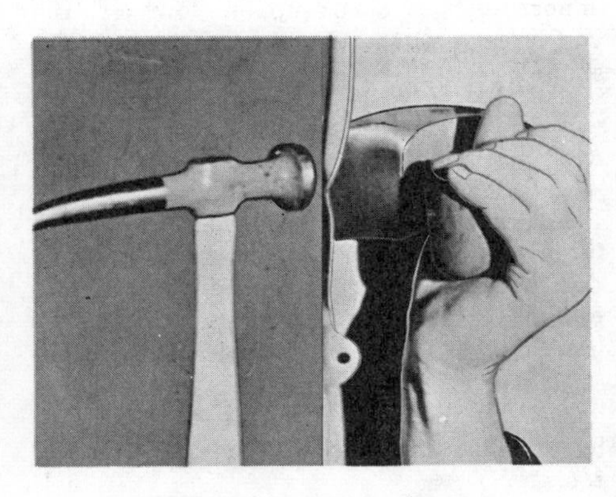

Reforming the fender bead with pick hammer and dolly.

Fig. 2-43. Steps in reversal of fender damage showing sequence of actions.

skirt, thereby strengthening the entire fender. The bead and the curved surface of the skirt will then hold the metal in position. Get the metal as smooth as possible with a hammer and dolly, using care not to stretch the metal.

File the repaired area, and use the high crown dolly and pick hammer to bring up low spots. By direct hammering with a hammer and dolly, flatten the metal raised with the pick. File as required until the metal is completely smooth. Straighten and reattach the fender bracket.

At this point the metal bumping operation is complete, and the job is ready for the metal finisher.

You can easily see that the job just described was complex damage of a simple type. You are probably wondering what happens when you encounter a job with the roof caved in and all the windows and doors smashed. Several subsequent chapters of this volume are devoted to straightening these more serious types of complex damage. However, before you move on to a study of straightening complex damages, you will require a knowledge of the power tools used in collision work. Power tools are available from several manufacturers, and are used by all progressive body shops throughout the country.

Checking On Your Knowledge

The following questions give you the opportunity to check up on yourself. If you have read the chapter carefully, you should be able to answer the questions. If you have any difficulty, read the chapter over once more so that you have the information well in mind before you go on with your reading.

1. What are the duties of a dingman in an automobile manufacturing plant?
2. What pressure variation in psi is possible with the two sides of the pick hammer if a blow of 100 pounds force is struck in both instances?
3. Why should you have a wooden or a hard rubber mallet in your kit of hand tools?
4. Why must your kit of tools contain both low crown and high crown dollies?
5. How is adjustment of a body file obtained so that the file can be used on surfaces with a contour?
6. What is meant by the term *line filing?*
7. At what angle are the file strokes to one another if you are doing X-filing? Cross filing?
8. What is meant by the term *direct hammering?*
9. Why is the use of a heavy roughing hammer usually inadvisable?

10. Which hammer is most generally used for bringing up small low spots?

11. When a light is used for locating low spots, how is it reflected to the body panel?

12. How does using a glove on one hand aid in locating low spots?

13. When your hand tools are to be left unused for a period of time, what should you do?

14. How can the working surfaces of hand tools be kept smooth?

15. Why must a hammer head be kept tight on the handle?

16. What hand tools are most generally used for reforming fender flanges and beads?

17. What is the name of the dolly block used for shrinking welds?

18. What hand tool is used with a shrinking dolly?

19. Is it possible to shrink metal by any other method than with a hammer and shrinking dolly?

20. Under what circumstances is a serrated face hammer used by some collision men?

21. Under what circumstances is a short shanked, square and round face hammer a valuable tool?

22. When is a long curved pick tool or a short curved pick tool used?

23. What tool is used to restore a smashed drip molding?

24. Why is oil sometimes applied to painted surface before straightening it?

Chapter

3 Welding and Cutting

A casual inspection of a modern car reveals little evidence of welding, yet all modern cars are welded from bumper to bumper. In fact, today's automobile could not be assembled at its present low cost without welding.

In body and frame straightening, and in all forms of collision work, it is often necessary to use welding techniques to reinforce frame members, and to weld in place whole new body panels and patches in old panels. These operations can be performed with oxyacetylene gas welding equipment, and most collision men have found it necessary to develop skill in the use of oxyacetylene equipment.

An oxyacetylene torch may also be used to melt and apply solder to body panels, to heat parts to permit bending, and to cut through body panels, inner body construction, and frame members.

An electric arc welder can also be used to cut metal or fuse two separate pieces or two edges together although no satisfactory method has been developed whereby the electric welder can be used for applying solder or heating parts prior to bending or shrinking.

If gas welding equipment is not available, a small blowtorch can be used almost as effectively for applying solder as the acetylene torch. A gasoline or alcohol blowtorch costs but a few dollars.

In shrinking metal (discussed in Chapter 4), it is necessary to heat small areas to a cherry red, then to pound the heated portions down. Here again, oxyacetylene equipment possesses a distinct advantage over any other. Some manufacturers of arc welding equipment, however, have developed a two-carbon torch that results in a flame which can be used for metal shrinking. However, a disadvantage exists in that during the application of the heat to the metal, the eyes and face must be protected, and the operator is, to a degree, working blind.

Arc welding, on the other hand, is generally conceded to be much faster and less costly than oxyacetylene welding. Electric welding equipment, satisfactory for most body panel jobs, can be purchased for as little as you may charge for a single job.

Any collision expert should be thoroughly familiar with both types of equipment, for as he goes from shop to shop, he must be able to use whatever equipment is placed at his disposal.

In collision work, it is often necessary to repair places where the metal has become rusted through, torn, or otherwise broken. The only process by which this can be done involves raising the temperature of the metal to the point where two pieces of metal or two edges of the same piece of metal are fused together. This process is called welding. Both gas welding and electric (arc) welding are explained and illustrated in this chapter.

Sometimes it is necessary to cut out badly damaged portions of body panels or fenders and replace them with new ones. In other instances, it is necessary to cut inner construction in order to gain access to the inner surface of the outer panels. Metal can be cut in several ways, and a later section of this chapter deals with a number of methods of cutting both sheet metal and the inner construction.

Welding or cutting with welding equipment leaves an uneven edge and surface. Regardless of this, it is necessary for the welder to leave the surface as smooth as possible. A discussion of the welder's responsibility in preparing the surface for metal finishing is given in the last section of the chapter.

The biggest problem with either gas or arc welding is achieving good *fusion*. Many times fusion and *adhesion* are confused in people's minds. In welding, the prime objective is to achieve good fusion of the two edges being welded. Fusion is the condition which exists when two materials actually flow together in a molten state and form one piece when they become hard. Adhesion is the condition which exists when two different materials are made to stick tightly to one another. This is especially true of soldering which is discussed in a subsequent chapter of this volume.

A process often confused with welding which utilizes the principle of adhesion is *brazing*. Brazing does not provide the same degree of strength as welding, and is actually a form of soldering. Never substitute brazing for welding in automotive sheet metal welding. It not only is an inferior method, but is usually considered as the mark of an amateur.

A material known as *flux* enables a welder to achieve either fusion or adhesion. The use of flux effectively eliminates the formation of oxide in the weld.

If oxide does form, flux will reduce and remove it from the weld. If oxide is not removed from the weld, the molten metal will be enclosed in a thin film of nonmetallic material, and any additional metal that may be added will adhere to this film rather than to break through it and fuse homogeneously with the other metal. However, flux is not used solely to dissolve the oxide, but also to float off such other impurities as sand, scale, and dirt.

Several good brands of flux are commercially available. Be sure to use the proper flux for the type of welding you are doing. It is advisable to follow the manufacturer's recommendations on this.

Gas Welding Methods

An oxygen acetylene flame can be used for fusing practically any kind of metal. Because oxygen and acetylene are both gases, the process is commonly called *gas* or *torch welding*.

Two tanks, one filled with oxygen and the other with acetylene, are used to contain the gases which are metered to a torch through hoses. The operator controls the metering by means of valves on the tanks and on the torch, Fig. 3-1.

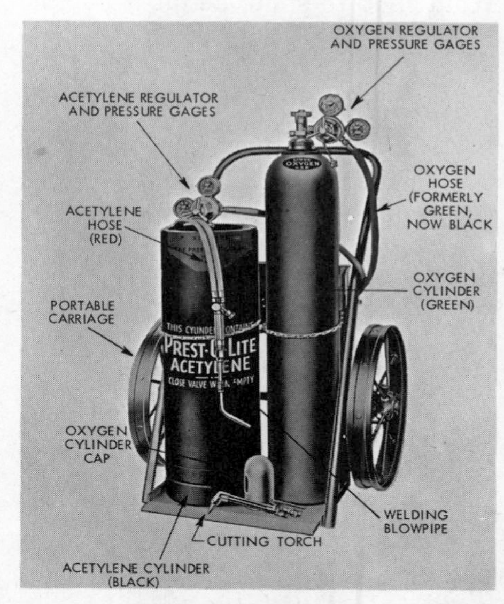

Fig. 3-1. Welding outfit and nomenclature. (Linde Air Products Co.)

The actual welding is done with the torch tip. A different tip is used with the same equipment for cutting. Both of these processes are explained in the following pages. First, however, you should understand why the gases at the end of the torch burn.

The standard oxygen tank is a seamless steel bottle about 5 feet high with walls about ½″ thick. The tank, when full, contains approximately 220 cubic feet of oxygen compressed to 1½ cubic feet. The oxygen, when compressed to this degree, exerts a pressure on the walls of the tank of 2,000 psi (pounds per square inch). Tanks of smaller capacity are available.

Oxygen alone is nonflammable, but it will actively support combustion. If no flame is in the torch tip and oxygen is allowed to escape, a film of ice will form around the tip. If oil or grease, which are forms of hydrocarbon, are brought into contact with oxygen under pressure, the mixture becomes highly flammable, even explosive.

The acetylene tank is similar in construction to the oxygen tank except that it is filled with a porous filler similar to a sponge. This filler may be made of either asbestos, corn pith, charcoal, or other material, depending upon the manufacturer. The filler is completely soaked with acetone, which dissolves and absorbs acetylene to allow more acetylene to be carried in the tank. Acetylene in a free state, not dissolved, can be safely compressed to a pressure of 14.7 psi; but the acetylene in a porous filler may be compressed until it exerts a pressure of 250 to 275 psi. Acetylene and oxygen are sold by weight.

The flame at the torch tip is a result of combustion of pure oxygen and pure acetylene. Two and one-half parts of oxygen are needed to unite with one part of acetylene.

It is not necessary to supply all of the oxygen through the torch. The torch is designed to supply one part each of oxygen and acetylene. The air surrounding the flame will supply the other one and one-half parts of oxygen necessary for perfect combustion and the creation of a neutral flame necessary for a perfect weld.

Equipment

The following items are the necessary components of a gas welding outfit. You will also need some metal on which to practice welding: (1) an oxygen tank with reducing valve, hose and connections; (2) an acetylene tank with reducing valve, hose and connections; (3) a welding torch and an assortment of tips—usually numbers 1, 2, 3, 4, and 5; (4) a set of welder's goggles with double glass for each eye (outer glass clear, inner glass smoke colored); (5) assorted welding rods; (6) a brick or metal top table or bench; (7) some thumb clamps and a vise; and (8) several pieces of 20 to 14 gage sheet metal.

Before you start assembling and setting up the equipment, there are several rules concerning its proper use which you should learn and always remember.

CAUTION:

(*1*) *Do not use oil or any greasy substance on any connections on a welding outfit.*

(*2*) *Do not connect the oxygen hose on the acetylene valve.*

(*3*) *Do not turn the oxygen torch valve on first.*

(*4*) *Do not leave a welding outfit without closing the tank valves.*

(*5*) *Do not leave the torch burning when it is not in use.*

(*6*) *Do not smoke or otherwise bring fire into the area where you are working with an oxygen tank.*

Observing these basic rules will prevent you from having accidents with your equipment.

Setting up Equipment. The first step in assembling a gas welding outfit is to remove the valve caps from the oxygen and acetylene tanks. Open and close each valve quickly to blow out any dust or dirt which might be carried to the regulators. This is known as *cracking the tank.* When cracking the tank, do not direct the high-pressure stream of gas toward anyone or toward an open flame.

Fig. 3-2. Gas welding tanks mounted on portable truck. (Linde Air Products Co.)

Next, connect the oxygen regulator, Fig. 3-2, to the oxygen tank. When you tighten the connection, do not hold the regulator in a fixed position. Allow it to come into position freely as the collar is tightened. This will eliminate any strain on the regulator and will reduce the wear on the valve seat.

Connect the oxygen hose (now black, but formerly green) to the regulator tightly. Be careful not to over tighten the connections. If you suspect that the connection is leaking, paint it with a solution of soap and water with the pressure at the tank turned on. Any leakage will show up in the form of a soap bubble.

The acetylene tank is hooked up in the same manner as the oxygen tank with a few exceptions. The acetylene hose is red and has left-hand threads which must be turned counterclockwise to tighten.

Connecting the Torch. Once the hoses are connected to the tanks, the torch can be connected to the hoses. On most equipment, there is no danger of interchanging hose connections because of the left-hand thread on the acetylene hose. However, a few older torches have right-hand threads on both the oxygen and acetylene connections, so it

TABLE 3-1. TORCH TIP SIZES AND PRESSURES FOR WELDING

Metal Thickness		Welding Head Size Number for Blowpipe				Pressures* (Psi) for Both Oxygen and Acetylene
(Inches)	(Gage)	OO-D	33	34	35	
		1				1
	28		1			1-3
				1	1	1-2
			1			2-4
	26			1		1.5-3
					1	1-2
		2				2
	24		2		2	1-4
				2		1-4.5
			3			2-3
		3				3
			3			2-4
1/16	16		4	4		2-3
					3	2-5
		4				4
3/32	13		4			2-5
				4		2.5-4
					3	4-6
		5				5
1/8	11		4,5			3-5
				4		3-6
					5	2-4
			5		5	4-6
3/16				6		4-6.5
			6			3-5
			6			5-8
1/4				6		6-10.5
					7	4-6
			7			4-7

*Regulator setting with twenty-five foot hose lengths. (Linde Air Products Co.)

TABLE 3-2. TORCH TIP SIZES AND PRESSURES FOR CUTTING

Metal Thickness (Inches)	Nozzle Size Number for Cutting Attachment or Blowpipe				Pressures* (Psi)		
						Acetylene	
	33	34	35	Type "E"	Oxygen	Four-Flame Nozzle	Six-Flame Nozzle
1/16	0				10-15	3-5	
	0				15-20	4-6	
1/8		1	1	1	10-13	2-3	1-2
	0				30-38	4-8	
1/4		1	1		17-24	2-5	1-3
				1	17-22	2-4	

*Regulator setting with twenty-five foot hose lengths. (Linde Air Products Co.)

is advisable to exercise care if this type of equipment is encountered.

Selection of Tip. After the torch is connected, it is necessary to select the correct tip for the job. The selection of tips is based on the thickness of the stock to be welded.

Since the numbering of tips has never been standardized, it is difficult to set up a specific rule. However, Tables 3-1 and 3-2 will be helpful.

The size of the tip used depends on several variables, such as the skill of the operator, the volume of the surrounding metal, the position in which the welding is done, and the kind of metal being welded. If a tip is too small for a job, much time will be wasted and poor fusion will result. If a tip is too large for a job, it is likely to produce poor metal in the weld due to overoxidation, and a rough job due to the lack of control of the flowing metal.

After a tip has been selected, install it in the nozzle. Adjust the nozzle at the union joint, Fig. 3-3, so that the tip will point correctly when the torch is held conveniently for operation and adjustment.

Adjusting Regulators. To adjust the oxygen regulator, make sure that the adjusting screw, Fig. 3-3, is turned all the way out and is free of spring tension so that when the oxygen pressure is released from the tank, it will not bang against the diaphragm and damage the nozzle. Open the oxygen tank valve fully. Open the oxygen valve on the torch handle one-quarter turn, then turn the adjusting screw on the

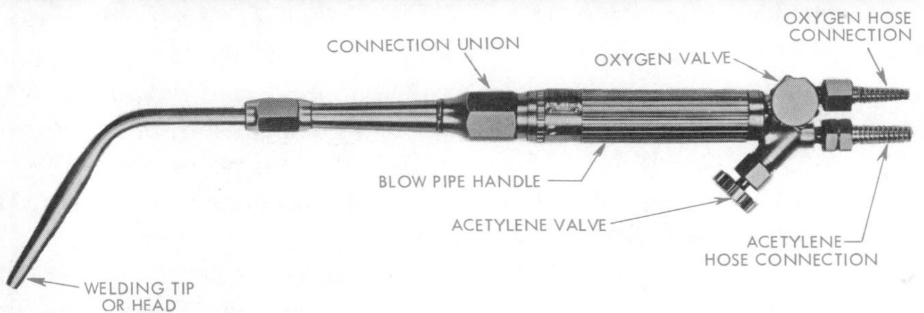

Fig. 3-3. Welding torch with nozzle in place. (Paul Lawrence Dunbar Vocational High School, Chicago, Illinois)

regulator clockwise until the proper pressure for the tip being used on the torch is registered on the pressure gage. Close the oxygen valve on the torch handle when the correct gage pressure is established.

The acetylene regulator can now be adjusted in the same manner with the exception that the tank valve need be opened only a quarter to one-half turn, or until the tank pressure registers on the tank pressure gage.

Lighting the Torch. A flint lighter, Fig. 3-4, is generally used for lighting the torch because it will produce a good-sized spark quickly.

To light the torch, open the acetylene valve on the torch handle about one-quarter turn and immediately spark the flint lighter at the end of the torch tip. If too much time elapses before the lighter is sparked, there is danger of a small explosion which may burn your hands.

When the gas is lit, turn the acetylene valve on the torch handle until the proper flame is established. For general purposes, you can consider the torch correctly adjusted when a yellow flame is produced which is just ready to break away from the tip and burns approximately 1/8″ away from the end of the tip. After the correct acetylene flame is established, open the oxygen valve on the torch slowly until the flame changes from a ragged yellow flame to a perfectly formed bluish tone. This is known as a *neutral flame* and is the proper flame for most welding.

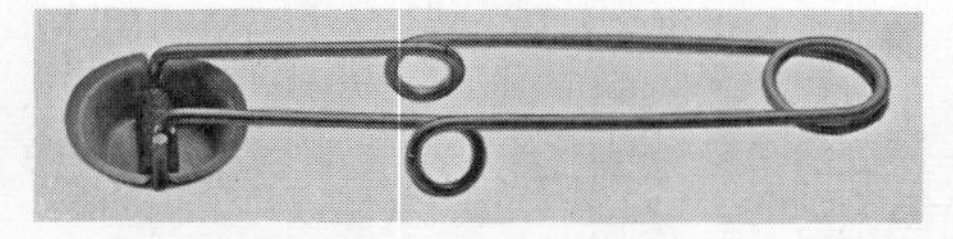

Fig. 3-4. Flint lighter or striker. (Linde Air Products Co.)

Welding Flames. Unless the oxygen and acetylene are combined in the proper amounts to produce a neutral flame, Fig. 3-5, the release of unburned carbon or oxygen will occur, and lower temperatures will result. The different types of flames you will encounter when the torch is not properly adjusted are shown in Fig. 3-5.

Free carbon in the welding flame will result in what is called a *reducing flame,* and will cause carbonization of the metal. This will cause slag and brittleness and will result in loss of heat, porosity of the metal, and you will have a difficult time fusing the two pieces of metal.

An excess of oxygen will result in a purplish colored flame, commonly called an *oxidizing flame.* This type of flame will cause rapid oxidation, slag inclusion, porosity, and again you will have difficulty in fusing the two pieces.

For combustion purposes, the acetylene obtains about one and one-half parts of oxygen from the atmosphere and one part is provided by the oxygen supply. If too much or too little is furnished due to improper adjustment of the reg-

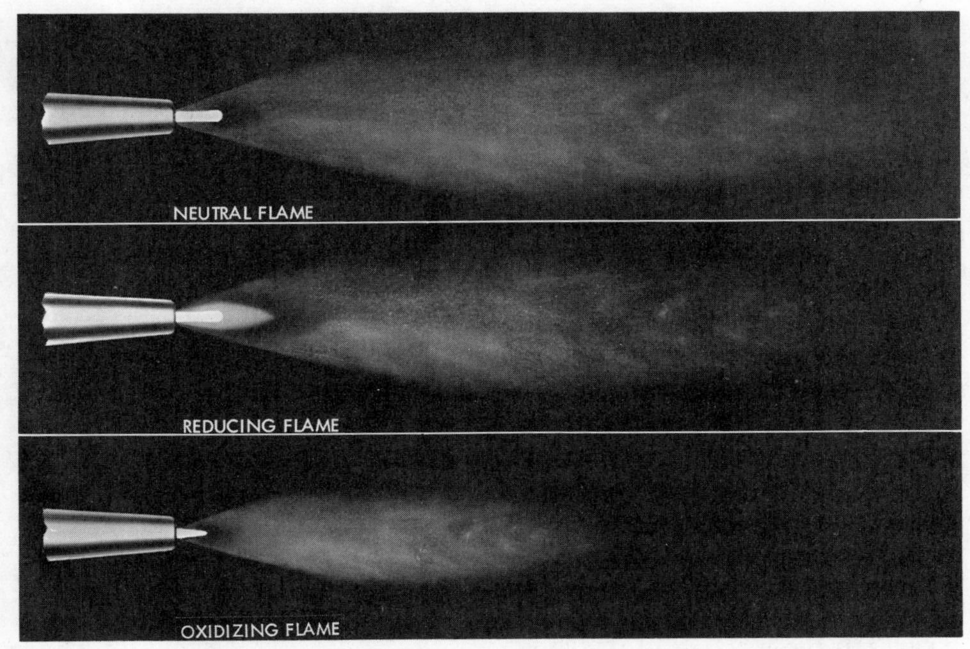

Fig. 3-5. Different types of flames: neutral flame (top), reducing flame (center), and oxidizing flame (bottom). (Linde Air Products Co.)

ulator or torch valves, the effects are noticeable at once by the appearance of the flame, by the sound of the combustion, and by the appearance of the weld metal. Proper adjustment of the welding flame is a vital factor of welding. It must be studied continuously if you expect to obtain good welds.

The sound of combustion is the sound made by the torch in the process of burning the acetylene and oxygen. When the flame is properly adjusted, it will burn softly and evenly. If too much oxygen is being delivered to the torch, the flame will burn with a sharp hissing sound.

If the pressure of both the acetylene and the oxygen is too great, the flame will burn with a harsh blowing sound, and the vertical cone will be too long. This type of flame will cause *blowing of the metal.* The force of the oxygen and gas is so great as it leaves the nozzles that it actually blows holes in the molten metal.

If too low a pressure is being used, it will permit the flame to burn within the tip. This condition will soon cause overheating of the tip. When the tip becomes hot enough to ignite the gases within it, backfiring or popping will result, spattering the metal, whereupon the continuity of the weld will be interrupted.

Carbonizing Flame. When an excess of acetylene is used, the flame will be ragged. Certain welding operations make it desirable to have a slightly carbonizing flame.

When welding aluminum, a carbonizing flame is desirable because it will prevent the formation of an excess of aluminum oxide, which interferes in the fusing of the metal. A carbonizing flame is also desirable when welding monel metal, stainless steel, and white or die-cast metal.

Oxidizing Flame. An oxidizing flame, as mentioned before, is injurious to the metal. An oxidizing flame can easily be recognized by the size of the flame cone (small and pointed) and by the brilliant blue color.

The use of too much oxygen will cause the metal to burn rapidly. This is a prime factor in cutting metal, so it can be seen readily that an excess of oxygen should not be used when you are trying to make a weld.

Manipulation of Torch and Welding Rod

Before you actually do any welding, you should become familiar with holding and moving the torch correctly. You will also have to familiarize yourself with adding welding rod to the weld. The welding rod provides the additional material needed for fusing two edges of metal together. The exercises given in this chapter will give you an opportunity to practice the movement of both the torch and welding rod.

Movement of the Torch. In these first exercises, it will not be necessary to light the torch because you are going to practice moving and holding the torch only.

In order to obtain the best weld, it is necessary to incline the torch at an angle of about 60° to the plane of the work. Fig. 3-6 shows the proper way of holding the torch with the tip inclined.

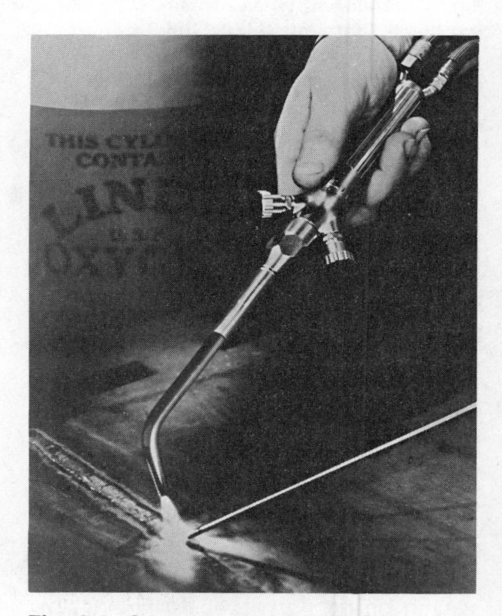

Fig. 3-6. Correct method of holding welding torch. (Smith Welding and Cutting Equipment Co.)

The torch should not be inclined too far. Otherwise, the molten metal will be blown ahead of the weld area. Neither should it be held in a nearly vertical position, for the flame will not then be utilized to its full value for heating the metal ahead of the weld area.

Whenever possible, move the torch from left to right rather than toward and away from yourself. It is much easier to observe the work when the torch is moved back and forth.

To make a proper weld, it is necessary to make a simultaneous fusion of the edges to be joined and the welding rod. This is accomplished by the movement of the torch, depending on the thickness of the stock being welded.

With thick stock, it is necessary to bevel or *chamfer* the edges to be joined, then butt them together and fill the bevel with molten welding rod. The proper movement to impart to the torch for this type of welding is illustrated by the lines in Fig. 3-7. The torch is oscillated in arcs large enough

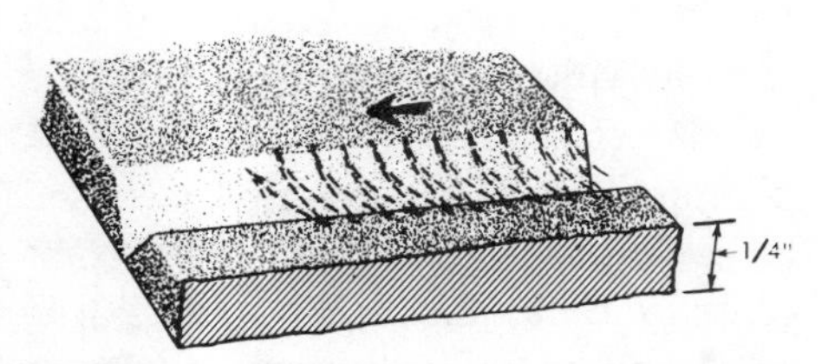

Fig. 3-7. Oscillation motion of torch for welding heavy stock.

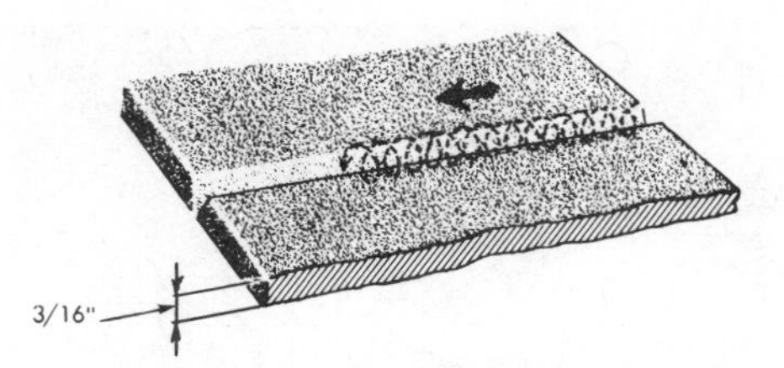

Fig. 3-8. Circular motion of torch for welding light gage metals.

to contact both edges of the bevel. The welding rod is held in the center of the bevel so the torch also contacts the rod. This movement allows the edges of the stock and the welding rod to be heated to the molten stage simultaneously.

When you are welding light-gage metals, you should impart a circular motion to the torch, Fig. 3-8. This circular motion should be in the direction of the welding. Experience will soon show you how large the circles should be for the different gages of metal which you will encounter.

Any motion of the torch, whether it be for either light or heavy stock, should be made in a constant and regular manner to produce a good appearance on the finished weld.

Adding Welding Rod. The welding rod plays an important part in welding. It must be held correctly and added to the weld at the proper time. Otherwise, a poor weld will result. Moreover, the rod should be inclined in a fashion similar to the torch. Fig. 3-9 shows how to hold

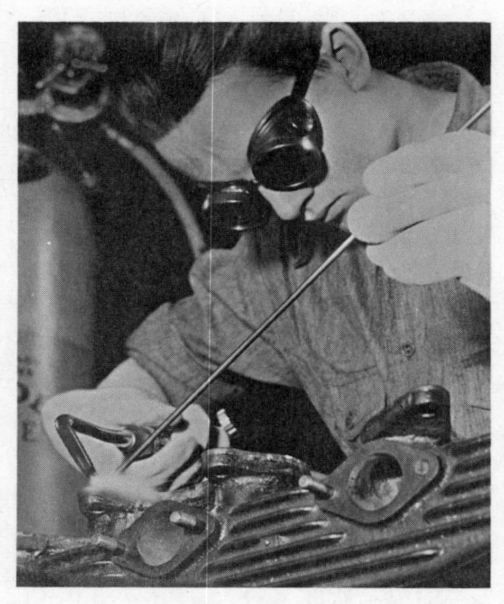

Fig. 3-9. Correct method for holding torch and welding rod. (Linde Air Products Co.)

the welding rod and torch in their proper relationship.

When the edges to be joined are heated to the molten stage, the welding rod should be brought into contact with them. As soon as the *bead* or *crater* is filled, the rod should be removed and the torch advanced slightly along the weld line. If the welding rod is added to the weld before the edges are sufficiently heated, poor fusion will result.

Exercises

You should perform each one of the exercises described here several times. By doing so, you will become quite proficient in the use of the welding equipment.

The only materials you will require are an old fender, some ¼", ⅛", and 3/32" steel plate, and some welding rod.

Welding of Heavy Stock. For your first attempt at welding, it is best for you to work with thick stock. Obtain some ¼" thick steel plates, and either file or grind a bevel on one edge of each so that when the plates are butted to one another, a V-shaped valley is created by the bevels. Be sure the bevel extends entirely through the section to be welded. A 45° bevel on each side usually will provide sufficient depth and width.

It is best to lay the plates on some nonflammable surface. Concrete is generally considered the best. Be sure that the plates are properly aligned and in the same plane so that after the two are welded together, an absolutely flat surface results with the exception of the bead left by the weld.

After the plates are prepared, light the torch and adjust the flame correctly. Use an oscillating motion as required when welding to the work. Preheat a section of the beveled edges. When they are molten, add the welding rod. This forms what is known as a *tack*. A complete weld is commonly called a *continuous tack*. As you complete a tack, move along the line of the weld making more tacks so that when you have completely

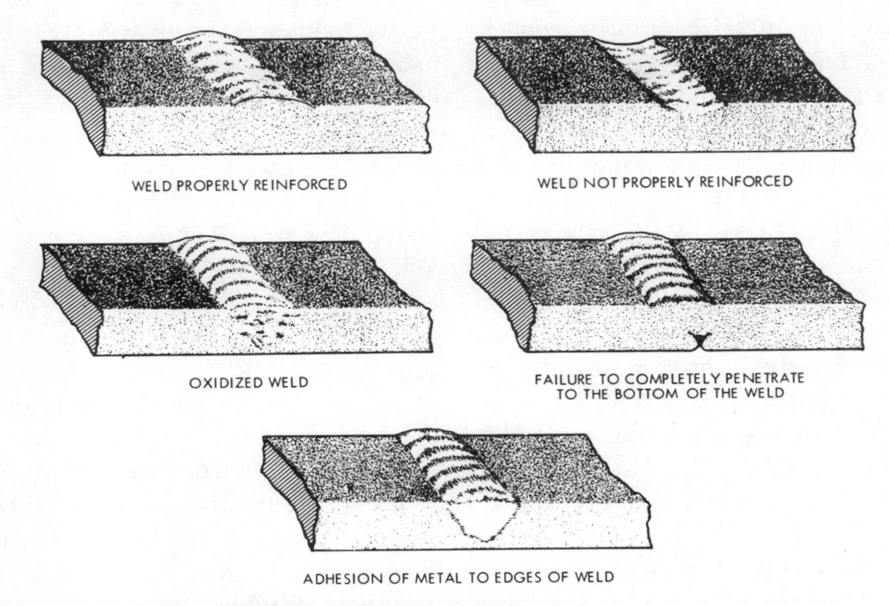

Fig. 3-10. Various weld conditions illustrated by results.

traversed the seam, you have a continuous tack.

Enough welding rod should be added to completely fill the bevel. There should be sufficient excess to form a bead above the finished surface. This bead is important for it reinforces the weld.

Fig. 3-10 illustrates the various conditions you may find when you have completed the weld. A properly made weld is shown in Fig. 3-10. Improperly made welds are also shown. Each one of these incorrect welds is due to some fault on the part of the welder.

The defect in the weld shown at (top right) is caused by not adding enough welding rod. The defect in the weld shown at (middle left) is caused by the edges being heated to the fusion point too quickly, with the result that a film of oxide forms on the edges which will not allow the welding rod and edges to fuse properly.

The defect in the weld shown at (middle right) is caused by failure of the welder to penetrate completely the stock which is being welded. The defect in the weld shown at (bottom) is caused by the welding rod and edges of the stock not being in fusion. That is, one is colder than the other. This results in what is known as adhesion rather than fusion. The warm metal merely sticks to the cooler metal and does not fuse with it.

Practice welding two pieces of ¼″ steel plate together until you can produce a weld similar to that shown (top left), Fig. 3-10.

Welding Light Stock. Perform the same operation with some ⅛″ or 3/32″ stock as you did with the ¼″ stock. Remember that you are now working with lighter material. To select a different tip for the torch, see the information given in Table 3-1 on tip sizes.

Because the stock is lighter, only a short time will be required to heat the metal all the way through. Move the torch in a circular motion, and add the welding rod when the metal is sufficiently molten to receive it. Practice this exercise until you can obtain a good weld every time.

Welding Sheet Metal. Several things must be taken into consideration when you are welding sheet metal. For example, the spread of heat will be much faster when the torch is applied to sheet metal than it will when heavier stock is being welded. If the weld is in only a small area, you will want to save as much paint on the surrounding surface as possible. When this is the case, you can place what is known as a heat dam around the area where the welding is to be done.

Heat dams are made from asbestos flake and water. Simply mix asbestos flake with water until a stiff paste is formed. Build a little mound 1″ to 1½″ thick and about 8″ to 10″ away from where you are going to weld. Completely surround the area being worked on and the heat will be confined to that area. Asbestos flake is the same substance which was used a few years back to insulate steam pipes in the basements of many houses.

Welding a Crowned Surface. For your first attempt at welding sheet metal you can use an old fender. Fasten the fender in a vise or other suitable clamping device so that it is held rigidly in the same position it is in when on the car. With a hacksaw, cut into the crown on top of the fender. Make a saw cut approximately 2″ long. Select the proper torch tip by consulting Table 3-1. Light the torch and you are ready to begin.

Use the correct movement of the torch, and heat the edges. Then add the welding rod, making a tack from above. As the surrounding crowned surface will rigidly hold the edges being welded, it will not be necessary to use clamps. Continue making tacks the length of the cut until you have a continuous weld.

You will notice that the heat has spread over a large area of the fender. Allow the fender to cool. Make another saw cut, construct a heat dam around it, and weld it up. Practice making welds in the crown of the fender from the top until you can obtain a good-looking weld which is properly reinforced.

Sometimes it is better to make the weld from underneath the fender. After you become proficient at making welds from above in the crowned surface, make another saw cut in the crown of the fender. Sit on the floor and make the weld from underneath. Simply heat the edges of the saw cut until they are in the proper molten state to receive the welding rod.

CAUTION:

Be sure to sit to one side of the area being welded so that the molten drops of metal which will fall off the weld do not drop on you or your clothing. Asbestos gloves can be purchased and should be worn whenever you are welding from underneath or whenever there is a possibility that the metal may drop on your hands. Practice making welds from underneath the fender until it is as easy for you as welding from above.

Welding Edge of Fenders. Welding the edges of fenders or other panels is not like welding a cut or tear in the center of a panel. The two edges are free to move back and forth independently of each other. For this reason, it is necessary to use a clamping device to hold the edges in line with one another until several tacks can be made, then remove the clamp.

With a hacksaw, cut into the practice fender anywhere along the edge. Make a cut approximately four inches into the fender. With a C-clamp, secure the two edges together and tighten the clamp, Fig. 3-11.

Manipulating the torch properly, make a tack as near the clamp as possible. Make several tacks at intervals along the line of the cut. Allow the tacks to cool, then remove the clamp. The edges are rigidly held by the tacks so you can now go ahead and make a continuous weld the length of the entire cut. Practice this exercise several times, then make the same kind of cut in the fender again and weld it from the underside.

It is a good policy, whenever you encounter a job of replacing or repairing fender splash shields, to inspect the edges of the fender to be sure no small cracks have started. Breaks in the edges of fenders are usually caused because a splash shield has been broken or come loose, allowing the edges of the fender to vibrate. This will cause cracks to start, then to grow with continued vibration.

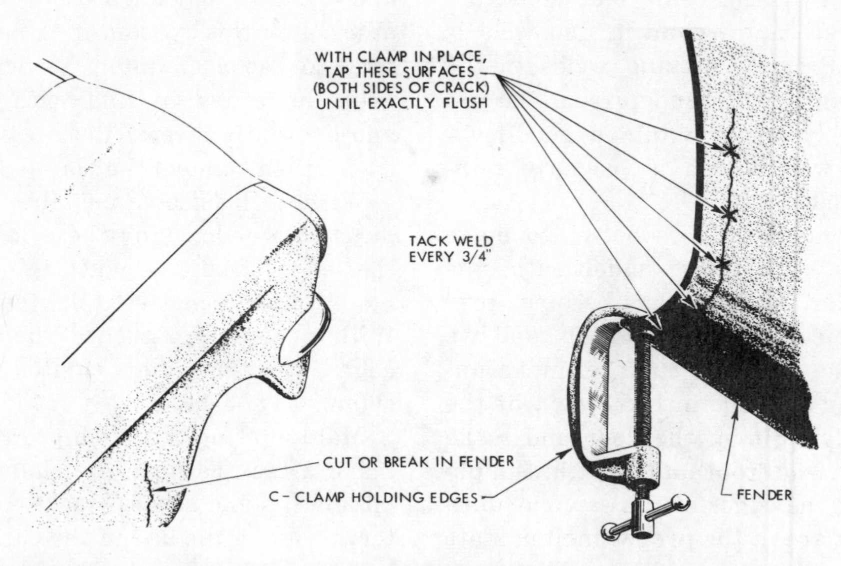

Fig. 3-11. Edges of cut in fender fastened with C-clamps prior to welding.

Cutting Sheet with Gas Torch. Four sizes of tips or nozzles are furnished for cutting sheet metal. These are graded according to the thickness of the metal to be cut, and are different from those used for welding. Usually, three to six small oxygen-acetylene orifices surround a center orifice which emits pure oxygen.

The oxygen and acetylene for the smaller orifices are controlled by an oxygen and an acetylene valve. The pure oxygen from the center orifice is controlled by an oxygen cutting valve. The purpose of the smaller orifices is merely to heat the area surrounding the cut to the point at which it will oxidize (burn) rapidly in the stream of pure oxygen from the center orifice.

An attachment is usually provided which screws into the handle of a regular welding torch, enabling it to be used as a cutting torch. This attachment takes the place of the regular torch tip from the handle to the end. A spring-loaded, push-type, oxygen valve, called the *cutting valve,* is a part of this attachment.

Working pressures are given by the manufacturers of cutting nozzles. Be sure to use the pressures specified by the manufacturer of the equipment with which you are working.

To cut sheet metal with the gas torch, preheat the metal with the torch. As soon as it becomes red hot, open the cutting valve, and move the torch along the surface only as fast as a clean, distinct cut can be obtained. Hold the torch at a constant distance from the work, and move it away from yourself so that you may watch the cut advance.

If at any time the torch is moved too fast and the cut is lost, it will be necessary to restart the cut. In this case, the oxygen supply should be cut off and the heating flames applied to the point where the cut was lost until the metal has been heated enough to start cutting again.

You can practice cutting with a gas torch by obtaining any old body panels which should be available from any body shop. Fix the tip on the torch for the gage metal with which you are working. Light the torch as you would for welding, preheat the area where you wish to begin your cut, then turn on the oxygen supply and start your cut.

You can mark where you want to cut with chalk so you will have a line to follow. The chalk will burn off near the torch, but it will help to guide you. It is virtually impossible to make any kind of a line which will not be burned off except a scribed line which is scratched into the metal surface.

Always keep the torch the same distance from the metal insofar as is possible. Move the torch only as fast as you can make a clean cut. The edges of the cut will appear ragged, but you should practice making a straight cut with as smooth an edge as is possible.

Arc Welding Methods

Arc welding is a process whereby the heat necessary to bring metal to the molten state is obtained by a continuous arc between a welding rod or a carbon rod and the work.

Arc welding probably is a little more difficult to master than torch welding, since it is necessary to strike an arc and to maintain this arc throughout the time you are welding. Arc welding is not difficult on heavy material in which large size welding rod is used and where high amperages are involved. Such welding, however, will represent only a small portion of the welding you will do in collision work. Most of your work will be on thin fenders and body panels that are equally thin.

In working on thin sheet metal

as employed in automobile body panels, the amperage used is comparatively low. Likewise, the size of the welding rod is comparatively small. It is more difficult, therefore, for the welder to establish and maintain the position of the welding rod. The distance the welding rod is held from the surface being welded establishes the length of the arc.

In arc welding, the arc is established by scratching the end of the welding rod on the surface to be welded. This is more easily accomplished if the surface is rough, as would be true if you were dragging the welding rod over a broken seam in the metal.

As the welding rod is dragged over this roughened surface, an electric spark is generated. The spark ionizes the air immediately surrounding the electrode. This ionized air becomes a conductor for electrical current if the welding rod is not pulled too far away from the surface and current continues to flow through this small air gap. This generates a tremendous amount of heat; both the end of the welding rod and the surface of the metal being welded are brought to a molten state, and fusing of the metal is accomplished.

In arc welding, only coated welding rod should be used. This coating is the flux necessary for the weld. This flux coating, of course, is not an electrical conductor, and it is necessary to remove the coating at the point where the welding rod is clamped into the holder. Sometimes the combination of welding rod holder and the rod itself is referred to as the *torch*. This is a carry-over of terms from oxy-acetylene welding.

In a measure, the size of the welding rod used controls the amperage flowing into the weld. As a rule, as you are developing skill in arc welding, you will start with a smaller than normal welding rod. This will reduce the possibility of burning holes in the sheet metal.

In the early stages of your development as an arc welder, you will want to reduce the amperage as much as possible until you have mastered control of the arc. However, the lower the amperages involved, the more difficult it will be for you to maintain the arc.

At one time, motor-generator welding equipment was in common use which delivered direct current to the welding rod. These welders, however, are rather expensive, and it is more difficult to strike and maintain an arc with a D.C. welder than with the comparatively inexpensive A.C. welder. Moreover, these motor-generator sets are heavy and are not as portable as the A.C. welders. For these reasons, the motor-generator D.C. welder outfits are fast disappearing from body shops. They are still popular, however, in welding shops that do welding of heavy parts.

The purpose of this section is to show you how, with an arc welder, to do the welding and cutting operations involved in collision work. For this reason, the instructions presented here are written primarily around the A.C. arc welder which you find in most shops.

This small equipment has a means of selecting different amperages that you will be using in the welding of body panels. Larger, more versatile arc welders will be found to have a wider selection of amperages and probably will have some advantages not possessed by these smaller models. Nevertheless, you can learn arc welding such as will be required in collision work with one of these small welders. When at some later date you encounter a larger machine, you will be able to apply the knowledge and technique you have learned with the small welder. The principles involved are identical.

Two different methods of arc welding are possible: carbon arc welding and metallic arc welding. In auto body shop practice, carbon arc welding is used only for aluminum. For this reason, detailed instructions are given here for metallic arc welding only.

The most popular electric arc welders are small, inexpensive,

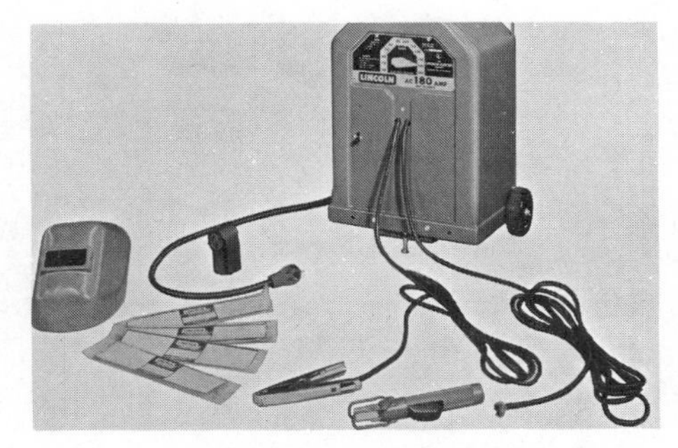

Fig. 3-12. Portable A.C. arc welder with accessories. (Lincoln Electric Co.)

portable A.C. welders similar to the one illustrated in Fig. 3-12. Also shown in this illustration are the necessary pieces of equipment for operating this welder.

Arc welding has an advantage over other kinds of welding in that the heat is concentrated right at the electrode (equivalent to the torch in gas welding). This means that distortion due to heat is minimized.

Protective Equipment

When you are working with arc welders, it is necessary to use certain protective measures to guard both your clothing and yourself from injury.

The rays emitted by the arc are similar in character to those given off by the sun and will cause sunburn of the arms and hands unless gloves, mitts, or protective sleeves are worn, Fig. 3-13. To protect the face and eyes from the harmful rays, protective shields made from

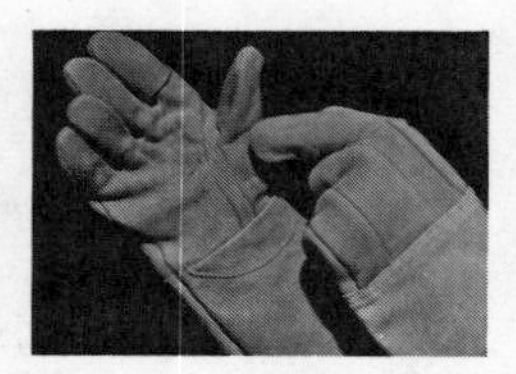

Fig. 3-13. Always wear hand protection when welding. (Lincoln Electric Co.)

pressed fiber and smoked glass are worn, Fig. 3-14. Some shields are held in the hand, leaving only one hand to operate the torch. Others are made so that they can be worn, leaving both hands free for handling the torch and the work.

On production welding jobs, to protect clothing from hot, spattering metal, leather aprons which extend from the chin to the knee are best. In automotive retail shops, welding is only an intermittent job and, other than gloves and face shields, no special clothing generally is used.

As a final precautionary measure, welding, wherever practical, should be done in a closed booth. Any other workers in the immediate area should not expose their eyes to the harmful rays emitted by the torch. These rays are so bright they can cause temporary blindness. Long exposure to them can cause permanent eye injury.

The welding rod is fastened in a holder similar to those shown in Fig. 3-15. These holders are so constructed that they allow the operator to hold the welding rod without receiving an electric shock and to manipulate it freely.

By being its own electrode, the welding rod melts itself down in

Fig. 3-14. Protective face shields and hoods: hand-held face shield, welding hood or helmet, welding hood with hinged window. (General Electric Co.)

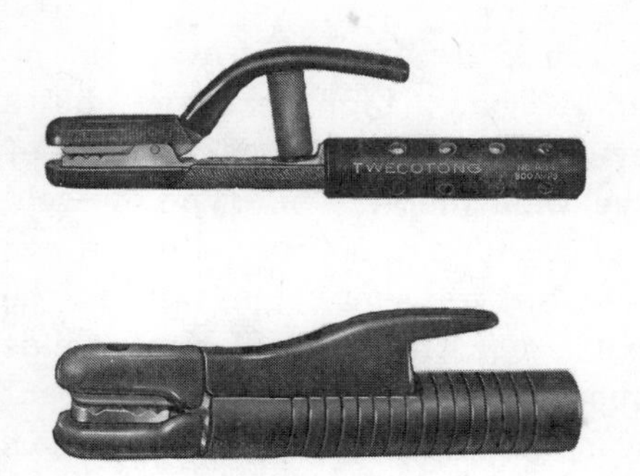

Fig. 3-15. Two common insulated holders. (Purity Cylinder Gases, Inc.)

the heat of its own arc, thereby supplying the necessary additional metal to complete a weld or to fuse together any two edges. With this process of welding, one hand is left free to either hold the work or to manipulate it as the operator desires.

In electric or arc welding, two things govern the quality of the weld. These are the uniformity of the arc and the current (amperage) used. Both, of course, are controlled by the operator.

Arc Length. The maintenance of a uniform arc is of the utmost importance in obtaining a good weld. Unless the filler rod fuses perfectly with the base metal edges being welded, a poor weld will result.

In order to bring about this proper fusion, it is necessary to maintain uniform heat during the welding operation. If a short arc is maintained, the welding rod will stick frequently and the edges of the work will not be heated to a molten state to receive the rod. If the arc is too long, the base metal will not be heated enough to fuse with the welding rod. The molten welding rod will fall on the cold base metal and will stick. Proper fusion will not take place, and a poor weld will result.

The correct length for the arc depends on the type of welding rod and the type of weld. For a coated rod, an arc of $\frac{1}{16}''$ to $\frac{1}{4}''$ is best. It is difficult to measure the length of an arc by sight. However, the sound made by the torch will be an even, steady buzz when the arc length is correct.

If the arc is too long, the torch will sputter because the arc is being broken and restruck almost instantaneously. This will cause the metal to spatter.

Overhead or vertical welding requires a shorter arc than welding downward. Welding rod of large diameter needs a longer arc than does that with a smaller diameter rod. Fig. 3-16 shows several examples of what can happen when an incorrect arc is used as well as an example of what a sound weld looks like when properly made.

The weld at the top of Fig. 3-16, has a rough bead and shows evidence of excessive spatter of the weld metal. This type of weld results from the use of an arc

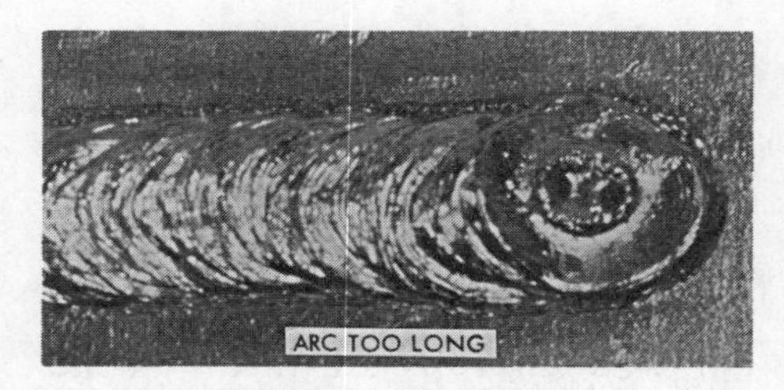

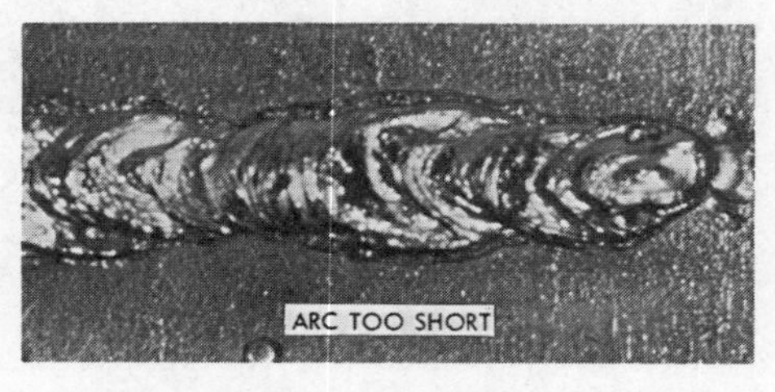

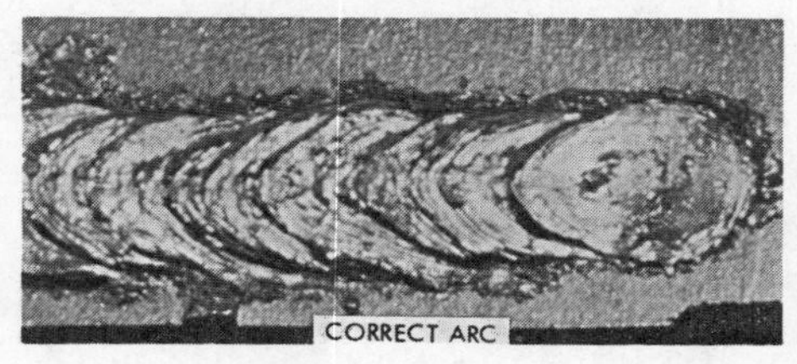

Fig. 3-16. This is how the welds appear when arc is too long; arc is too short; arc is the correct length.

which is too long. The weld in the middle has a high bead and shows evidence of poor penetration of the weld metal. This type of weld will result from the use of an arc which it too short. The weld at the bottom is the way all good welds should look. The proper current was used, the proper arc length maintained, and the welding rod was manipulated correctly.

Current Value. The amount of current used in arc welding has a direct bearing on both the soundness of the weld and on the ease with which the weld is made.

Most arc welding machines have automatic voltage control. Table 3-3 gives the current or amperage value for arc welding mild steels with coated rods.

The welds shown in Fig. 3-17 are examples of using incorrect

TABLE 3-3. CURRENT VALUES FOR ARC WELDING WITH COATED ROD

Metal Thickness	Rod Size (Inches)	Amperage Range
Light-Gage Sheet Metal Up to Approximately 7/64" Thick	1/16 5/64 3/32	10-30 25-45 40-70
Mild Steel Up To Approximately 3/16" Thick	1/8 5/32 3/16	50-130 90-180 130-230
Mild Steel Up To Approximately 5/16" Thick (Frames, Etc.)	1/8 5/32 3/16 1/4	60-120 90-160 120-200 190-300

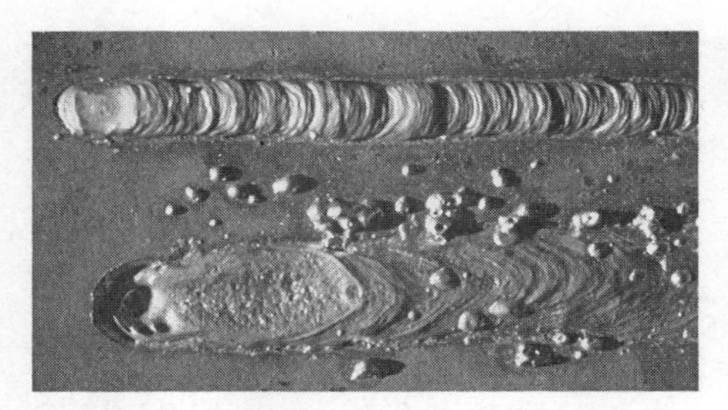

Fig. 3-17. Examples of welds where incorrect welding currents were used. (Lincoln Electric Co.)

welding current. The weld shown at the top was caused by the use of a welding current that was too low. Poor penetration resulted, and instead of obtaining proper fusion, the weld metal merely adhered to the improperly heated base metal, producing an unsound weld. In the weld shown at the bottom, too high a current was used, which caused spattering.

The amperage can be controlled on all arc welding machines. Amperage can be adjusted by a rheostat, providing an infinite range of amperage, or it may consist of an assortment of sockets into which the holder cord jack is plugged.

All such welding equipment carries an instruction plate which indicates the amperage level. The small welder, in Fig. 3-12, is provided with a dial control for simple current selection.

All welding equipment have simple controls. However, the larger machines, capable of delivering high amperage provide a much greater range of amperage. Nevertheless, a few minutes' study of the instruction plate on any of these machines will reveal just how the controls are operated.

To give yourself the best opportunity to control the current you are using, you should pay strict attention to the sound which the arc is making. A good arc will give off a continuous crackling sound and the molten metal will pass across the arc stream in a steady but invisible flow.

Exercises in Arc Welding. An inexpensive small A.C. arc welding unit similar to the one illustrated in Fig. 3-12 can be used. This welder can be plugged in to any 110 volt A.C. light socket which means you can work in your own basement or garage.

Some welding equipment operates on 220 volts. Be sure to read the rating plate on the equipment. Obtain some ¼″ or ⅛″ steel plates. Prepare and position them for a butt weld. Bevel the edges (45°) and lay them side by side on a nonflammable surface.

Coated rod is generally used for arc welding. It is much easier to strike and hold an arc with coated rod than with bare rod. You can strike an arc by scratching the welding rod against the work the same as you would if you were striking a match. It is necessary,

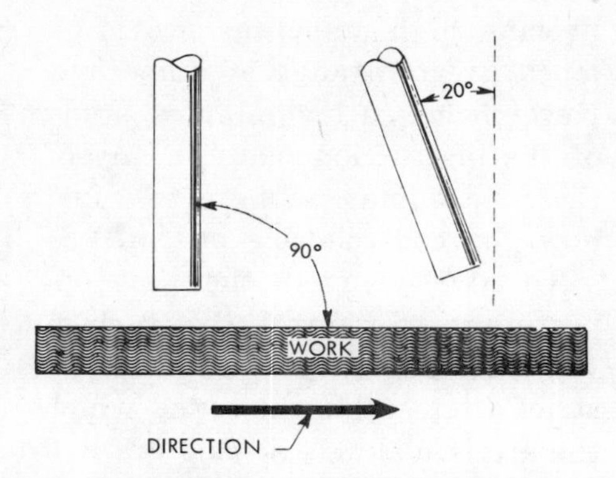

Fig. 3-18. Angles for holding welding rod.

of course, to hold the welding rod in a holder which is properly connected to the welding machine.

Fig. 3-18 shows the different angles for holding the welding rod. The metal is more easily directed if the welding rod is inclined about 20° as shown, although many welders hold the rod in a vertical position.

After the arc is established, the welding rod is slowly burned away and it is necessary to pay particular attention to the sound the arc is making. If you do this, you will have no difficulty in maintaining the correct arc length.

Move the arc along just fast enough to keep depositing the proper amount of welding rod after a crater has been formed in the base metal to receive it. The smoothness of a weld is dependent upon the uniformity of the arc and the speed with which it is moved.

If you should accidentally break the arc, exercise care in restriking it because flaws are apt to occur after such interruptions. If this happens, strike the arc ahead of the weld, then come back and heat the last crater made, then move on.

Closing the Weld. When you have succeeded in welding the seam between your first practice plates, you will notice that there is a crater at the end of the weld. It is necessary to fill this crater to strengthen the weld. Simply move the rod at right angle to the seam when the end of the weld is reached and at the same time move it away until the arc is broken. If the crater is not filled sufficiently, restrike the arc and go over the same spot again.

Sheet Metal Welding. Welding sheet metal is more difficult than welding heavy stock. More things must be taken into consideration.

The main point in welding sheet metal is to have the proper current setting on the arc welder. Because of the thinness of the metal, it is possible to burn holes through it quite easily. Use the lowest current setting which will still give you the heat necessary to bring the work to a molten state for proper fusion with the welding rod.

For your first exercise in welding sheet metal, you can use an old fender. Fasten the fender in the same position it is in when on a car, and make a saw cut 2″ long in the crown part of the fender.

After you have made the cut in the fender, obtain some heavy wire or even a piece of coat hanger wire. Lay the wire lengthwise in the cut, strike an arc with the torch, and fill in around the wire with welding rod. The wire in the cut will help you to keep from burning the metal while you become more familiar with manipulating the torch with a steady motion.

Try this method of welding several times, then do a weld without the wire in the cut.

After you become proficient at making welds in the crown of the fender, make some cuts in the edge of the fender and weld them. Practice making the welds from underneath. Be sure when you are welding from under the fender that you work so your hands and arms are to one side of the weld. This will eliminate the possibility of any hot metal falling on you.

Practice each of the different exercises several times or until you can produce a sound weld in a minimum of time no matter which way you are doing it.

Cutting With Arc Welder. The same equipment is used for cutting with the arc welder as is used for welding. A welding rod is used which is slightly larger in diameter than those used for welding the same gage of metal, and the amperage is set higher.

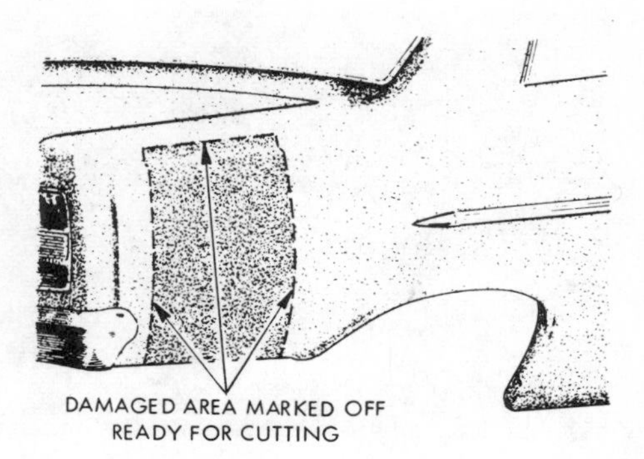

Fig. 3-19. Damaged area ready for cutting.

To cut with the arc welder, insert a welding rod in the holder and strike an arc as you would for welding. Instead of moving the torch over an area to preheat the metal, simply hold the torch in one place until a hole is burned through the sheet. As soon as a hole is made, thrust the tip of the welding rod into the hole and move the rod along as the arc burns out the metal along the line which you wish to cut.

To practice cutting with an arc welder, you can use the same panels on which you have been practicing with the hand tools. Fig. 3-19 shows a rear fender panel which is marked in preparation for cutting out the damaged area. Fig. 3-20 shows the fender in the process of being cut away and after the damaged portion has been removed. Notice in Fig. 3-20, at left, that the operator is standing with the torch tilted away from himself.

Fig. 3-20. Fender being cut away, and fender with damaged portion removed. (Lincoln Electric Co.)

Cutting Methods

As has been pointed out in the preceding pages, it is possible to cut metal with either a gas torch or an electric torch. However, each of these methods of cutting leaves a ragged edge and is rather slow.

The cutting methods described in this section do not involve the use of the welding equipment, although a cutting operation is followed normally by welding. But a hand chisel or power saw can follow a drawn or scribed line exactly.

Cutting with a Chisel. A special chisel which makes a smooth cut 1/16″ wide is available for cutting body panels. The cutting edge of this chisel is curved so that the shaving which is removed curls neatly out of the way. The chisel is provided with a sharp point so that the cut can usually be started without first drilling a hole.

Fig. 3-21 shows this chisel being used to cut a door panel. It will be noted that the lower part of the panel has had an irregularly shaped piece removed. This irregular cut was merely made to demonstrate the versatility of the chisel. Usually, your cuts will be straight across the panel, since this is the best method for making a patch.

Hold the chisel as shown in Fig. 3-21. With the chisel tilted in this manner, the hammer boss provided lays at a convenient angle. Hit the boss as indicated to pierce the panel. To cut the panel, strike it, in the direction of the desired cut. By hitting the chisel with

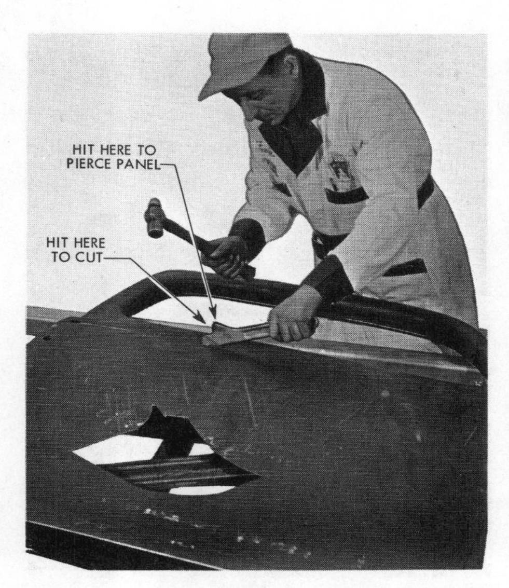

Fig. 3-21. Using chisel to cut sheet metal. (Anzich Mfg. Co.)

hammer blows of medium force, it will cut out and curl up a strip of metal $\frac{1}{16}''$ wide.

You can scribe a line on an old fender or body panel with a pencil or scriber (scratch awl) and practice cutting along the line. Practice until you are able to produce a straight, neat cut in a reasonable length of time.

Power Chisels. With the advent of air power in shops and the adaptation of air power to wrenches, drills, etc., power chisels came into being. A set of air chisels engineered specifically for body shop work is shown in Fig. 3-22.

As most shops have air operated equipment, you will undoubtedly encounter power chisels early in your career. Operation of a power chisel is simple and safe. The chisel locks into the power gun and is held in place by a quick release spring. The air to the power gun is controlled by a regulator at the butt of the gun. This enables the operator to increase or decrease power, depending on requirements. The unit has a spring-loaded squeeze trigger for instant OFF-ON control.

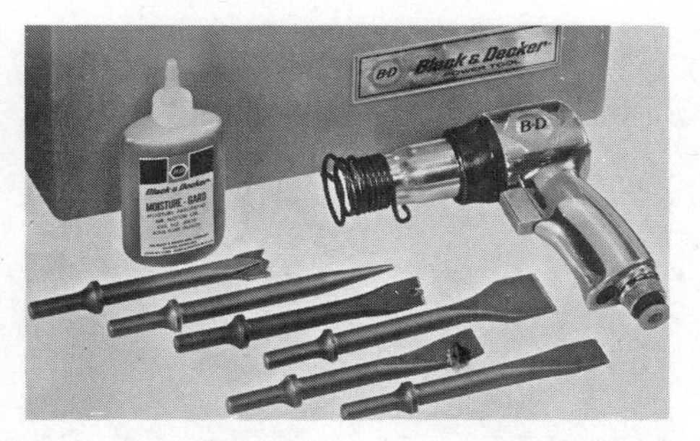

Fig. 3-22. Power chisel kit. (Black and Decker Mfg. Co.)

Power Saws. Two kinds of power operated body panel saws are in common use in body shops. One is a saw having its own motor and constructed expressly for this purpose. It is a machine having a short piece of regular hacksaw blade which is moved in and out at a fast rate in short strokes. The other is an attachment for an electric drill which converts the rotary motion of the drill to reciprocal or in-and-out *motion.* A hacksaw blade is also used in this machine, as shown in Fig. 3-23.

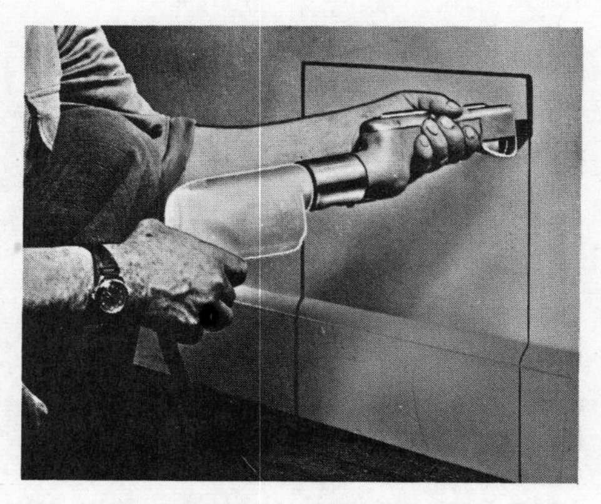

Fig. 3-23. Use of power saw attachment for electric drill. (Tri-Saw Corp.)

Cutting with either machine is a simple matter and one which will not require much practice to learn. If you are starting to cut in the edge of a panel, simply bring the moving blade against the panel and move it forward along the cutting line only as fast as the metal is cleanly cut. Too much pressure against the blade, or forcing it along at too great a cutting rate, will result either in short life for the blade or breakage.

When it is desirable to start your cut in the center of a panel or back from the edge, it may be necessary to drill starting holes which will accommodate the blade of the saw. This can most easily be accomplished by drilling three $\frac{3}{16}''$ holes so that they overlap and form a slot long enough so that you can insert the blade of the saw through the panel. Then turn on the saw and start your cut.

If a saw of the type shown in Fig. 3-23 is used, however, no starting holes are necessary. The saw blade is merely held almost parallel to the surface to be cut with the tool resting on the curved portion below the blade. After the saw is started, the tool is slowly tipped to a perpendicular position.

You will find that it is much easier to replace a piece of an auto body or fender panel if the edges to be welded are smooth. This makes it possible to cut the panel patch to the exact dimensions of the repair.

Typical Welding Jobs

Automotive bodies and frames generally are of welded construction. In most instances, both body sheet metal and the body inner construction are built up by spot welding.

Recently, portable spot welders have been used more frequently in body shops. A spot welder is shown in Fig. 3-24 and its use indicated in Fig. 3-25. Spot welding is useful for a variety of welds, lap joints and

Fig. 3-24. Portable spot welder, showing ease of movement and applicability. (Ford Motor Co.)

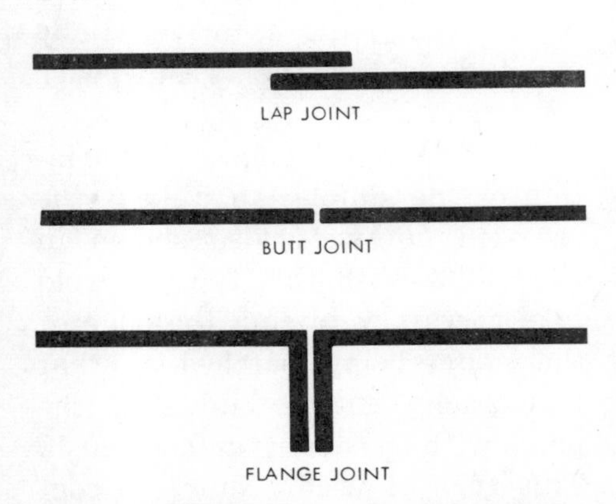

Fig. 3-25. Different types of welds or joints.

flange joints, Fig. 3-26, and recessed lap joints.

Although instructions for using spot welders vary among the different brands available, they are relatively simple to follow. The repair man must use an electrode large enough to provide the intense heat necessary to fuse the metals being joined.

Unlike other forms of welding where a welding rod is introduced into the joint to form a fusing agent, spot welding is a direct fusing of two pieces of like material. Spot welding is fast and economical (no expensive welding rod is used). It produces a surface that can be quickly prepared for the refinisher.

Complete details on electrode sizes and heat ranges for various metal thicknesses are supplied with the welders when they are purchased. There are no rules of thumb for spot welding. Each piece of equipment must be used as directed by the manufacturer.

In collision work, however, most body welds are formed on flanges which permit seam welding to be used.

In the replacing of a portion of a panel, the usual practice is to form flanges on the two pieces and to perform the welding on the flanges rather than the outer surface. This holds the amount of metal finishing to a minimum.

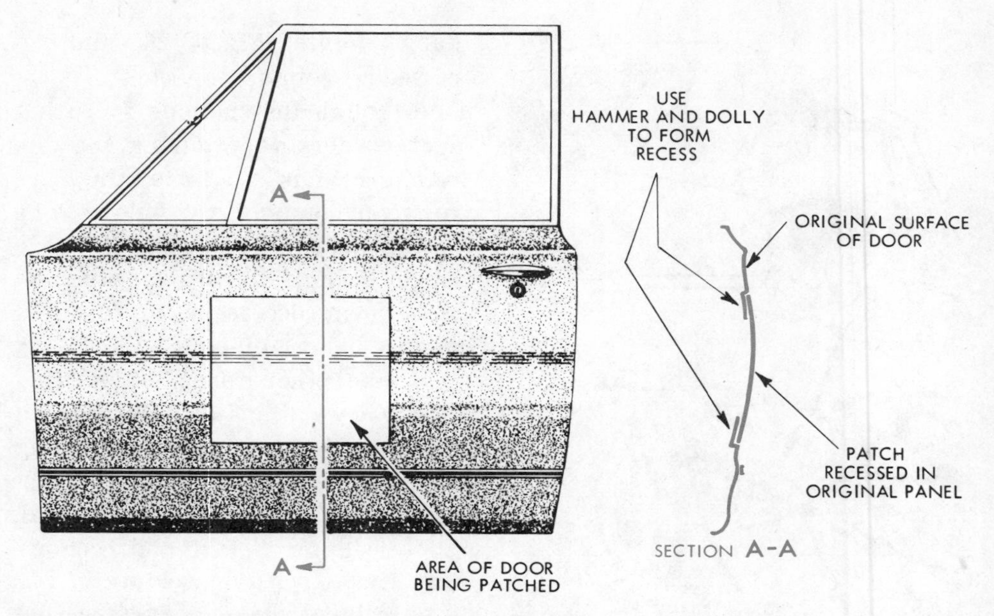

Fig. 3-26. Welded recessed lap joint on door panel.

In body repairing, tears in the metal, particularly on fenders and shields, are frequently encountered. These also are welded with either the gas torch or the arc welder.

This section is concerned with showing you when different welds are made, where they are made, and why. The different types of weld joints with which you will be concerned in body work are shown and a description of where each should be used is given.

Types of Welds for Light Sheets

Several different types of joints can be used in welding sheet metal. The common ones are shown in Fig. 3-25.

Lap Joint. The lap weld is an easily made weld. This type of weld, of course, leaves a step in the surface which makes it impossible to perfectly match the original contour. Lap welds of this type, however, can sometimes be used where the joint is covered by molding or trim or is otherwise concealed.

Recessed Lap Joint. A variation of the simple lap weld is the recessed lap weld also shown in Fig. 3-26. With this type of weld it is necessary to sink the edge of the panel being patched so that the patch can be laid into the panel with the outer surfaces flush. This type of weld requires a considerable amount of time to prepare, but results in good welds. The depth of the recess, of course, should be exactly equal to the thickness of the panel in order to make certain that the two surfaces will be flush after welding.

Flange Joint. The type of weld which produces what is probably the most reliable joint, and which also produces the joint most easily finished by the metal finisher, is called a flange weld, Fig. 3-25. With this type of weld, it is necessary to take a little more time with the preparations. The edges of the pieces to be joined must be flanged inward from the outside finished surface. The flange may be formed by using a hammer and a suitable right-angle edge of a dolly. In some cases where a weld is to be made in a prominent place in a panel, a strip of ¼″ x 1″ steel can be formed to match the contour of the inside of the panel at the point where the joint is to be made. This strip should extend for the full length of the joint. With small screws and nuts, fasten the strip ½″ to ¾″ from the point where the panel has been cut. (The holes drilled in the panel can easily be filled while you are making the weld.)

Form the flange over this steel strip rather than over a dolly. The strip will prevent any change in the panel contour as the flange is formed. Once the flange is formed it will hold the contour. The strip is then removed and fastened to the new panel, and the flange is formed on it in the same way.

Butt Joint. The butt weld shown in Fig. 3-25 is quickly and easily prepared. This is the main reason why it is so extensively used. Particularly where the weld can be made from the inside, the butt weld saves a lot of work for both the welder and the metal finisher. However, most cases of buckled panels occur as a result of welding a butt type joint.

Screws Hold Unwelded Joint. Joints made with flange or lap joints can be fastened together with a number of self-tapping screws. This permits you to match the contours of the new and the old panels before you start to weld. With recessed lap joints, the threads of these screws may be tacked in place as you are welding. The heads of the screws are ground off as the surface is later finished. With a flange joint, the screws can be tacked in place and left right in the flange.

Any of the welds described in the preceding can be used whenever you are replacing a portion of a damaged panel. One of the factors governing the type of weld to use is the location of the weld. In some instances, it will be impossible to perform a certain operation in the preparation of the weld because of interference with some other panel. In other instances, the weld itself might interfere with the function of other panels or mechanisms after it is made. You will have to decide which type of weld most effectively and efficiently will do each job.

Frame Welding

Frame welding is much the same as welding sheet metal. The major difference is in the thickness or gage of the metal with which you are working. It is mandatory that the frame be just as strong after the repair as it was before it was broken.

Since the frame holds the body together and gives it rigidity, it is essential for the frame to be sound and strong. Secondly, the suspension members cannot function properly in a crooked frame.

Whenever a frame is broken, the seam of the break is welded together, then a reinforcement plate is welded over the broken section. As most of the frame members are of channel stock, this reinforce-

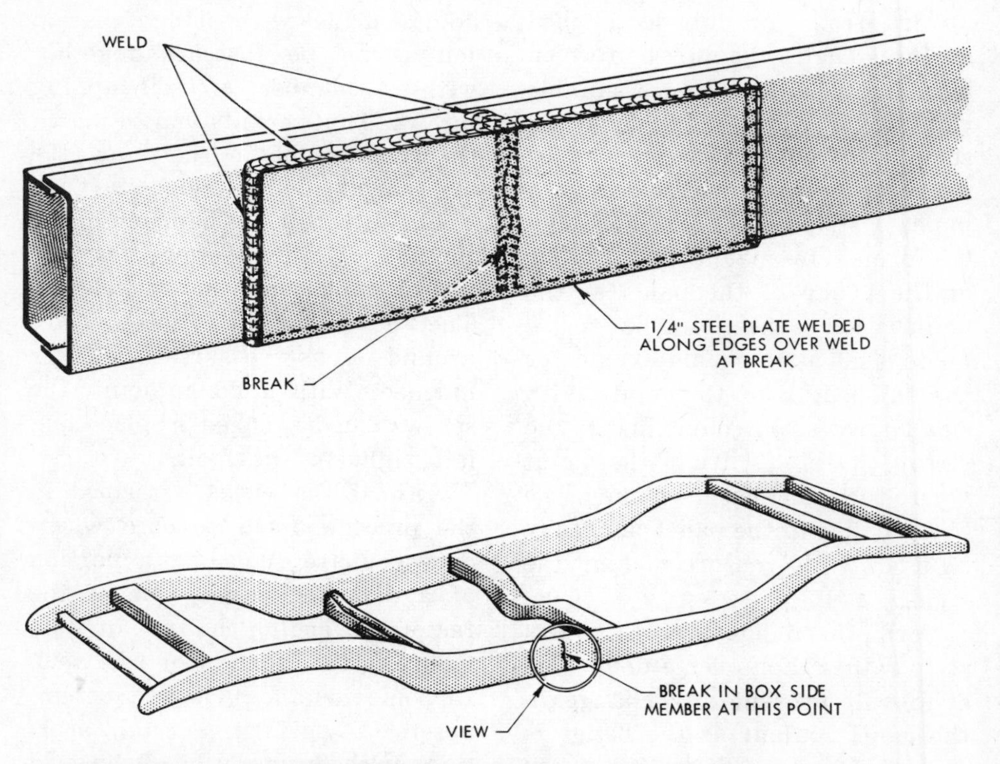

Fig. 3-27 Frame repair example showing patch weld of heavy metal.

ment plate is often made of channel material. Whether or not the reinforcement plate should be placed around the outside of the damaged member or on the inside depends on whether there would be any interference with body or chassis parts by its being installed on the outside. This can be decided only at the time the particular repair is made. Fig. 3-27 shows an example of frame repair.

Preparing Metal for the Finisher

Whenever a weld is made, the surface left by the weld is not smooth. Since the intention of all body repairs is to restore the finish to a like-new condition or to its original smoothness, it is obvious that a good deal of finishing work is required after welding.

The welder is not concerned with metal finishing, which is a trade all in itself (a subsequent chapter of this volume is devoted to it). However, the welder is charged with the soundness of any weld he has made. It is in this respect that the welder is slightly concerned with metal finishing.

Even though flux is used during the welding process, a certain amount of scale or oxide is left on the weld when it is finished. This scale must be removed before the soundness of the weld can be seen. Usually, it is ground off with a disk grinder. However, if a grinder is not available, it can be removed by hitting the weld with several sharp blows from a body mallet.

The amount of finishing necessary after welding is controlled by the type of weld used. All welding on outside surfaces of a body should be done from underneath or from inside if possible. This will leave the weld metal stacked toward the inside of the body, and a minimum of filing or grinding will be required.

Checking On Your Knowledge

The following questions give you the opportunity to check up on yourself. If you have read the chapter carefully, you should be able to answer the questions. If you have any difficulty, read the chapter over once more so that you have the information well in mind before you go on with your reading.

1. What process for fusing metal together is meant by the common name *torch welding?*
2. About how many pounds per square inch pressure is exerted on the acetylene cylinder when it is filled with acetylene?
3. How much pressure is exerted on the oxygen tank when it is filled with oxygen?
4. Is acetylene sold by weight or pressure?
5. Is oxygen sold by weight or pressure?
6. The flame at the tip of the welding torch is the result of what elements?
7. What are the necessary components of a gas welding outfit?
8. What six basic safety rules govern the operation of a gas welding outfit?
9. What color is generally used for the oxygen hose?
10. Generally, what color is an acetylene hose?
11. Why is it that on most welding equipment there is no danger of interchanging the oxygen and acetylene hose connections?
12. What is the name of the tool used most commonly for lighting a gas welding torch?
13. What is the purplish colored flame called which results from the use of too much oxygen?
14. In order to obtain the best weld, it is necessary to hold the torch at what angle to the plane of the work?
15. What type of motion should be imparted to the torch when you are welding light-gage metal?
16. How much should the welding rod in gas welding be inclined to the plane of the work?
17. When should the welding rod be brought into contact with the work?
18. What will be the result if the welding rod is added to the edges to be joined before they are sufficiently heated to receive it?
19. How is the heat necessary to do arc welding derived?
20. Is it necessary to wear any kind of protective garments when you are arc welding?
21. What kind of current is most commonly used for arc welding in collision shops?
22. In electric or arc welding, what two things govern the quality of the weld?
23. What one control is usually provided on most small, portable, A.C. welding machines?
24. How is an arc struck on an arc welder when you are ready to weld?
25. What are four different kinds of weld joints that can be used in body sheet metal welding?

Shrinking, Soldering and Metal Finishing

Chapter

4

This chapter is designed to develop in you the knowledge of what is required and the skills needed in the preparation of automotive bodies and sheet metal for the painter. The trade of metal finishing employed in automotive factories involves bumping and filing, as presented in Chapter 2; welding, as presented in Chapter 3; and the use of power grinders and sanders for the purpose of preparing the surface for the painter, as presented in this chapter. This trade involves, as well, the shrinking of stretched metal, the sinking of welds and the building up of contours with solder, and the preparation of the metal for the painter.

Establishing the metal finisher's responsibility for the surface is important. When the metal finisher fails to properly prepare the surface for the painter, the painter is required to use other expedients, such as putty glazing, which often can result in an inferior paint job.

Shrinking Stretched Metal

When body panels and fenders are formed in dies under high pressure, the sheet metal is stretched and drawn, then compressed. This displaces the metal molecules within each grain or crystal of metal that makes up a metal mass. The high pressure of the press, squeezing the metal, locks the molecules in this new position and they will resist any subsequent force which tries to change their arrangement.

The metal in its new stressed form still has some elasticity. That is, the metal can be bent or twisted within its new form. When the distorting force is removed, the elasticity of the metal will cause it to resume the shape that it had when the molecules of the metal were locked into the new form in the stamping press dies.

It is the objective of the collision man to avoid destroying this natural tendency of the metal to return to its original pressed shape. This is not always possible in collisions where a normally smooth surface is badly creased. These creases represent a portion of the metal which has been distorted beyond its *elastic limit* and in which the molecules have been displaced to new positions. They are no longer locked in the arrangement that was given to them in the forming die.

The exercises that were presented in Chapter 2 were intended primarily to relieve the new strains created by such creases or folds so that the natural forces existing in the surrounding metal could return it to its die shape.

Each hammer blow struck on a body or fender panel does, in a small measure, exactly the same thing that the original presses did. That is, it stretches, draws, or compresses the metal and has a tendency to lock the molecules in a new position. The body hammer, however, does not do this as well as the original forming dies.

Every time you strike the surface of a panel in direct hammering, you are stretching the metal slightly. This is why it is so important that in all dinging, you hold the number of separate blows down to just what is required, because every blow will further stretch the metal. In many cases, the amount of hammering required is so slight that the stretching of the metal is negligible and cannot be detected. Nevertheless, on occasion you will encounter excessive stretching, usually the result of correcting complex damage.

Stretched metal is often found when you are reworking a fender or panel which has been excessively hammered by some amateur. When the metal has been stretched, it is not possible to make it conform to its original contour by using the hammer and dolly alone. In such cases, the metal will have to be shrunk.

In Chapter 2, a method of cold shrinking by means of forming ribs in the stretched area was discussed. In that exercise, a shrinking dolly was used to sink a valley through the stretched area, thus effectively reducing the bulge.

Such a method can be used if an oxyacetylene torch is not available to you for hot shrinking.

Hot Shrinking. Hot shrinking is accomplished by heating a small portion (an area about the size of a nickel) of a panel red hot. This causes the metal to expand and rise slightly above the surrounding surface. While the metal is red hot, if a dolly having no crown is placed under the heated portion and the heated portion is hit several times with a hammer, the heated metal will be compressed. When that particular spot cools, it will have lost most, if not all, of its crown. But repeating this process on the stretched area of the panel, the stretched metal can be shrunk. The purpose of this section is to show you how to shrink metal that has been stretched, using this method.

Hot shrinking is a simple process, but one which requires careful timing and the proper tools. The tools required are those which are used for many other operations in body work. You should have a welding torch equipped with the same size tip as used for welding the thickness of sheet with which you are working, a body hammer or mallet, a shrinking dolly, a medium sized sponge, a container, and water.

The hot shrinking operation is shown graphically in Fig. 4-1. A stretched condition is depicted; heat is applied by the torch, and then the heated area is struck with the body hammer, and finally with the hammer and low crown dolly. The heated area is immediately quenched with a sponge dipped in cold water. The sequence is always the same. Review it, rehearse it, and then you are ready for practice on a body panel.

If you can find a discarded fender, door, or body panel that is stretched, use it for your first attempt at shrinking metal. If you are unable to locate a stretched area, merely assume that some area is stretched.

Arrange your tools so that they are within easy reach, as it is necessary to change quickly from one tool to another when shrinking.

Locate the highest point in the stretched section of the panel with which you are working. Light the torch and heat a spot the size of a nickel in the center of the high spot to a cherry red, Fig. 4-2.

Use a circular motion when you are heating the spot. Be careful not to burn through the metal. As soon as the spot is cherry red, place the shrinking dolly under the spot and strike it several sharp blows with a hammer or mallet. The dolly block must be held loosely against the underside of the panel exactly centered under the hot spot. The hammer blow must hit the hot spot

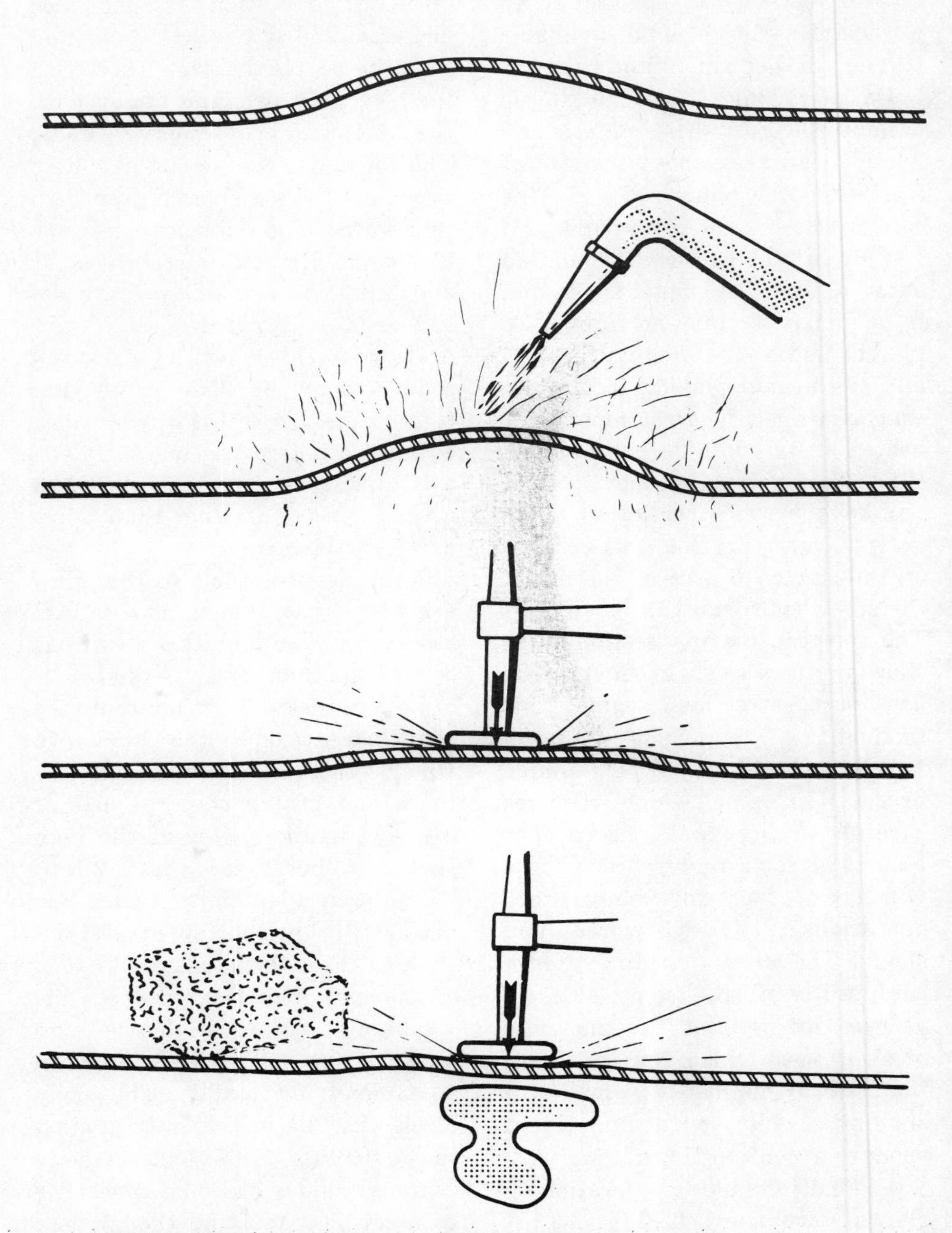

Fig. 4-1. Shrinking operation. (Minnesota Mining and Mfg. Co.)

Fig. 4-2. Using torch to heat spot in stretched section of hood panel. (Paul Lawrence Dunbar Vocational High School, Chicago, Illinois)

Fig. 4-3. Hammering down the high spot on a hood panel. (Paul Lawrence Dunbar Vocational High School, Chicago, Illinois)

accurately and with sufficient force to push the metal down while it is still red hot. Fig. 4-3 shows a high spot on a hood panel being hammered down.

After four or five hammer blows, the heated spot will turn black. Quench it immediately with the water-filled sponge. Fig. 4-4 shows the same spot on the hood being quenched with the water-filled sponge.

Repeat this operation, taking the next highest spot in the stretched section of the panel until the bulge is finally shrunk down below the level of the surrounding surface. It then can be brought up to its correct level by direct hammering.

Fig. 4-4. Quenching a heat spot. (Paul Lawrence Dunbar Vocational High School, Chicago, Illinois)

Practice this operation a number of times. You will find that you can do an adequate job after just a few attempts. However, there are a few rules which you should observe at all times during a shrinking operation that will help you to do a much better job than would ordinarily result.

CAUTION:

Never quench a red-hot spot. Wait until the metal has turned black.

Never heat an area greater than that where pressure can be applied with the hammer and dolly.

Never use anything but an acetylene torch for heating a stretched section.

Never attempt to shrink a panel until the panel has been roughed out.

Always hammer the stretched section outward before applying heat.

If the stretched part of the surface is small, heat a smaller spot.

It is possible to shrink metal without quenching each spot with water. However, the shrinking operation is much faster when each spot is water quenched. Fewer heat spots are required if the heat expansion is drawn out by quenching rather than by additional spots.

In some panels it is possible to use a spoon for the backing tool for the hammering operation. This is particularly true where it is necessary to shrink a section in a door panel or over inner construction of a body panel.

Whenever you are performing a shrinking operation, exercise care to avoid overshrinking the panel. This will cause the metal to warp and buckle both in and around the stretched area. However, if this condition does occur, heat a small spot in the area where the panel is buckling, apply a dolly block or spoon with enough pressure to hold the buckling section up, then allow the metal to cool. Do not use the hammer or water in this instance.

Soldering Methods

When adjoining panels do not match exactly, it is customary in automobile body factories to build up the lower panel with solder. In collision work, these same points must be built up the same way. In addition, any part of the body or fenders can also be built up with solder. Solder is expensive and heavy. In each instance, you must weigh the possibility of bringing the panel up to where it belongs by other means as against the time and cost of building it up with solder.

In many cases where you cannot get behind the damage to push it out without spending too much time in disassembly of trim panels, hardware, or inner construction, it will be practical to build up the low spot with solder.

Body soldering is performed with either an oxyacetylene torch or a blow torch and is referred to as *torch soldering*. A soldering iron is seldom used. This section deals only with torch soldering as practiced in automobile body shops.

In body repair work, it is often impossible to leave a completely smooth surface with the bumping tools. Also, irregularities are left in any surface that has been welded because the seams of the weld are sunk. It is necessary for all of these irregularities to be removed from the surface before the job can be completed. As it is not possible to sand or grind these small indentations out of a surface without removing too much metal, thus leaving the structure weak, some other means is necessary.

Solder is the material used for filling the depressions, and *soldering* is the method of applying the solder. It is necessary to file or grind the solder smooth after it has been applied to a surface, but this presents no problem because solder is a lead compound which is easily worked in either the molten or cold state.

The most commonly used method of soldering is with a torch, using a paddle to work the solder into the place where it is needed.

Preparation of the Surface. Before solder can be applied to a metal, it is essential that the surface be absolutely clean. This means that any paint remaining on a surface after it is dinged out must be removed. Paint can be removed either with a file or with a disk grinder.

In some instances, the surface needing solder build-up will be covered with rust. Rust can be removed in the same manner as paint, either with a file or with a disk grinder. Failure to completely remove rust or paint before soldering is attempted will result in a poor soldering job. The solder will not stick to the surface, and it will break away when you attempt to blend the contour of the soldered and unsoldered areas together.

Another condition which you will encounter is a surface where welding was done. In most cases, the welder will have removed the oxide crust which is formed by welding. If he has not, it can be removed as described in Chapter 3.

After the scale left by the welding process is removed, it is necessary to prepare the weld so that solder can be applied. A weld leaves a rough surface. In order to have a smooth surface after the finish operations are performed, it is necessary to force the welded area below the normal contour of the surface, then to build up the contour with solder. This process is called *sinking the weld.*

The sinking of welds is a hand operation. The best time to do it is after the weld has cooled so that the metal being formed is cold. The seam of a weld where a fender was torn is shown in Fig. 4-5. The metal finisher is using a hammer and dolly to sink the weld.

Fig. 4-5. Hammering seam below original surface.

The tools used for sinking welds are also used for shrinking stretched panels as described in Chapter 2.

By not sinking the weld until it has cooled, any defects in the surface will immediately become apparent when the metal is struck with a hammer. The seam of the weld is sunk approximately 1/8″ below the normal contour of the surface. This depression is filled with solder, filed smooth, and an unbroken contour will result. A welded seam ready for soldering is shown in Fig. 4-6.

You should practice sinking welds until you can perform the

Fig. 4-6. Welded and ready.

operation with little or no difficulty. The easiest type of weld to sink for your first attempt is one where the weld runs into the edge of a fender. Simply start from the edge and work back along the seam.

After you have practiced and become proficient at hitting the dolly squarely with the hammer, sink a weld where it is necessary to start in the middle of a panel. Exercise care in this operation, as there is danger of deforming the surrounding area if you do not hit the dolly squarely.

Tinning. The process of tinning prepares a surface for receiving and holding solder. Tinning is actually the first operation of soldering. Before any tinning is done, you should be certain that the surface is clean. In the case of a surface where welding was done, sanding and wire brushing may not remove all of the oxide scale. Sometimes a welded surface is rough and a wire brush or a grinder will not get into all of the small depressions. The scale can be removed in cases like this by applying muriatic (hydrochloric) acid to the rough spots with a small brush.

WARNING:

Never allow the acid to contact either your clothing or your body. If you should get some on your hands, rinse them immediately in cold water.

When the surface to be soldered is absolutely clean and dry, light the torch and pass it back and forth, applying heat to the surface. This is called *preheating.*

Immediately after the surface is preheated, the flux should be applied, followed by the tinning coat of solder. Acid core solder is usually used because the flux is contained in the center of the solder. This solder comes in rolls of different sizes and is sold by the pound.

The solder wire is about 1/8" in diameter. Heat the entire area until it is hot enough to melt the solder. Then apply the solder and smear it over the surface with a rag until the entire area is covered. Always cover an area a few inches larger than that actually needing a solder build-up.

If acid core solder is not available, regular body solder and tinning acid may be used. Preheat the surface, apply the acid with a brush, heat the surface until solder will melt, then smear it over the area with a rag.

Building Up. The actual application of solder is often called building up the contour. After the surface is tinned, the solder can be applied. If acid core solder is used, play the torch over the area just enough to keep the tinning coat hot so that it will hold the solder as it is applied. Heat a portion of the solder until it is ready to droop, then push it against the panel.

If the area being worked on is overheated, the solder will run. Keep applying solder in this fashion until a sufficient amount has been deposited to build the surface up to a higher contour than the original. How to handle the surface from this point on is explained later.

If regular bar solder is used, the torch is applied to the tinned surface to heat it, then to the bar of solder. Heat the end of the bar until approximately one inch of it becomes soft and starts to sag, then quickly press it against the hot tinned surface. Continue applying solder in this manner until a sufficient amount has been deposited to build the surface up to the desired point.

Solder is applied in the same way on either a horizontal or vertical surface. On a vertical surface, however, you will find it is necessary to keep the solder hot enough so that it can be worked, yet not so hot that it will run. Solder should be applied on a vertical surface in somewhat smaller amounts at each application than on a horizontal surface. The torch should be passed over the applied solder just often enough to keep it in a workable condition.

Paddling. As soon as enough solder has been applied, it is necessary to smooth it and work it into the general shape of the finished contour. This process is called *paddling*.

Before it is applied to the solder, the paddle should be covered with a light film of regular engine oil. This will prevent the solder from sticking to the paddle.

Heat is applied over the entire area from time to time so that it is just below the temperature necessary for working the solder. Local areas are then heated to a workable state, and the solder smoothed to the desired contour with the paddle. Fig. 4-7 illustrates an acetylene torch and solder paddle being used to smooth solder over a fender. Notice that the

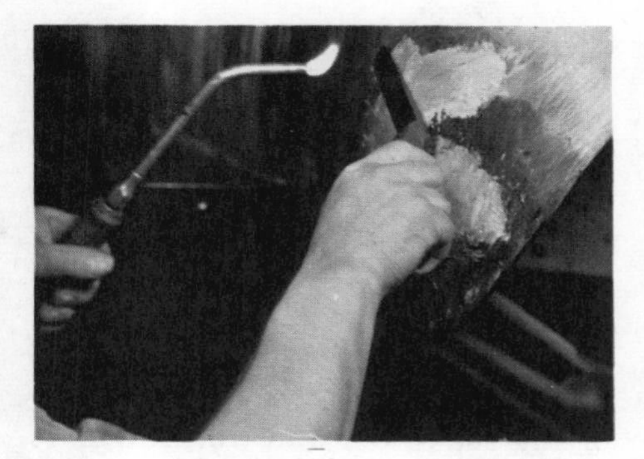

Fig. 4-7. Spreading solder with torch and paddle.

torch is applied only as necessary to keep the solder in a workable state.

Be sure to keep plenty of oil on the paddle at all times during the paddling operation. When one portion of the surface is smoothed to the desired contour, move along until the entire surface has been worked. Do not overheat the surface, for the solder will run off, and a second application will be necessary.

The area covered by solder should always be slightly greater (a few inches on every side) than that actually needed. This will make it easier to obtain the desired contour during the finishing operation. When solder is applied to a weld that has been sunk, the surface should be built up beyond what it was originally. When you are using solder to fill a deep depression, be sure to keep the entire mass heated all the way to the bottom during the shaping process. If the bottom is allowed to cool, it may become impossible to work it further. Any attempt to reheat it will result in the surface melting and running off entirely.

Establishing the Contour. After the solder is paddled smooth, it is necessary to allow it to cool thoroughly before the finish contour is established. If any finishing is done while the solder is hot, the surface will peel or pit and additional work will be necessary to make it smooth.

Because solder is much softer than the surrounding steel body sections, it cuts away faster. Therefore, disk grinding is not advisable. It may remove more solder than is desired, leaving a low spot in the body contour and, after painting and polishing, the low spot will show up as a *bull's eye*. Don't cut too far.

Finish the edges of the soldered area first, and then finish the center of the area. Shape the area with a body file first; then with an open cut solder float file. The float file cuts slowly and smooths out large file marks and small ridges.

Fig. 4-8 shows a fender with a soldered surface filed smooth. It should be pointed out that this fender was photographed merely to show what can be done with solder. If it is necessary to apply this amount of solder, it is more economical to replace the fender.

Fig. 4-8. A smooth soldered fender.

Exercises

Your first attempt at soldering should be to apply solder to a contour that is only slightly dented. Before you apply any solder, however, make two or three templates from a piece of cardboard so that you can check the final contour two or three ways. A template is made by cutting one edge of a sheet of cardboard so that, when held edgewise to the surface, it fits the contour snugly except for where it bridges the low spot to be filled with solder. Apply the solder as described here. Smooth it, and as soon as it is cooled, file or grind it to the desired contour.

As you develop the feel of applying the solder and working on it you can move along to filling deeper depressions or larger areas.

As a final exercise, you should apply solder to a vertical panel, and then work it smooth. Attempt only a small area until you can manipulate the tools quickly, then you should have no difficulty.

Don't become discouraged if on your first attempts at paddling you lose the solder you so painstakingly applied. Just start over again. Everyone goes through this experience. Keep on trying until you can handle the solder expertly.

Grinding Materials and Methods

While the body file cannot be completely replaced, many of the jobs that can be done with a file can be done just as well and much faster with a grinder. A grinder can be used to remove rust or paint from the surface, to grind out minor irregularities in the metal, to locate low spots, and to develop the contour of areas built up with solder. The grinder most commonly used in collision shops is the portable disc grinder, two sizes of which are shown in Fig. 4-9.

The technique of grinding with a disc grinder is different than that required with a drum or cone

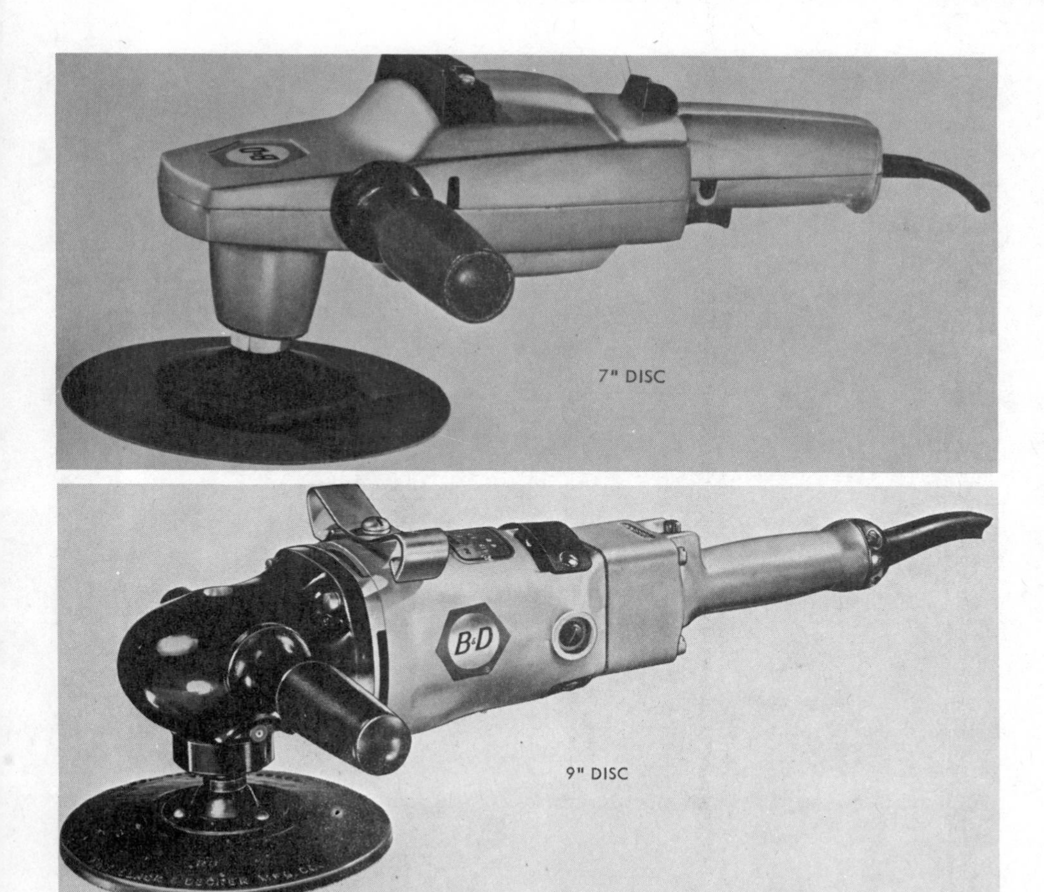

Fig. 4-9. Portable disc grinders for light and heavy grinding (Black and Decker Mfg. Co.)

grinder. These grinders are discussed later in this chapter. However, the disc grinder will be your primary source for power grinding in actual practice.

In the automotive body factories, special drum type grinders are used almost exclusively for finish grinding. But even where the disk grinder is used for most jobs, mandrels are available which will permit their use as a drum or cone grinder.

The abrasive for drum grinders is in the form of a replaceable sleeve which is fastened to the mandrel. Drum or cone grinders are used mainly for grinding of hard-to-get-at places. They are time saving devices to be used for special contours such as around headlights, fender joints, panels

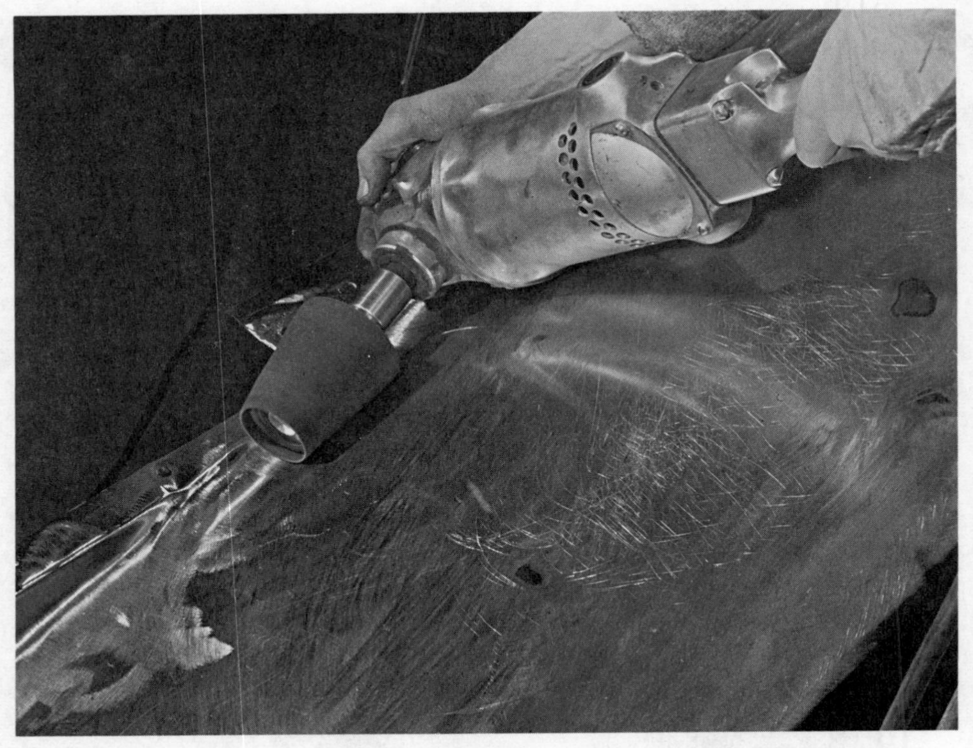

Fig. 4-10. Cone mandrel in an electric grinder. (Minnesota Mining and Mfg. Co.)

adjacent to rear decks, etc. Fig. 4-10 shows a cone mandrel in use. Cone mandrels are used with coated abrasive cloth cones. Cone mandrels and drum type grinders are operated in the same manner as the disk type grinder.

Abrasives. But before one uses grinders he needs to learn something about abrasives. Five different minerals are commonly used for manufacturing abrasives. Three of these—*garnet, flint,* and *emery*—are natural mineral abrasives. The other two are *aluminum oxide* and *silicon carbide,* which are manufactured at high temperatures in huge electric furnaces. Garnet, a semi-precious jewel, is by far the most important of the natural minerals. Emery and flint break down easily and are better suited for household use than for industry.

Aluminum oxide is the more important of the two manufactured agents. It is the toughest, most durable abrasive available. The manufactured abrasives are best for use in the automotive field and in industry at large where the work is chiefly on metal.

The abrasive is put on a backing which is either of paper, cloth, or a combination of the two. For dry grinding or sanding, high-quality glues are used for anchoring the abrasive grains to the backing. For wet sanding, resins are used as the binding agent.

Grit Sizes and Grades. Choosing the abrasive best suited for a grinding operation, you should specify the grade; the type of backing and weight; and the adhesive used to anchor the abrasive mineral to the backing, commonly called the *bond.* In general sanding or grinding operations the coarseness or fineness of abrasive particles may be designated in one of three ways: by symbols, by mesh number, or by both.

SYMBOLS: 3/0, 2/0, 1/2, 1½, 2, etc.
MESH NUMBERS: 400, 320, 280, 180, 100, 50, 24, etc.
BOTH: 9/0-320, 5/0-180, 2/0-100, 1½-40, etc.

You may have encountered one of these designations if you have ever purchased sand paper or emery cloth at your local hardware.

As the list shows, twenty grades are commonly available in coated abrasives although only a very few are normally used in automotive refinishing operations. For automotive collision and refinishing operations, typical grade or grit sizes:

16 Coarsest	150
20	180
24	220
36	240
40	280
50	320
60	360
80	400
100	500
120	600 Finest

abrasive designation would be: #24 Grit, Open Coat Resin-over-Resin Bond, Heavy Duty Fibre-Disc Backing. This would be the abrasive disc selected for removing old paint and rust.

To visualize the meaning of this grade size, think of a Grade 24 as a grain size that could just narrowly pass through a screen having twenty-four holes per lineal inch. By comparison, a Grade 220 would then pass through a screen having 220 holes per lineal inch.

In the choice of a grade for a sanding operation it is important to use a grade no coarser than necessary to efficiently remove the desired quantity of paint, filler or metal. The use of an unnecessarily coarse grade might grind at a faster rate than a finer grade but the scratch imparted would very likely require grinding with additional grades to remove the coarse scratch and bring the metal to a desired condition.

Backings. Paper backings are used in coated abrasives primarily for their flexibility. A-wt, the lightest weight paper, is used most commonly in sheet form by hand, hand blocked or on reciprocating sanders. A-wt paper is the most flexible of the paper backings as well as the lowest in tear resistance. As additional strength and tear resistance is required, the user may choose, C-wt, D-wt or E-wt backings which offer progressive increases in strength but also tend to be progressively less flexible:

Paper—A-wt–C-wt
D-wt – E-wt
Cloth —X-wt
Fibre —Heavy Duty

Cloth backings offer the ultimate in tear resistance as well as the abrasive anchorage essential to heavy duty sanding.

Fibre backings are used in disc form only and provide the user with an extremely durable backing. Fibre offers a firm base for supporting the abrasive and with high abrasive anchorage comes exceptional durability.

Coated abrasives fall into two additional classifications based on how widely the abrasives are spaced. If the abrasives are close together, it is referred to as *close coat*. If the abrasives are widely spaced, it is called *open coat*.

Fig. 4-11. Open coat and close coat abrasive discs.

In close coated abrasives, the abrasive is applied in such quantity as to entirely cover the backing. In open coat abrasives, the backing is usually 50 to 70 percent covered, Fig. 4-11. This leaves wider spaces between the abrasive grains. The open coating provides increased pliability and good cutting speed under light pressures. Open coated abrasives are used where the surface being ground is of such nature that closely spaced abrasive minerals would rapidly fill up, as shown by the disk at the right, Fig. 4-11. This disk is now valueless since, through improper use, its grinding ability has been reduced to zero.

In the manufacture of coated abrasives, the abrasive minerals are applied to the backing either by the gravity method or by the use of an electrostatic field. The electrostatic field method is the more popular. In this method, a powerful electrostatic field compels the abrasive grains to follow its lines of force and become anchored in the glue with their long axes at right angles to the backing (standing on end). Since the lines of force are evenly spaced, the abrasive grains are evenly spaced. This upending of the abrasive crystals provides sharper, faster cutting power. Both types of abrasives may be produced by either method.

Grinding Disks. Since the coated abrasive disk does the actual cutting, selection of the right grit and coating for each job is important. Grinding disks represent a considerable portion of body shop expense. While they speed up the work considerably, it is important that you never lose sight of the fact that the disks are expensive. The cost of grinding disks varies with size, grit, and brand. Nevertheless, to enable you to appreciate the waste each time you see a torn disk or one loaded with paint, you can assume that each disk costs more than fifty cents. Thus, it becomes apparent that the skill that must be developed in their use must include not only doing the job in a satisfactory manner, but understanding and following practices which will permit full value received as well.

Bonds. Two basic systems of bonding are used: glue-over-glue and resin-over-resin. Bonds are also composed of two separate adhesive applications called the *make* and *size coats.* The function of the make coat is to adhere the proper quantity of abrasives to a backing. After solidification of the make coat in drying chambers, a second adhesive coating (size coat) is applied over the abrasive to firmly anchor the particles to the backing. The glue-over-glue bond is used where a high degree of flexibility is required. The resin-over-resin bond produces an abrasive with exceptional resistance to grain loss for heavy duty grinding applications. In addition, the smooth surface of a resin-over-resin construction offers further benefits in its ability to resist clogging or *loading* of the area between the abrasive particles with the residue from the grinding operation.

CAUTION:

1. *Excessive disc speed can endanger you, the operator. Discs have a speed limitation. At higher speeds, pieces may fly off, and you could be injured.*
2. *Excessive speeds heat up the metal surface without penetrating. This can cause metal warp. Metal warp is an extremely tedious problem to correct, either by solder or plastic filling.*
3. *Excessive speeds result in excess wear on the disc, requiring needless replacement of expensive discs.*

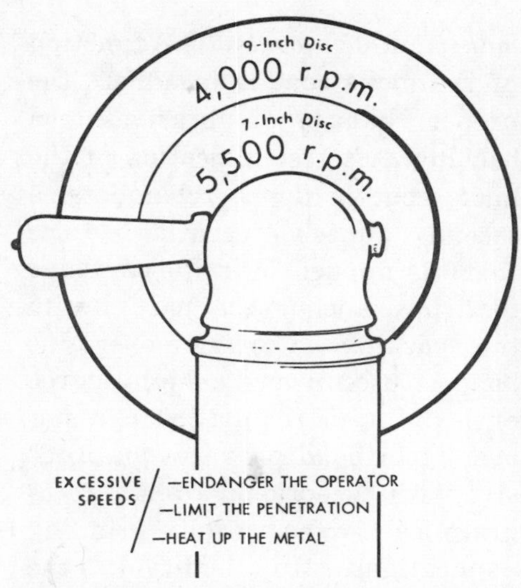

Fig. 4-12. Maximum tool speeds. (Minnesota Mining and Mfg. Co.)

Fig. 4-13. Cutting down disk for further use. (Minnesota Mining and Mfg. Co.)

An important factor in the operation of a disc grinder is tool speed, or the speed of the disc. Recommended maximum speeds for the popular 7″ and 9″ disc grinders are shown in Fig. 4-12. The speed on a 9″ grinder should not exceed 4000 RPM. The speed on a 7″ grinder should not exceed 5500 RPM. Speeds in excess of these maximums work against you instead of hurrying the job.

Disks 9″ in diameter have 82 percent more abrasive area than 7″ disks. The outer edge of the larger disk runs 32 percent faster. Discs can be cut down, Fig. 4-13. Cutting down sanding and grinding disks when they become worn or filled amounts to a considerable saving over a period of time.

Anything that will stick to the abrasive surface will quickly render it ineffective. For this reason, it is important to use only widely spaced abrasives when grinding anything that might have a tendency to clog the grit. This includes all kinds of paint, waxes, etc.

Backing Plate. In most disk grinding, the disk is placed directly on a slightly *flexible backing plate* assembly usually made of molded rubber. The degree of flexibility is controlled by the thickness of the plate and the material of which it is made. Wood, hard rubber, and a phenolic plastic material all have been used as backing plate material.

Very little flexing of the grinding disk is required when working on a convex surface, and a backing plate the full size of the grinding disk can be used. When working on a concave surface, it is necessary to have the disk flex enough to permit it to follow the contour.

To permit grinding concave surfaces, many metal finishers use two 9″ grinding disks with a 7″ backing plate, Fig. 4-14. The two grinding disks are placed back to back. By this method, the outer inch of the disk has only the support of the second disk and can flex enough to match most of the concave surfaces you will have to grind. With the outer one inch consisting of merely two grinding disks back to back, you will be able to grind right down into a

Fig. 4-14. Backing plate assembly. (Minnesota Mining and Mfg. Co.)

sharp corner. If care is used, this double disk can be used to reach down into drip moldings to remove rust.

If you have a 9″ grinder, you should have both a 9″ and a 7″ backing plate. The 7″ backing plate will also permit you to cut down disks worn on the outer edge, thus almost doubling the disk life.

Grinding Principles. As we have indicated, most of the grinding you will be doing will be with a disk grinder. The disk grinder can be used for removing paint, revealing low spots, shaping the contour of areas built up with solder, grinding down welds, and cutting away metal. The actual use of the disk grinder involves not only full knowledge of abrasives, but considerable skill as well.

Several general rules govern the use of the disk grinder. If you observe these rules, you will more easily and quickly be able to become proficient in the use of the grinder. These rules are considered good shop practice and are more for your own safety than anything else.

CAUTION:

The first thing you should do when you are going to use an electrically operated device is to see that it is properly connected and grounded, Fig. 4-15. Shop floors are usually of cement and are relatively good conductors of electricity. If the grinder is not properly grounded, you may receive shocks when you are using it.

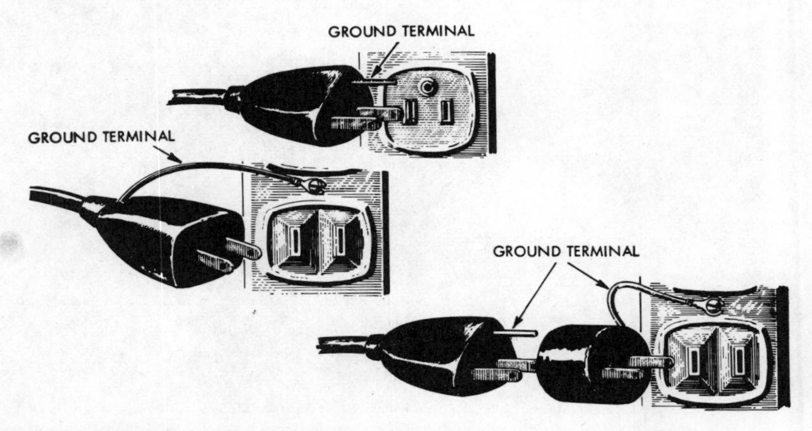

Fig. 4-15. Three types of electrical plug grounding terminals for shop safety.

Always wear goggles to protect your eyes from flying particles of metal and from the small abrasive particles that come loose from the grinding disk. Always replace torn disks as soon as the tear is noticed. Torn disks may catch in the work and twist the grinder out of your hand.

Always maintain a balanced position when you are using the grinder. This position not only permits you to have perfect control over the machine at all times, but it will also permit you to work for longer periods without tiring.

When you operate the grinder, hold it as flat as possible without permitting the center connecting bolt to come in contact with the surface being ground. Hold the grinder so that only 1½″ to 2½″ of the outer edge of the disk is in contact with the surface being ground. The grinder must never be tilted so that only the edge of the disk contacts the surface. Failure to observe this will cause gouges or deep scratches in the metal which will be hard to remove.

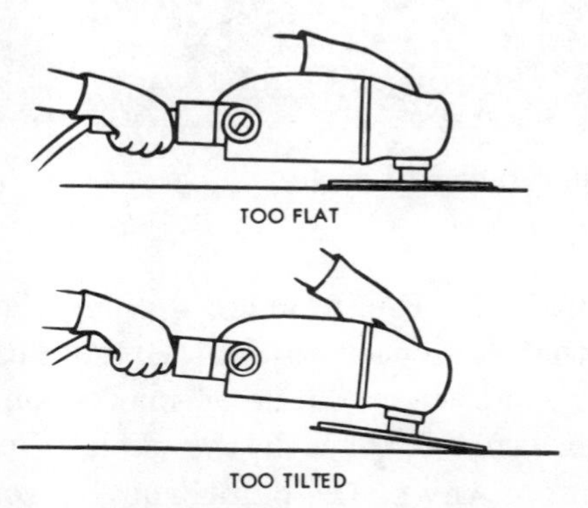

Fig. 4-16. Incorrect methods of holding a disc grinder.

The correct and incorrect methods of holding the grinder are illustrated in Figs. 4-16 and 4-17.

Move the grinder from left to right, overlapping the previous stroke with each new stroke. Make the cutting lines clean and straight as possible. Move the grinder in the same manner whether you are removing paint, rough grinding, or finish grinding. For most grinding operations, finish grind the long way on the repaired surface.

Auto Factory Use and Collision Shop Practice. In automobile factories, No. 80 grit is generally used for finishing the metal, for the metal finisher is working with bright, unpainted, new metal. In collision shops, you will be working with old metal that has previously been painted, and in some cases you will be working on metal that has rusted. Moreover, you will be working on surfaces that have been reworked with hammer and dolly, and in some cases with contours that have been built up with solder. In collision shops, even the finishing operation is generally performed with No. 50 grit.

Generally, only three different grades of disks will be used. What they are and what they are used for

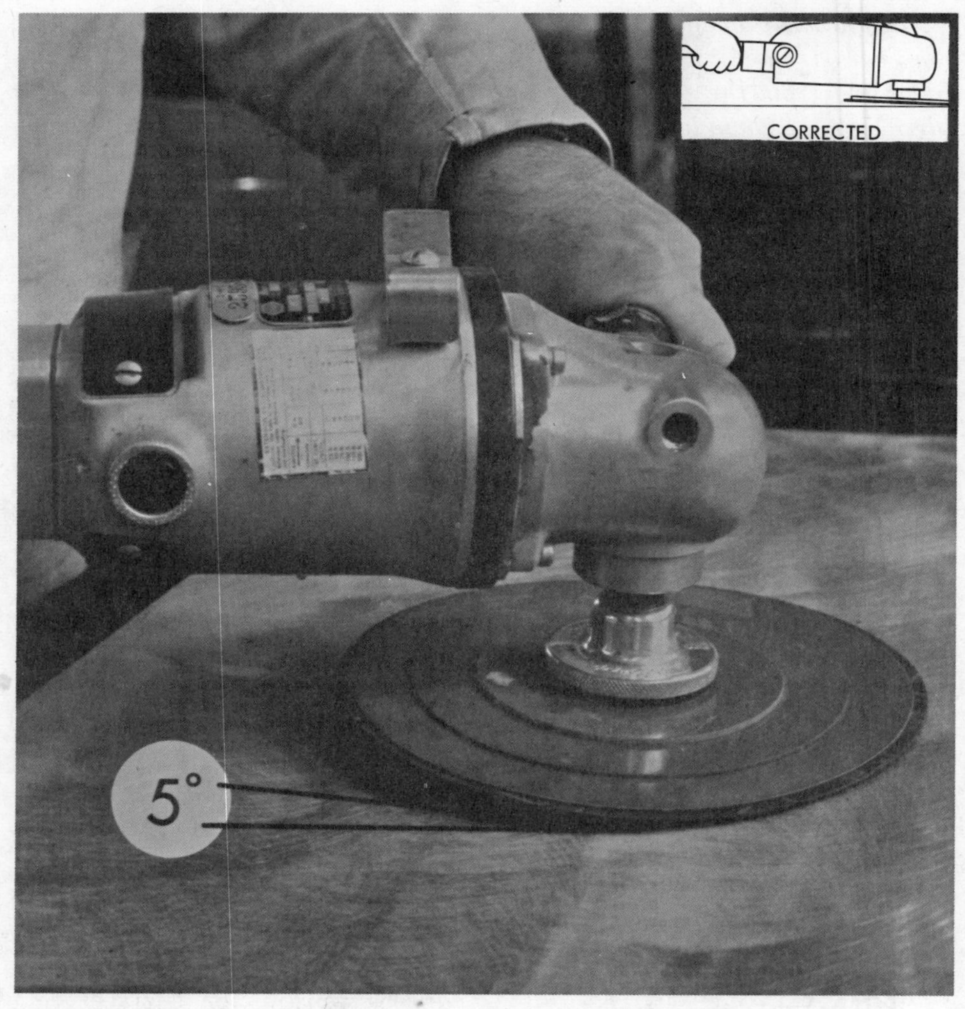

Fig. 4-17. Correct method of holding the disk grinder; note 5° angle.

are pointed out in the following paragraphs.

16B Disk. The 16B disk is coated with a coarse, open coat abrasive. It must be used with caution to prevent making deep scratches in the surface. This disk is most generally used in rough grinding surfaces that have been painted. Grind until you notice a volume of sparks coming from beneath the disk, then stop. Any of the paint, rust, or solder left on the surface is not likely to fill subsequent discs.

Close Coat No. 24 Grit Disk. The No. 24 grit close coat disk is used for several purposes in the body shop. It is most generally used for removing welds and for use in place of the file in showing up high and low spots in the bumping operation. It is also used in removing paint and rust.

Close Coat No. 50 Grit Disk. The only function of a No. 50 close coat disk is for performing finish operations on metal surfaces, both steel and solder. This disk will remove the scratches left by the No. 24 grit disk.

Grinding Exercise

Use an old fender, door, hood, or body panel for practicing with the disk grinder. Fasten the fender or panel in such a manner that you have a horizontal surface to work on and so it cannot move about as you move the grinder back and forth over the surface.

Place two 9″ open coat, No. 16 grit disks back to back, and fasten them to the grinder backing plate. Be sure the center hold-down bolt is securely tightened. It is well to disconnect the grinder from the source of power whenever you are changing or installing a disk. Doing so will eliminate any chance of accidentally starting the grinder.

Hold the grinder with your right hand so that the grinder disk lies on the surface to be ground with the side of the disk farthest away from you touching. Let the handle lie loosely in your hand. You will only be using the one hand in this exercise. Be sure the disk is contacting the surface correctly, then turn on the switch.

You will find that by turning your wrist slightly, the grinder will start to move in one direction. Allow it to travel about ten or twelve inches, then turn your wrist the other way and the grinder will move in the opposite direction. Continue with this exercise until you have made about twenty or twenty-five complete strokes of from eighteen to twenty-four inches long. At the completion of each stroke, move the grinder about ¾″ farther away from you. Do not lean on the grinder or otherwise try to apply pressure. The weight of the grinder itself will provide sufficient pressure.

Stop the grinder and compare what you have done to the two surfaces, Fig. 4-18. What you are trying to do is to obtain a surface covered with innumerable scratches which cross each other, and to entirely eliminate parallel scratches. If you find you are making the grind marks all in one direction, change the angle of the grinder or the way you are holding it until you are able to obtain the correct crisscross pattern.

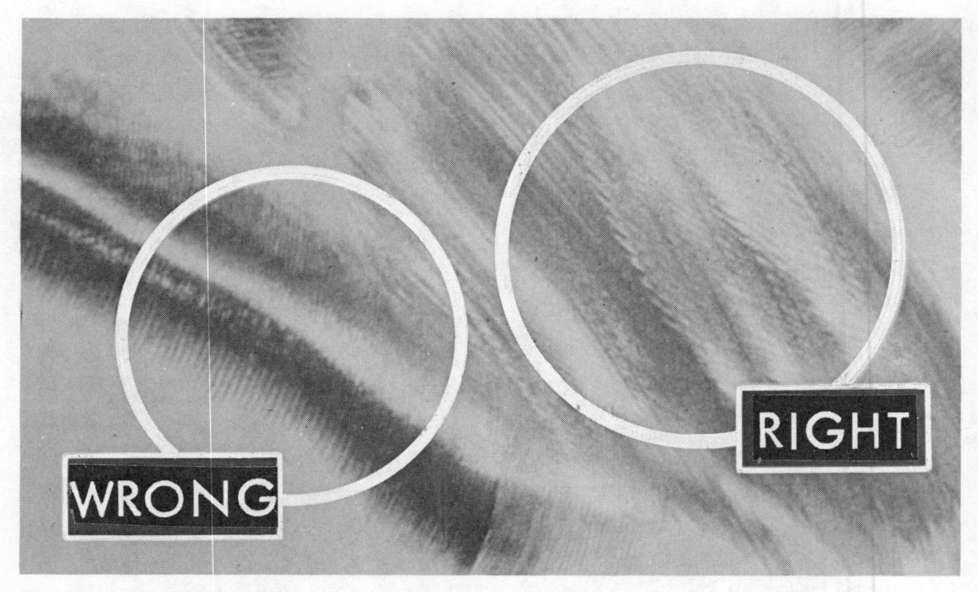

Fig. 4-18. Correct and incorrect patterns left by grinding.

When all of the paint has been removed from the practice surface, remove the No. 16 open coat disk, install a No. 24 close coat disk, and continue the exercise.

After all of the marks made by the open coat disk have been removed with the close coat disk, if the grinder marks are still crossing each other as they should, change to a No. 50 close coat disk. You are now finish grinding.

All of these exercises (on a horizontal surface) are performed with one hand. You will find that it is easier to obtain the correct grind pattern if you just allow the grinder to lie on the surface and let the machine do the work. When you are satisfied with the way you grind a horizontal surface, move the fender or panel so as to provide a vertical surface to grind in the next exercise.

Vertical Grinding. In grinding a vertical surface, you will have to use both hands. However, remember that in the previous exercise it was apparent that very little pressure was required on the grinder. In this exercise, you will use the second hand merely to support the weight of the grinder and to assist in the guidance of the machine. Do not push the grinder against the surface; merely let it contact the surface.

Continue to practice on a vertical surface until you can grind this way as well as you can on a horizontal surface. Don't fail to change the grinder disk each time the disk has filled its function.

The disk grinder is a valuable tool which can save you a lot of manual labor. For example, you can use the grinder instead of a file to aid in the location of low spots. However, don't lose sight of the fact that the grinder removes metal fast. Unless you are careful in its use, you will grind the body panels or fenders too thin. When you use a grinder to locate low spots, just pass the grinder over the surface lightly.

Remove the low spots with the pick hammer, then lightly grind the surface again. Repeat the process until you have successfully removed the low spots from the entire damaged area.

Preparing Metal for the Painter

The preparation of the metal for the painter involves doing whatever is required to provide the painter with a surface to which the paint can adhere. The surface must be free of deep scratches, otherwise the paint will not be of uniform thickness or the deep scratches may show after the paint is dry.

A surface which is sufficiently smooth is established by the use of No. 50 close coat abrasive. This may be accomplished with a disk, cone, or drum grinder, or any combination of them.

As a final operation, the metal finisher should remove any sharp edges left by the grinding operation. Lightly scuff the entire surface that has been ground or filed with No. 30 to No. 120 grit sandpaper or emery cloth held in the hand.

In all grinding or sanding, remember that the painter must taper the edge of the paint in all directions from the damaged area. This enables him to have a smooth paint job with no ridge where the new paint overlaps the old. Leave the paint intact where you are not working so he will have something to work with. Anything you do toward tapering the edge of the paint around the damaged area while you are grinding will save the painter some hand work.

Complete Repaint Jobs. On jobs that are going to be completely repainted, the metal finisher usually removes all rust from the body whether it happens to be in the collision damage area or not. Places in which rust is liable to form are along fender seams, along body panel seams, around door locks and windows, or under chipped paint.

At the same time you are using the open coat disk grinder to remove the paint from damaged sections on complete repaint jobs, inspect the rest of the job for rust and remove any you find. If, in grinding away rust to get bright metal, you find the panel has rusted through, repair it either by welding or soldering, whichever is required.

A Typical Shop Job. In Chapter 2, a typical fender job was discussed and illustrated. At that point the surface was brought back to its normal contour.

On such a job, after the fender is straightened and made as smooth as possible with a hammer and dolly, the grinder comes into play. First, remove all the paint from the damaged area, Fig. 4-19. Use a No. 16 grit, open coat disk, otherwise the disk will load up with paint. An open coat No. 24 grit disk may be used for synthetic enamel finishes if preferred.

Be sure to use the grinder so that the scratches run crisscross instead of parallel to each other. Correct and incorrect patterns left by grinding were shown in Fig. 4-18. This will save considerable work and time later on. Pick up the low spots with a pick hammer or dolly as soon as they are revealed. Don't try to grind them out. Again use the hammer and dolly and grinder or file as required to smooth out the metal. In the early stages, use chalk on the surface to check the smoothness of the metal instead of frequent grinding.

Fig. 4-19. Remove paint from damaged area. (Paul Lawrence Dunbar Vocational High School, Chicago, Illinois)

Once all of the low spots are removed, regrind the surface with a No. 50 grit, close coat abrasive until it is entirely smooth. Some shops use as high as a No. 80 close coat disk for the final finish grinding operation. A metal finisher is shown grinding the final surface in Fig. 4-20.

At this point the job is ready for the paint shop with the exception of the final operation of going over the entire damaged area by hand

Fig. 4-20. Finish grinding chalked surface. (Paul Lawrence Dunbar Vocational High School, Chicago, Illinois)

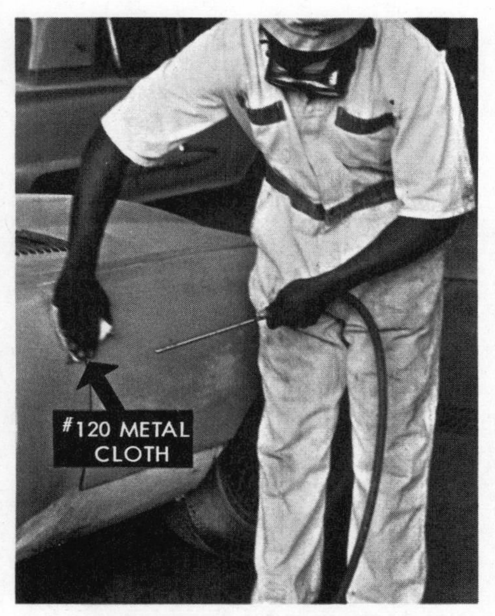

Fig. 4-21. Remove burrs. (Paul Lawrence Dunbar Vocational High School, Chicago, Illinois)

with fine sandpaper or emery cloth. This operation will remove burrs or sharp edges left by the finish grinding operation, as indicated in Fig. 4-21.

CAUTION:

Always wear goggles for eye protection when you are grinding. Always maintain a balanced position to make your work easier and to avoid the possibility of an accident. Never apply excess pressure. Let the grinder do most of the work. Remember to hold the grinder fairly flat so that you avoid creating gouges or low spots.

The grinder is a tool which can save much manual labor, but it must be handled with care. When using the grinder, do not allow your clothing to come in contact with the rotating disc. Body grinders are very powerful, and the disc may snag your clothing, draw itself close to your body, and cause injury.

Grinders, as well as other heavy duty shop tools, are provided with electrical grounding terminals at their plugs. Make sure the terminals are in operating condition so that you will not receive an electrical shock. The plugs and receptacles should be checked by a qualified electrician at least once a year for safety sake.

Checking On Your Knowledge

The following questions give you the opportunity to check up on yourself. If you have read the chapter carefully, you should be able to answer the questions. If you have any difficulty, read the chapter over once more so that you have the information well in mind before you go on with your reading.

1. When hot shrinking, how large should each heat spot be?
2. What are the tools used for a hot shrinking operation?
3. What type of motion should be imparted to the torch when a heat spot is made?
4. What color should the heat spot be when it is quenched with water?
5. Should the entire stretch area be heated at one time?
6. Can other than an oxyacetylene torch be used for hot shrinking?
7. Is it possible to shrink stretch areas without quenching each heat spot with water?
8. Are more or less heat spots required when water is used?
9. Is it possible to apply solder to a surface if rust or paint is still on the surface?
10. What material is used for building up contours or filing depressions in a finished surface?
11. What is the name of the method used for applying this material to the depressions?
12. When a wire brush or a grinder will not suitably clean a welded surface for soldering, what other method of cleaning can be used?
13. What is the process called for preparing a surface for solder?
14. Name two materials which may be used for tinning a surface.
15. Why should the soldering paddle be dipped in oil before it is used to spread solder?
16. If any grinding or filing is done to establish a contour while solder is hot, what will the result be?
17. Name three natural minerals which are abrasive in nature.
18. Which of the natural mineral abrasives is the most important?
19. What are the two types of coating in which abrasives are applied to backing?
20. Name two methods which are used for applying the abrasive to the backing. Which is the more popular?
21. What are the three things to specify in ordering abrasives for automotive collision work?
22. What grit grinding disk is usually used in collision work for rough grinding?
23. What grit grinding disk is usually used in collision work for removing welds and showing up high and low spots?
24. What is the function of a No. 50 close coat disk in collision work?
25. When grinding on a body panel with a disk grinder, how much of the grinding disk should actually come in contact with the work?
26. What undesirable condition will be created if only the edge of the disk is allowed to contact the work?

Power Tools

Chapter

5

In the preceding chapters, the use of the various hand tools for restoring the body and sheet metal to its original contour were presented. However, in actual collision work, a large percentage of the jobs you will encounter require the use of power tools to push or pull large areas or sections back to, or somewhere near, their original position.

Power is supplied by hydraulic jacks which can be extended to the desired length and for which a number of attachments are available for pushing or pulling.

As explained in Chapter 1, the outer skin of the body is fairly light-gage metal, placed over a framework of heavier, stiffer metal which is reinforced with various types of supports and braces. In addition to the damage (as the result of a collision) to the outer skin of the body that may be apparent, this inner construction also becomes damaged.

Since the inner construction is attached to the outer skin, the outer skin is prevented from returning to its original shape. This means that the inner construction must be restored to its original shape and position, either before or at the same time that the outer metal is corrected. In some instances, you will find that once the inner construction has been restored to normal position, the outer panel will have been corrected at the same time.

The inner construction of automobile bodies is of much heavier metal than the outer panels and cannot be restored to normal by the same processes. Once the interior trim panels have been removed where the side of the automobile body has been pushed in, you may find that the inner construction has been bent and permanently deformed.

Quite often this occurs at a point where the inner construction is attached to the body sills. Since the body sills are rigidly fastened to the vehicle frame, they represent the strongest part of the body. When the force of the impact is received above the sills, the inner construction usually bends at or near the body sill. Correction of the damage to the inner construction is generally accomplished by applying pressure to the damaged member or members.

In damage of this kind, the piece that is attached to the body sill will be bent or kinked. Where a sharp kink or crease has been formed at any point in the inner construction, use heat while the pressure is being applied. This permits the metal to go back to its original shape with little danger of cracking. If you attempt to straighten sharp kinks cold, you may crack the metal, since body metal is of low-carbon steel. Little or no loss of strength occurs due to heating.

Power Tools. In using power tools, it is important that you understand that power is being applied at both ends of the jack. That is to say, power is being applied to whatever the jack is resting against and to whatever it is pushing against at the other end. This makes it necessary to block the base of the jack, usually with a piece of 2 x 4 or several 2 x 4's, at the point you are pushing from, to spread the force over a large area. Use a *special adapter* of some kind at the end with which you are pushing. In general, these adapters localize the pressure, whereas the 2 x 4 or block at the other end spreads the pressure over a larger area, thus does not result in the deforming of any parts.

In addition to being required for straightening body inner construction, power tools are useful in providing support or pressure at otherwise inaccessible portions of the outer panels. They control pressure in a degree than is impossible with hand tools, on panels and fenders themselves.

The use of power tools in many instances will permit backing up your work with a dolly at places where it would be impossible to hold a dolly and still manipulate a hammer. In progressive body shops, it is not uncommon to see as many as four power jacks being used at one time on a single job. The use of more than one jack on a rather involved damage saves considerable time in resetting of the power tools.

Power dollies are used in essentially the same way as hand dollies are used in either direct or indirect hammering. The power dolly can be used to apply pressure to the low part of the damage, and the crease around the damaged area is relieved by indirect hammering, or by spring hammering through a spoon. Generally, however, power dollies are used for direct hammering rather than for indirect or spring hammering. Rubber heads on the jack will apply pressure to the low areas for indirect hammering. Being compressible, they will follow the work, thereby reducing the number of separate jack adjustments required.

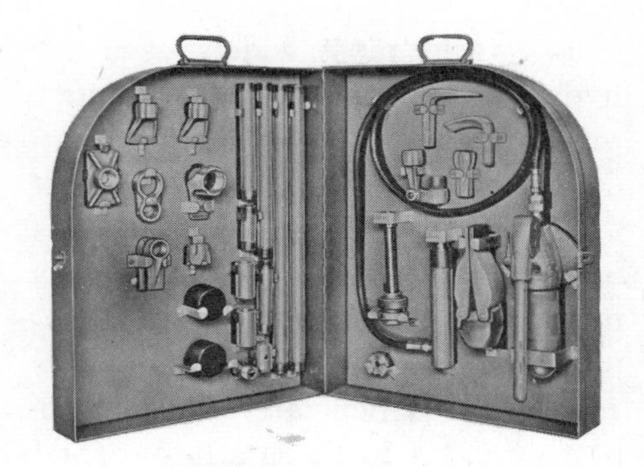

Fig. 5-1. Small power tool set.

Although the use of power tools will speed up and make easier a great many jobs, you will find that practically every job will have to be finished with hand tools. The number of power tools available to you will largely control the speed with which you can do collision work. In some cases, lack of power tools or adapters may limit you to certain types of jobs.

An economical way of getting started would be by the purchase of a small power set similar to the one shown in Fig. 5-1. This set will handle a fairly large percentage of the jobs you encounter. As your business increases and you purchase heavier equipment, this assortment of power tools will be of value as a second set which in many instances can save considerable time.

Jacks As Expansion Devices

The basic part of power tool equipment, the *jack,* is the part of the equipment that actually supplies the power. A body jack consists of three basic units as shown in Fig. 5-2.

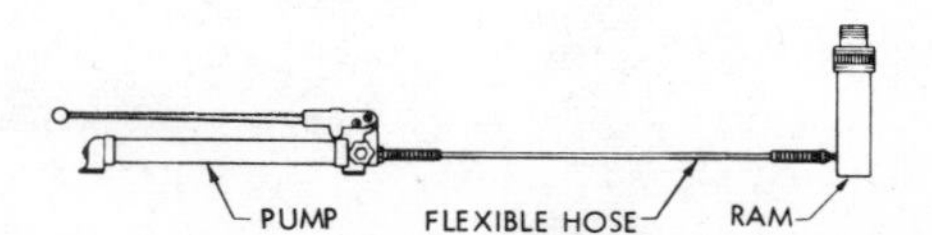

Fig. 5-2. Basic units of jack. (Blackhawk Mfg. Co.)

The jacks most widely used are hydraulically operated (oil under pressure) and are similar in principle to the kind of hydraulic jack used in tire repair work. The jacks used in body work are, of course, much more powerful than common car jacks. *Pneudraulic jacks* (jacks in which air pressure is used to exert force on a liquid [oil] column which in turn pushes the ram) are also used to some extent in body shops. Regardless of how the power is developed inside the jack, however, the principles involved for their correct application are the same.

Types of Jacks

Only the different types of hydraulic jacks which are generally available are discussed here. However, you may consider the information set forth as applicable to pneudraulically operated equipment, because the different types described are also available in pneudraulically operated jacks.

The types of jacks in general use in body shops are either direct-acting or remote-controlled. A jack which exerts power in either direction is called a *push-pull jack*. These jacks may be *either* direct-acting or remotely controlled. Any

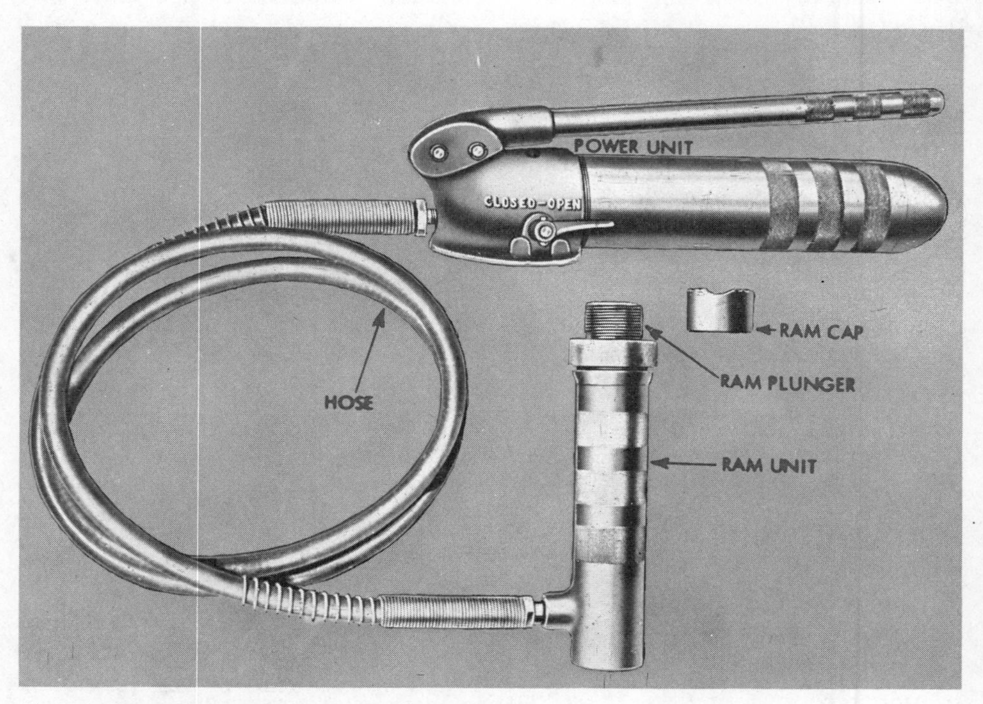

Fig. 5-3. Remote controlled jack showing parts of a set.

job may be done with any one of these types. The main difference in jacks is in the manner in which the setup for the repair at hand is made. Probably the most commonly used jack is a remote-controlled type similar to the one shown in Fig. 5-3.

A *direct-acting jack* is one in which the power unit or hydraulic pump is integral with the ram. With this type of jack, the action may be in only one direction or it may work in either direction (push or pull).

In *a remote-controlled* jack, the hydraulic power supply unit is separate from the ram unit of the jack. The two units are connected by a reinforced rubber hose. This hose is of sufficient length to permit you to work freely about the vehicle.

A push-pull jack is one in which the plunger in the ram unit can be moved under power in either direction at the discretion of the operator.

Jacks in which the ram unit can be moved by power only in one direction pull an attachment such as chains or pull plates. These attachments convert the push action of the plunger to a full, powerful pull action.

The ram unit of all jacks is basically the same. All the threads on the ram and the ram plunger are standard pipe threads. The threads on all of the tools and attachments match the threading on the ram and plunger, Fig. 5-4, from one manufacturer to another.

It will be necessary for you to do your own maintenance work on any power equipment which you may purchase, as well as on the power equipment at your disposal in any body shop where you may work. Moreover, there are several things which you should remember when you are using power

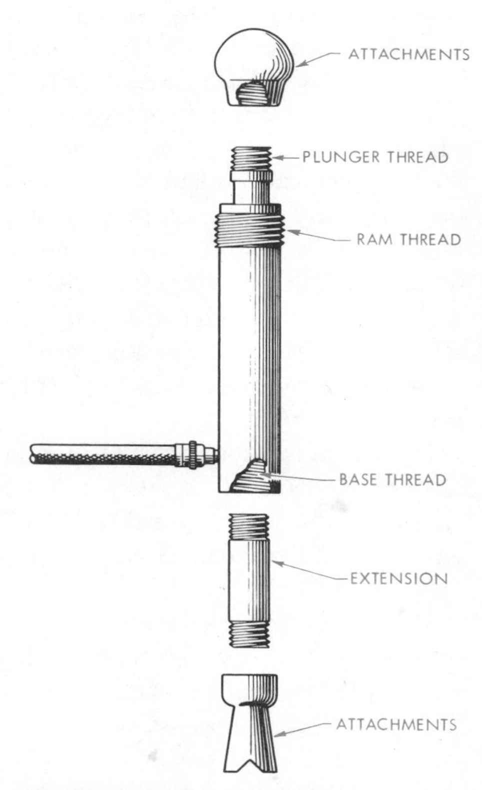

Fig. 5-4. Arrangements of ram unit of jack. (Blackhawk Mfg. Co.)

equipment that will lengthen the life of the equipment appreciably.

Care of the Hose. On the remote-controlled jacks where the hydraulic pressure is supplied to the ram through a hose, it is well to exercise care so that the hose does not become damaged.

The hose is made from oilproof rubber reinforced by woven steel wire which is covered on the outside by a fabric and rubber combination. Do not permit heavy objects to drop or fall on the hose. A sharp, hard impact may kink the wire strands in the hose. Because of the rubber covering, the kink may not be noticeable. Subsequent applications of pressure will subject the kinked wires to a bending and unbending process which will eventually cause them to break. With the wires broken, the fabric by itself will not be strong enough to withstand pressure, and the hose will leak or break altogether.

In making setups with the jacks, always be careful to anchor the ram unit so that its pushing force will not tend to bend or break the hose fitting.

Do not subject the hose to high pressure if it is twisted or kinked. Frequent use under such conditions will cause hose failure.

Care of Ram Threads. Whenever the ram is not in use, the attachments provided for protection of the plunger threads and the ram body threads should be in place, Fig. 5-5.

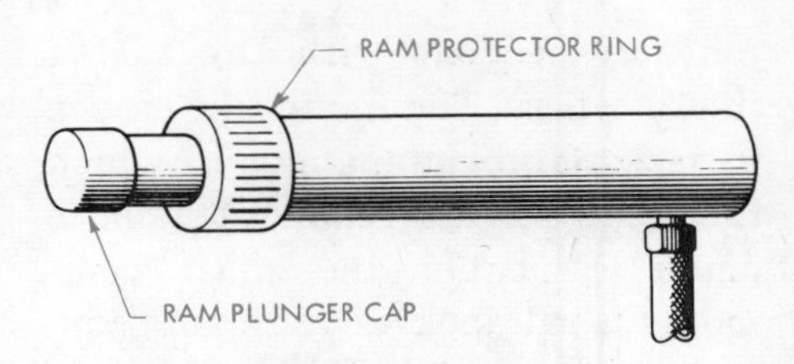

Fig. 5-5. Plunger cap and ram protector ring in place. (Blackhawk Mfg. Co.)

Use all of the threads when you make connections, and always turn the attachments until they are tight. This will assure long thread life. Always keep the threads in both the ram and the attachments clean and free from grease. Threads that are gummed up prevent proper connection, and damage may result when pressure is applied. Whenever threads become marred or bent, they should be straightened or filed so that the proper fit can be obtained when connections are made.

Adding Oil to Pump Unit. The only part of the jack needing attention is the pump or hydraulic unit. It is necessary to replenish the supply of hydraulic oil in the pump periodically.

Add oil according to the manufacturer's recommendations for the particular jack with which you are working. Do not add an excessive amount of oil or the pump will not operate properly. In an emergency, SAE 10w engine oil can be used for filling the hydraulic unit. However, most jack manufacturers specify a fluid of their own. You should never use hydraulic brake fluid, shock absorber fluid, alcohol, glycerine, or castor oil. These fluids will corrode the valve seat and cylinder wall surfaces, and will dissolve the sizing which seals the pores in the pump leathers.

Care of Chains. The following precautions will prolong the life of the chains:

Do not twist the chain excessively while making a setup.

See to it that the chain is wrapped around the frame or frame member several times, so that the load is distributed over as many links as possible.

Protect the chain links whenever they rest on sharp corners. This may be done with wood blocks or old tire casing.

Always fasten the chain hook securely to a chain link. If the hook does not grasp the link adequately, the entire setup can slip, causing further damage.

Tools and Attachments

Tools and attachments harness and direct the powerful force of the hydraulic power units. These tools and attachments, when coupled to the ram and the ram plunger, make possible hundreds of working combinations. All of the tools and attachments are described and illustrated in use in this section, and are presented here so as to familiarize you with the equipment with which you will be working. Later in this chapter, the principles of power tool application are presented.

As each of these pieces of equipment has several uses, only the main application is described and illustrated here. After you understand what the tools are and become familiar with their working principles, you will be able to apply this knowledge to making up special combinations to suit any job you may encounter.

Some of the tools can be attached directly to the ram or ram plunger. However, the majority of the setups you encounter will require either that you use several different tools in sequence or that you apply power over so wide a space that the ram, with plunger extended, will not reach. Tubing is available for spanning distance, and an adapter is supplied with each set of tools for quick setups.

With any of the power tools, it is always necessary to anchor the jack firmly against something before power is applied. Different attachments, called jack bases, are available for this purpose.

Pushing Tools. Certain of the tools described in this section are used for a variety of pushing operations. The tool is usually named for the main operation for which it is designed, although it may be used for other operations. A set of pushing tools is shown in Fig. 5-6.

It is often necessary to perform an operation where two panels can be pushed back to normal by pushing directly from one to another. This is referred to as a spreading operation. The tools used for this type of work are described in this section, as well as push-pull attachments and chain

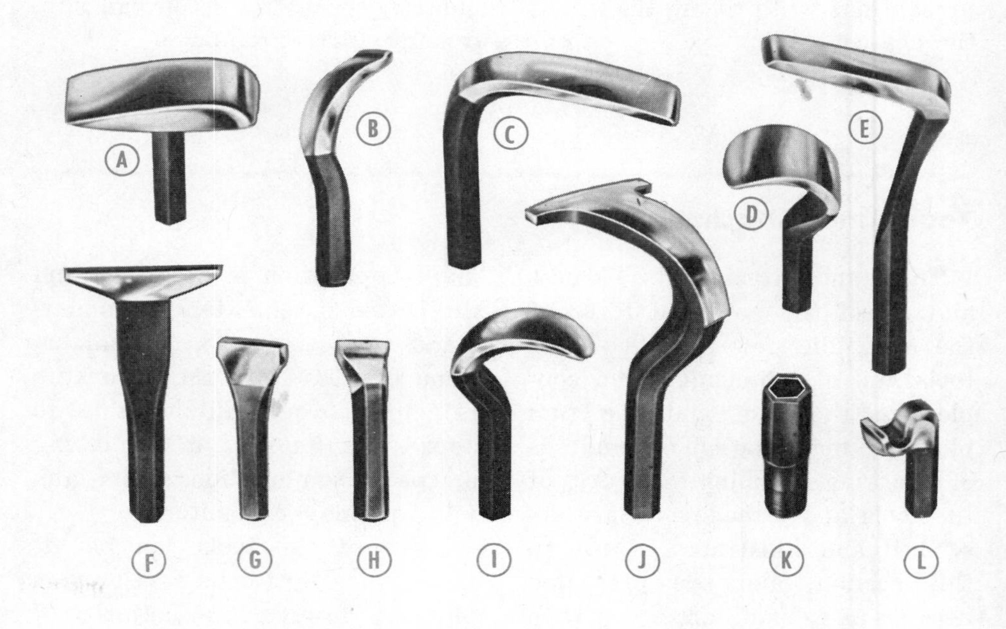

(A) POWER DOLLY
(B) DRIP MOLDING SPOON
(C) COWL AND LOWER QUARTER PANEL SPOON
(D) CORNER AND HEADER PANEL SPOON
(E) QUARTER PANEL PUSHER SPOON
(F) QUARTER PANEL MOLDING SPOON
(G) CALKING IRON
(H) OFFSET PUSHING TOOL
(I) UPPER REAR QUARTER PANEL SPOON
(J) TOP RAIL SPOON
(K) HEX ADAPTER
(L) FENDER HOOK

Fig. 5-6. Pushing tools for many purposes and conditions of service.

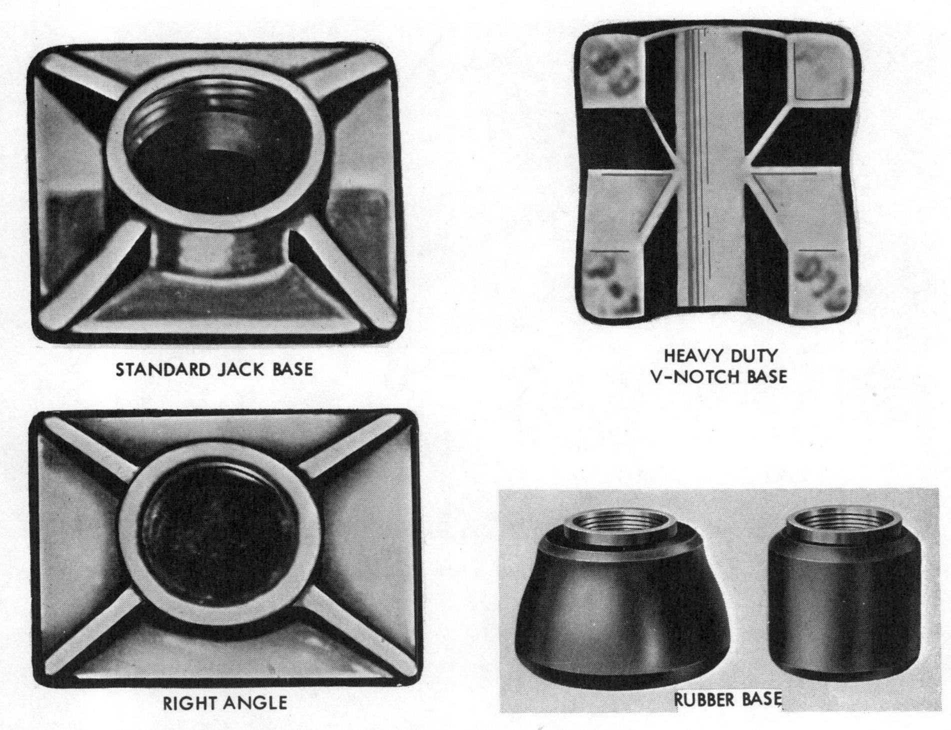

Fig. 5-7. Jack bases for various applications shown in use.

attachments commonly used with one-way jacks.

Jack Bases. The standard jack base is used in all operations where a special base or other attachment is not required, Fig. 5-7.

The heavy-duty V-notch base is used mostly for holding the jack when pushing either frame sides or cross members into alignment, Fig. 5-7. The notch in the end of this attachment permits you to anchor the jack against any edge of the frame which is strong enough to withstand the pressure of the application.

Rubber jack bases usually come in a variety of shapes and sizes, Fig. 5-7. They are particularly valuable since they conform to almost any shape under pressure and distribute the pressure over a fairly large area. They likewise permit you to straighten damage or apply pressure in some instances without damaging the paint. Fig. 5-8 shows three rubber bases being used in a setup for applying pressure to a window opening.

The right-angle jack base is very versatile and can be used in a large number of setups. It is particularly

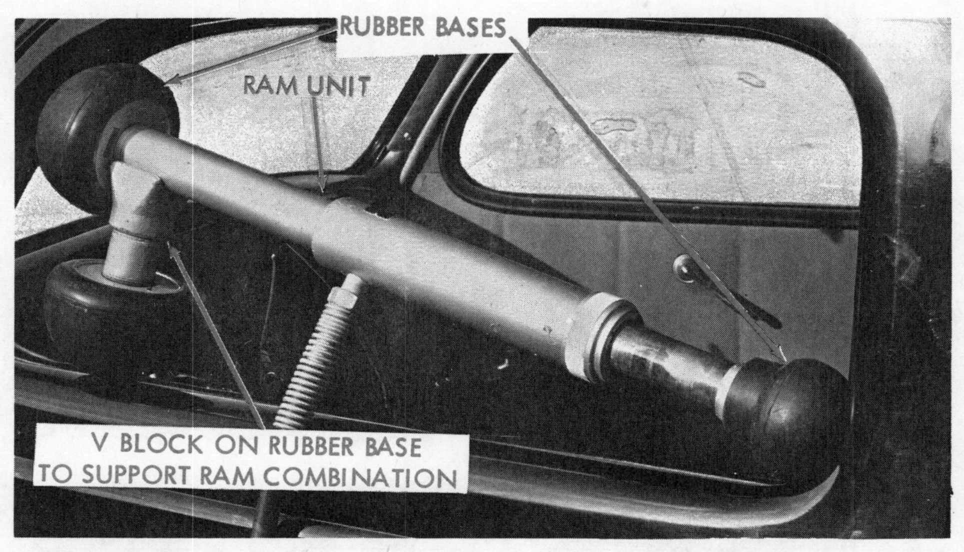

Fig. 5-8. Rubber bases used in applying pressure to a window opening. (Blackhawk Mfg. Co.)

useful on frame work. The sharp point, Fig. 5-7, is especially useful for pushing into alignment those parts of a frame where two members come together to form a sharp, right-angle corner.

Adapters, Tubing and Caps. The hex adapter, Fig. 5-9, couples directly to the ram plunger. Most of the spoons and pushing dollies have hex shanks which slip into the hex well in the outward end of the adapter. The hex arrangement allows you to position the tool six different ways without disturbing the jack setup. You can also slip the tool in and out of the adapter quickly.

The ram cap connects directly to the end of the ram, Fig. 5-9. It

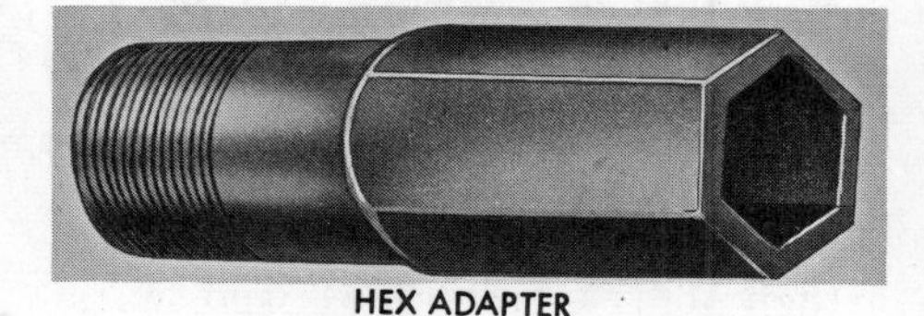

HEX ADAPTER

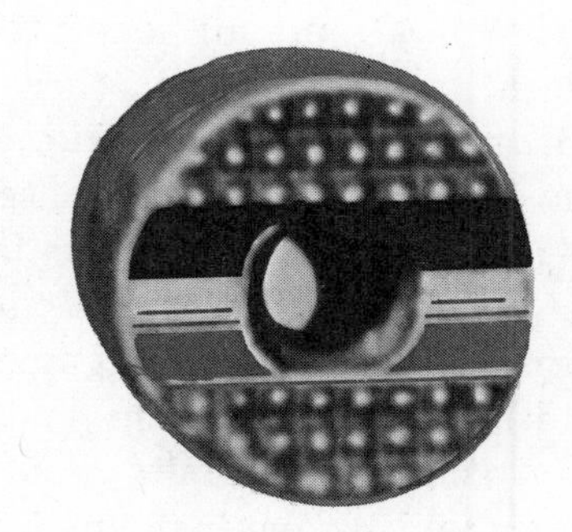

RAM CAP

Fig. 5-9. Accessories for ram.

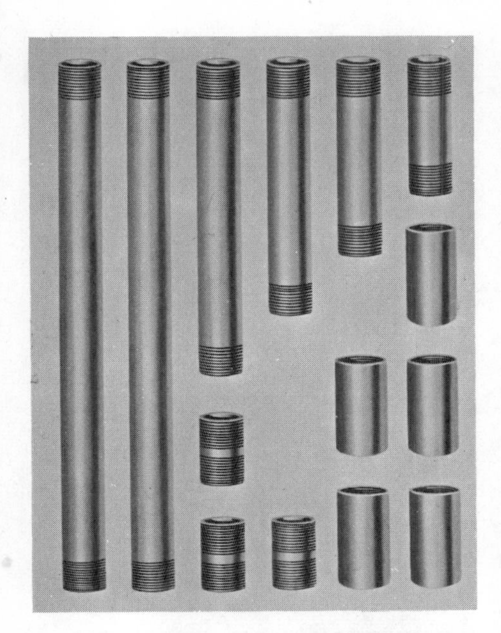

Fig. 5-10. Tubing set for extending the ram arm safely and strongly.

is used where a straight push is required when the space available for working is limited.

A tubing set is illustrated in Fig. 5-10. Tubing is usually made from seamless steel. The tubing couples to the ram or the ram plunger. It is fully threaded and chamfered for speedy coupling. The connector nipples have holes along the side so that a screwdriver can be used for tightening.

A quick coupling tubing set is shown in Fig. 5-11. With this set, the tubes slip together and are fastened in place with a snap pin.

Fig. 5-12 shows a typical setup where several lengths of tubing are used to span a distance.

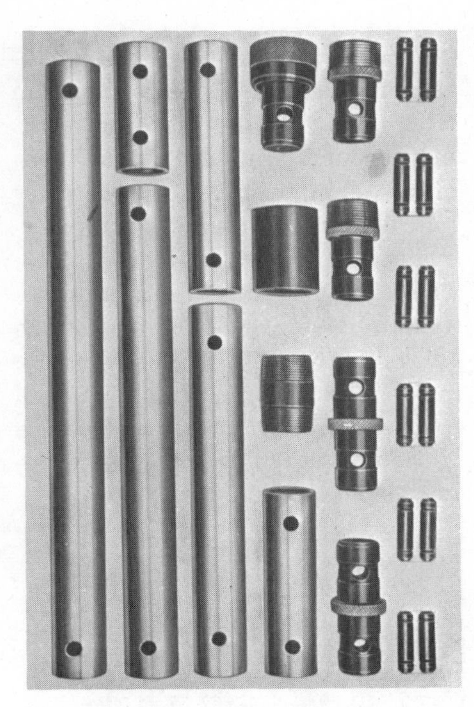

Fig. 5-11. Quick coupling tubing set.

Fig. 5-12. Setup involving the use of tubing.

Offset Pushing Tool. The application of this tool in conjunction with the hydraulic jack for working around an obstructed area (thus eliminating the necessity for removal of inner reinforcements) is illustrated in Fig. 5-13. The offset design of this tool makes it suitable for pushing operations on radiator shells, grilles, fenders, and body brackets. It can be used to push directly into reveal panels without disturbing the surrounding panel sections.

Fig. 5-13. Offset pushing tool in use.

Spoon Tools. A cowl and lower quarter panel spoon is shown in Fig. 5-14 being used to push out a left-hand cowl panel. This spoon is designed to fit most quarter panel and cowl contours by reaching behind inner construction.

Fig. 5-14 also shows a drip molding spoon being used to jack out kinks and dents in the drip molding section of a top panel. The lip on this spoon enables you to hook it under the drip molding without danger of its slipping. You

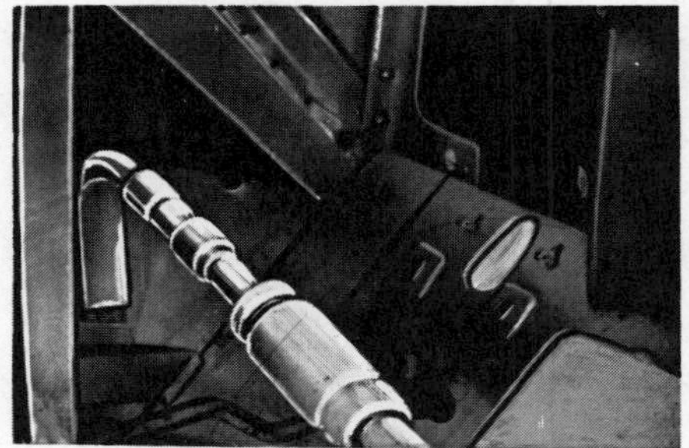

COWL AND LOWER QUARTER PANEL SPOON

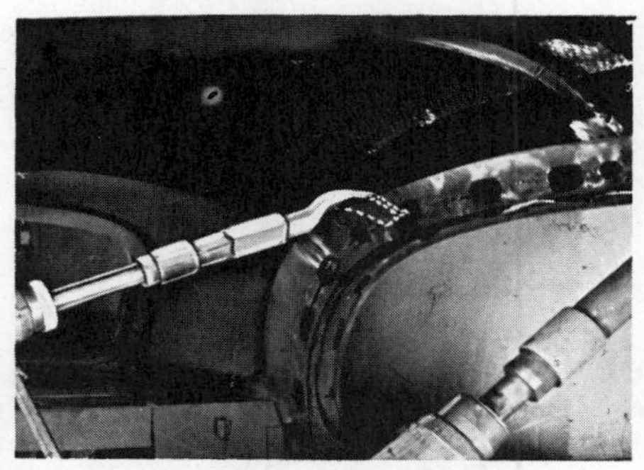

DRIP MOLDING SPOON

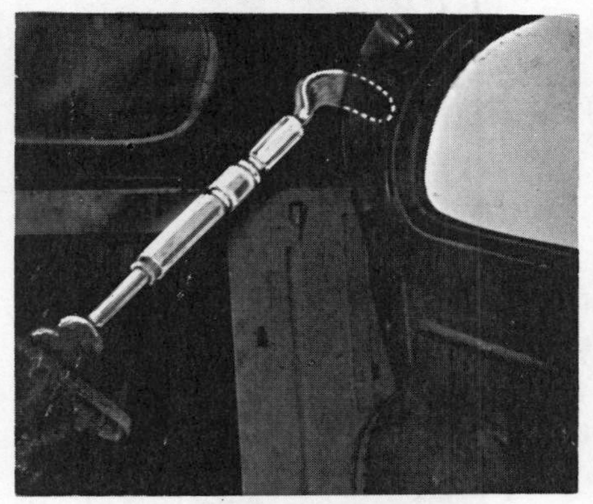

UPPER REAR QUARTER PANEL SPOON

Fig. 5-14. Spoon tools in use.

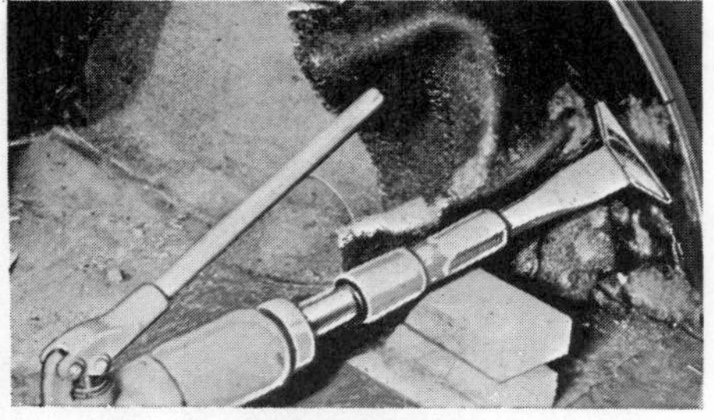
QUARTER PANEL MOLDING SPOON

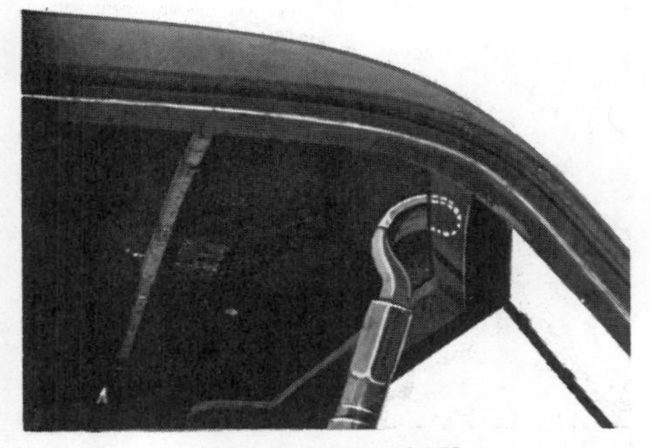
CORNER AND HEADER PANEL SPOON

QUARTER PANEL PUSHER SPOON

Fig. 5-14 (continued)

TOP RAIL SPOON

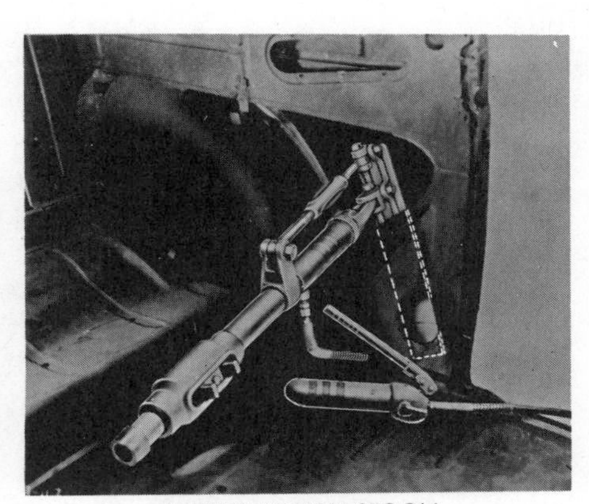
ROCKER ACTION SPOON

Fig. 5-14 (continued)

will find this tool useful when it is necessary to push an upper quarter panel out as well as up.

On most cars, the high crown radius of the upper rear quarter panel spoon is necessary for working around the upper back sections. This type of spoon is shown in Fig. 5-14 also.

The same figure illustrates a quarter panel molding spoon being used for pushing out the rear quarter panel moldings.

The corner and header panel

spoon is used to get in behind header panel inner construction to push up crushed panels. Such an operation is illustrated in Fig. 5-14. This tool can also be used as a high crown dolly for dinging.

Because of the long working end, the quarter panel pusher spoon is used for getting behind inner construction around the quarter panel area. It is particularly useful for getting behind drain gutter inner construction without removing the drain gutter, as shown in Fig. 5-14.

The top rail spoon is used in the same manner as the quarter panel pusher spoon. It is designed for use in straightening roof rail outer panels without removing the roof rail inner construction. The spoon has a deep throat and a curved surface anvil which will match the contour along the side of metal roofs. The top rail spoon is shown in use in Fig. 5-14. A rocker action spoon is also shown in use in Fig. 5-14. It has a universal hinge arrangement which permits the anvil spoon to adjust itself in four different directions. This enables you to easily reach behind inner construction. The rocker-action spoon can be used for both roughing operations and finish work on all surfaces and in all areas except those having special shapes or contours.

Power Dolly. A power dolly, shown in Fig. 5-15 applying pressure to a damaged rear hinge pillar, is usually used where a straight push is needed. You will find a straight push is often an essential operation when you are working on pillars, metal floor panels, up-

Fig. 5-15. Power dolly in use.

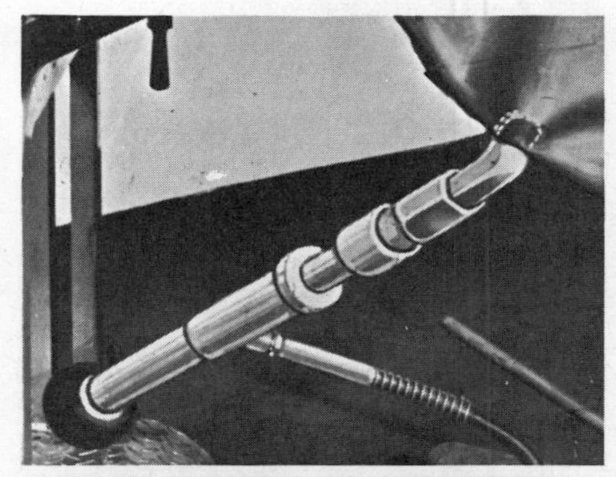

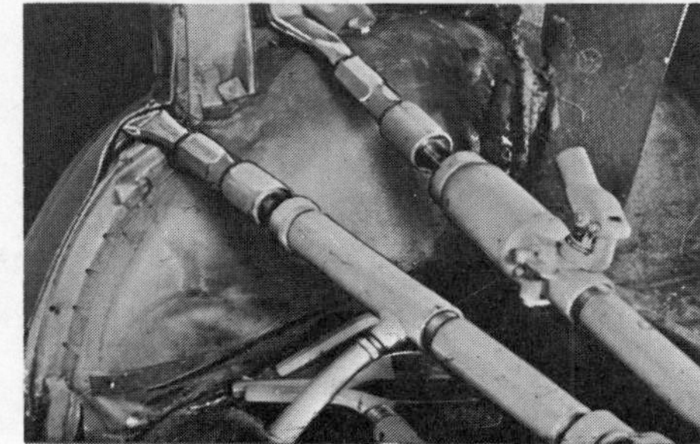

Fig. 5-16. Other ram accessories.

per dash panels, or in trunks.

Fender Hook and Caulking Iron. The fender hook is used for relieving backward strain in fenders prior to roughing them out. A typical setup off the car is shown in Fig. 5-16.

The caulking iron is a heavy-duty tool used mainly in quarter panel work. Fig. 5-16 also shows a caulking iron being used to push a rear quarter panel molding into alignment. The caulking iron may also be used for pushing and aligning frames, dash panels, and curved inner construction.

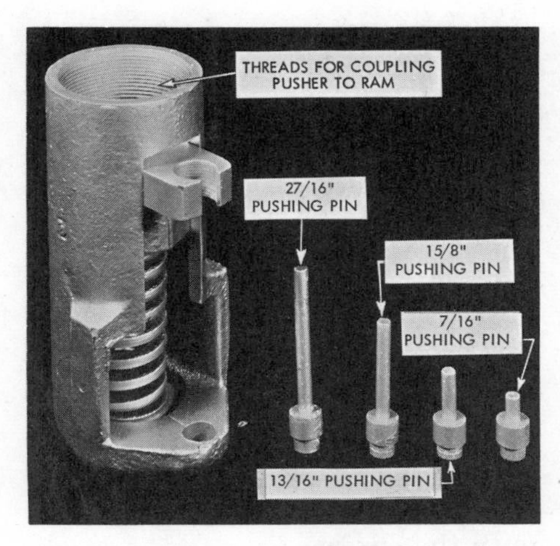

Fig. 5-17. Hinge pin pusher and pin assortment. (Blackhawk Mfg. Co.)

Hinge Pin Pusher. Hinge pins are often difficult to get at for removal. Usually, the hinges are built as close to the body as possible to provide a smoother, more streamlined appearance. The operation is sometimes a long and laborious procedure without a suitable tool for removing hinge pins. With a hinge pin pusher, Fig. 5-17, the job is relatively simple.

Hinge pin pushers consist of the pusher itself and pusher pins of various lengths and diameters. The pusher is the part of the tool which is connected to the jack. Different lengths and diameters of pins enable you to work on a large variety of cars and with situations in which the damage has caused the hinge area to be deformed.

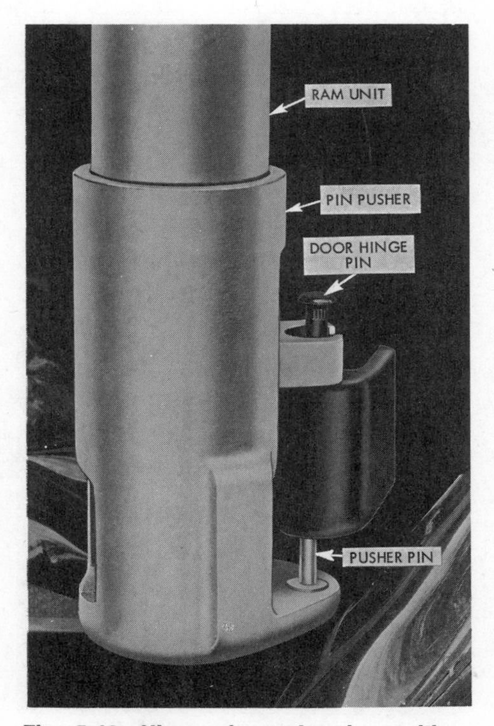

Fig. 5-18. Hinge pin pusher in position. (Blackhawk Mfg. Co.)

Fig. 5-18 shows the hinge pin pusher in position for the first operation in removing a hinge pin. Hinge pins can be installed as well as removed with this tool.

It is not always necessary to use a pusher pin to push in a hinge pin because the hinge may be so narrow that the broad head of the pusher pin will not fit the hole. In this case, you can install the hinge by simply removing the pusher pin from the hinge pin pusher. Use the bottom lug of the pusher to push the hinge pin in until it is flush with the surface.

Spreaders. The V-type toggle action spreader is for use where it is not necessary to reach too far between the units being spread. It is particularly useful, Fig. 5-19, for spreading grille bars, fender panels, and hoods.

The V-type toggle action spreader attaches directly to the ram unit of the jack. When power is applied, the ram plunger comes forward and actuates the jaws of the spreader through a cam action which forces the jaws apart. When pressure is released, the plunger returns and the jaws of the spreader, being spring loaded, immediately close. In Fig. 5-19 a V-type toggle action spreader is being used to separate grille bars.

You can see from the illustration that this tool is easily adaptable for working in small spaces because it does not require much operating space when it is attached to the ram.

The hydro method spreader also employs a toggle action. This

HYDRO-METHOD SPREADER

V-TYPE TOGGLE ACTION SPREADER ON FRONT GRILLE SECTION

Fig. 5-19. Two types of spreaders shown in typical applications.

spreader, shown in use in Fig. 5-19, has a maximum spread of 16″ and a minimum closed width of 1½″.

A hinged dolly effect is incorporated in the end of each jaw which allows it to follow contours and permits the body repairman to do direct hammering while the dolly acts as the backing tool.

A small wedge-type spreader which will lie in the palm of your hand is available. This spreader, Fig. 5-20, has several attachments which screw into the bottom side of the lower jaw. These attachments allow a variety of actions in a confined working space. This tool is especially useful for removing small dents, low spots, or kinks from panels where it is difficult to reach with other tools. The attachment shown at left has a rocking action which allows the spreader to be used at an angle.

The second attachment is called a mushroom pick. It is used for removing larger dents or creases. The extended edge can be used to reach behind beads or lips. The third attachment is used for bringing out pinpoint type dents and other small dents. The blunt-nosed attachment shown at right is also used for removing very small dents and low spots. The use of spreader attachments expands the use of the spreader, Fig. 5-20.

Push-Pull Attachments. The push-pull tools are used with either direct-action or controlled, push-pull jacks. (Chain setups for pulling are described under chain attachments.) A group of push-pull tools which are typical are illustrated in Fig. 5-21.

These tools are made for use in extremely close quarters and will withstand extreme pressures. Because most frame straightening is done with the body in place on the frame, it is often necessary to work close against the under portions

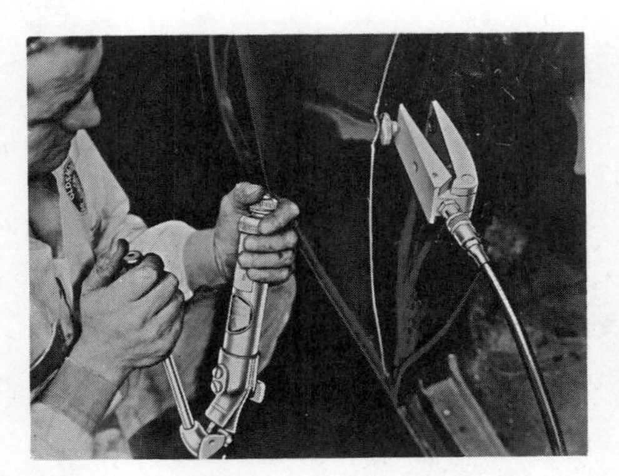

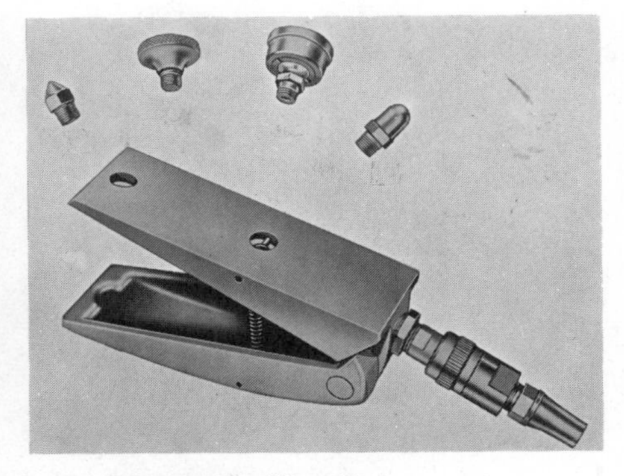

Fig. 5-20. Small wedge spreader with attachments. (Blackhawk Mfg. Co.)

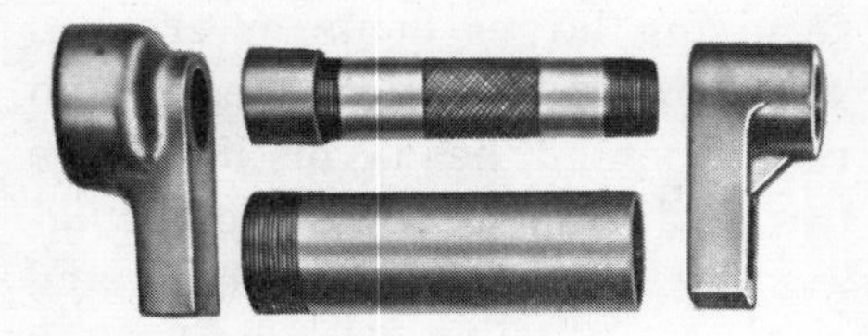

Fig. 5-21. Push-pull tools.

of the body. In such instances, you will find these tools particularly helpful.

Chain Attachments. Chain attachments are used primarily on one-way, remote-controlled jacks. However, certain setups in frame straightening require the use of chains regardless of the type of jack used. Chain attachments are also used extensively for straightening axles and other suspension members.

Various attachments are necessary for attaching the chain to the jack. These attachments are shown with the jack in various arrangements in Fig. 5-22.

The large chain attachment is threaded onto the ram body. A ram cap is placed over the end of the ram plunger. When pressure is applied so that the ram moves outward, a pulling effect can be achieved when the chain is hooked as shown. Any of the jack bases can be used instead of the ram cap, depending on the kind of surface.

Two of the attachments pictured in Fig. 5-22 are illustrated

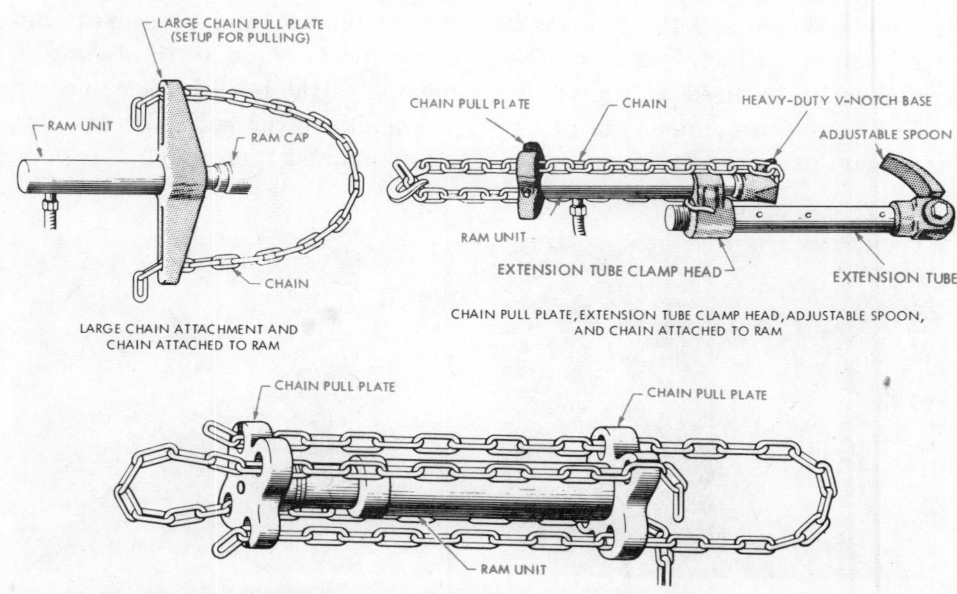

Fig. 5-22. Chain pull attachments and sets. (Blackhawk Mfg. Co.)

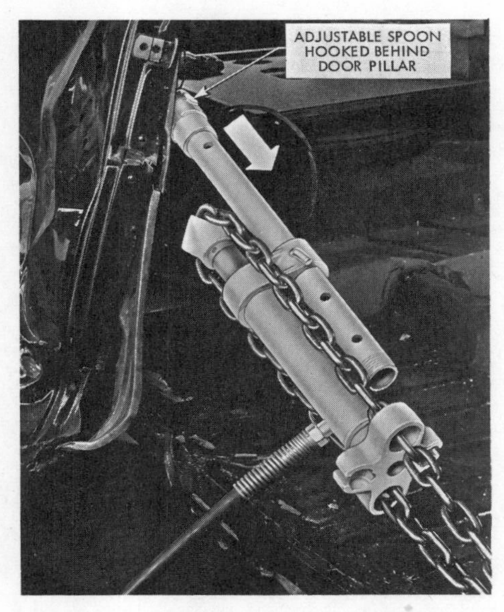

Fig. 5-23. Chain attachments used in pulling rear panel section. (Blackhawk Mfg. Co.)

in use on an actual job in Fig. 5-23. This is a combination setup in which the adjustable body spoon is hooked behind the rear door post while the chain is anchored to the frame. The arrow indicates the direction of the pull.

The setup of chain and chain attachments shown at the bottom in Fig. 5-22 is shown in actual application in Fig. 5-24. This combination of attachments gives a two-way pulling effect. It consists of the two chain plates which attach to the ram and plunger and the two chains which hook around the frame members, as shown. The direction in which the frame will move is indicated by the arrow.

Fig. 5-24. Chain and attachments being used to pull diamond shaped frame into alignment. (Blackhawk Mfg. Co.)

Application of Power Tools

The previous sections of this chapter have served merely to introduce to you the power tools. No attempt has been made to explain how they are used.

This section deals with the techniques of using power tools. Because of the tremendous power developed by the jacks, it is necessary for you to harness it in the proper fashion or more damage will be created to add to the damage which you are attempting to straighten.

The application of power tools to various types of jobs is presented in this section. The methods most commonly used are discussed and illustrated. These methods embody the principles of power application which you should remember when you are devising setups on your own.

Using Body Hammers with Power Tools. Where deep damage is encountered, much time can be saved and a satisfactory job can be accomplished by using either indirect or direct hammering with power equipment. Power equipment is indispensable where you cannot reach the underside of the damage with a hand dolly.

In this application, the power tool plays the same role as your one arm and the dolly block or backing tool in hand hammering. The difference is that instead of the return effect imparted from the dolly to the panel when the dolly bounces up after each blow, the power tool exerts a continuous force. As the panel is straightened, the tool is forced right along behind it by additional applications of power from the jack. By this method, the panel will be quickly returned to its normal contour.

When you intend to do direct hammering, apply the power tool directly underneath the point where you intend the hammer blows to strike.

When you intend to do indirect hammering, apply the power tool on the deepest portion of the ding, and hammer around the outside, following the upward movement of the panel with the power tool until the damage is corrected.

Whether you are using power tools or hand tools, always remember the one basic rule of all collision work: The corrective force should be applied as near as possible in a direction directly opposite to the force which caused the damage.

Pushing Out Body Panels. Instances will sometimes occur where it will be necessary for you to bring a damaged body panel to a near normal contour by use of power tools alone. When this is the case, apply the power for pushing out a body panel in a manner similar to that shown in Fig. 5-25.

In this instance, you do not push at the deepest portion of the dent. Instead, work around the outer edges of the damaged area in an ever-decreasing circle. The dent will be *walked* right up out of the surface and you will have a contour ready for the finishing operations. If power is applied directly at the lowest portion of the ding without relieving the strain as the pressure is applied, the metal may become kinked or stretched.

Spreading Force over an Area. It is sometimes necessary to anchor the jack against a panel which will not bear the force which the jack will exert when pressure is applied. However, if the force is distributed over a large area of the panel, no damage will result. Fig. 5-26 illustrates a setup where a piece of 2 x 4 lumber is used to distribute the

DAMAGING FORCE

DO NOT PUSH AT DEEPEST POINT OF DENT
WORK AROUND OUTER EDGE AS ILLUSTRATED
THIS PREVENTS KINKING AND
STRETCHING OF METAL.

PUSHING OUT BODY PANELS

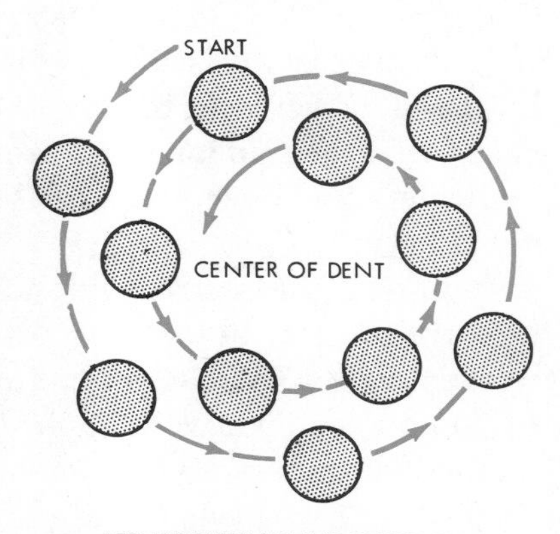

APPLY POWER (AS INDICATED IN
SHADED AREAS), CENTER OF DENT
WILL SNAP BACK AUTOMATICALLY.

Fig. 5-25. Pushing out body panel from center of dent. (Blackhawk Mfg. Co.)

Fig. 5-26. Board used to distribute force of jack base. (Blackhawk Mfg. Co.)

Fig. 5-27. Jack anchored on board against quarter panel.

force of the jack base. In this case, the roof needs straightening. To exert the proper force, it is necessary to base the jack against the floor which would not withstand pressure concentrated in a small area without becoming damaged. By using the board, the force is spread over the floor, and the roof can be straightened easily.

In Fig. 5-27, another instance of using a board to spread force over an area is illustrated. The jack in this setup is based against a piece of 2 x 4 which is laid in the curve of the quarter panel inner construction. Without the 2 x 4 the quarter panel would not be able to withstand the pressure.

Application of Several Lines of Corrective Force. With complex types of damage, it is expedient to use more than one jack to exert pressure against several points of the damage area alternatively. A setup involving the use of three different jacks to push out a rear quarter panel is shown in Fig. 5-28.

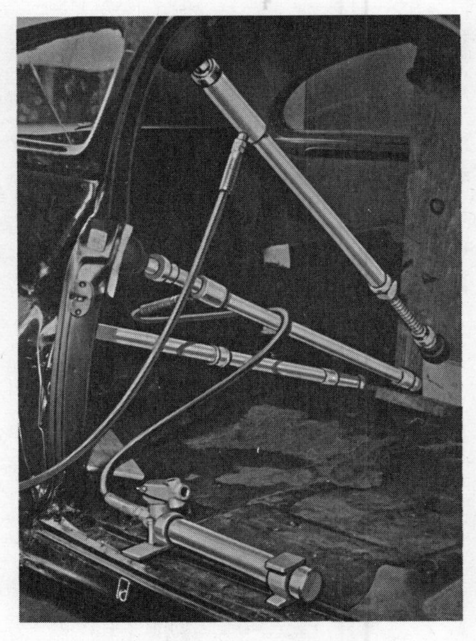

Fig. 5-28. Pushing out rear quarter panel. (Blackhawk Mfg. Co.)

You can see from this illustration that boards are used to distribute the power exerted by the jacks against the undamaged area from which the pushing is to be done.

Two of the jacks are equipped with rubber flex heads and the necessary extensions so that the heads can be properly applied. The other jack is used with a quarter panel pusher spoon. The combination of two jacks with flex heads, positioned near the roof, prevents distortion to other parts of the body while the quarter panel is straightened by pressure on the lower setup.

Pressure is applied to each of the jacks alternately and in small amounts so that the movement of the panel is not great enough to dislodge the other units which are being employed in the setup.

When you encounter complex damage and as you study the damage to determine the line or lines of destructive force, the need for more than one jack will immediately become apparent. On a dual setup, always remember to spread the pressure as much as possible on the base end of the jack to prevent distortion of the panel from which the pushing is being done.

Some of the jobs, accomplished in a small shop with multiple jacks, may in a large shop be done with a larger piece of equipment. In Fig. 5-29 a center pillar is being straightened with a piece of power equipment that is capable of exerting pull by chain while maintaining a support at both top and bottom of the car body through the use of rigid arms. Because the unit has a pull range of from 10,000 to 40,000 pounds, it is protected from backlash in case of mechanical failure of the door pillar.

Fig. 5-29. Straightening center pillar with power pull equipment. (Guy-Chart Tools Ltd.)

Miscellaneous Power Tools

Certain tools used in the automobile repair shop for general repair work are also used on body repair and collision work. Some of these pieces of equipment are hydraulically operated and some are operated by air (pneumatically).

Most of the tools explained and illustrated in this chapter have been of the type that derive their power from the application of hydraulic pressure. However, there are tools on the market which use air pressure instead of hydraulic pressure. The most commonly used tools are hydraulic.

Air equipment is equally fast and easy to operate as the hydraulic equipment and the principles of application are the same.

Pneudraulic Pump. The pneudraulic (air and hydraulic) pump, embodies both the principles of pneumatics and hydraulics. This type of jack is operated by an air-over-hydraulic system which is similar to that used in many large trucks and busses for their braking systems. Shop air is applied to the oil reservoir in the ram. Release of this jack is either automatic or manual. This means that any amount of pressure you apply to the work will be held until you turn the release valve to *release*.

Fig. 5-30. Using pneudraulic pump to straighten windshield pillar. (Chicago Pneumatic Tool Co.)

Fig. 5-30 shows a pneudraulic pump being used to straighten the rear section of a car which has been damaged. The pump is being used with a portable body and frame straightener with which you will become familiar during your study of frame and unitized body straightening and repair in Chapters 7 and 8.

This tool can also be used to operate stationary presses similar to the one shown in Fig. 5-31. When the pump is used in this fashion, the addition of an extra reservoir is necessary to boost the amount of pressure which is built up by the pump.

Pneumatic Fender Iron. Calling this tool, Fig. 5-32, a *fender iron* is somewhat of a misnomer because it can be used for repairs other than on fenders. The fender iron consists of a yoke with an air hammer attachment. The end of the yoke opposite the hammer face is so designed that several different dollies or dies, Fig. 5-33, can be attached, depending on the contour of the surface being worked. The upper die hammers on the outside of the surface while the lower dolly backs up the surface being hammered.

In addition to having several dollies which can be interchanged on the yoke, several different yokes are also available, Fig. 5-34.

These yokes are different so that the tool set will be useful in a

Fig. 5-31. Pneudraulic pump operating forty-ton hydraulic press. (Chicago Pneumatic Tool Co.)

greater variety of places. Some yokes are short and some are deep for reaching up under a fender or out into the middle of an all-metal top. Any of the dollies in the set will fit any of the yokes, which means that this tool can be used for almost any contour where you

Fig. 5-32. Pneumatic fender iron comprised of yoke, air hammer, and dolly heads. (Chicago Pneumatic Tool Co.)

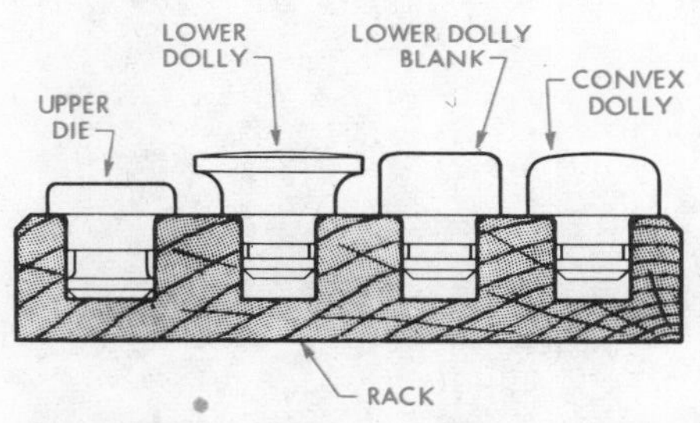

Fig. 5-33. Dollies used with pneumatic fender iron. (Chicago Pneumatic Tool Co.)

can directly reach the damage.

A regulator valve on the pneumatic fender iron controls the air pressure at the discretion of the operator. If care is not used in the operation of the fender iron, it is possible to stretch the metal when you are hammering.

A high-speed cylinder head and a high-speed piston are available for use with the fender iron. They will double the number of blows per minute which the fender iron will strike on the surface. The high-speed cylinder head should never be used without using the high-speed piston, however, or else the tool may be damaged.

It is always necessary to metal finish the job after the damaged surface has been hammered back to a near normal surface.

Shop or Arbor Press. In the course of repairing damage to an automobile, it is sometimes necessary to straighten the bumpers or other easily removable parts. Because of the thickness of the bumper metal, it is not possible to straighten a bumper unless it is rigidly held and has a great deal of pressure applied to it.

An arbor press is usually used for this purpose. Fig. 5-35 shows a hydraulically operated arbor press which is mounted on a rigid base, but is portable. In this press, the bumper is merely laid on the supporting members. This leaves the center of the bumper unsupported. Pressure can be applied to the unsupported section of bumper through the hydraulic pump and ram, and the damage can be straightened.

Arbor presses vary in size from the small one pictured in Fig. 5-

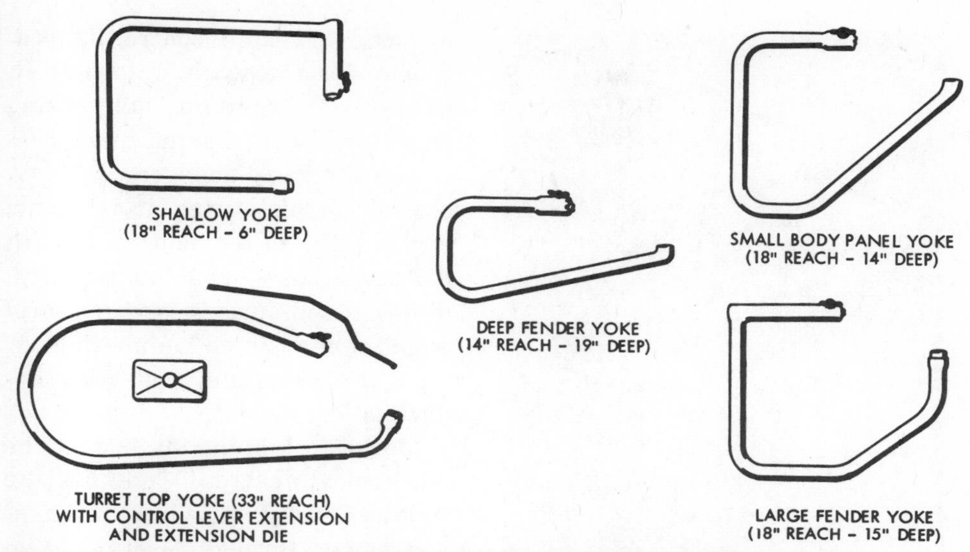

Fig. 5-34. Yokes used with pneumatic fender iron. (Chicago Pneumatic Tool Co.)

35 to sizes which are able to develop many tons of pressure. An arbor press is usually standard equipment in any shop which is doing automobile repairing, whether the shop has a body repair shop or not.

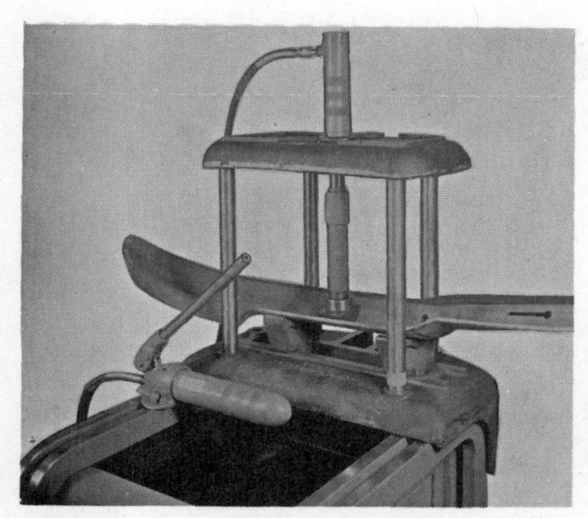

Fig. 5-35. Arbor press with bumper in press.

Some inexpensive arbor presses rely on the leverage and gear principle to derive their power. A long handle is geared to a spindle coming down to an anvil. By rotating the handle, the spindle is raised or lowered to contact the work. After the spindle contacts the work, the operator can apply the necessary pressure at the handle to move the spindle and make whatever displacement is desired.

Leverage Dolly. The leverage dolly is not a power-operated tool, but it is considered a power tool because it provides power through leverage. It is used mainly on metal tops to aid direct or spring hammering. A rubber base keeps it from slipping or damaging the floor. The long arm enables the

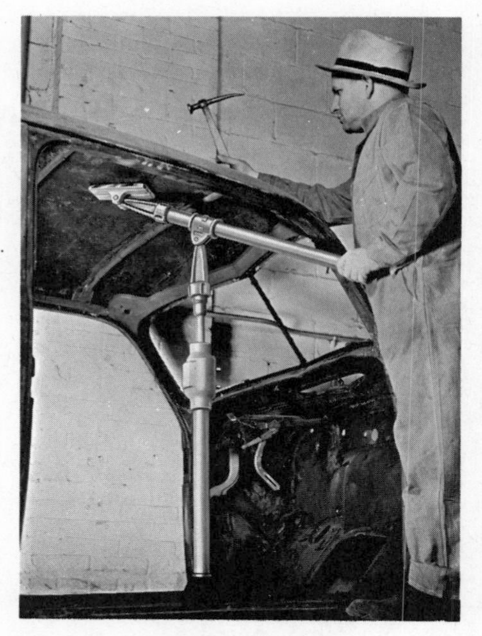

Fig. 5-36. Leverage dolly in use.

operator to readily control its location under the work. Fig. 5-36 illustrates the leverage dolly being used for spring hammering.

The leverage dolly can be purchased complete with attachments for length adjustment and with different bases and dollies with different contours. It is very useful when doing finish-hammering of tops after roughing out with hydraulic equipment.

Mechanical Push-Pull Jack. The mechanical push-pull jack, like the leverage dolly, provides mechanical power through leverage, Fig. 5-37. The jack may be adjusted for pulling or pushing by sliding the body off the shaft and replacing it in reversed position. The jack is

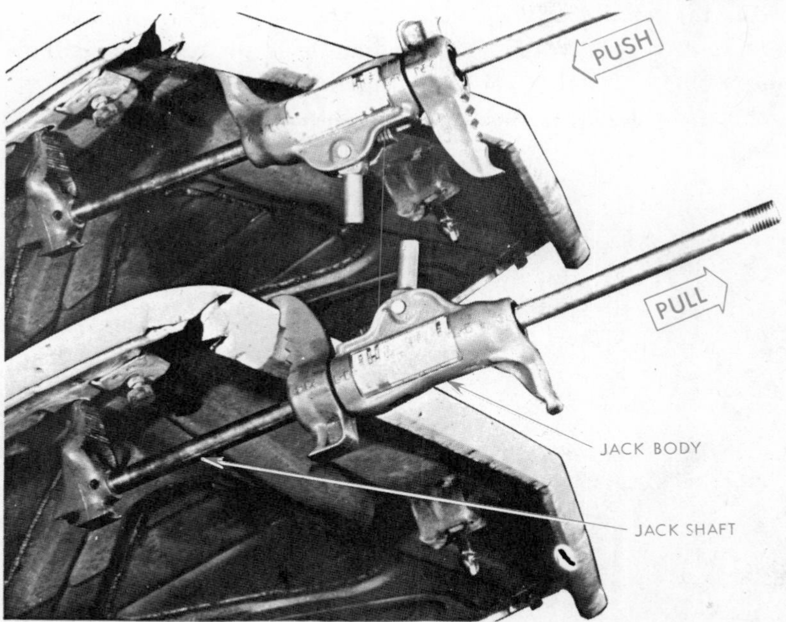

Fig. 5-37. Straightening a hood with a mechanical push-pull jack. (Guy-Chart Tools, Ltd.)

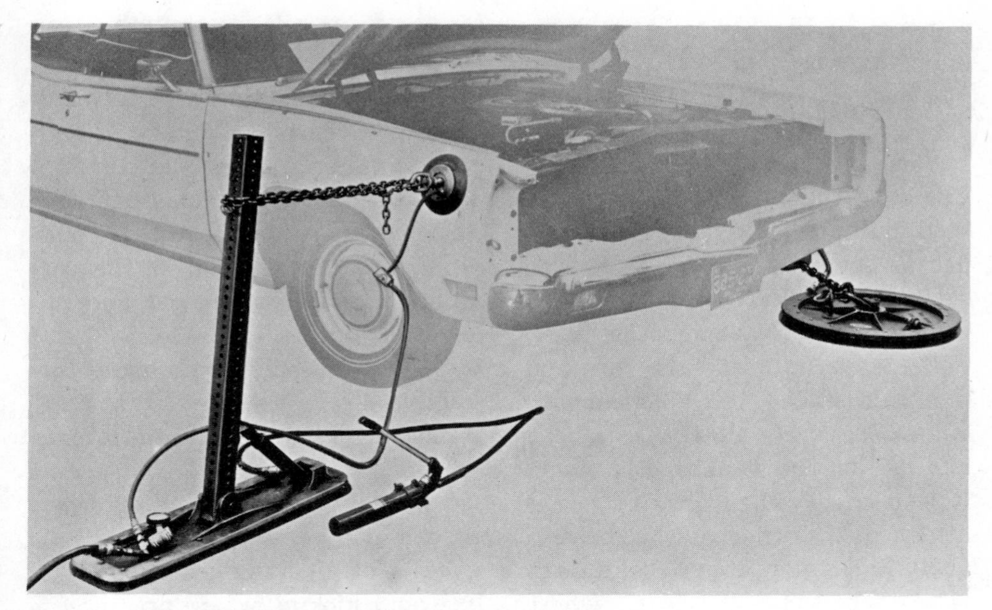

Fig. 5-38. Vacuum powered pulling set. (Ford Motor Co.)

Fig. 5-39. Portable vacuum anchor with chain attached. (Ford Cotor Co.)

compact, light in weight, and requires no hoses or hydraulic fluid. Various accessories can be purchased.

Vacuum Powered Pulling Set. The components of a vacuum powered pulling set are shown, connected for use, in Fig. 5-38. The set consists of a power stand, the round portable anchor, the panel puller and chain and the ram and pump kit. The portable anchor, Fig. 5-39, can be moved to the car and laid on the floor exactly where it is needed. When an air hose is attached, the anchor becomes a 6000 lb suction cup. The anchor is attached to the car, where needed, by chain or cable.

A power stand and panel puller are shown in Fig. 5-40. The power stand has a suction cup area in the base. The panel puller is a suction cup in itself. It can readily be seen that minor dents can be quickly pulled out with this arrangement. For more serious damage, a constant pulling pressure can be maintained while your hands are free to work with jacks or other tools.

With a combination of the vacuum powered pulling set and anchor shown in Figs. 5-38, 5-39 and 5-40, it is possible to do many corrective exercises around a damaged car. The anchor can be used to hold frames when the frame horns are bent either up or down. It can also be used to hold various pieces of jacking equipment to prevent kickup when pressure is applied.

Fig. 5-40. Power stand and power puller, vacuum operated. (Ford Motor Co.)

Fig. 5-41. Panel puller. (Ford Motor Co.)

Fig. 5-41 shows a close up view of the panel puller. The puller has a 250 lb capacity on regular shop air supply of 50-60 PSI. Each of the units described here has its own vacuum venturi which develops vacuum from the regular shop air supply. Venturis have no moving parts and therefore require no maintenance.

Checking On Your Knowledge

The following questions give you the opportunity to check up on yourself. If you have read the chapter carefully, you should be able to answer the questions. If you have any difficulty, read the chapter over once more so that you have the information well in mind before you go on with your reading.

1. What is probably the most commonly used hydraulic jack?
2. How is a one-way acting jack adapted to a pulling operation?
3. How many different types of hydraulic jacks are in general use in collision shops?
4. What attachments can protect threads on a ram cap body?
5. In an emergency, what kind of oil can be used to fill the hydraulic unit in a jack?
6. What is provided with most jacks to add distance?
7. With a quick coupling tubing set, how do the tubes fasten together?
8. What arrangement that connects directly to the ram is provided for quickly adapting power tools to a dolly?
9. For what two reasons is a rubber jack base of great value?
10. V-block type jack bases are used almost exclusively on what type of collision work?
11. What is the major value of an offset pushing tool?
12. When is a power dolly used?
13. In what respect is a rocker action spoon different from all other body spoons?
14. In how many different directions can a rocker action spoon be adjusted?
15. What tool is available for removing hinge pins?
16. What feature of a toggle action spreader causes the jaws to close immediately if the pressure is released?
17. What effect is incorporated in each jaw of a hydro-method spreader that allows the spreader to follow contours?
18. Chain attachments are used primarily with what type of jack?
19. When power tools are used with either direct or indirect hammering, they replace what hand tool in a hand hammering operation?
20. What can be used to spread jack force over a large area?
21. When it is necessary to remove damage by using power tools only, how is pressure applied to the damaged area through the jack and attachment used?
22. Can more than one jack be used at one time to remove damage?
23. What power arrangement is necessary for straightening bumpers which have been bent?
24. Is a leverage dolly a power-operated tool?
25. What are some of the advantages of the mechanical push-pull jack.

Chapter

6

Doors, Hoods, and Deck Lids

The straightening of doors, hoods, and deck lids and their fitting into or alignment with the openings provided for them is not only an important part of collision work, but is a service that almost every auto mechanic is, on occasion, called upon to perform. At least a portion of the material presented here can be used by other than accomplished collision men.

Door fitting actually is considered a trade within itself in the automobile factories. In some instances, the trade includes not only car body and truck cab doors, but deck lids and hoods as well. The material presented in this chapter will equip you to master this trade, and will also provide you with the necessary knowledge to make repairs.

Aside from the serious damage to doors, hoods, and deck lids that will be encountered as a result of collisions, these parts can become distorted or sagged as a result of misuse and, in some instances, as a result of normal use. The readjustment of hinges, striker plates, and locking mechanisms to provide a uniform clearance around the door is considered as a part of alignment.

Doors, hoods, or deck lids that have become damaged in a collision fall into the classification of collision work. However, these parts must be aligned to match the body after they are straightened or repaired. In addition to the straightening and aligning presented in these sections, information on replacement is also given. Replacement panels for many popular cars are generally available.

Door Panel Replacement

Outer door panels are usually damaged in any collision which involves the side of an automobile. As a general rule, the door can be satisfactorily restored with a minimum of straightening, bumping, and metal finishing. When the damage is severe, involving rips or tears in the metal, when part of the panel metal is missing, or where bends or kinks exist beyond the point where the panel can be straightened economically, either the panel or the complete door should be replaced.

Rusted Panels. As cars grow older, the bottom of the panel often rusts through. In these cases, it is generally economically practical to replace the panel only. All doors are provided with drain holes at the bottom so that water which runs down the outside of the glass between the door panels can run out. Most of the rusting through that you will encounter will be the result of failure to keep these drain holes open.

Where a door panel has rusted through, you can reasonably expect some damage to the inner construction as well. In some cases, you will have to weld in reinforcements to strengthen rusted inner construction. Look particularly at the inside of the lower corners.

Complete vs. Part Panel Replacement. When a door is made, the door panel covers the entire door. That is, in addition to the lower portion of the door, the same piece of metal extends on around the window opening. Replacement panels, however, end just below the window opening. Such a panel is considered a *complete door panel.*

In repairing doors, whether you install the complete panel or whether you install only a portion of it is determined by a number of separate considerations. Of course, if the entire door panel is damaged to the extent where it cannot be repaired, the entire door panel must be replaced. When a complete panel is replaced, openings must be provided for door locks, hinges, decorative strips, etc.

If the door panel below the lock is replaced, then these extra steps are avoided. In some instances where the bottom of a door is rusted through, and only the lower portion of the panel is to be replaced, you may even find it possible to make the repair without removing body hardware, such as window regulators and door glass.

Replacing a portion of a panel in such a way that the joint is at some point not concealed by a decorative strip or an abrupt change of contour requires careful matching of the two contours. Moreover, a joint of this kind should not be welded by any process which might cause undue expansion of the metal, since it is virtually impossible to shrink the metal if a flange type welded joint has been made in the center of the contour.

The decision as to which kind of panel is going to be installed (whether it will be a complete panel, a panel cut under a molding, or whether the panel joint is to appear at some point below this) must be made before you actually start to work on the door.

Body Patch Panels. Just as many car and truck manufacturers and a number of independent manufacturers provide or make available replacement door panels, so also are a number of body panels available both in the form of complete panels or of patch panels.

When a particular automobile model for some reason starts to rust through at a given panel, the replacement parts manufacturers in some cases have a replacement patch panel on the market before the car manufacturer does. Needless to say, in the case of body repairs, these patch panels permit a satisfactory repair of panels at a fraction of the cost of the entire panel. The following instructions on the replacement of door panels apply equally to the installation of such patch panels on other parts of the body. Body patch panels, consequently, are not covered elsewhere in this volume.

Panel Replacement Considerations

With the wide variation in design among the many makes and models of cars and trucks, it is obviously impossible to give detailed instructions and illustrations here on each. However, the panel is replaced in the same manner regardless of the make or model of the vehicle. A discussion of the considerations involved and detailed instructions on how to effect panel replacement are given here in the following paragraphs.

Several things should be considered and evaluated before panel replacement is made. It is necessary to decide how much of the panel needs replacement, then to determine just how much of the panel it is economical to replace. Several factors must enter into and govern any decision concerning panel replacement. All of these factors are reviewed so that when you encounter badly damaged panels, you will be able quickly to reach a decision as to what is needed.

For example, a door may be so badly distorted or otherwise damaged that it will be necessary to replace the entire door. This is determined by the time and material required for the repair as compared to the cost of the new door. Don't fail to take into account the considerable amount of work of transferring the hardware, glass, and trim to the new door.

Door Locks. Whether or not it will be necessary to remove the door lock depends on how much of the panel is replaced. If the entire panel is replaced, cut off the old panel either at the belt line or the belt molding. In either case, the removal and relocation of the door lock is required.

Some replacement panels come with all of the necessary holes already in them. Generally, however, this is not the case, and when the entire panel is replaced, a hole must be cut in the new panel to accommodate the lock. While this is a fairly easy operation, it does consume some time. Whenever possible, therefore, you may want to cut off the old panel below the door handle.

If it is necessary for you to relocate a door lock hole in the new panel, use a hole saw of the correct size. It is generally easier to locate and cut the hole after the replacement panel has been fastened in place.

Door Glass. If only the lower portion of a panel is replaced, it may not be necessary to remove the door glass for the operation. An exception to this would be if the door is sprung so that the entire door needs straightening. The window might crack during the straightening operation. If the inner panel is distorted enough that hammering is necessary, it is best to remove the glass.

When the glass is left in the door, it should be kept in the fully raised position during the time the replacement is taking place. This will keep the regulator mechanism up out of the way and the glass held firmly by the frame.

Interior Trim. The interior trim of the door consists of the trim pad, window garnish molding, door lock handles, and the door and window regulator handles. Any time all or any portion of the door panel is replaced, the interior trim pad must be removed.

Openings are provided in the inner panel through which you can work. These openings, of course, are normally covered by the trim pad. Completely remove the trim pad. If you merely loosen it at the bottom, the trim may be torn or otherwise damaged while you are working on the door. The trim should be removed carefully so that it can be used again after the panel replacement is completed.

Moldings. If the belt moldings are to be removed, the operation should be done after the interior trim pad is removed. Once this pad is removed, you can see which type of fastening is used to hold the molding in place. Working from the inside, you can remove the molding without damaging either the molding or the fasteners.

Door Removal. Whenever a panel or a portion of a panel is replaced, the door should be removed. You will find that the ease of working on the door after it is removed more than offsets the little extra time involved in removing and reinstalling the door.

Types of Joints

How much of the panel is replaced governs the type of joint used to fasten the remaining portion of the old panel and the new panel together.

Recessed Lap Joint. A recessed lap joint is used only when the entire panel is replaced and the old panel is cut off either at the belt line or above the molding, Fig. 6-1. A considerable amount of both time and skill are involved in preparing a recessed lap joint. However, a fine finish job can be done with this type of welded joint if the one panel is recessed to a depth which is exactly equal to the

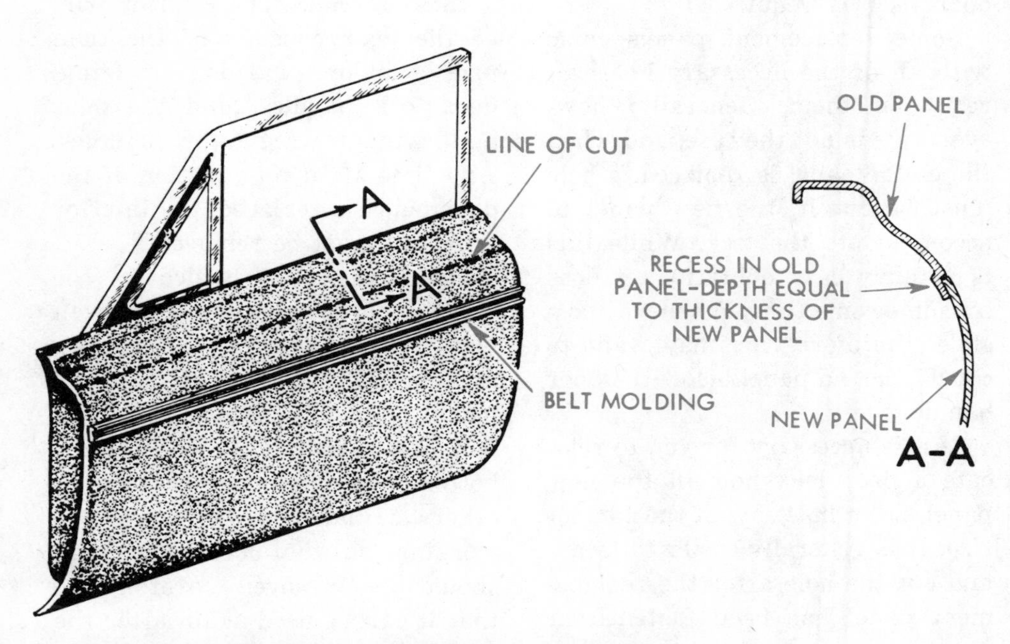

Fig. 6-1. Recessed lap joint on door and cut-away section.

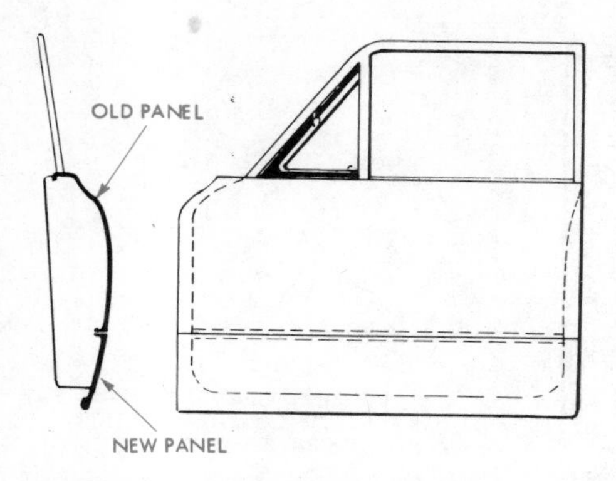

Fig. 6-2. Flange joint on door.

thickness of the other panel.

Flange Joint. A flange joint is usually used when only the lower portion of a door panel is replaced. An example of this is shown in Fig. 6-2. This type of joint cannot be used where there is any chance that it will interfere with the inner workings of the window mechanism or the door lock mechanism. A very nice finish job can be attained with this type of joint, provided the flanges are accurately formed and care is used in matching the contour of the two panels exactly.

Butt Weld Joint. A butt joint can be used wherever it is possible to conceal the joint. This usually means that it can be used at any point where the joint comes under a molding. An example of this is shown in Fig. 6-3. A butt weld is quickly made. However, it generally is not considered as strong as a lap or flange joint. For this reason, it is not generally used where the strength of the weld is a factor in the repair.

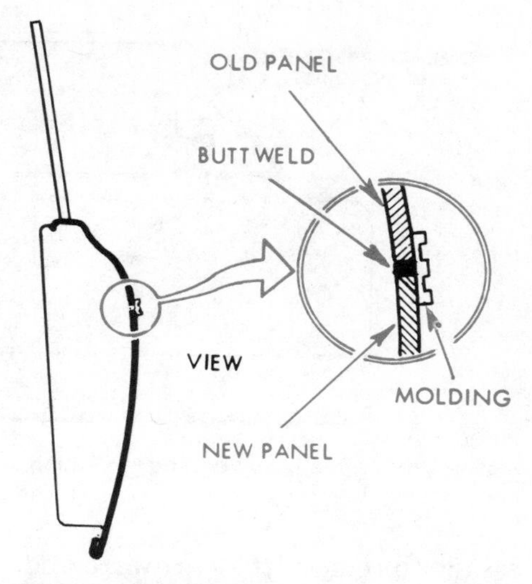

Fig. 6-3. Butt weld joint on door.

Removing Old Panel

The way in which the old panel is removed depends on how much of it is removed. The old panel is cut off at one of three locations: at the belt line, at the belt molding, or somewhere below the molding. These three different possible locations for a cut are shown in Fig. 6-4, which shows a door ready for the cutting operation. Once the cut is made, some additional work is necessary to remove the old panel.

Cut Made at Belt Line. When the entire panel is to be replaced, the old panel is cut off at the belt line. As previously mentioned, it nec-

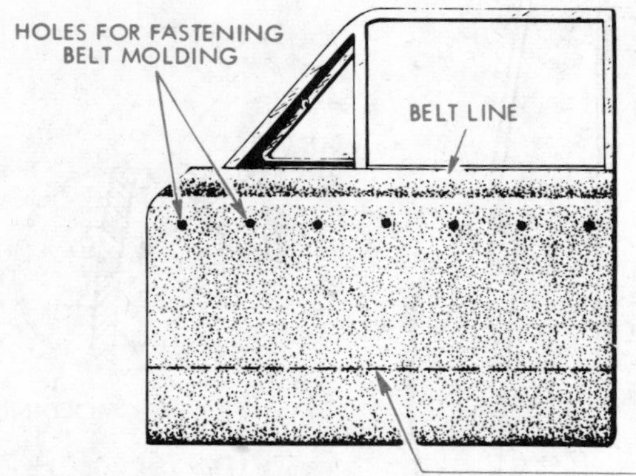

Fig. 6-4. Door ready for cutting operation.

essary to remove the hardware and trim from the door before a complete panel is removed. A door ready to have the complete panel removed is shown in Fig. 6-4.

The belt line acts as a natural line to follow. The actual cut is made with either a power saw or a special cutter. The method of cutting is determined by the type of joint you intend to make. Generally, the power saw or cutter is preferable for all kinds of joints. Cuts with welding equipment leave rough edges which require a lot of work, and are not practical except for flanged joints. Even with flanged joints, considerable extra work is involved in preparing the flanges if the edges of the metal are too rough.

Fig. 6-5 shows the door panel being cut with a special cutter. The panel is cut all the way across in this manner. If a lap joint is desired, the extra panel material for the lap may be left either on the old panel or allowance made for it on the new one. The other panel is cut straight across.

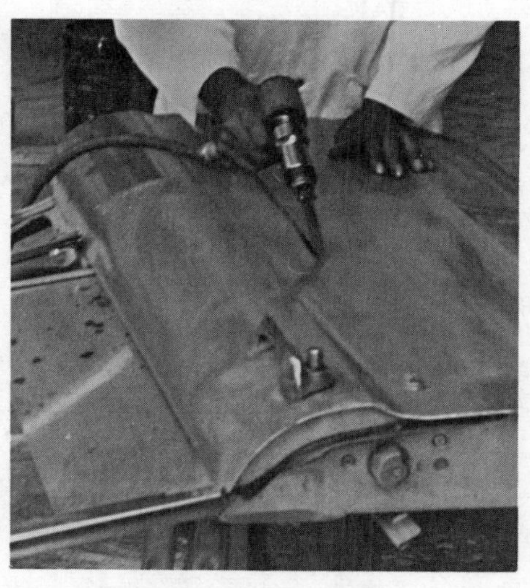

Fig. 6-5. Cutting door with special cutter. (Paul Lawrence Dunbar Vocational High School, Chicago, Illinois)

Where a recessed lap joint is made at the belt line, the extra

Fig. 6-6. Recessed lap joint with inset. (Anzich Mfg. Co.)

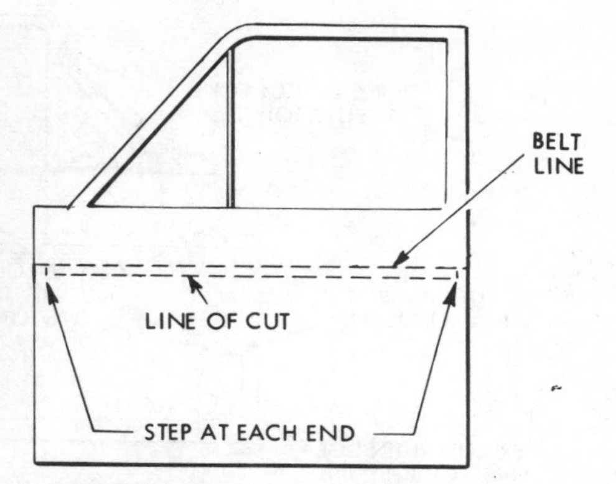

Fig. 6-7. Line of cut for lap joint at belt line.

material generally is left on the old panel. This extra metal is then recessed or sunk the exact thickness of the new panel. The new panel lies on top of this recessed portion with the visible joint straight across the door at the belt line.

An instance of where the recess is formed in the new panel rather than the old is shown in Fig. 6-6.

If you are forming the recess in the old panel, make the cut ¾″ below the belt line. Start the cut at the inside edge of the inner construction on one side of the door. Cut straight across to the inside edge of the inner construction on the other side. Then make a vertical cut to the belt line, ¾″ up. Then, using a hacksaw, make a cut on the belt line through the outer panel where it is folded over the inner construction. Fig. 6-7 is a sketch showing the exact line of the cut. The new panel and the old will butt at the step portion of the joint and will lap in the center.

Cut Made at Belt Molding. One advantage of cutting the panel at the belt molding is that the joint is later concealed by the molding. This permits the use of the easily made and easily finished butt joint. A flange or lap joint may interfere with installation of the molding.

The hardware and trim must be removed. The belt molding is removed and the cut is made directly under the molding. The cut should exactly intersect all of the holes used for fastening the mold-

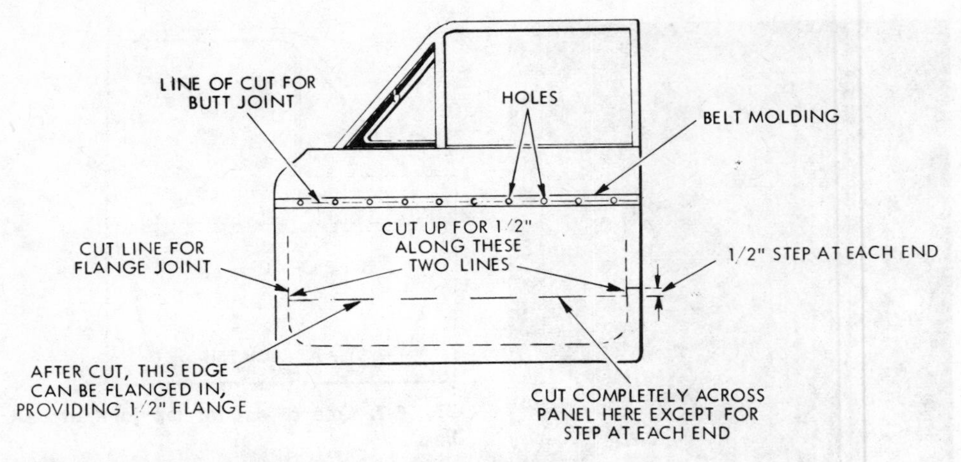

Fig. 6-8. Cut lines for butt and flange joints, showing dimensions.

ing in place. Scribe a line to intersect the molding holes and make the cut along this line. Finish the cut over the inner construction with a hacksaw, Fig. 6-8.

Cut Off Lower Portion Only. Where only the lower portion of the panel is to be replaced, much of the hardware and decorative trim can be left on the door. In some cases, you may not have to remove either the glass or the window regulator. The glass should be run all the way up during the entire procedure.

The most satisfactory joint is the flange joint. To form the flange, a step must be cut at both ends of both the old and the new panels.

Scribe a line straight across the panel at the point where the final joint is to be made. If you want a ½″ flange, scribe a second line ½″ below the first. If you want a ¾″ flange, use a ¾″ measurement.

The long cut is made along this second line between the inner surfaces of the door inner construction, straight across the panel. Two vertical cuts ½″ (or ¾″) long are then made toward the top of the door, up to the upper line. The length of this vertical cut establishes the width of the flange you will be forming. The two horizontal cuts, one on each end, are made with a hacksaw. Saw through the outer skin only and continue the cut around the edge of the door flange.

Removal of Flange. After the cut is made across the panel, it is necessary to loosen the old panel around the edge to remove it. The outer panel is folded around the inner panel at its outer edge. Grind through the folded edge as shown

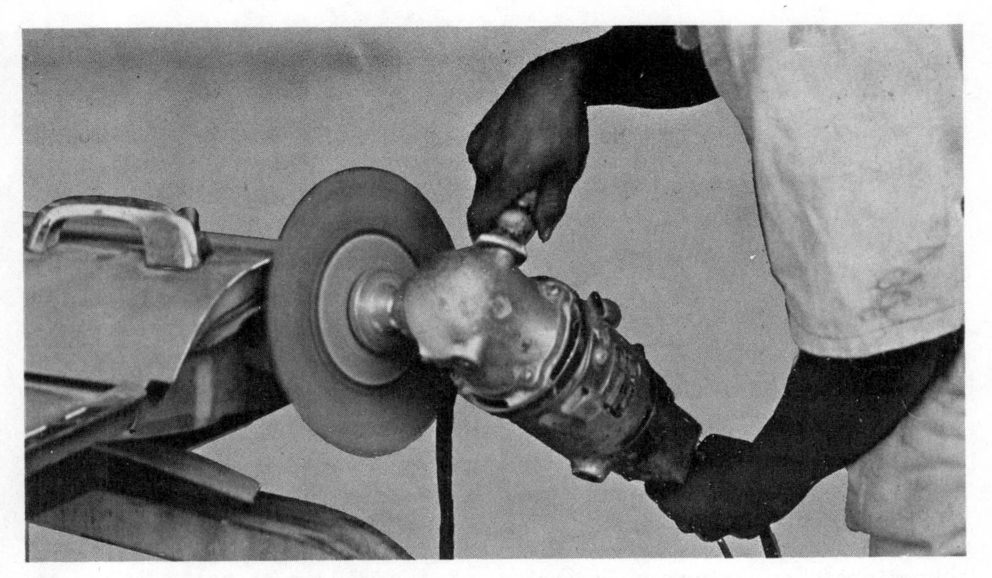

Fig. 6-9. Grinder in position for cutting off edge of door panel. (Paul Lawrence Dunbar Vocational High School, Chicago, Illinois)

in Fig. 6-9, and the old panel can be lifted off. Be careful during this operation not to grind too deeply or you will grind away a portion of the inner panel A grinder in position for cutting the edge of the outer panel is shown in Fig. 6-9.

The final operation in removing the old panel is to remove the flanging strip of outer panel, which is left on the inside of the edge of the inner panel after the grinding operation. When the door is manufactured, the door outer panel is folded around the edge of the inner panel and is spot welded. It is these spot welds which hold the flanging strip in place. With a hammer and chisel, break the spot welds and remove the flange.

Inspection and Repair of Door. During the process of removing the old panel, some damage may be inflicted on the outer edge flange of the inner panel. If this flange is bent or otherwise distorted, it must be straightened. Straighten any damage to the inner panel. Weld any cracks, breaks or tears. Give the entire door a close visual inspection and correct any damage found.

If you have to straighten the door, it is a good plan to check the door in place in the door opening to see that it matches both the contour of the body and fits the door opening before putting the new panel in place. If it does not fit, it can be straightened by one of the methods presented earlier in this chapter.

Preparing the New Panel

Several things have to be done to the new panel before it can be installed. The preparation necessary depends on the type of joint used to secure the old and new panels together. The steps necessary in preparing a new panel for the three commonly used types of joints are covered here.

Butt Joint. When a butt welded joint is used, little preparation is required. Be sure the edges to be joined are straight and meet each other perfectly. Be sure enough material is allowed around the outside of the door for forming a flange around the entire edge of the door. The panel can then be fastened in place.

Recessed Lap Joint. As previously mentioned, either the old or the new panel can be recessed to make a recessed lap joint. In general, it is easier to sink the recess in the old panel since it is held rigidly in the door and will not tend to flop around while you are sinking the recess.

If the recess is formed in the old panel, the new panel is merely cut straight across.

In some instances where an abrupt change of contour occurs, it is possible to eliminate the recessing operation and just lay the new panel on top of the old, as shown in Fig. 6-10.

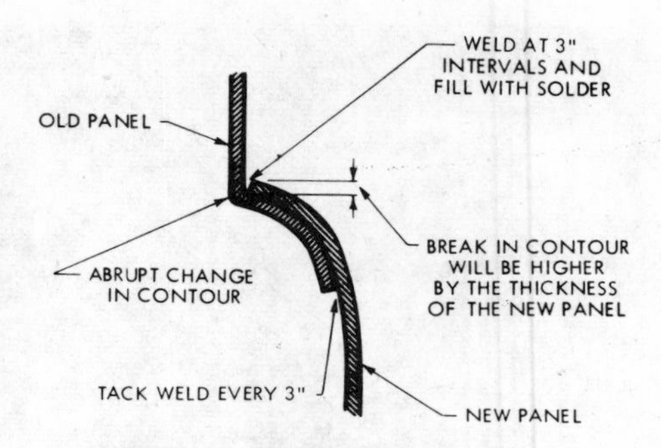

Fig. 6-10. Lap joint not recessed.

Forming the Recess. The ideal way to form a recess would be to have a dolly with a 1/16″ step running its full length. Scribe a line on the underside of the panel at the point where the step is to occur. This will be 1/2″ farther from the edge of the panel than the point where the outer surface of the two panels will meet. Using two C-clamps, clamp the dolly at one end of the panel with the step on the scribed line. Use a square-headed hammer as shown earlier in Fig. 6-3.

Form the edge of the panel down into the step in the dolly. Use the other side of the same hammer to hammer the corner into the corner of the recess in the dolly. Fig.6-11 illustrates several of the points involved in the formation of the recess.

Complete the recess for the full length of the dolly, then move the

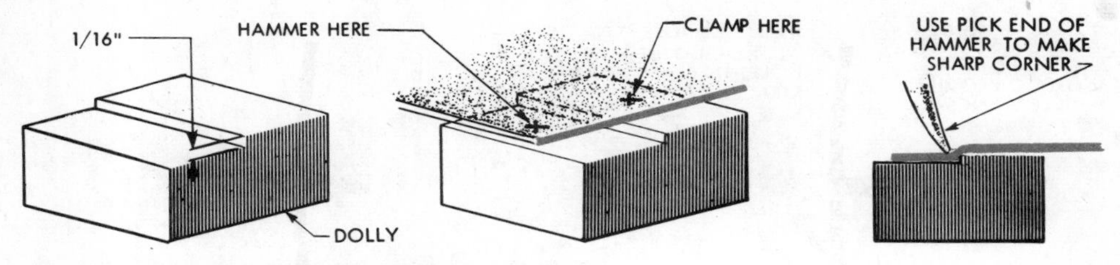

Fig. 6-11. Forming recess for making a lap joint.

dolly about 1½″ and form the recess this additional distance. Complete the recess each time before moving the dolly, and continue across the panel. Each time the dolly is moved, make sure the step of the dolly is on the scribed line.

A less accurate, but generally satisfactory, recessed lap can be made without the recessed dolly just described. However, a dolly having a square edge is required.

Bend the panel to a 45° angle as shown in Fig. 6-12. Then make a second bend as shown in the same figure. It may make the job easier if you make hacksaw cuts in the edge of the panel at about 3″ intervals. These cuts should be about ⅔ the width of the lap.

Lay the new panel on the door to make certain it is the right size and that enough material is available all around the edge for turning at least a half-inch flange around the inner panel.

Flange Joint. Once a flange is formed on a curved panel, it will hold the curvature of the panel. However, in the forming of the flange, there is always a possibility of changing the panel curvature slightly. This, of course, could cause some difficulty in making the two contours match for the entire length of the joint. Generally, the flange is formed with a square-

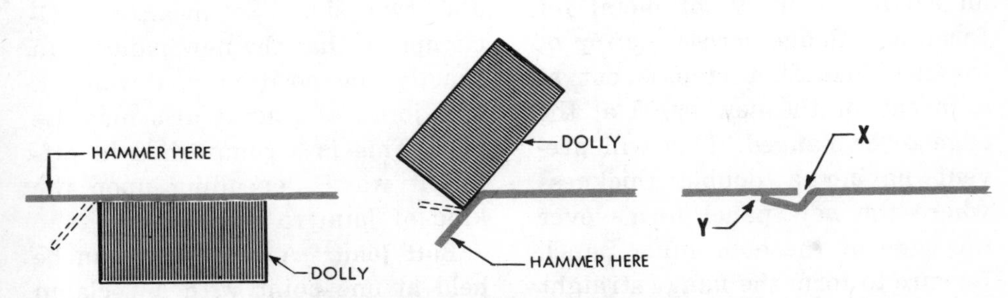

Fig. 6-12. Alternate method of recessing metal for a lap joint.

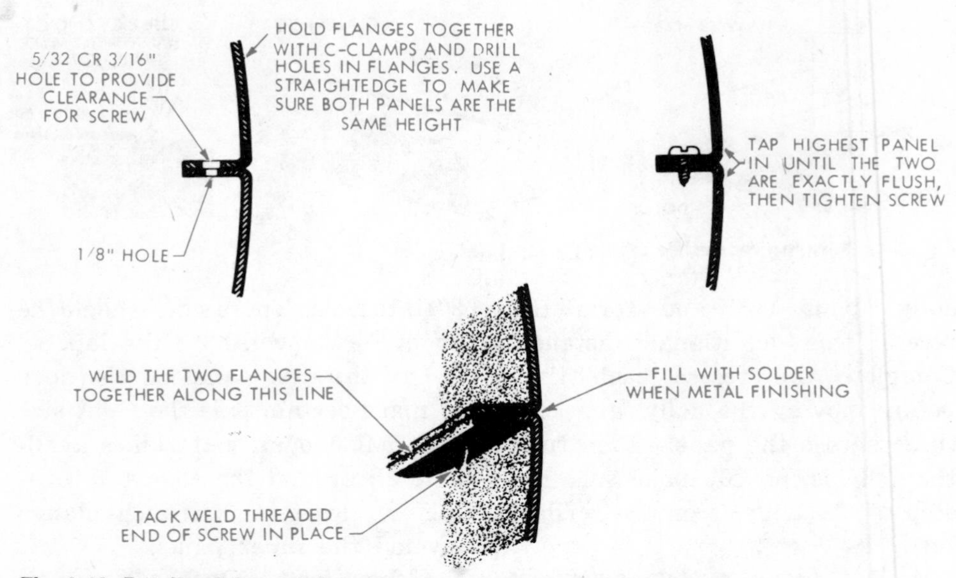

Fig. 6-13. Details of flange joint where motion may stress the joint.

edged dolly and a hammer. However, if you are doing a lot of work on one particular model, you might find it advisable to make a form for making flanges. Fig. 6-13 shows several views of a flanged joint.

The flange is formed on both the old and the new panels. This means that it is necessary to allow an extra ½″ or ¾″ of metal for forming a flange across the top of the new panel. A step is cut at each end of the new panel at the edge to be flanged. This will prevent having a double thickness where the new panel forms over the edge of the door inner panel. Be sure to form the flange straight so that it will fit perfectly against the flanged edge of the old panel and not protrude above it.

Securing the New Panel in Place

It is necessary to hold the panel securely so that it cannot move out of position during the welding operation. Regardless of the type of joint to be made, fasten the new panel to the door at the bottom and two sides by means of C-clamps so that the new panel is in exactly the position you want it. The joint, of course, also must be held. This is accomplished in different ways, depending upon the kind of joint to be made.

Butt Joint. A butt joint can be held at one point with a C-clamp until a tack weld can be made to hold the joint. Arrange the C-clamp so that it grips both the old and new panels equally, then tack weld the two panels together at both sides of the C-clamp. Make the welds as close to the clamp as possible. Move the clamp several inches and repeat the operation.

If good tacks are made every few inches, it may not be necessary to do further welding. The remainder of the joint can be filled with solder. Generally, however, a better job is obtained if a continuous weld is made. If possible, weld the joint from the inside as well.

If the weld is made from the inside, it will not be necessary to sink the weld. If you cannot weld from the inside, weld from the outside. Sink the weld about 1/8″ and fill the valley thus formed with solder as a part of the metal finishing operation.

When welding a continuous seam in a butt type joint with an arc welder, you may find the welding job will be speeded up and the danger of burning through the panel reduced if you lay a piece of soft wire in the joint. As you weld, the wire and the two edges of the panel are fused together.

Lap Joint. Either a straight lap joint, Fig. 6-10, or an accurately recessed lap joint of the type shown in Fig. 6-11 can be fastened with self-tapping screws spaced about 4″ apart. Drill a 1/8″ diameter hole through both panels at 4″ intervals, then enlarge the holes in one panel to provide clearance for the screw. Tighten the screws in place.

Weld the joint on both sides. Either remove the screws or tack the threads of the screws to the panel. If you remove the screws, weld up the holes. If you tack the screws in place, you will grind off the heads during the metal finishing operation and will fill in around the screw with solder.

If the recessed lap joint is of the type shown in Fig. 6-12, the depth of the recess may not be exactly the thickness of the panel, and a different procedure is required.

With the panel in place in the recess, as shown in Fig. 6-12, lay a straight edge across the joint. If the two panels are not flush, raise or lower the panel by bending the edge of the lower panel with a pair of pliers. Tack weld the two panels together at the edges of the overlap, both inner and outer. Make a weld every two inches.

The recessed lap joint at the belt molding (Fig. 6-6 in which the recess was formed in the new panel rather than the old) was completed without welding. The new panel was lapped under the old one approximately one-half inch. The two are fastened together by six or eight self-tapping, sheet-metal screws.

Simply drill six to eight one-eighth inch holes through the panels, countersink the holes in the outer panel, and install the screws. Provide sufficient holes to accommodate whatever device is used to retain the molding in place. If desired, the exposed edge of the overlapped panel can be soldered, although it is not absolutely necessary. Then install the molding and the whole joint will be concealed.

Another method of joining panels with a lap joint is by using *pop rivets*. Several types of pop rivet tools are available. An inexpensive tool is shown in Fig. 6-14. Notice the rivet lying alongside the tool. Insert the rivet in the tool. Then insert the rivet into the hole and press the rivet flange against the surface and squeeze the handles. The rivet will be pulled back up into itself and its outer edge will bead on the under side of the work. The panels are drawn together and the excess rivet outside is cut off, leaving the rivet smooth on both sides.

Commercial rivet tools are available for heavier duty requirements. Rivets can be obtained in standard sizes and lengths. The rivet tool is especially suitable for joining panels or light inner con-

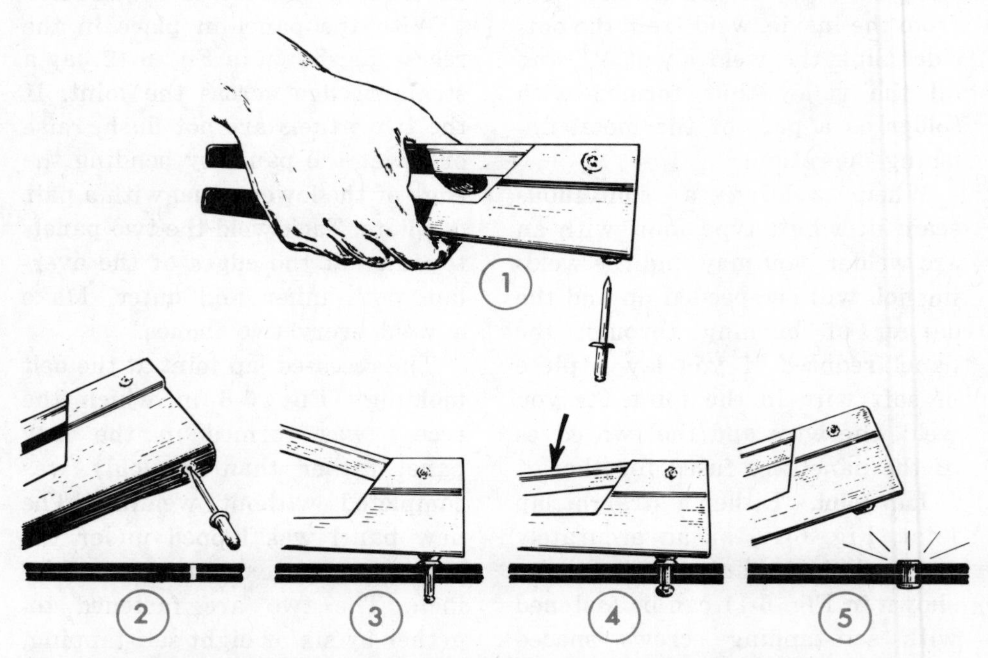

Fig. 6-14. Blind or pop rivet tool in action. (United Shoe Machinery Corp.)

struction where the rivets do not show.

Flange Joint. The flange type joint, where the flanges are accurately made, permits a perfect match of the two contours. Using a C-clamp, hold the two flanges together at the center of the joint. Make sure the two surfaces of the panel are the same height, then drill the flanges at a point near the clamp, as shown in Fig. 6-13. Install a self-tapping screw and run it up snug but not tight. Use a straightedge. If one panel is higher than the other, tap it down until they are flush, then tighten the screw.

Move the C-clamp about four inches and repeat the foregoing procedure at four-inch intervals to one end of the joint. Starting four inches from the first screw, install a screw every four inches from the center out to the opposite end of the joint. Always start at the center of the joint and work out toward the edges. Details of fastening the flanged panel in place are shown in Fig. 6-13.

Trimming. After the new panel has been fastened in place, it is necessary to trim off excess material around the edge of the door. The trimming operation is done in the same manner, regardless of the type of joint that was made on the door or where the joint was made.

Turn the door over on the bench,

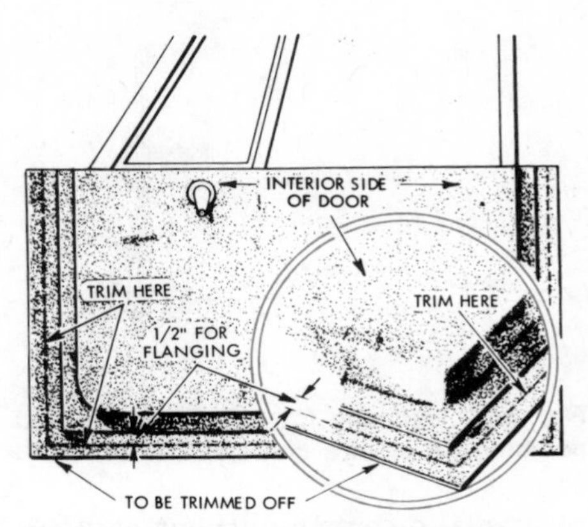

Fig. 6-15. Trimming new panel edges.

or other type of rest on which you have been working, so that the inner panel side is up. Mark around the edge of the new panel, allowing approximately one-half inch for forming a flange around the inner panel. How to trim the new panel is shown in Fig. 6-15.

The actual cutting off of the excess material can be accomplished with a pair of ordinary tin snips. This will leave a smooth edge which can be turned over the edge of the inner panel to form a flange.

Notching. Special consideration must be given to the corners of the new panel before it can be flanged around the inner panel. The corners will either be rounded or square. Each case must be handled in a slightly different manner.

If the corner is rounded, it should be notched as shown at left in Fig. 6-16. This notching will permit the metal to be flanged

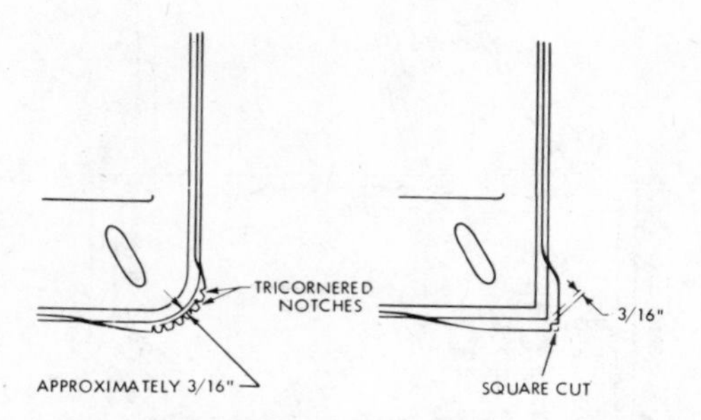

Fig. 6-16. Notching for round corners and notching for square corners.

around the corner without causing wrinkles or cracks which would spoil the entire job. Notice that the notches are only cut to approximately $\frac{3}{16}''$ from the inner panel. If the notches are cut too deeply, the opening formed by the notch will show on the outside edge of the door after the flange is formed. You will have no difficulty in forming this small amount of metal into shape.

If the corner is square, the notching should be done as shown at right in Fig. 6-16. In this instance, an actual cut is taken out of the metal which takes the whole corner out of the new panel. When the flanging is done the two edges will form one solid flange at this point. The dimensions for such a cut are given in Fig. 6-16. These dimensions can be followed, no matter what type or size door you encounter. As when notching for round corners, you should not notch too deeply or else the cutout made by the notch will show when the new panel has been flanged over the inner panel. The deepest portion of the notch should be approximately $\frac{3}{16}''$ away from the inner panel. The notch can be made easily with tin snips or a hacksaw.

Flanging. After the new panel is fastened in place and the necessary notching has been done at the corners, the edges of the panel can be flanged. This completes the job of fastening the new panel into place on the door. Start at the top of the replacement panel on either edge of the door and form the flange with a hammer and dolly. Forming the flange is simply a matter of turning the new panel around the outer edge of the inner panel all around the edge of the door. Fig. 6-17 shows a body man in the process of forming a flange around the edge of a door.

Notice that the panel is first turned down by the body man at a 90° angle to the plane of the panel for a distance. The body man then goes back and finishes turning the edge under to complete the flange. This will prevent splitting the edge of the metal as might result if the flange were turned under in one operation.

After the flange is completed, tack weld the flange to the door inner panel at intervals of about three inches. It is usually a good plan to weld up the relief cuts that

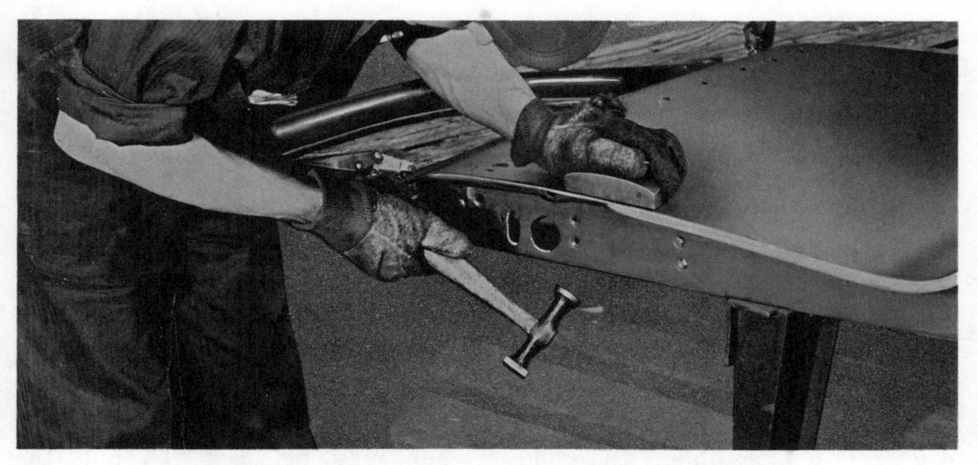

Fig. 6-17. Flanging outer panel around inner panel. (Anzich Mfg. Co.)

were made in the panel at the corners of the door.

Metal Finishing. If any screw holes are left in the outer panel, they should be filled with solder, then filed and sanded smooth. All welds which show from the outside should be ground down, covered with solder, then filed smooth. If, when soldering along a joint made at the belt line, you accidentally fill the holes for the belt molding with solder, redrill them. The door should be all ready for the refinisher when the panel replacement is complete.

Installing Hardware and Trim. The door should be mounted on the car before the hardware and trim are installed. Holes for the door handle and lock are sometimes provided in replacement panels. If not, they must be drilled at this time. Even when holes are already provided, it may be necessary to do a certain amount of filing to get them to line up properly so that all parts fit snugly in place and join with the right fasteners.

Be sure the belt molding and other trim moldings are firmly in place. If they are part of a continuous molding, be sure they mate perfectly with adjoining body moldings.

Install the interior trim last. Be sure the handles for the door lock and window regulator are in the same relative position as the handles on the opposite door of the vehicle. Try all the door mechanisms to make certain they are operating properly before installing the interior door trim panel.

Door Straightening

In some instances, considerable work might be saved for the painter if you wait until the door is painted before you install the door hardware and trim. This is particularly true if you have made a panel joint under the belt molding. The joint should be painted to protect it from rusting. This, of course, is not possible if the molding is in place.

All of the various holes such as are used for door locks, handles, or moldings, should be made before the door is painted.

This section deals with the correction of damage to car doors which can be considered major or serious, and which may involve the removal of the door from the car.

The different aspects of straightening typical door damage are presented in the following paragraphs. Although typical damage to a door is pictured during the various stages of straightening, you will encounter doors where some of the operations discussed here will not be necessary.

Since the instruction given in previous chapters covers the removing of minor dings from panels, little mention of straightening such damage is made here.

Roughing Out. The roughing out operation is used to restore the general contour to the damaged panel. It involves the application of force to the damaged area in either a driving, pushing, or pulling operation. The damaged metal can be driven back into shape with a hammer and dolly, or a hydraulic jack may be used. To pull the metal back into place requires the application of tension to the panel surface. Each method has advantages and limitations. However, all straightening or roughing out operations will require the use of one or a combination of these methods.

Driving Out Panel Damage. This method is used for minor dents or in combination with the pulling or pushing of more severely damaged panels. It involves the use of common body hand tools such as hammers, dolly blocks and spoons. The important thing to remember, in using a driving force, is the possibility of serious upset or reverse to the panel surface. Only minor dents should be driven out if the panel has a low crown or nearly flat surface.

Pushing Out Damaged Areas. This method involves the use of a hydraulic jack to apply a steady force to the damaged area. The damaged sheet metal must transmit this pushing force to the edges of the panel. This procedure requires extra care to prevent buckling at the point of force application, particularly in the case of flat or nearly flat surfaces.

Pulling Out Damaged Areas. The main advantage of this method of panel straightening is that the tendency for upsetting is greatly reduced. The application of tension or a pulling force finds its greatest use in roughing out low crowned, nearly flat panels. The amount of tension used in straightening should be limited by the yield point of the metal. Too much tension will result in metal stretching. (Fig. 5-41 in the previous chapter shows a typical vacuum panel puller being used to straighten a damaged door.)

The important things to keep in mind when using tension are: use rigid attaching points, spread the force over as wide an area as possible, align the pull with the crown of the panel and do not exceed the actual yield point of the metal.

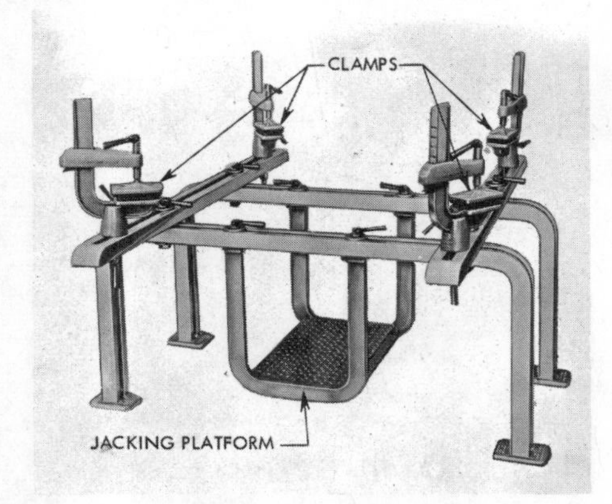

Fig. 6-18. Holding unit for doing door straightening.

One method of straightening a damaged door is by using a holding unit such as shown in Fig. 6-18. This unit consists of a clamping device mounted above a jacking platform. Fig. 6-19 shows a damaged front door clamped in position on a holding unit in preparation for roughing out the damaged area with power tools. A rigid device for holding the door is necessary, otherwise the door might be sprung during the straightening operation.

Fig. 6-19. Door in position on holding unit.

As discussed in Chapter 5, a rocker action spoon can be used with a jack to perform the first operation. The rocker action spoon, because of its ability to reach under inner construction and its general versatility, is ideally suited for this job. Fig. 6-20

Fig. 6-20. Door with damage partially removed.

Fig. 6-22. Cutaway panel showing face of rocker action spoon.

shows the door after both a fourteen and an eighteen inch rocker spoon have been used to rough out the panel. Fig. 6-21 shows one of the different setups which are necessary to produce the result are shown in Fig. 6-20.

By using both a fourteen and an eighteen inch spoon, only two setups were necessary on this job. Otherwise, it would have been necessary to move one single spoon several times. You can note also that the spoons have a low crown contour which nearly matches that of the door panel being straightened.

Whenever you are using a rocker action spoon for door straightening, be sure to position it to match the contour of the surface being worked. Fig. 6-22 shows a portion of a door panel cut away

Fig. 6-21. Fourteen inch rocker action spoon positioned for straightening upper half of door.

Fig. 6-23. Hammer and low crown surfacing spoon being used.

so you can see how the face of the spoon should fit the contour.

At the same time the rocker action spoons are used, a hammer and low crown surfacing spoon are used from the outside to relieve the strain by spring hammering, Fig. 6-23.

Checking Door Fit. Once the panel is restored to its approximate normal contour, remove the door from the holding fixture and try it in the door opening of the body. This will permit you to determine if the inner construction has been distorted. If the inner construction has been distorted so that the door contour does not match the body, or if too much or too little clearance exists around the door, the inner construction should be straightened at this time before the panel is finished. The holding fixture and power tools are also used to straighten the door inner construction before door panel straightening can be begun.

Hand Bumping. After the roughing out and the correction of any misalignment or distortion of the inner construction, continue with the rocker-action spoon in much the same manner as with a hand dolly. It absorbs the blows of the hammer for either direct or indirect hammering, or through the surfacing spoon as in spring hammering. Fig. 6-24 shows the door panel ready for metal finishing.

Fig. 6-24. Door panel hammered smooth, ready for grinding.

Welding. After the door is bumped out and ready for the metal finishing operations, any necessary welding should be done. Cracks or tears cannot be welded until after the bumping is done, as a buckled metal condition may result. If a panel has a tear in the center and is severely dinged over the entire area, the edges of the tear will be quite far apart. As the surface is straightened, the edges of the tear will brought closer together until, when the bumping is done, they may almost touch.

If the welding is done before the panel is bumped smooth, it will be necessary to fill the tear with weld. Then, when further bumping is done, you will find that you have too much metal in the panel and it will buckle.

Shrinking. If a door panel is found to be stretched after the bumping operations, it will be necessary to shrink the stretched portions before the metal finishing can be done.

All bumping and any welding necessary should be done before stretched areas are removed. If an attempt is made to remove a stretched portion of a panel before the bumping is complete, it might be necessary to repeat the operation after further bumping.

Metal Finishing. After all the necessary roughing, bumping, welding, and shrinking operations are done, metal finish the door to prepare it for the painter. The door pictured in the sequences here is the same door pictured in the sequences in roughing out and hand bumping. In Fig. 6-25, the position of the door has been changed slightly in the holding unit to provide a better working position for grinding. Grind the damaged area, using a No. 16 open coat disk. As the paint is removed, the low spots are revealed, and pick tools can then be used for raising them, Fig. 6-26.

Fig. 6-25. Panel in position for grinding.

Fig. 6-26. Use pick tool to remove low spots or to relieve them.

The intelligent collision man will remember that any grinding operation, such as the one explained above and shown in Fig. 6-25, requires eye protection. In the illustration, the repairman is shown wearing cup goggles for the protection of his eyes.

Care must also be exercised when prying, Fig. 6-26. The proper tool is the safe tool. The pry bar should be used for prying operations rather than the screw driver which may be at hand.

In checking your progress with the pick tools, use the body file, Fig. 6-27 rather than the grinder. You will find the job will be speeded up and less physical effort will be required. The file is given a slight convex adjustment to eliminate the possibility for the surface to become wavy. With the blade slightly convex, you can file ex-

Fig. 6-27. Body file being used.

actly where you want. Whether you file a large or a small area is determined by where you start and end each stroke. If low spots exist that cannot be raised, fill them with solder.

After all the low spots have been eliminated, disk sand the panel with a No. 50 closed coat disk to make it perfectly smooth and ready for the painter.

If it is possible, obtain an old door and practice a door straightening job. If a holding fixture is not available to you, one can be improvised. Create some damage in the practice door, then follow the operations in the sequence given. You will find that the damage will be quickly and easily removed using the pick tools and body file as you have been taught.

Door Alignment

Door alignment actually is a separate trade in many of the automotive factories. Door alignment is also a necessary part of collision work. Much of door alignment has nothing whatsoever to do with the car having been involved in a collision. Rather, it is the result of what might be considered normal usage.

A large percentage of the misaligned doors you will encounter can be corrected whether or not you have mastered the techniques involved in the other aspects of collision work. The purpose of this section is to show you how to align doors regardless of the kind of misalignment. The following paragraphs will show you what misalignment consists of, the kinds of misalignment you will encounter, and how you will check for them. Each of the factors of misalignment, and any condition of the door which results in misalignment is discussed. Just what you can do and how to do it are presented under each heading.

An additional aspect of door alignment has to do with the dimensions of the door—how the door fits into the opening of the body, and how the opening in the door fits the glass. How to check and correct the window openings, how to make a comparative check of the door as compared to a door known to be correct, and how to check the door opening in the body by X-checking are also presented in this section. In each of these instances, the method of checking and the means of making the corrections are presented.

What Misalignment Is. The doors of an automobile body or the doors of a truck cab are misaligned when they do not fit the contour of the body or when they are not centered in the door opening. Doors must also provide a good seal against dust, water, and air. In order to do this, they must match the contour of the body at all points. When closed, doors must be centered in the opening provided for them. This is necessary for two reasons. If the door is not centered, it will not close properly and the gap around the door will not be uniform.

Centering the door in the opening involves moving the door up or down and forward or backward. In addition, it may involve moving either the top or the bottom of the door forward or backward and leaving the other end of the door in its original position. It may even be necessary to move the top and bottom of the door in opposite directions.

Doors will be encountered which fail to match the contour of the body in several different ways. The door can bulge out too far at the center, or it may be too flat with the result that the top and bottom of the door do not fit into the body opening as they should. In the example, it is assumed that the degree of bulge is the same at both the front and rear of the door. However, in addition to these cases, you will also encounter doors which bulge too much or too little at one side of the door, while at the same time the opposite side of the door matches the contour perfectly.

Sometimes you will encounter jobs where the trouble appears to be misalignment of the door, when actually the door itself is not the cause of the fault. In cases where the door does not match the contour of the body, it might be well to X-check that portion of the body at the front of the door and at the back of the door to determine whether the reason of the failure to match body contour is due to distortion of the body or distortion of the door itself.

In some cases, a lack of uniform clearance at the front of the door might be due to a mispositioning of the front fender or quarter panel. This possibility should be considered before any great amount of work is performed on the door itself. It may be necessary to correct the quarter panel damage before door alignment can be checked properly.

How To Check Door Alignment. Door alignment is checked by making a close visual inspection of the door and its relation to the surrounding body panels. First open and then close the door, observing the up-and-down movement of the edge of the door at the lock pillar. If, as the door latches, you get an up-or-down movement, the door is out of alignment. Look also for signs of rubbing or scraping by the door on the scuff plate or sill. If scrub marks are found, a condition known as door sag exists.

With the door closed and properly latched, notice the outer surface contour of the door in relation to the surface contour of the adjacent panels. The contour should match perfectly.

With the door closed and latched, look for uniform spacing at the front, top, and rear of the door. The door should center exactly in the opening provided.

Kinds of Misalignment

All of the different possibilities of door misalignment are listed and illustrated in Fig. 6-28. The conditions listed in (1) through

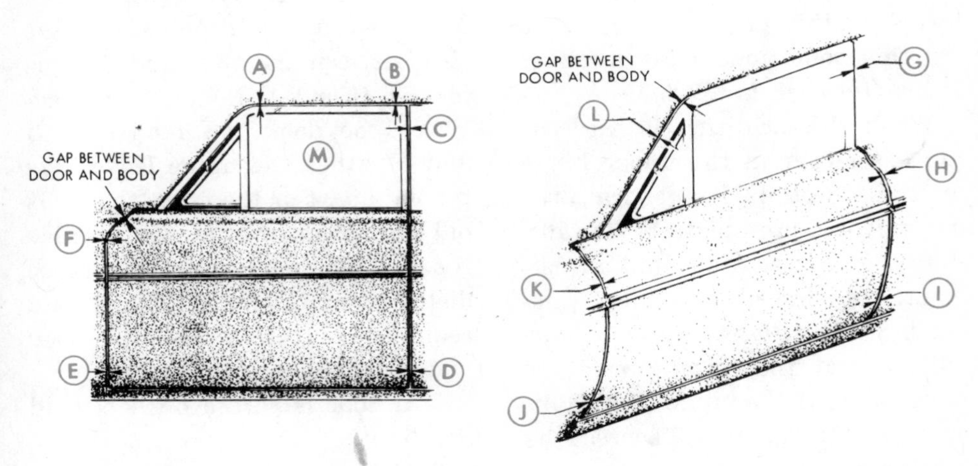

(1) B more than A
(2) D more than C
(3) C and D more than E and F
(4) C and D less than E and F
(5) C and D normal, E and F too wide
(6) C and D normal, E and F too close
(7) C more than D
(8) M window does not fit opening
(9) G flush, H and I stick out
(10) H flush, G and I stick out
(11) I flush, G and H stick out
(12) G and H flush, I sticks out
(13) G and I flush, H sticks out
(14) H and I flush, G sticks out
(15) L flush, G and K stick out
(16) K flush, G and L stick out
(17) J flush, K and L stick out
(18) K and L flush, J sticks out
(19) J and L flush, K sticks out
(20) J and K flush, L sticks out
(21) J and L flush, G, H, and I stick out

Fig. 6-28. Kinds of door misalignment as illustrated in this section.

(8) are discussed here under those headings. The cause and correction of each type of misalignment is given in each case. The conditions listed in (9) through (21), Fig. 6-28, are cases where the door does not match the contour of the body and the appropriate contour corrections must be made.

(*1*) *B More Than A*. When the gap between the door and the body is more at *B* than at *A*, the gap at *D* will be more than the gap at *C*. This condition is commonly called door sag. It is possible for *B* to be more than *A* without having door sag if the opening in the body happens to be distorted at this point. A correction for this condition is given under *Door Opening in Body*.

When the condition is sag, the fault is either in the upper hinge or the dovetail. In general, the dovetail is more apt to be at fault than the hinges. A dovetail adjustment, as described under sidehead, *Striker Plates and Dovetails,* will correct the misalignment in most cases. If the hinge is at fault, a hinge adjustment will correct the condition.

(*2*) *D More Than C*. When *D* is more than *C* the condition again is usually *door sag*. In this case, *B* will be more than *A* and the correction will be made as just described under *B More Than A*. When the door opening is distorted at this point, causing a wider gap between the door and body at *D* than at *C,* the correction is made as described under *Door Opening in Body*.

(*3*) *C and D more Than E and F*. When the opening between the body and door is more at *C* and *D* at *E* and *F* either the hinge leaves at E and F either the hinge leaves are too close, or the front fender is out of alignment. If the hinges are at fault, it will be necessary to make a hinge adjustment. If the front fender is too far to the rear, it will be necessary to move the fender forward.

(*4*) *C and D Less Than E and F*. When a condition where the gap between the door and body is less at *C* and *D* than the gap between the door and fender at *E* and *F* either the hinge leaves are too far apart or the front fender is out of alignment It is also possible for the opening in the body to be distorted at *C* and *D*. This would require correction as discussed under *Door Opening in Body*.

If a door is forced open beyond the limit of the hinge, the hinge will be sprung. The correction in this case will be to close the hinge leaves as described under *Hinges*.

If the front fender is too far forward, it will be necessary to move the fender to the rear by making one of the possible fender adjustments.

(5) *C and D Normal, E and F Too Wide.* When the opening between the door and body is normal at *C* and *D,* but the opening between the fender and door at *E* and *F* is too wide the fault is usually in the fender and not the door. In rare instances, the opening in the body might be distorted to cause this condition. The correction usually lies in moving the fender to the rear a suitable amount to close the gap at *E* and *F* to normal.

(6) *C and D Normal, E and F Too Close.* When the gap between the door and body is normal at *C* and *D,* but is too wide between the door and fender at *E* and *F,* the front fender is usually at fault. The fender has been moved to the rear, and a fender adjustment is needed.

(7) *C More Than D.* If the gap between the door and body is more at *C* than it is at *D,* the trouble usually lies in the hinges. Of course it is possible that the door opening is out of alignment, but this possibility should be explored last. Door openings are discussed under *Door Opening in Body.* If the hinges are at fault, it will be necessary to adjust the hinges.

Window Does not Fit Opening. In cases where the window glass, Fig. 6-28, does not fit the opening, the trouble lies either in the way the glass is mounted or in the door itself. This can be checked by merely raising the glass and determining whether or not it makes proper contact across the top in the fully raised position. An adjustment of the window glass in the regulator may correct this condition. If it does not, the fault is in the door itself, and it will be necessary to correct the opening with power tools.

Striker Plates and Dovetails. The function of a striker plate is to hold the door in the closed position. The function of a dovetail is to limit the up-and-down movement of the door when it is in the closed position.

Several types of striker plate and dovetail arrangements are now in common use on the different makes of cars. In Fig. 6-29, an arrangement is shown where a rotary latch is used and where the striker plate and dovetail are separate. In this case, the dovetail is mounted on the door and slides into the recess provided in the striker plate assembly when the door is closed.

Fig. 6-30 shows another arrangement where the striker plate and dovetail are separate. A rotary latch is used in this case, and the way the striker plate and dovetail mesh is merely a variation.

In Fig. 6-31, no dovetail is used. The striker plate is also the guide for the door. The housing over the door latch rotor performs the func-

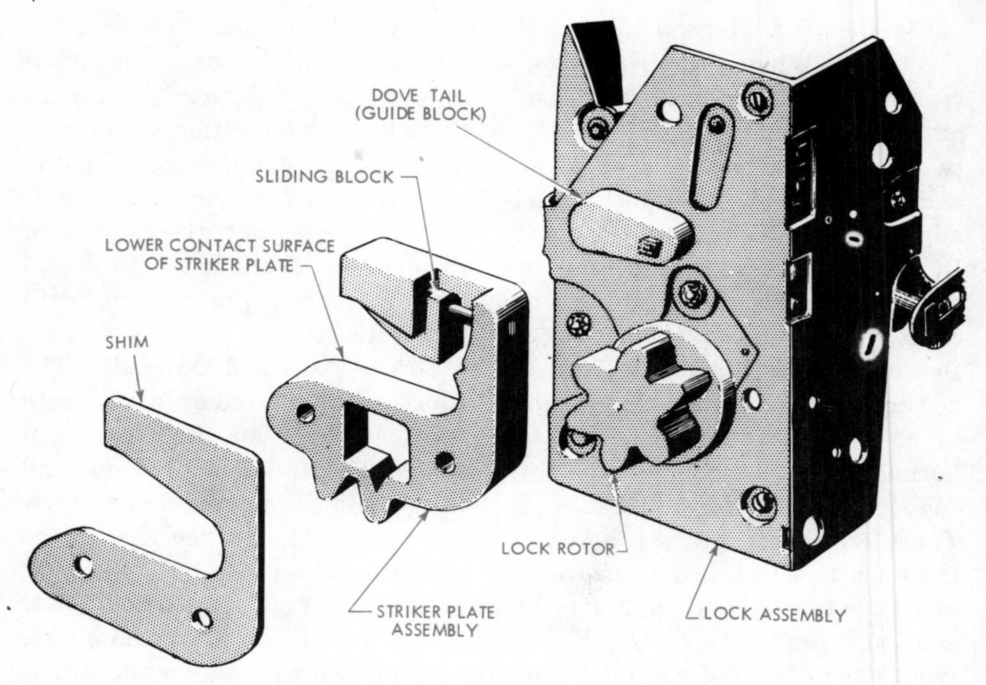

Fig. 6-29. Separate striker plate and dovetail. (Ford Motor Co.)

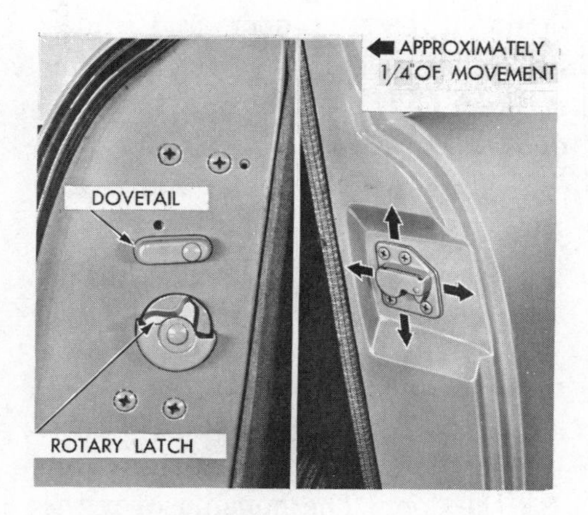

Fig. 6-30. Door lock striker plate and dovetail. (Dodge Div., Chrysler Corp.)

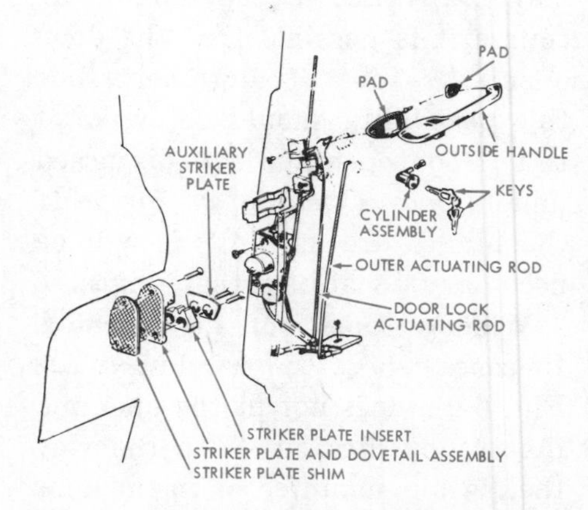

Fig. 6-31. Combination striker plate and dovetail. (Ford Motor Co.)

tion of the dovetail or guide block.

Striker Plate Adjustment. In all cases when a striker plate needs adjustment, check to see if it is worn to the extent that it needs replacing. The striker plate needs adjustment when the door fits too loosely, or sometimes when the door will not close. It is possible to have a striker plate loosen and move in when the door is shut. If it moves in far enough, the latch will not close over it and the door will not fasten shut. In cases like this, the striker plate should be loosened and moved outward, then retightened.

In cases where the door is not closing tight enough, note the distance the door sticks out beyond the body. The striker plate must be moved inward slightly more than this distance before the door will close and latch properly. Loosen the screws holding the striker plate until it is possible to move the striker plate by tapping it lightly with a mallet. Tap the striker plate inward the desired distance, then tighten it securely in place. Open and close the door to check the door fit. It may be necessary to readjust slightly to get the desired fit.

Dovetail Adjustment. On cars so equipped, a dovetail adjustment is necessary only when you wish to move the lock side of the door up or down slightly. A dovetail adjustment will not correct an excessive sag condition, but it will align the door if the door is only slightly out of alignment.

As when adjusting the striker plate, you should check the door in the closed position to see how much movement is required. Then loosen the screws holding the dovetail until it can be moved by tapping it lightly with a mallet. Tap it in the direction desired. When it has been moved into the proper location, tighten the screws securely. Close the door and open it a few times to be sure the dovetail is seating properly, then check the alignment. It may be necessary to readjust slightly to get the exact alignment desired.

Hinges. A non-adjustable hinge arrangement used in some cars is shown in Fig. 6-32. A device called a *door check* is used with most hinge arrangements to prevent the door from opening beyond the limit of the hinge travel.

Door hinges figure in the correction of door alignment quite frequently. It is not uncommon for an individual to catch the door of his car on some immovable objects and to spring the hinges. Hinges can be adjusted in several different ways: by spreading and by closing and, in more recent models, by moving the hinges with adjustments which are provided.

Hinge Spreading. When a con-

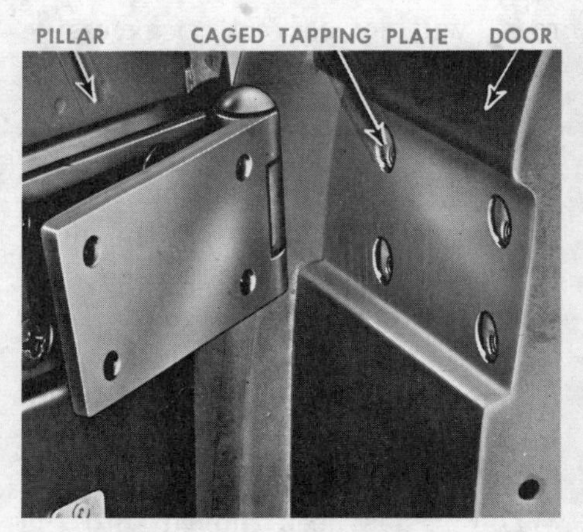

Fig. 6-32. Non-adjustable hinge arrangement, and fiber block in position for spreading lower hinge. (Ford Motor Co.)

dition of door sag is encountered on cars without adjustable hinges, it is usually necessary to spread the leaves of the lower hinge. This moves the bottom of the door toward the lock pillar. You will undoubtedly encounter situations where it will not be possible to entirely correct by spreading the lower hinge. In these cases, it will be necessary to close the upper hinge leaves.

If it is determined that the lower hinge needs spreading, it can be done easily and quickly. With the door closed, determine how much the hinge needs spreading. This can be done by measuring the clearance between the door and the lock pillar at the lower corner of the door. Check this dimension against what the clearance should be. The amount to spread the hinge is the difference between what the clearance should be and what it actually is.

Open the door and place a fiber block, slightly thicker than the distance which you wish to move the door, between the hinge halves as shown in Fig. 6-32, right. Fasten the fiber block in place with glue or some other sticky substance. With the block in place, close the door tightly.

It may be necessary to open and close the door several times to obtain the desired spread. It may also be necessary to use another block of a different thickness to get exactly the alignment desired. Be careful not to overspread the hinge. It is better to spread a little at a time until the desired spread has been accomplished than to spread too much.

Closing Hinges. When it is found desirable to close a non-adjustable hinge to attain perfect door alignment, it is necessary to remove the hinge from the door and the body. With the hinge removed, the distortion will be evident.

Place the hinge in a vise, then tighten the vise until the hinge leaves are close together and parallel when they are in the closed position. It is usually necessary to close the upper hinge more often then the lower one. However, the closing is accomplished in the same manner in either case.

Before reinstalling the hinge, make certain that the hinge mounting surface on both the lock pillar and the door is straight. If it requires straightening, a good job usually can be done easily and quickly with a hammer and a low crown surfacing spoon. Place the spoon against the pillar or door surface and hammer against the back face of it until the surface is straight. It may be necessary to move the spoon about slightly as the hammering is done in order to get the entire mounting surface straight.

After the hinge mounting surfaces are straight, install the hinge. Replace the weatherstrip if it was removed and cement it firmly in place. Try the door a few times to make sure it is perfectly aligned.

Hinge Adjustment. When you are correcting door alignment on a car that has adjustable hinges, remove the door lock striker plate to allow the door to hang free on the hinges. When properly adjusted, the door should be centered in the door opening.

If the door does not require a correction of the contour, it can be aligned by the adjustment provided at the hinges. The front doors can be adjusted, fore or aft, up or down, or in and out. The adjustment point may vary between models as to whether the adjustment is made at the door end, or the pillar end of the hinge. Fig. 6-33, top shows two possible hinge arrangements and the adjustments possible with them.

You will notice immediately that the major difference is whether the adjustment is made at the door end or the pillar end of the hinge. In all cases, the cap screws are threaded into floating type tapping plates. For this reason the cap screws should not be loosened too much. If the adjustment required can be accomplished at the pillar end of the hinge, it will not be necessary to remove the door trim panel.

Fig. 6-33, bottom shows rear door hinge adjustment points. The major difference in these two arrangements is that it is not necessary to remove the door trim pad

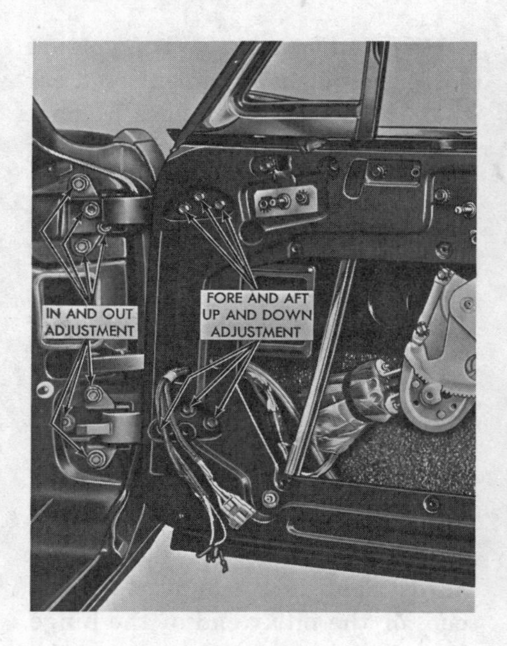

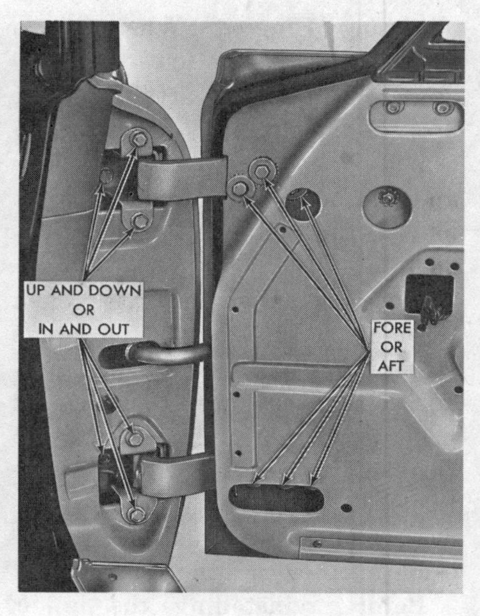

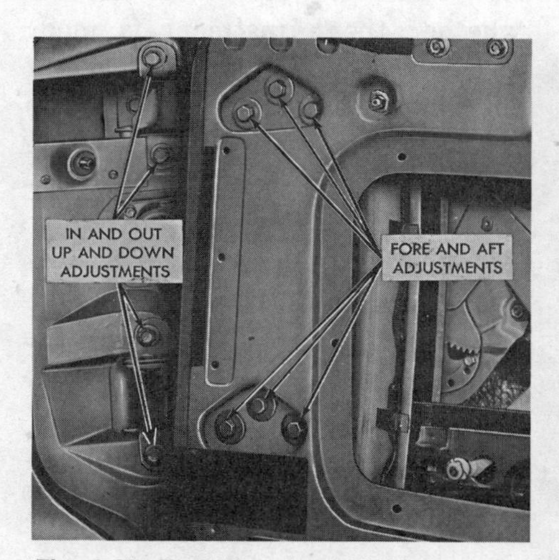

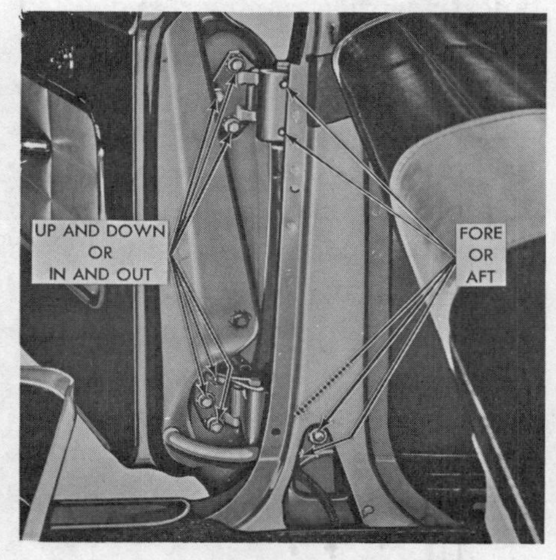

Fig. 6-33. Typical front door hinge adjustments (top) and rear door hinge adjustments (bottom). (Lincoln-Mercury Div., Ford Motor Co.)

to accomplish the adjustments.

Door Dimensions. In cases where a door is severely damaged and a good deal of straightening is necessary, it is a good policy to check the door before any attempt is made to reinstall and align the door with the body.

Make measurements on the damaged door, working from points that can be easily established on an undamaged door. Then make a measurement on the undamaged door, using the same points to measure from as you used on the damaged door. Compare the readings obtained to determine whether or not the damaged door requires further attention. Always be sure to take the measurements from the same points on both doors.

Window Openings. When the window does not fit the opening, and it is found that the difficulty is in the door itself and not in the way in which the window glass is mounted, the correction necessarily involves collision techniques.

The window opening can be checked by trying the glass to see how it fits in the closed position, or by taking comparative measurements with the opening in a door known to be in alignment.

Always exercise care not to push the door out too far in correcting window openings, since a good, snug fit with the edge of the glass is desired all around the floor.

Door Opening in Body. When a door is known to be in alignment, but does not fit the opening in the body, the opening in the body needs correcting. In many instances, a misalignment condition in the door opening will be discovered only when the door is placed in the opening.

A quick check of the gap around the door between the door and the body will quickly show where the opening is off. The two most commonly used methods of determining whether or not the opening is in alignment are checking the known dimensions and X-Checking the frame.

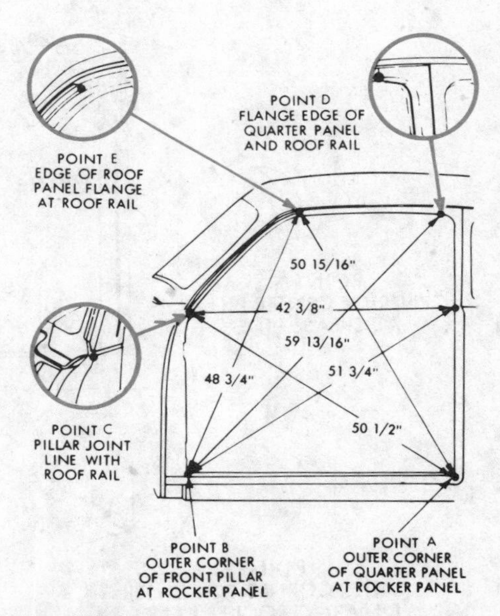

Fig. 6-34. Front door opening dimensions. (Ford Motor Co.)

Checking Known Dimensions. It is sometimes possible to obtain the dimensions for door openings from car manufacturers. When this can be done, it is a simple matter to check the dimensions of the door opening against what the dimensions should be. Any discrepancy immediately shows where the opening needs realigning. An example of how known dimensions are taken on a front door is shown in Fig. 6-34. An example of how known dimensions are taken in a rear door is shown in Fig. 6-35. In each case, enough cross dimensions are made so that a misalignment condition can be isolated to a small area. After the extent of misalignment of the opening is determined, the corrective measures can be applied.

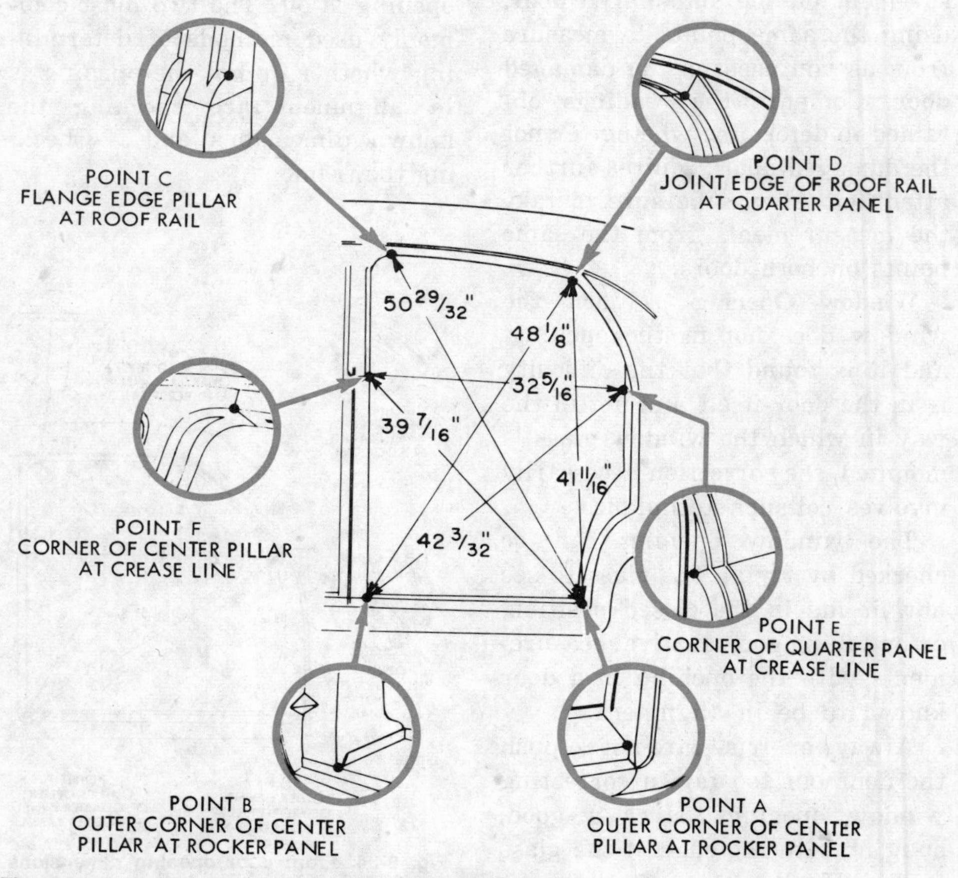

Fig. 6-35. Rear door opening dimensions. (Ford Motor Co.)

Correction of the door opening involves the use of power tools and collision techniques. Some good examples of the techniques involved were given in Chapter 5.

X-Checking. If the door opening is suspected of being out of alignment, and the dimensions of the door opening are not known, the opening can be compared to another opening on either the other side of the car or on another body of the same make and model. The basic principles of X-checking, as discussed in Chapter 1, are merely applied to comparing the one door opening with the other.

To check for misalignment of the door opening, a quick comparison of the over-all dimensions is made first. If this check shows the opening to be correct, no further check is needed. How to compare a door opening with one known to be correct by the X-checking method is shown in Fig. 6-36.

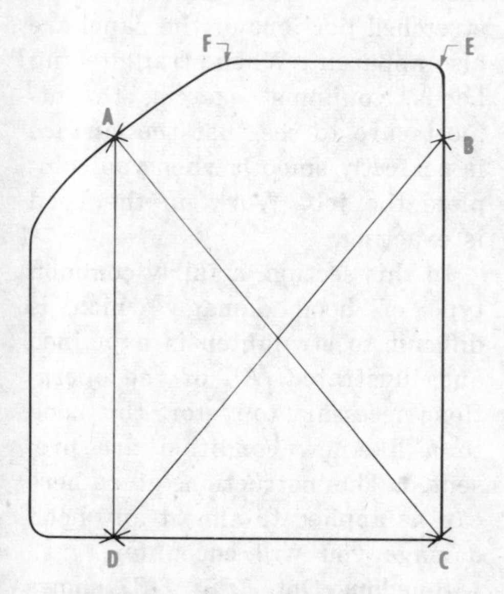

Fig. 6-36. Door opening comparison reference points for x-checking.

First, arbitrarily establish point *A* on the sloped portion of the door opening. A plan that will work on most cars is to establish points *A* and *B* seven inches below point *E*. Set your body trammel so that when one end is placed at *C*, the other end of the tram is seven inches below *E*. Draw a reference mark at the end of the tram. This is point *B*.

Move the tram to the slope of the door and let it hang from the point where it touches the bottom of the opening. Mark point *A* at the upper end of the tram and point *D* at the lower end.

Turn to the undamaged opening to which you want to compare the damaged one. Mark points *A*, *B*, and *D* in the same way you did on the first one. Dimensions *A* to *C* and *B* to *D* should be the same on both openings. Compare dimensions *A* to *B* and *D* to *C*. This comparison, plus the comparison of the two diagonal dimensions, will quickly show how much the opening has been distorted and will provide a clue as to the correction needed to make the door fit it.

Hood Straightening

The hood of an automobile or truck is substantially anchored when it is closed. Many models have spring-loaded hinges so that the tension of the spring holds the hood firmly in place at the hinged side. At the front or other point of locking, a sturdy latch holds that end or side of the hood down under spring tension.

Completely around the hood—front, back, and around the two sides—a number of rubber pads are provided, on which the hood rests. When the hood is open, however, it is virtually unsupported. It is held in place by the hood hinges alone. This means that for any hood straightening operation involving the use of power tools, the hood will have to be removed and held in some manner to permit the application of power tools.

Generally, when damage occurs to the hood, you will find that the hood flange will crack. As a first step of any hood repair, the flanges should be rewelded to prevent the crack from extending during the time the hood is under pressure from the power tools.

Minor damage, local in area, can usually be corrected by using a hand dolly and hammer. In cases where the damaged area is extensive, time can be saved by using power tools. Nevertheless, if you do not have power tools available or if you do not have a suitable means of holding the hood to permit the use of power tools, a surprising amount of the damage can be readily worked out by use of the hand tools alone.

The hood of an automobile is constantly under the eye of the driver and passengers. Any defects in workmanship, such as ripples or low spots, can be easily seen from the driver's seat. Any bulges or stretched portions of the panel are also apparent. When straightening hoods, you must exercise the utmost care to see that the surface is perfectly smooth when you complete the job. Work on the hood is exacting.

In this section, a fairly common type of hood damage which is difficult to straighten is explained and illustrated. All of the operations necessary to restore this hood to a like-new condition are presented. The instructions given here can be applied to almost any hood damage you will encounter.

Roughing Out. Fig. 6-37 shows a damaged antique hood of heavy

Fig. 6-37. Damaged antique hood clamped in holding unit.

metal clamped securely in a holding unit. The damage is toward the front of the hood, adjacent to the high crown area of this particular hood. This means that it is in the section of the hood most easily seen by the driver.

Notice that the hood has been clamped in the holding unit with the damaged area directly over the jacking platform. Fig. 6-38 shows the damaged section partially straightened. An eighteen-inch rocker action spoon was used, along with the necessary tubing, a small rubber base, and a direct-acting jack.

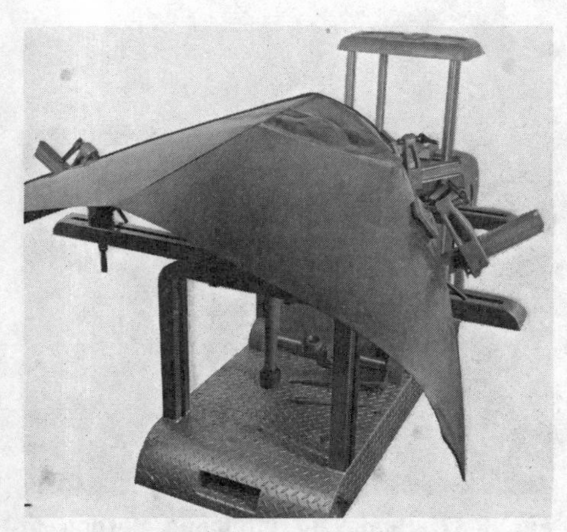

Fig. 6-38. Damage partly removed.

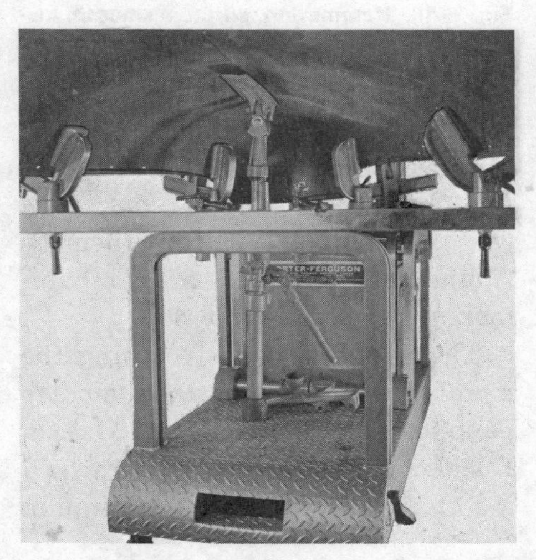

Fig. 6-39. Rocker action spoon and jack positioned for removing damage.

Power was applied from the underside with the jack based on the jacking platform, Fig. 6-39. Note that the rocker action spoon is positioned directly under the center of the hood. This minimizes the chance of stretching the metal beyond the point where it can be restored to normal within a body shop.

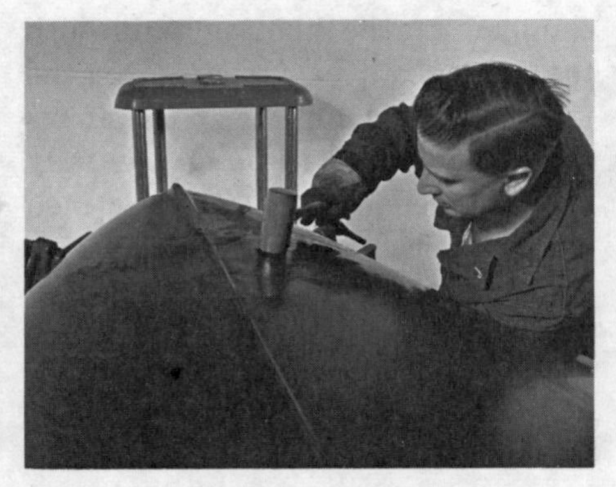

Fig. 6-40. Hammering surface smooth, using dolly and light hammer.

Hand Bumping. After the surface has been roughed out with the power tools, it can then be further straightened with a hammer and dolly, Fig. 6-40.

The possibility of stretching the metal is ever present when you are hammering on a hood. Use a wooden mallet, if possible, to hold metal stretching to a minimum. Fig. 6-41 shows the hood bumped out in preparation for the removal of the paint. A grinder with a No. 24 open coat disk is used for removing the paint. The low spots are brought up with a pick hammer. It may be necessary to alternately file with a body file and work with the pick hammer to remove all of the low spots.

Shrinking. During the final hand bumping operation of removing low spots, any stretched portions of the damaged area will become visible. These stretched areas should be shrunk back to normal at this time. It will generally be necessary to pick up additional low spots created by the shrinking operation. Fig. 6-42 shows a stretched section being shrunk by the method explained in Chapter 4. Figs. 6-43 and 6-44 show the subsequent hammering and quenching operations required.

Fig. 6-41. Hood roughed out.

Fig. 6-42. Removing stretched portion of hood with heat spots.

Fig. 6-43. Hammering heat spots in stretched area.

Fig. 6-44. Quenching heat spots with cold water and sponge.

The heat spots should be about the size of a nickel and they must be hammered down while they are still cherry red. The heat spots

Fig. 6-45. Filing hood for intermediate stage of finishing.

should not be quenched until after the metal has turned black.

Metal Finishing. After all the roughing, hand bumping, shrinking, soldering, and welding that may be necessary are done, grind or file, Fig. 6-45 the entire damage

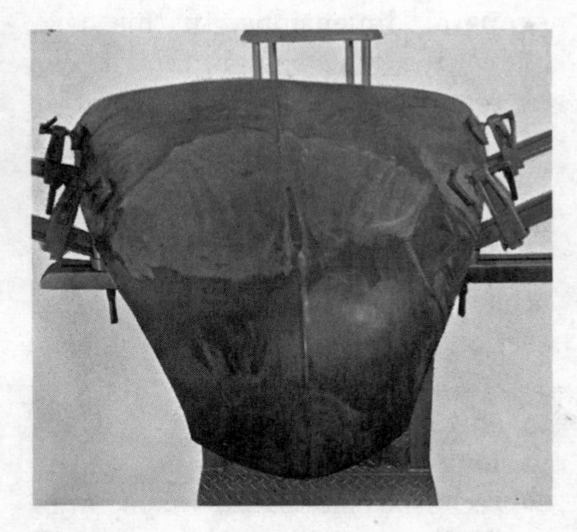

Fig. 6-46. Surface ready for the painter.

area. Use a No. 50 close coat disk to finish the area. This removes all of the minute scratches left by the file and leaves the surface ready for the painter, Fig. 6-46, when the finished body work is transferred from the body shop to the paint shop.

Hood Alignment

Any time a car is involved in a collision where the grille, a front fender, or hood is damaged, an alignment problem usually arises. Even though each damaged panel is bumped out and straightened, they usually do not fit together as they did originally.

In some instances, you will find that misalignment is due to a condition that exists in the hood itself. At some previous time, perhaps, the hood may have been damaged in a collision, and whoever straightened the job may not have restored it to its original shape or dimensions. In this case, of course, the misalignment can be repaired by making a correction of the hood.

You will often find that you can make up for a discrepancy in one part by an adjustment in some other part. The purpose of this section is to define what is meant by proper hood alignment. How to check hood alignment and the various things that can be done to correct the particular aspects of hood alignment are also discussed.

With the large variation in body design and the large number of makes and models of cars and trucks on the road, it obviously would be impossible in a volume of this kind to give a step-by-step procedure for the alignment of each type of hood. This section, rather than presenting a procedure for alignment for a specific make or model, is designed to acquaint you with principles of alignment and to point out to you the methods whereby the desired results can be achieved.

Proper Hood Alignment. Automobile hoods, when latched in position, are generally held in place at the rear with spring-loaded hinges and at the front with a spring-loaded latch, both of which pull the hood downward under tension. The hood itself rests on small blocks of hard rubber or on a lubricant impregnated fabric sometimes known as antisqueak.

In most automobiles, the front grille work, the two front fenders, and the hood are intended to form a smooth-flowing silhouette. If any of the parts stick forward or are to the rear of their normal position, a step appears in the contour. Hood alignment, or at least one aspect of hood alignment, involves the maintenance of a smooth-flowing visual contour for these separate parts at the front end.

At the rear of the hood, the cowl is recessed so that when the back of the hood is in this recess, the outer surface of the hood flows in a continuous line which matches the surface of the cowl immediately adjacent to this recess. If the hood is too high or too low, a step occurs in the silhouette.

If the hood is too far forward, a large gap exists between the rear of the hood and the raised portion of the cowl. On the other hand, if the hood is too far rearward so that less than a normal gap exists between the back of the hood and the cowl, it is possible that when the hood is raised, it will strike the cowl panel and chip the paint on either or both the cowl panel and the hood.

The contour of the hood must match the contour of the cowl exactly, that is, the two surfaces should be exactly flush with each other at all points when the hood is closed.

On the sides of the hood, a uniform gap should exist for the full length of the hood on each side. As explained previously, a number of rubber blocks are provided for the hood to rest on. Since the hood is under tension, the gap at the point where the rubber block should be might be less than normal if one of these blocks is missing. On the other hand, if the hood, when held down under tension by the hinge springs or the latch springs, fails to touch the rubber blocks, then not only will the gap at that particular point be wide, but noise and vibration may result.

All of the various kinds of hood misalignment that might occur are shown in Fig. 6-47. In the list accompanying the illustration, each condition of misalignment is given. Each condition is numbered. This number agrees with the number of one of the following paragraphs where the condition is fully discussed, and the correction needed is given.

(*1*) *A Too High, B and F Normal.* When the center of the hood sticks up and both rear corners are down, a hinge adjustment will usually correct the condition. It may be possible in some instances to draw the hood down by tightening the screws which hold the hood to the stiffener which runs crosswise near the rear of the hood. If a hinge or a stiffener adjustment does not remove the condition, a contour correction is needed.

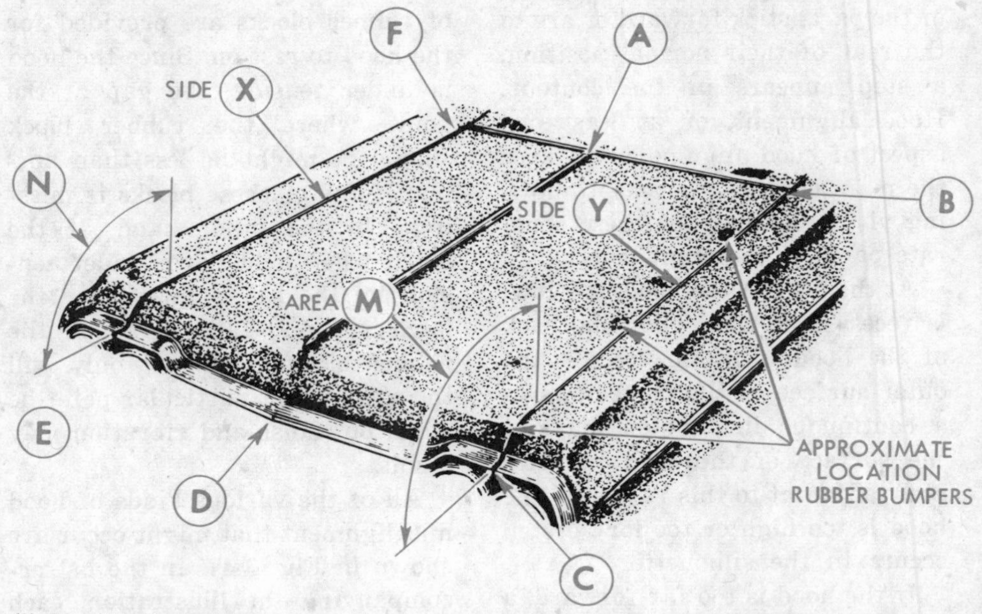

(1) A too high, B and F normal
(2) A normal, B or F too high
(3) A, B, and F too high
(4) A, B, and F too close to cowl
(5) A, B, and F too wide
(6) C sticks out, D and E normal
(7) E sticks out, C and D normal
(8) E and C normal, D does not match contour
(9) C, D, and E too far forward
(10) side X too wide, side Y normal
(11) side X too close, side Y normal
(12) side Y too close, side X normal
(13) side Y too wide, side X normal
(14) sides X and Y too wide
(15) sides X and Y too close
(16) side X too wide at area N, normal at E and F
(17) side X too close at area N, normal at E and F
(18) side Y too close at area M, normal at B and C
(19) side Y too wide at area M, normal at B and C

Fig. 6-47. Hood misalignment possibilities and check list.

(2) A Normal, B or F Too High. When the center of the hood is down at the rear, but one or both of the corners at the rear stick out, a hinge adjustment is necessary. On occasion, a contour correction will be necessary.

(3) A, B, and F Too High. Where the hood sets too high all across the rear, a hinge adjustment is necessary. However, you should make a quick check to be sure that nothing is holding the hood out of alignment before a hinge adjustment is made.

(4) A, B, and F Too Close to Cowl. Even though the rear of the hood is supposed to rest on the cowl in the recess provided, a gap between the edge of the hood and the shoulder of the recess is necessary. If this gap is too narrow, the hood may catch on the cowl when it is opened, causing the paint to chip on both the hood and the cowl. In this case, it is necessary

to move the hood forward. This is done by hinge adjustment.

(5) *A, B, and F Too Wide.* Aside from the fact that a wide gap between the hood and the cowl looks unsightly, the hood may stick out in the front at the grille and the latch may not work properly. In this case, a hinge adjustment is needed.

(6) *C Sticks Out, D and E Normal.* When a corner of the hood sticks out at the front, the hood may be cocked in the hood opening, and another condition of misalignment may exist at some other portion of the hood. In most instances, however, the contour of the hood is out of alignment and needs attention.

(7) *E Sticks out, C and D Normal.* Again, this is a condition where one corner of the hood does not fit properly at the front. The same correction applies here as it does for the previous condition.

(8) *E and C Normal, D Does not Match Contour.* Usually, the center of the hood at the front is made to match the contour of the grille or to line up with a molding or ornament. When the fit is poor at this point, one of several things may be wrong.

If the hood fits well at all other points, the grille and the front-end sheet metal may need adjusting. Since the hood latches into the hood strainer it is possible that the strainer is too low or too far forward. The correction of all of these possibilities is discussed subsequently. If the opening is not at fault, the contour of the hood is out and needs attention.

(9) *C and D Too Far Forward.* When the front of the hood is too far forward, it is a good idea to make a quick check to determine whether or not the gap at *F A B* is too wide. If it is, an adjustment is necessary to move the hood to the rear. Another possibility to explore is whether or not the fenders and front-end sheet metal are too far to the rear. An adjustment will correct any undesirable condition found. If the contour of the hood is not correct, this same condition can exist, and a correction of the hood contour will be necessary.

(10) *Side X Too Wide, Side Y Normal.* When the gap between the hood and the fender is too wide at one side but is normal at the other, the hood opening is too large. An adjustment of the fender will correct this condition. If the hood itself has been badly damaged, it may have too much contour to one side of the center line, and a contour correction is needed.

(11) *Side X Too Close, Side Y Normal.* When the gap between the hood and fender is too close at one side but normal at the other, a fender adjustment is indicated. If

this does not solve the problem, it will be necessary to correct either the hood opening or the hood contour.

(*12*) *Side Y Too Close, Side X Normal.* This condition is like the one above. The correction is the same as described when side *X* is too wide, and side *Y* is normal.

(*13*) *Side Y Too Wide, Side X Normal.* Again, the condition described here is a problem involving the gap between the hood and fender. The correction is the reverse of that given in (*10*). Instead of closing the gap, widen it.

(*14*) *Sides X and Y Too Wide.* When the gap between the hood and fenders is too wide at both sides, one or the other of two conditions exists. Either the opening for the hood is too large and the fender needs to be adjusted closer to the hood, or the contour of the hood needs correcting.

(*15*) *Sides X and Y Too Close.* When the gap between the hood and fenders is too close at both sides, the opening or the hood contour is at fault, and the correction necessary is the same as (14).

(*16*) *Side X Too Wide at Area N, Normal at E and F.* A hood may have a contour which sweeps downward at the front. The hood opening sometimes becomes narrower at the front. Both of these factors contribute to a type of hood misalignment commonly encountered. Where the hood sweeps downward, it is apt to fit too closely, or not well at all. The correction needed is dependent to some extent on the type of damage which has been inflicted on the hood. The correction in this case can require either attention to the hood opening or a correction of the hood itself.

(*17*) *Side X Too Close at N, Normal at E and F.* The condition described here is another possibility of misalignment between the hood and the fenders. The correction needed is noted under (16).

(*18*) *Side Y Too Close at M, Normal at B and C.* When the hood does not fit at the portion described here, the correction needed is explained under (16).

(*19*) *Side Y Too Wide at M, Normal at B and C.* The correction needed when the hood and fender contour does not match is given under (*16*).

Checking Hood Alignment. Hood alignment is easily and quickly checked in most instances by a visual examination. With the hood in the closed position, check the gap all around between the hood and the adjacent panels. The gap should be uniform. If it is not, one of the conditions of misalignment shown in Fig. 6-47 exists.

Each manufacturer has specifications for what the correct gap should be. Whenever possible, you should work to the manufacturer's specifications. However, in the absence of specifications, a good general rule to follow is to see that the gap is not greater than 1/4" nor less than 1/8". If the clearance at the joint is not within specifications, it is necessary to shift the hood or make some other adjustment of the width of the opening to correct the misalignment.

In some instances, it will be necessary to examine the hood opening and the hood separately to see which one is at fault. When this is necessary, it is done by a method of *X-checking*. The hood opening is measured as shown in Fig. 6-48. Any misalignment in the over-all opening will be obvious as soon as the dimensions for *X* and *Y* are compared. The measurements, of course, should be the same.

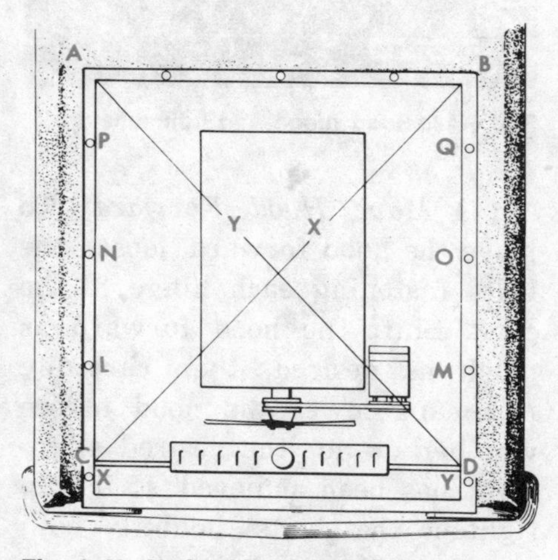

Fig. 6-48. X-checking hood alignment.

To more closely isolate a condition of misalignment, X-measurements can be taken from points *A* and *B* to any of the corresponding opposite points along either side of the opening. The points shown in Fig. 6-48 are the holes in which the rubber pads or bumpers which support the hood are secured.

Hood Opening. When a condition of misalignment exists that affects the hood opening, it will usually be necessary to shift either the fenders or the front end sheet metal. In some cases, only one fender will be the cause of misalignment. The reason for this may be that the fender is too high, too low, too far forward, or too far toward the rear.

A high or low condition can be quickly corrected by loosening all of the fender attaching bolts. Using a 2 x 4 for a lever, either force it up or down.

If either fender is too far forward or too far back, a hydraulic jack can be used. Simply loosen all of the fender attaching bolts, then anchor the jack so that pressure can be exerted in the desired direction. Tighten the attaching bolts before the pressure from the jack is relaxed.

In some cases, both fenders will be misaligned. In this case it will be necessary to loosen the attaching bolts of both fenders. The fenders can then be moved as necessary.

Occasionally the hood, when properly aligned at the rear, will be misaligned at the front. The hood should lie evenly between the fenders at the grille. If the opening is too narrow, the bolts which attach the fender to the radiator support bracket and the grille should be removed. A hydraulic jack should then be placed between the fenders as far forward as possible. The fenders should be forced apart until the proper distance exists between them. This distance can be determined by measuring across the front of the hood, then adding the desired clearance on each side to the measurement taken.

Before the pressure is relieved on the fenders, shims or flat washers should be placed between the fender brackets and the radiator supports. These shims will hold the fender in the new position.

As soon as the shims are installed and the bolts tightened, remove the jack and bring the hood into the closed position. If too much clearance exists, it will be necessary to repeat the operation and remove shims until the desired clearance or fit is obtained.

It may also be necessary to move the front-end sheet metal up or down. All of the attaching bolts holding the hood strainer in place should be loosened. The hood strainer can then be raised or lowered and secured in place by the use of shims or washers. It may be necessary to straighten some of the support brackets in order to effect the desired alignment of the front-end sheet metal.

Hood Hinges. The hood hinges on most cars are constructed so that they can be adjusted to move the hood forward or rearward, or to move either rear corner in or out or up or down, Fig. 6-49.

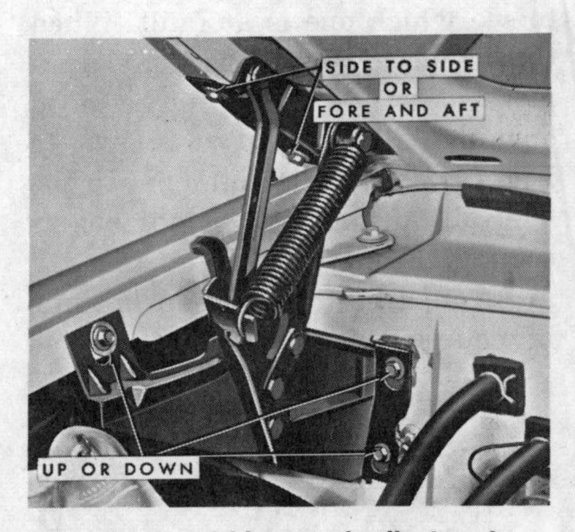

Fig. 6-49. Hood hinge and adjustments.

(*1*) *Move Hood Forward.* To move the hood forward, loosen the bolts fastening each hinge to the cowl. Shift the hood forward as much as desired, then carefully raise and lower the hood to see whether or not the desired alignment has been achieved. If it has, tighten the bolts holding both hinges to the cowl.

(*2*) *Move Hood Rearward.* To move the hood to the rear, loosen the hinge attaching bolts at both hood hinges. Move the hood to the rear as desired, then work the hood to see whether or not it is in proper alignment. If it is, tighten the bolts fastening the hinges to the cowl.

Whenever the hood is adjusted rearward, be sure that the safety catch (if one is used) holds properly when the hood is in the unlatched position.

(*3*) *Hood Rear Corners.* After all of the adjustments are made, you may find that the bottom rear corner of the hood is either too close to the fender or too far from it when the hood is closed. When this condition exists, it can be corrected quickly and easily by bending the hood hinge plate on the cowl. If the plate is bent toward the cowl, the corner of the hood will be forced away from the fender. If the corner is too far from the fender, bend the plate away from the cowl and the hood will be brought closer to the fender.

A large pry bar or a monkey wrench with a piece of pipe on the handle, or even a bar of steel, can be used as a tool for the operation of bending the hood hinge plate to match the height of the hood and the width of the opening above the cowl. As all must be done at the same time, it is a trial and error process of many fittings.

Fig. 6-50. Hood latch and adjustments. (Lincoln-Mercury Div., Ford Motor Co.)

Hood Latches. A typical hood latch is shown in Fig. 6-50. The hood can be adjusted up and down to match the top contour of the front fenders by moving the hood latch lock dowel up or down, unlocking the locknut before the adjustments, and finally locking it again in place when through.

Contour Correction. Whenever any condition of misalignment exists where it is necessary to correct the contour of the hood, it will be necessary to remove the hood. After the hood has been removed, it can be corrected by the usual collision methods. It is necessary, however, to fasten the hood in a rigid device to effect any contour corrections. Detailed instructions on contour correction were described previously in this chapter.

Deck Lid Straightening

As is true of doors and hoods, the deck lid on an automobile is securely held in place when closed. A lock or latch keeps the lower edge under tension. In many designs, the hinges are spring loaded so the upper edge also is under tension.

With the deck lid opened, as would be required to correct any collision damage that may have occurred to it, the deck lid is supported only by the hinges. This means that in any instance where the use of power tools is required, it will be necessary to remove the deck lid and hold it in a suitable holding fixture. Even if you do not have a holding fixture, the deck lid should be removed. All of the pressure that you must apply to the deck lid will be transferred to the hinges. There is a possibility that during the correction of the deck lid damage you may cause some damage to the body through the hinges.

The principles involved in straightening the deck lid are much the same as those involved in straightening any door.

One disadvantage you will encounter in working on deck lids lies in the fact that in some areas, the deck lid inner construction leaves little space between the inner construction and the outer skin or panel. This means that some long, thin spoons and long picks are almost a necessity. Even with these tools, you will often find it necessary to remove a portion of the inner construction during the bumping operation, then weld it back in place after the outer skin is corrected. Time can be saved by drilling small holes through the inner construction which will permit the use of a punch as a pick. In all operations of this kind you always have the possibility of filling in with solder where it is too difficult to bring the surface up to the required smoothness.

Many kinds of damage occur to the deck lid, since it is subject to rear collisions and is often damaged when the vehicle is struck at the quarter panel. It would be impossible to present all of the possible varities of damage that can occur to a deck lid on even one make or model of car. When one considers the large number of makes and models that are on the road, the problem is even more apparent. For the purpose of illustrating the techniques involved in deck lid

Fig. 6-51. Deck lid mounted in holding unit, and eighteen inch rocker action spoon in position.

straightening, the example shown in Fig. 6-51 might be considered as typical. It is felt that these steps will apply to almost any kind of damage that you will encounter. This particular deck lid was restored to normal, and various stages of its correction were photographed.

When you encounter a seriously damaged deck lid, the advisability of replacing rather than repairing it should be considered. Estimate the amount of time that you will have to spend to correct the deck lid, then compare this cost to that for a new part. This is particularly true if the top and quarter panels of the car have been damaged. By using a new deck lid, you will be providing yourself with one part, the condition of which you know, and the deck lid can be used as a template or gage in restoring the other panels to normal.

Roughing Out. When a deck lid is to be straightened, a much more satisfactory job can be done if the deck lid is removed from the car and placed in a suitable holding device. A deck lid which has had the lower right-hand corner pushed in is shown correctly mounted in a holding unit in Fig. 6-51, left. Inspection of the damage has shown that it will be possible to straighten the damage without cutting away a portion of the inner construction.

The first step in straightening the damage is with an eighteen-inch rocker action spoon used in conjunction with a hydraulic jack. Fig. 6-51, right shows the spoon in use. It is necessary to insert the spoon through the small opening in the center of the deck lid, then position it so that it will push out as much damage at one time as possible. While pressure is main-

Fig. 6-52. Spring hammering on deck lid.

tained against the underside of the surface with the rocker action spoon, spring hammering is done on the outer surface, Fig. 6-52.

Hand Bumping. As soon as the surface is comparatively smooth and all sharp ridges have been re-

Fig. 6-54. Illustrating depth of deep-throated spoon.

moved, a bumping hammer and a deep-throated door spoon are employed, Figs. 6-53 and 6-54. The great depth of the deep-throated door spoon, Fig. 6-54, allows you to reach to the very edge of the panel on most deck lids.

When the surface has been made as smooth as possible by bumping, use a pick tool to raise the low spots. Fig. 6-55 shows a

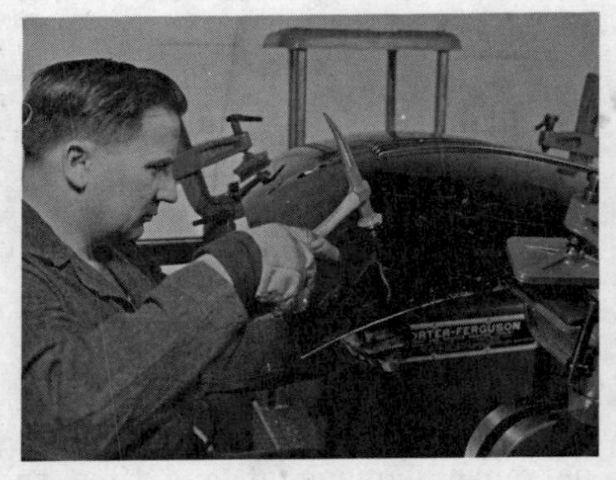

Fig. 6-53. Bumping hammer and deep throated spoon being used on deck lid.

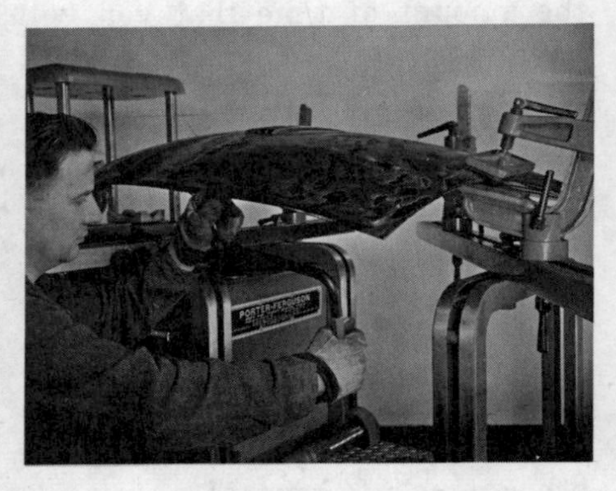

Fig. 6-55. Deep-throated pick tool in use.

Fig. 6-56. Illustrating depth of deep-throated pick tool.

deep-throated pick tool being used on the deck lid to raise the low spots near the edge. Fig. 6-56 shows the same tool laid alongside the deck lid to enable you to see the reach which is possible with this tool.

Remove any low spots revealed by filing. A different type of pick tool, which has an offset to increase efficiency when working in close places, is shown in Fig. 6-57. This tool is inserted between the inner and outer construction when in use, usually with a prying action. It may be used to strike a light blow when tapped with a hammer, but spring action will dull the blow.

Metal Finishing. After all of the bumping operations are performed, any welding or shrinking necessary should be done before the finishing operations are started. When all the low spots are removed, the surface can be filed and sanded smooth.

Fig. 6-58 shows a body file, which has been given a slight concave adjustment, being used on the deck lid. Care should be exercised not to remove too much metal. To make the surface ready for the painter, use a grinder with a No. 50 grit close coat disk.

Fig. 6-57. Deep-throated pick with offset point for remote areas.

Fig. 6-58. Body file being used on deck lid to adjust the deck lid contour.

Deck Lid Alignment

Proper deck lid alignment should be maintained at all times. An improperly aligned deck lid will allow water and dust to enter the luggage compartment which may cause damage to anything which is being carried in it.

Whenever a deck lid is repaired or replaced, close attention should be given to its proper alignment. All surface damage must be corrected before you attempt to align the lid.

Several methods of aligning deck lids are commonly used depending on the type of equipment available and on the extent to which the lid is misaligned.

Proper deck lid alignment exists when the deck lid matches the contour of the body at all points. Deck lid misalignment is easily checked by visual inspection of the gap all around the deck lid between the deck lid and the body. However, it is often necessary to check more closely for deck lid alignment.

A simple but effective way to make this check is to chalk the edge of the body flange which contacts the deck lid weather strip. Be sure the chalk is rubbed on evenly all along the flange. Close the deck lid, then open it. The chalk will be transferred to the weather strip at each point where contact is made. If a chalk line is visible around the entire weather strip, the lid is sealing perfectly. Wherever the chalk line does not appear, the deck lid is not sealing properly, and realignment is necessary. If the trouble is in the contour, it will be necessary to correct it.

In some cases where the deck lid does not seal properly along the bottom edge, it may be possible to correct it by adjusting the latch or the hinges. An adjustable hinge arrangement is shown in Fig. 6-59. If you make this adjustment and still do not get proper alignment, it

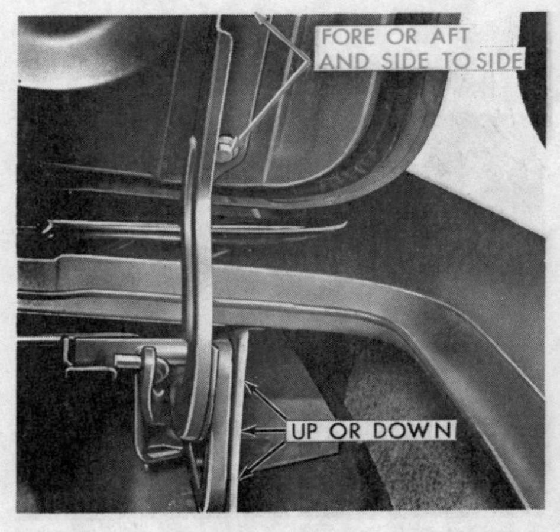

Fig. 6-59. Deck lid hinge adjustment. (Ford Motor Co.)

may be necessary to bend or twist the deck lid.

Bending or twisting operations can often be done with hand tools, either with a door-bar unit or with power tools. Some deck lids are more rigid than others due to the construction. In cases like these, it will be necessary to use a door-bar unit or power tools.

Twisting Deck Lid by Hand. Fig. 6-60 shows a method of providing a fulcrum point for raising one side of the lid, thereby forcing the other side down. No power tools are involved. In this case, the deck lid did not fit properly along the left side. A mallet was placed between the deck lid and the body on the right-hand side. By closing the deck lid against the mallet, the side opposite the mallet (left side) was forced down. Never apply strong pressure against the mallet. Check the alignment and sealing. If necessary, repeat the operation until alignment is achieved.

Matching Deck Lid with Body Contour. Another situation you may encounter is that created when the deck lid does not fit the contour of the body. This condition may exist at several points around the deck lid, along the roof panel, along the extension panel, or along the lower back panel on either side of the deck lid. Sometimes it is not the fault of the deck lid. The panels adjacent to the deck lid may be misaligned.

If the deck lid does not follow the contour of the roof panel but works freely, the roof panel is out of alignment. Place a power jack between the floor pan and the underside of the roof panel just back of the drain gutter, as shown in Fig. 6-61.

Fig. 6-60. Method of twisting deck lid by hand. (Ford Motor Co.)

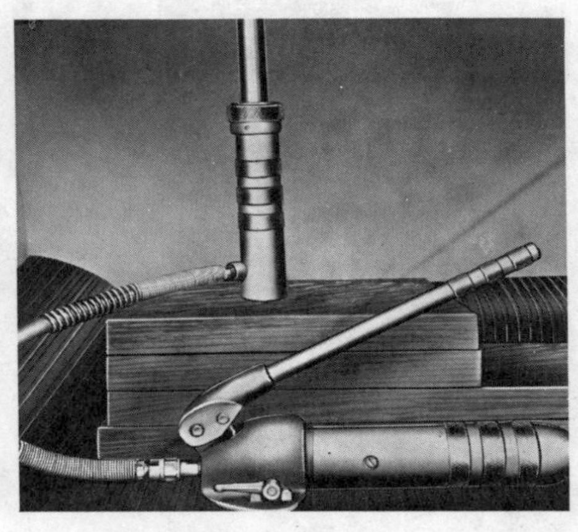

Fig. 6-61. Hydraulic jack in place to raise roof panel. (Ford Motor Co.)

Place the base of the jack against a 2 x 6 to distribute the strain on the floor pan over a larger area. Raise the roof panel until the proper contour is obtained. Do not apply excessive pressure against the roof panel with the first application. Check the fit along the roof panel. If necessary, repeat the operation until the proper contour is obtained.

If the misalignment is along the extension panel above or forward of the tail light openings, it can usually be corrected by the use of a rubber mallet only. Determine the location of the misaligned section of the extension, then strike the top surface in the center of the misaligned area with the rubber mallet, Fig. 6-62. Be sure to hit close to the drain gutter with the flat surface of the mallet. It may be necessary to strike several blows to obtain alignment.

If the deck lid does not fit properly along the lower back panel, place a piece of paper between the deck lid and lower back panel. Close the deck lid, then pull the paper. If the deck lid is sealing properly, you will not be able to pull the paper out.

Make this same check at both ends and at the center of the deck lid next to the striker plate. If proper contact is not made at the striker plate, adjust the striker plate. If contact is made at both ends and not at the center after the striker plate has been adjusted, use two mallets, one at each corner, and apply pressure as shown in Fig. 6-63. You will encounter cases when you can hammer the lower back panel out toward the deck lid by striking the inside of the back panel with a mallet.

If the deck lid is tight at the cen-

Fig. 6-62. Method of aligning center of deck lid extension panel. (Ford Motor Co.)

Fig. 6-63. Method of aligning center of deck lid with lower back panel. (Ford Motor Co.)

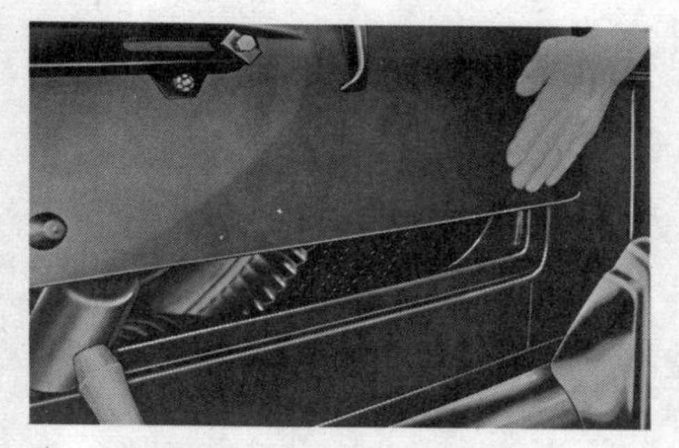

Fig. 6-64. Fitting deck lid lower corner to lower back panel. (Ford Motor Co.)

ter but no contact is obtained at either or both lower corners of the deck lid, one or two methods can be used to make the correction. The first is to hold the deck lid part way open, then to strike the corner of the lid that is not making contact with a rubber mallet. The second is to place a mallet between the deck lid and the lower back panel at approximately the center of the panel. Apply pressure against the deck lid on the side that is not making contact as shown in Fig. 6-64. Repeat as many times as necessary to correct the curvature of the deck lid so that it will fit snugly.

Checking On Your Knowledge

The following questions give you the opportunity to check up on yourself. If you have read the chapter carefully, you should be able to answer the questions. If you have any difficulty, read the chapter over once more so that you have the information well in mind before you go on with your reading.

1. Can doors, hoods, and deck lids become misaligned as a result of other than a collision?
2. What can be done to help prevent rusting at the bottom of door panels?
3. When is it necessary to remove the door lock during panel replacement?
4. When a door glass is left in the door during a panel replacement, what position should it be in?
5. When a door panel is replaced, is it always necessary to remove the interior trim from the door?
6. Why should the interior trim pad be removed before the belt moldings are removed?
7. When a door panel is to be replaced, is it practical to leave the door on the car?
8. What are the governing factors in establishing the type of joint to be used when a door panel is replaced?
9. What kind of joint is generally used when it falls under a molding or is concealed by a decorative strip?
10. When an entire panel is to be replaced, where is the old panel generally cut off?
11. Why are power saws or special cutters preferable to torch cutting when removing door panels?
12. How are the corners of a replacement panel prepared for flanging around the inner panel?

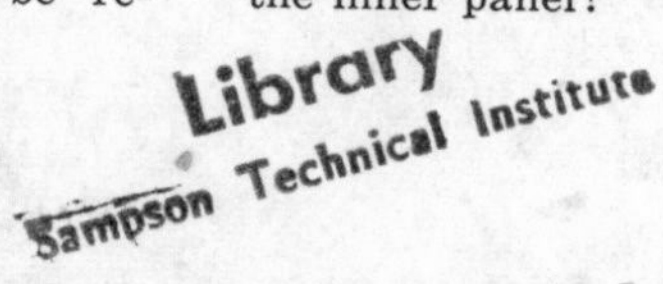

13. When scrub marks are found on a door sill or scuff plate, what kind of door misalignment is indicated?

14. What is the function of a door striker plate? A door dovetail?

15. What can be accomplished by a door dovetail adjustment?

16. What device is used with hinges to prevent the door from opening beyond the limit of the hinge travel?

17. In what ways can hinges generally be adjusted?

18. In either of what two ways are all contour alignment problems corrected?

19. What is the name of the equipment most commonly used for correcting door contour?

20. Why is it generally necessary to remove and hold a hood rigidly during a straightening process?

21. What adjustments are usually provided at the hinges of hoods?

22. When aligning a deck lid, is it possible to do any aligning operations with other than a door-bar unit?

23. Where is chalk applied in connection with checking decklid alignment?

24. What conditions may exist when the deck lid does not fit the contour of the body?

25. How is paper used to check the seal between the deck lid and the lower back panel?

26. Name three instances where a rubber mallet can be used to align the deck lid with body panel contours.

27. When is proper deck lid alignment said to exist?

Frame Straightening

Chapter

7

As pointed out in Chapter 1, the frame is the foundation of the automobile. This also holds true in unitized construction where the underbody takes the place of the frame. It is therefore of the utmost importance to first determine the extent of collision damage to the frame and then correct it before doing other work. This chapter explains and illustrates how to determine and correct frame damage. We shall also see what the resulting damage to other units of the automobile can be when the frame is damaged.

Not only must the collision repairman be able to check a frame or underbody to determine what damage exists before attempting to repair it, but it is necessary also to determine if frame or underbody misalignment exists before you attempt to correct body alignment. The principles and the actual practice used in checking frame alignment are presented here.

The separate parts of an automobile or truck frame are usually riveted together. Unitized underbodies are almost exclusively welded. Rivets are used because of their great structural strength and their resistance to shearing. These properties exist only if the rivets are properly installed. The second part of this chapter explains rivets and their correct installation.

Some shops specialize in frame straightening only, and many small collision shops farm out their frame straightening jobs. These smaller shops, however, must be able to determine whether or not a frame is misaligned in order to know whether or not it must be sent to the frame shop.

Whether you will be working in a shop specializing in frame straightening and possessing large, expensive equipment or in a small shop with but little equipment, the principles involved in checking a damaged frame or an underbody

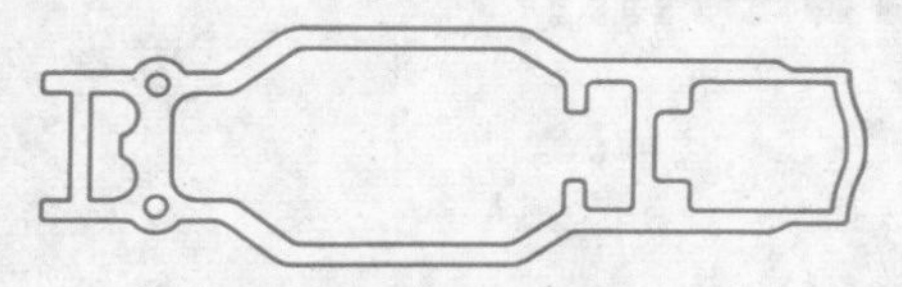

PERIMETER FRAME

This frame is separate from the body and forms a border that surrounds the passenger compartment. It extends forward for power train and suspension support . . . it extends to the rear for trunk and suspension support. Generally, it consists of box or channel-type rails joined by a torque box at the four corners. The torque boxes transfer the primary loads to the frame . . . however, the complete frame relies heavily on the body structure for rigidity.

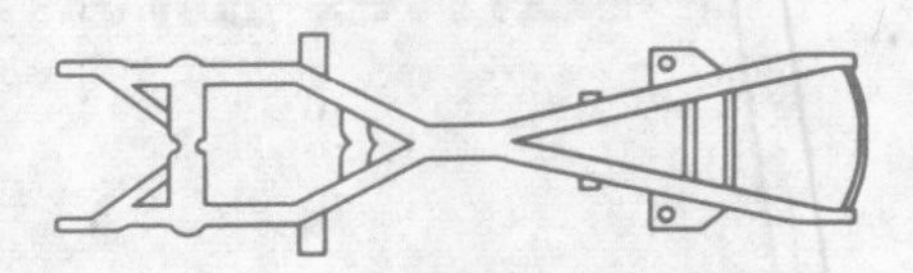

X-TYPE FRAME

Designed as an elongated letter X, this type of frame narrows to a strong junction at the center section. It has considerable front and rear stiffness and a rigid center section. Usually, it has three or more crossmembers to provide torsional stability. However, there are no crossmembers in the center section of the vehicle. This frame forms a rigid structure for the vehicle for mounting the power train, running gear and the body components.

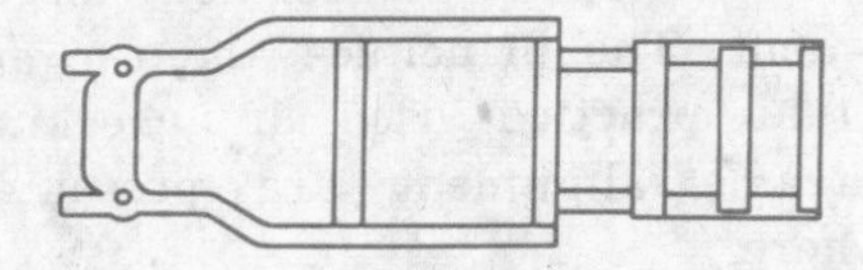

LADDER FRAME

Historically, this type of frame was the forerunner of the various types found on today's vehicles. The ladder frame is similar to the perimeter frame, but the rails do not completely surround the passenger compartment. The rails have less offset and are built on a more direct line between the front and rear wheels. This structure generally has several crossmembers and is reasonably rigid within itself. It forms a strong support on which the body is mounted.

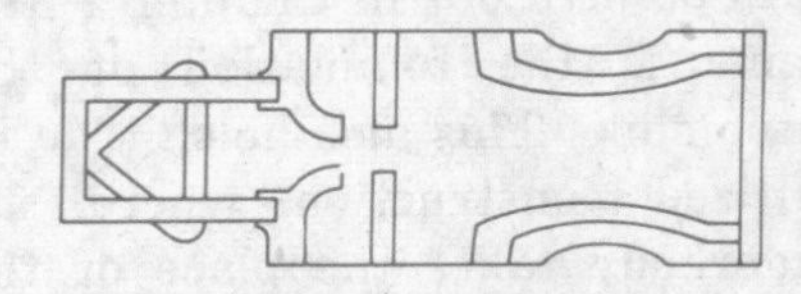

UNITIZED CONSTRUCTION

In this type of construction, every member is related to another so that all sections tend to be load-bearing members. The floor pans, rocker panels, etc. in the lower portion of the body are integrally joined so as to form a basic structure. Heavy reinforcement is used where the engine and suspension are mounted. The front portion generally looks like a separate frame . . . however, the rails are welded to the body structure thereby forming an integral support.

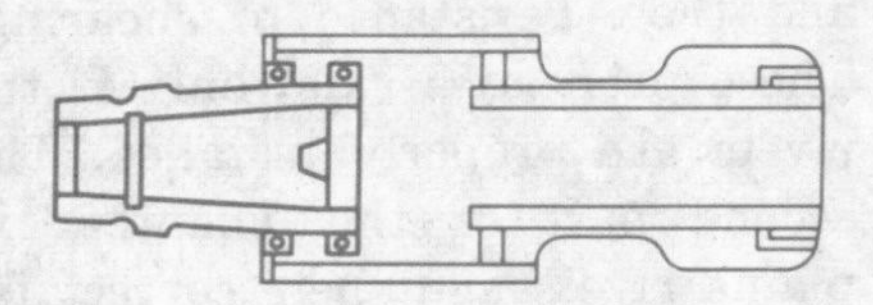

UNITIZED WITH BOLT-ON STUB FRAME

This configuration is found in several models and is particularly noticeable in some front-wheel drive vehicles. A strong, heavy stub frame is utilized to support the engine, accessories, power train and running gear. This frame may have strong, sturdy crossmembers and will extend backward under the floor pan. Back of the cowl, the remaining structure follows the conventional unitized or integral design. The front stub frame is bolted to the unitized body section.

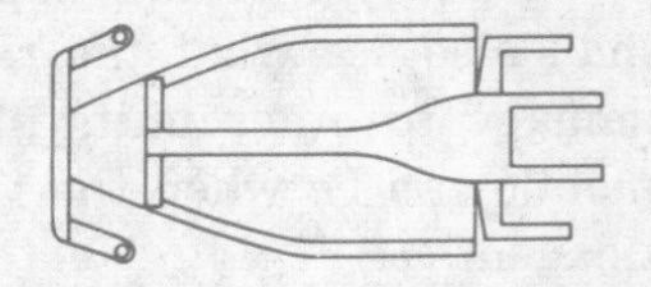

PLATFORM CONSTRUCTION

Somewhat similar to unitized construction, this underbody consists of a reinforced, fairly flat section that forms the entire lower portion of the car. Volkswagon and similar types of cars utilize this construction technique. The lower section which includes the floor pans is a bolt-on assembly which is joined to the body. Therefore, this section depends on the rest of the body for rigidity. It serves as a support member for the engine, running gear and body structure.

Fig. 7-1. Basic types of frames and underbody construction. (Blackhawk Mfg. Co.)

are the same. These principles are discussed in the following sections.

Regardless of the equipment used, a bent frame member must be held at one or two points and the corrective force or pressure must be applied at another point. How this is done, along with illustrations showing typical setups, is described later. It will be necessary to adapt the hook-up to the particular type of frame which you encounter.

During the straightening processes, as a result of necessary heating or excessive working, frame members often lose part of their original strength. It is entirely possible, too, that at some time you will encounter frames having inherent weaknesses. Some types of truck operation, moreover, result in unanticipated shock loads for which the manufacturer has not provided. In all of these cases, you will have to reinforce the frame. The last section discusses the subject of frame reinforcement and shows you just how reinforcements are accomplished.

A misaligned or weakened frame may cause a number of other misalignments in a vehicle. For this reason, it is important that a frame be repaired immediately if it has been damaged or misaligned.

For your convenience, the basic types of car frames and underbodies are shown in Fig. 7-1.

Frame and Unitized Underbody Misalignment

Misalignment and Vehicle Control. In addition to the structural significance of a weakened frame or underbody, the control of the vehicle can be affected. A car or truck with a damaged or weakened frame or underbody can be a menace on the highway, not only to the people who are riding in the vehicle, but also to people and property along the right of way.

Frame or underbody misalignment usually has an effect on the steering control. The steering mechanism is dependent on the frame for support. The suspension parts for both front and rear wheels are also attached directly to the frame. The proper control of the car depends on these units being correctly adjusted and in correct relationship, not only to each other, but to the center line of the vehicle as well. The adjustments in some cases are fine measurements which are immediately affected by any change in the shape or natural position of the frame or underbody.

You have undoubtedly seen examples of one type of misalignment in which a car seems to travel in a partially sidewise manner, commonly called *dog tracking*. It is often necessary for the driver of such a vehicle to struggle constantly to maintain a straight course. The effort required to maintain a straight course with such a vehicle becomes greater as the speed of the vehicle is increased. Misalignment of frame or underbody also can cause tire wear, may affect the brakes, and often accounts for binding of the controls.

Misalignment and Vehicle Performance. Aside from the effect a damaged frame or underbody has on steering control and tire wear, it can also place undue stress on other mechanical parts of the vehicle. The alignment of the engine with the clutch and transmission may be affected. This could cause a manual transmission to jump out of gear, and might result in premature clutch failure.

Any radical change in the angle of the transmission to the rear axle may cause excessive wear in the universal joints, noise in the rear axle, or axle failure. Whenever the frame or underbody has been damaged by a collision, there is a possibility of a partially ruptured hydraulic brake line which could ultimately lead to a complete brake failure. Electrical connections also may be broken or strained.

Importance of Alignment. It is impossible to properly align any part of the body when the frame or underbody is out of alignment. If you attempt to align a door, deck lid, or hood before you correct the damage to a frame or underbody, you will be unable to do a satisfactory job and will end by doing the job twice.

Riveting of Rigid Frames

The various members of most automobile frames are riveted together. Since it is often necessary to remove a cross member to get at the transmission or clutch assembly for repairs, some center cross members may be fastened in place with bolts.

Always fasten a new frame member in place in the same way the original member was installed. If rivets were used, use rivets. If bolts were used, use bolts. However, if bolts were used and if the bolt holes have become enlarged from wear, redrill the holes so they are round, and install the next size larger bolt. This is generally necessary to prevent unwanted movement between the two members.

Equipment. Frame rivets can be satisfactorily installed with a ball-peen hammer and a backing-up tool. The surface of the back-up tool that contacts the rivet can be flat. A better job, however, will result if the back-up tool is provided with a depression which fits the rivet head.

The hammer should weigh at least 2 pounds and the backing-up tool at least 10 pounds. A 1½″ to 2″ diameter steel bar 20″ long with a rivet set (depression) in the end will provide good backing.

Various air and electrically operated rivet guns are available. These require very little instruction since their use is obvious. There is danger in the use of these tools, however, that the head may be properly formed on each end without the hole being properly filled. When using these tools, make sure first of all that they have enough power to handle the rivet size being used. You should check to determine if the rivets are hot enough so they can be expanded in the hole.

Riveting. In general, frame riveting is done only with hot rivets. Hot rivets are easier to form than cold rivets, and a much neater job can be done on forming the upset rivet head. The main reason for using hot rivets is that when a cold rivet is installed in a hole that is not in complete alignment with the mating part, it may not fit the hole. A hot rivet will squash out and fill the entire hole so that a shearing action between the two parts is prevented.

If a rivet is installed so that looseness exists between the parts being joined, wear will develop. The slightest movement between the parts will set up a shearing action and the rivet will eventually be cut off or will break. Proper riveting is most important.

In all instances, the two frame members that are to be riveted together should have enough rivet holes that two of them can be used to firmly bolt the two parts together. Use a long, tapered punch to pry the holes into alignment. Install the two bolts and tighten them securely.

Successful riveting requires fast work. Have everything you need right where you can put your hands on it. This will include the hammer, backing tool, tongs, and a punch.

PROCEDURE:

The rivet must be white hot. Working fast:

(1) With the tongs grasp the rivet next to the rivet head and enter the rivet in the hole.
(2) Immediately hit the rivet head hard with the backing tool. This blow must be hard enough to assure that the flange of the

rivet head will be tight against the frame member.

(3) With the backing tool held firmly against the rivet head, hit hard on the other end of the rivet. This is the blow which expands the rivet in the hole. If this step is not well performed, all subsequent steps will fail to fill the hole. If you are slow, the rivet will lose its heat and its softness. If the backing tool is not held firmly against the rivet head, the head will move away from the frame member and it will be difficult to tighten the rivet. Work fast, hold the backing tool firmly against the head, and hit a hard flat blow with the hammer. The steps to this point are shown in Fig. 7-2.

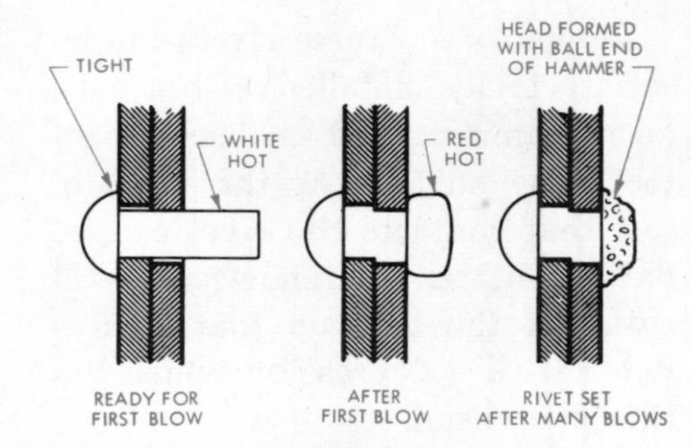

Fig. 7-2. Stages of hot riveting.

(4) If a rivet head has not started to form, as shown in the center illustration, Fig. 7-2, hit a second, harder blow.

(5) Use the ball end of the hammer and form a head on the rivet. The backing tool must be held firmly against the rivet throughout the entire operation.

Checking Frame Alignment

The principles of measurement presented in Chapter 1 apply to frames as well as to bodies. These principles remain the same regardless of the kind of equipment used. Less detailed instructions on how to put these principles to use are required it a complete frame checking and correcting machine, such as shown in Fig. 7-3, is used.

If you understand the principles of checking frame alignment with an improvised setup, you will have no difficulty in applying what you have learned to one of these machines. Learning how to check frame alignment with a few basic tools will give you a better appreciation of these machines. It will make you self-reliant and better able to make quick preliminary frame checks away from the shop, as may sometimes be necessary. All frame checks not made on frame

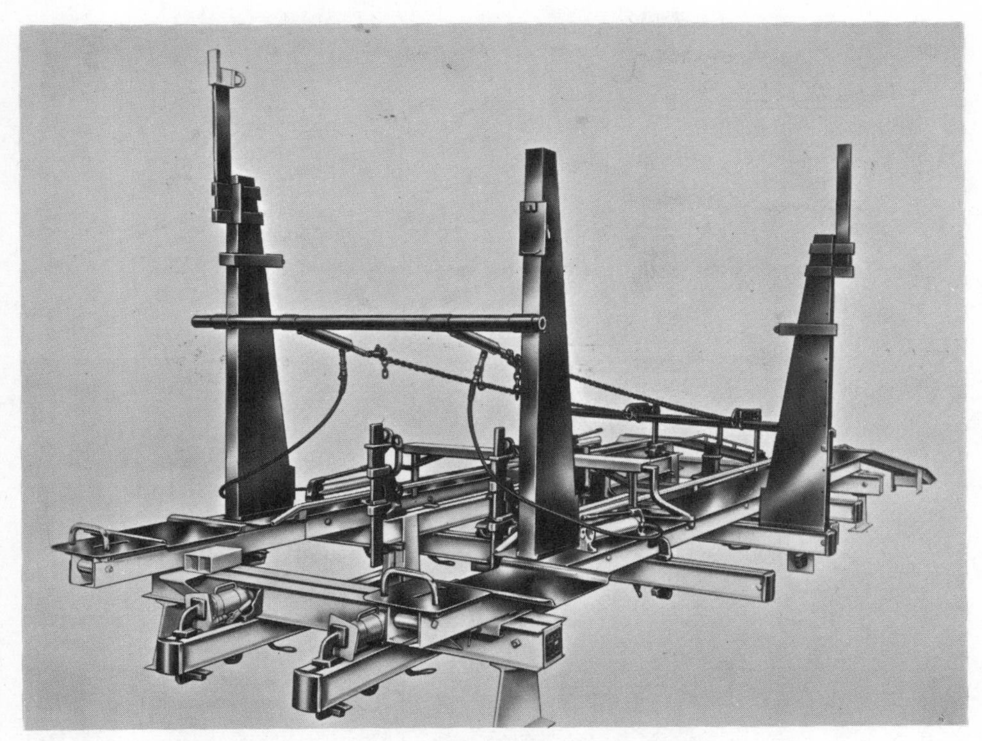

Fig. 7-3. Combination body-frame correction service. (Bear Mfg. Co.)

straightening machines should be made on a level floor.

The importance of frame alignment has been emphasized throughout this entire volume. Assuming you have an appreciation of its importance, this section merely tells you how to check for misalignment. A frame may look like it is in alignment, but it may not be.

Equipment. Frame alignment can be checked with a steel tape and a tram gage, which are generally available in even the smallest shops. The tram gage used in body work, Fig. 7-4, is satisfactory. However, a larger gage with a hinge in the center, or a sliding arrangement, will be more versatile for frame work. The hinge in the center permits the tram gage to be used like a pair of dividers. This permits you to check frame dimensions even though some intervening part makes it impossible to make a direct, point-to-point measurement with a tram gage or

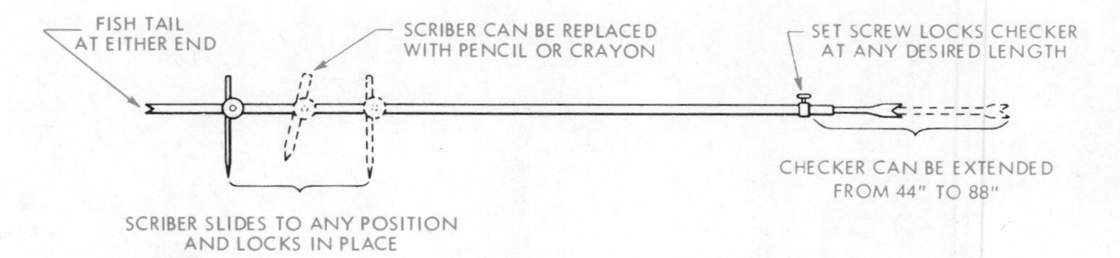

Fig. 7-4. Telescoping tram gage developed for cross body checking.

Fig. 7-5. When three self-centering gages are used to check for vertical frame alignment, the frame is free from vertical misalignment only if all three gages are in horizontal alignment. (John Bean Corp.)

a steel tape. Self-centering gages are also used to check frame alignment. The gages are called *self-centering* because the pins in the center of the gages always remain at the center no matter how far the gage is extended. Self-centering gages are held in place by small pins which fit into the jig holes in the frame side rails, Fig. 7-5.

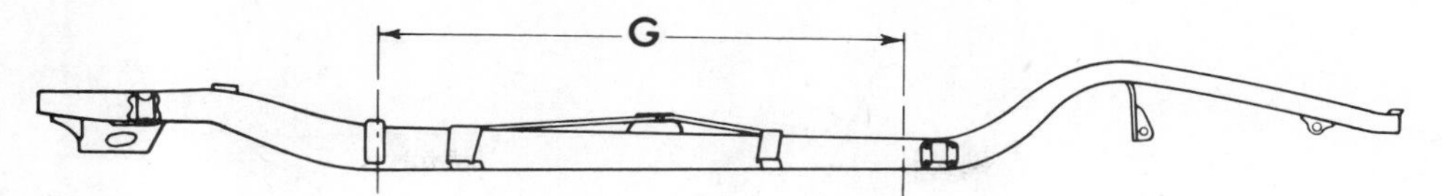

Fig. 7-6. G is the center section of the frame.

Center Section Alignment. In most cars the center section of the frame is designed so that it will be level when the car is under the anticipated normal load. What is meant by frame center section is shown in Fig. 7-6.

Leveling. Place the four corners of the center section on horses of equal height so that they are the same distance from the floor. The frame must rest firmly on these horses. This will mean that instead of supporting the frame, the axles will be hanging from the frame. The springs should not be supporting any of the load. All these frame aligning operations should be done on a smooth, level floor. The floor is used as a reference point and is known as the *datum line* when measurements are taken. A frame setup on blocks for an alignment check is shown in Fig. 7-7. It must be borne in mind, however, that most frame alignment checks are made on the vehicle.

Measuring Height. Make a visual check to see whether or not any of the corners do not touch the horses. If one corner doesn't touch the horse, either this corner is bent up or one of the other corners is bent down. Before any further checking is done, loosen all of the frame-to-body bolts. It is possible that some condition of misalignment in the body is holding the frame out of alignment.

If the corner is still up after the body bolts are loosened, continue with further checks of the center section, but keep this particular point of misalignment in mind.

X-Checking. When the four corners of the center section are established at the same height from the floor, all that remains is to X-check the center section from one corner to the other, comparing the diagonals. These measurements are designated as *X* and *Y* in Fig. 7-7. If the diagonals are not the same, the frame is probably swayed at the center section or it has become diamond-shaped from a corner collision. Exaggerated forms of frame sway and diamond-shaped frame are shown later.

Front Section Alignment. After the alignment of the center section has been checked, the alignment of the front section can be checked. The front section of the frame is

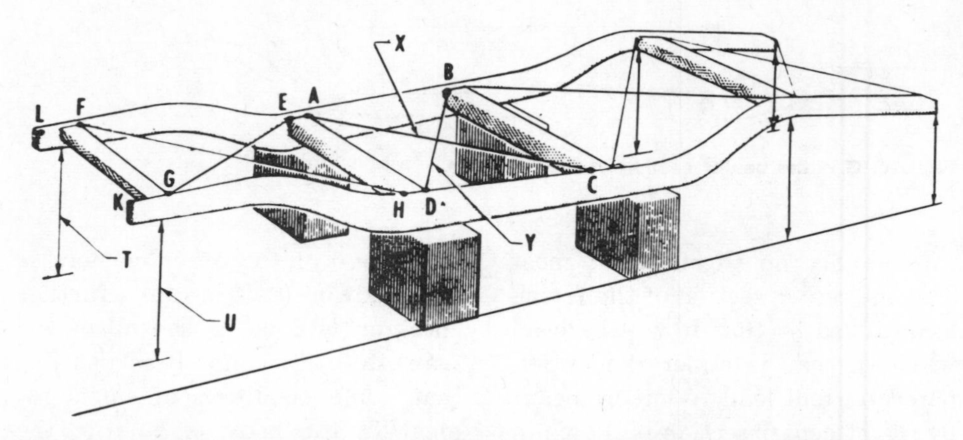

Fig. 7-7. Checking frame alignment from floor to selected points along the chassis.

considered as all of the frame forward of the center section.

With the frame resting on the horses under the center section, make measurements *T* and *U*, Fig. 7-7. This will quickly establish whether any twist exists which has raised or lowered one corner. The front section is then X-checked from *E* to *G* and *F* to *H*. If these two measurements are not the same, the frame is either swayed, diamond-shaped, or buckled up or down. For example, if *EG* is longer than *FH*, the frame is swayed to the left. If *FH* is longer than *EG*, the frame is swayed to the right.

Further X measurements can be made out to the extreme ends of the frame *K* and *L*. These measurements will establish whether or not the frame ends, or *horns* as they are sometimes called, are out of alignment. The horns can be bent in or out or up or down. Height measurements from the tips of the horns to the floor will show which one is bent either up or down.

To isolate the exact point or area of misalignment, smaller areas of the front section can be X-checked. Measurements also can be made at any point along the side of the frame to the floor. Always be sure to measure from like points at both sides of the frame. These measurements will be the same at each side of the frame except where the misalignment exists. If one side is higher from the floor than the other, the frame is either twisted or buckled upward at that point. If one side is lower than the other side, the frame is buckled downward at that point.

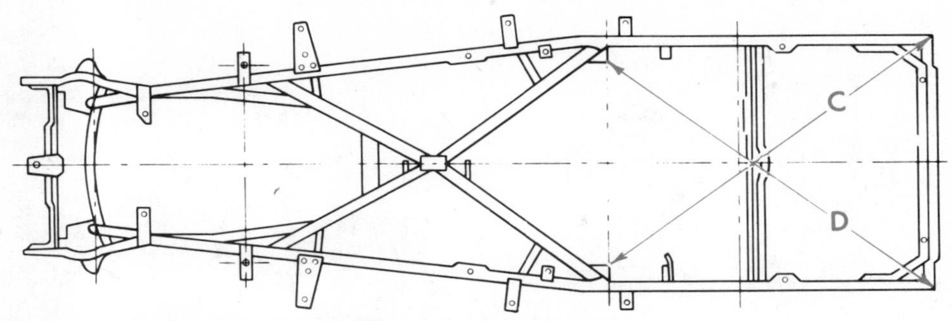

Fig. 7-8. Checking frame rear section in a horizontal plane.

Rear Section Alignment. The rear section of the frame is considered as that portion of the frame from the center section to the rear.

The first measurements are height measurements from the two extreme rear corners to the floor. If one of these dimensions is more than the other, either one corner is up or the other is down or the frame rear section is twisted. Next X-check the rear section at *C* and *D*, Fig. 7-8. If *C* is more than *D*, the frame is swayed to the left. If *D* is more than *C*, the frame is swayed to the right. A diamond-shaped frame can also cause either of these measurements to be more than the other.

To locate the exact point or area where the misalignment exists, smaller areas of the rear section can be X-checked. Always measure from like points at both sides of the frame. Measurements also can be made from any point along the frame to the floor. Measurements, when compared, should be the same. Any difference will indicate that the frame is either buckled or twisted in that area. How to correct both of these conditions is described in the following sections.

Checking Unitized Underbody Alignment

The same principles hold true for underbody misalignment and frame misalignment in a car that has rigid frame construction.

A regular frame machine with frame centering and leveling gages is also equipped for handling unitized underbodies. A unitized underbody, with lineal dimensions and master locating hole for checking alignment with such a machine is shown in Fig. 7-9. All frame di-

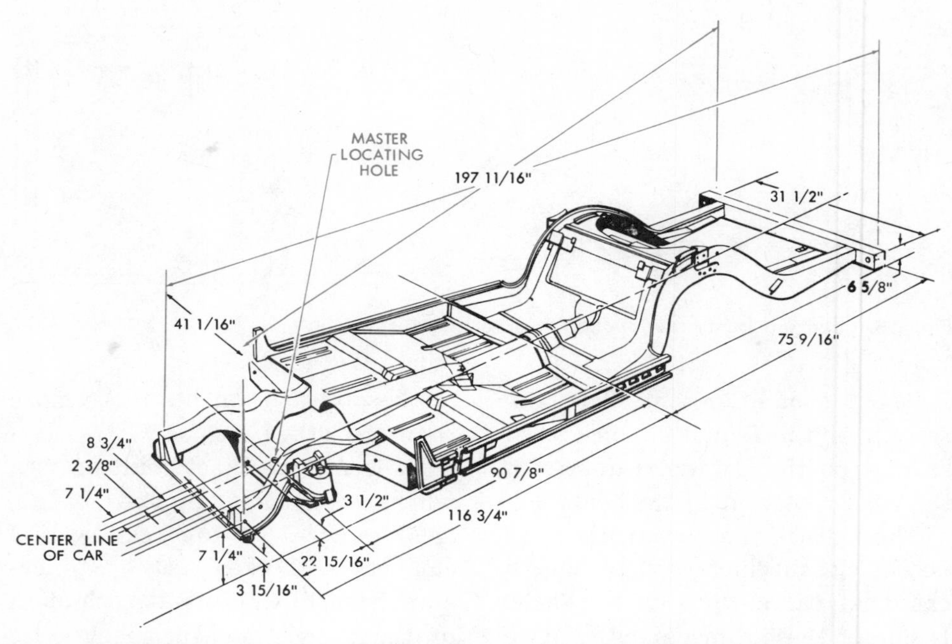

Fig. 7-9. A typical unitized underbody with lineal dimensions and the master locating hole for checking alignment with a frame machine. (Lincoln-Mercury Div., Ford Motor Co.)

Fig. 7-10. X-checking a vehicle and frame with a two-point tram gage. (John Bean Corp.)

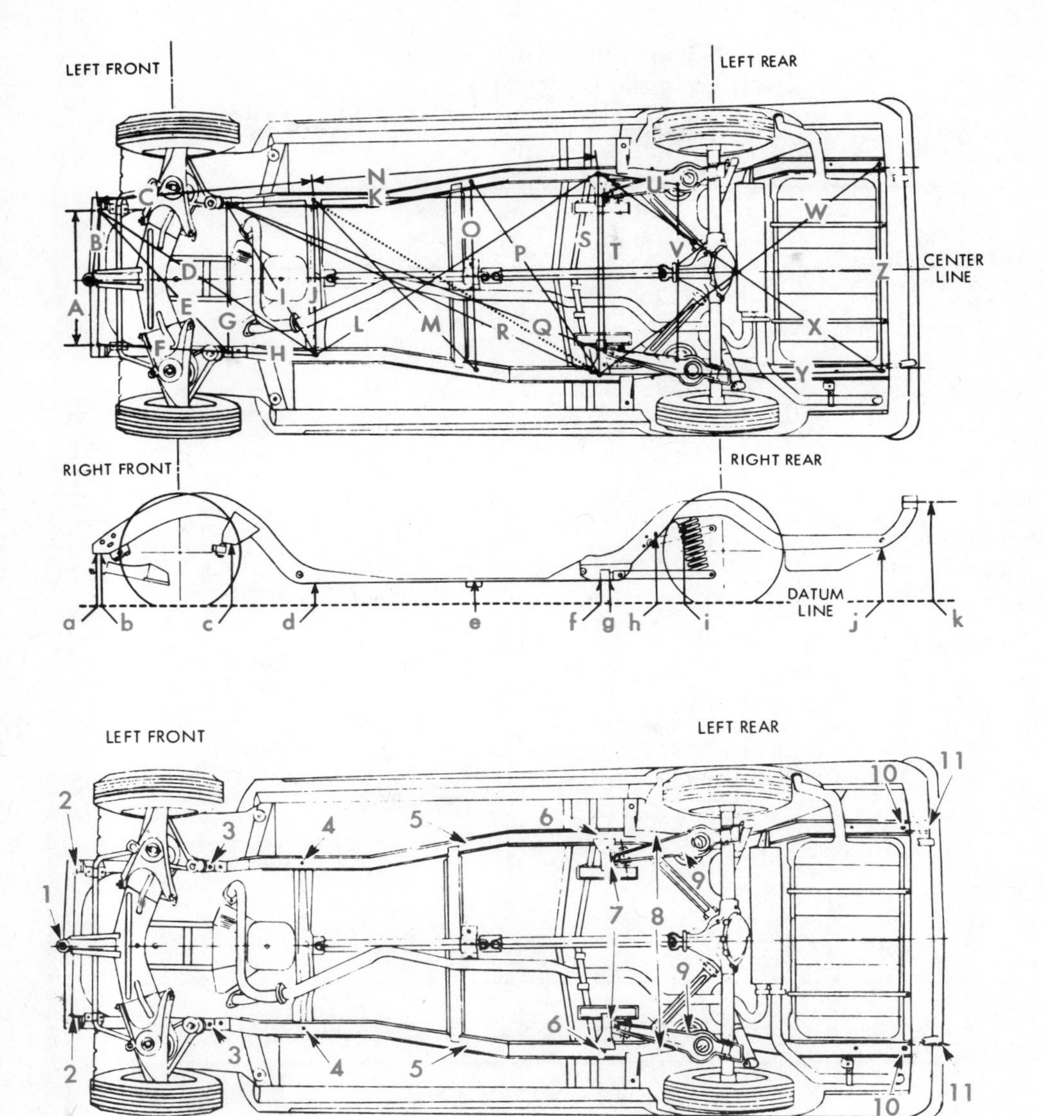

Fig. 7-11. This car frame shows vertical and horizontal dimensions and tram gage reference points. The actual dimensions in inches can be found in Table 7-1.

TABLE 7-1 DIMENSIONS AND
REFERENCE POINTS SHOWN IN FIGURE 7-11

HORIZONTAL:

Fig. Ref.	Dimension (Inches)	Ref. Point	to Ref. Point	
A	28-29/32	2	2	
B	14-15/32	1	2	(either side)
C	48	2	4	(same side)
D	56-5/8	2	4	(opp. side)
E	40-29/32	2	3	(opp. side)
F	27-23/32	2	3	(same side)
G	31-5/32	3	3	
H	20-9/32	3	4	(same side)
I	37-3/16	3	4	(opp. side)
J	31-5/32	4	4	
K	81-29/32	3	7	(same side)
L	69-1/2	4	6	(opp. side)
M	48-25/32	4	5	(opp. side)
N	59-7/8	4	6	(same side)
O	38-3/16	5	5	
P	46-11/16	5	6	(opp. side)
Q	87-23/32	3	7	(opp. side)
R	87-19/32	3	6	(opp. side)
S	40-1/8	6	6	
T	31-21/32	7	7	
U	17-23/32	6	9	(same side)
V	37-23/32	9	9	
W	69-23/32	6	10	(left side)
X	68-15/16	6	10	(right side)
Y	55-7/8	6	10	(same side)
Z	42	10	10	(same side)

VERTICAL

Fig. Ref.	Dimension (Inches)	Datum Line to Ref. Point
a	12-1/2	1
b	12-7/16	2
c	14-3/8	3
d	6-1/16	4
e	6-1/16	5
f	6	6
g	6-1/32	7
h	14-11/16	8
i	16-13/32	9
j	10	10
k	18-21/32	11

mensions are checked with reference to the master *locating hole* which is attached to a frame machine.

The body tram gage, Fig. 7-10, is an accurate method of determining underbody alignment, but self-centering gages are also widely used. On unitized bodies, self-centering gages are mounted by means of C-clamps, magnetic adapters, or special studs screwed into the bottom of the body.

Some typical alignment check and reference points are shown in Fig. 7-11. All of the checks can be made with a tram gage. Fig. 7-11, top, shows letters which represent frame dimensions. Table 7-I lists the same letters with the corresponding dimensions in inches. Fig. 7-11, bottom, shows numbered tram gage reference points. Table 7-I lists the tram gage reference points and the distances between them.

Straightening Frame Damage

Once you know where to hold and where to apply pressure, straightening is best accomplished on a *frame straightener*. Modern frame straighteners permit several setups to be made at one time. Even

Fig. 7-12. Wheel balancing as well as body and frame straightening may be done on this frame and body press. (John Bean Corp.)

without a straightener, you can correct almost any damage by improvising setups.

Illustrations of typical damaged frames are shown in this section. Heavy black arrows show where corrective force is applied and heavy black blocks show where the frame is to be held. Light arrows indicate that the member should be pulled to simplify the correction. These illustrations also show where heat is to be applied.

A rack type frame and body press, which can be used for both frame straightening and underbody damage correction, is shown in Fig. 7-12. If a frame and body

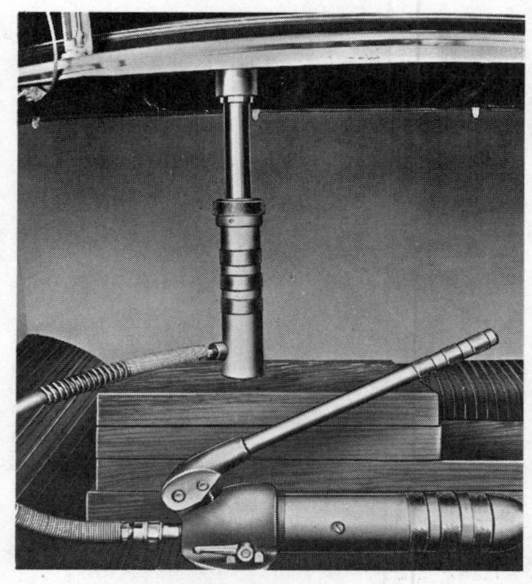

Fig. 7-13. The hydraulic ram is one method of applying the push necessary to correct bodies and frames damaged by collision. (Ford Motor Corp.)

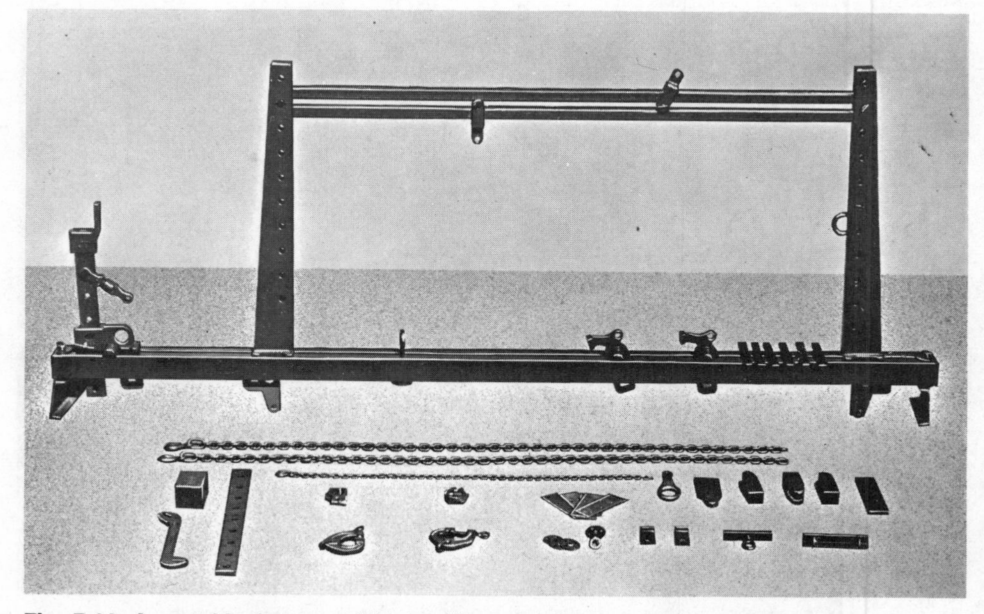

Fig. 7-14. A portable frame and body aligner is shown with its various clamps, chains, and pull plates in the foreground. When in use, a hydraulic ram is installed to apply force.

press is not available, portable hydraulic equipment as described in Chapter 5 may be used.

A *hydraulic ram,* Fig. 7-13, is a simple portable tool available for frame and underbody straightening. A hydraulic ram can often be applied directly against the damaged frame or underbody, thereby saving valuable time needed to set up more elaborate equipment. However, other equipment must be used if the hydraulic ram cannot be applied directly and at the correct angle to the damage.

The portable *body and frame aligner* shown in Figs. 7-14 and 7-15 uses the type of hydraulic ram shown in Fig. 7-13. With the hydraulic ram supplying mechanical power, the aligner is able to apply corrective force at any angle on all sections of the body or frame. However, the *frame straightener and body press,* Fig. 7-12, is a more complete tool than the porta-

Fig. 7-15. The portable aligner is straightening a unitized underbody. The underbody has no center cross member to exert force against. Therefore, clamps are installed on the pinch welds below the rocker panels. A length of tubing, along with the clamps and chains, serves as a temporary cross member against which corrective force is exerted. (John Bean Corp.)

ble body and frame aligner. Consequently, it often provides a faster repair because more than one hookup or correction can be made at the same time.

Use of Heat in Straightening. Frame side rails and cross members are usually formed from low-carbon steel. Strength is imparted to the frame members during the rolling and forming processes, but this surface hardness is partially lost if heat is used during frame straightening. This loss of surface hardness is often the lesser of two evils. Any attempt to straighten a severely crimped or buckled frame while cold may cause cracks in the bent part or ruptures in welds. Heat is also used in straightening underbody damage.

Because a frame is constructed from comparatively thick material, bending or otherwise twisting it work-hardens it in the area of the bend. Any further attempt to force it to another position may cause it to crack or break. For this reason, it is advisable to apply heat to the damaged portion of the frame, then to perform the straightening operations necessary while the frame is still red hot. Heat is applied with an oxyacetylene gas torch. If a sharp bend exists, heat should be used whether the frame is in the car or not. If the damage is such that the use of heat is called for at some point where it might damage the body, raise the body away from the work.

The heat should be applied directly to the damaged portion which you want to bend or reshape. The frame will bend in the heated area first. Unless the heat is applied properly, the corrective bend will not be made in the right place, and instead of having one bend to correct, you will have two.

If the frame is not believed to be strong after the straightening is completed, it should be reinforced, as discussed later.

Application of Heat. Actually, only a very little heat is required to bring the color of the heated member to a dull red, at which time it is at the proper temperature to be worked. The temperature should be kept below 1200° F, or a cherry red, since excessive (white hot) heat could weaken the frame member and cause permanent damage. Extra care must be taken when applying heat to a unitized underbody because of the differences in the gage of the metals in the sub-frame.

If heat must be applied, start to heat the buckled portion or damaged area well out near the edge. Fan the flame over the entire buckled area so that it is heated uniformly. Best results can be obtained by moving the flame in an ever decreasing circle until the area is entirely heated.

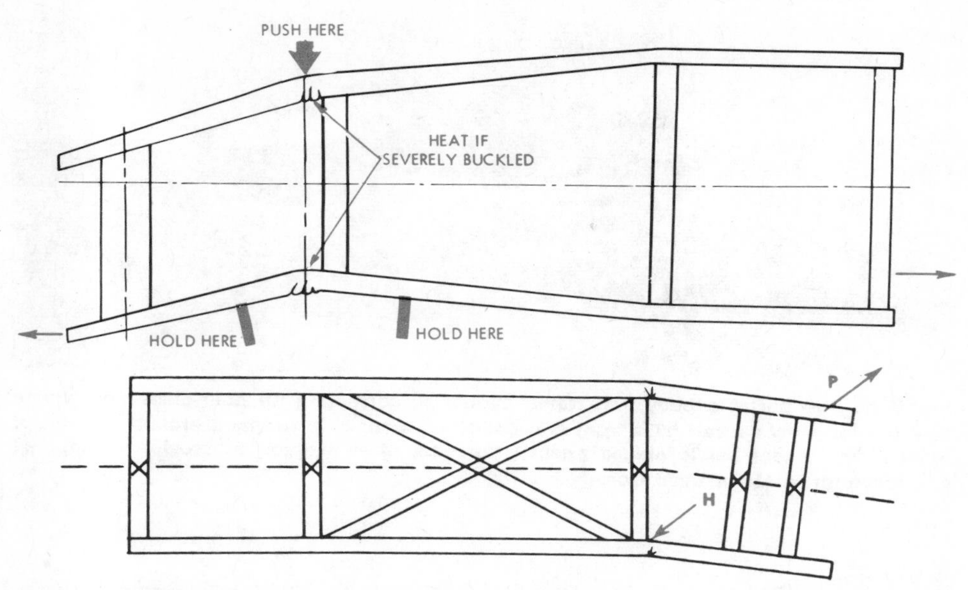

Fig. 7-16. Two methods of correcting side sway damage from a front end collision. (Top: Bear Mfg. Co.; Bottom: John Bean Corp.)

Do not spot-heat any portion of the area. Spot-heating will be likely to damage the metal itself, and will undoubtedly make correction of the original damage more difficult. Heating at first well out toward the edge of a buckled area will remove the chill from the surrounding area. This prevents the heated area from cooling so fast that it hardens before the damage is corrected.

Sway. Sway from a front end collision is shown in Fig. 7-16. In addition to showing the line of damaging force, this illustration also shows directions in which the corrective force can be applied. The illustration also shows where heat should be applied and two methods of correcting the frame. Fig. 7-17 shows a frame in the process of being corrected for front end sway.

It may be necessary to push the damaged portion beyond its normal straight line position to overcome any spring back which might occur. You can decide whether or not to use reinforcements after the frame is straightened.

Two other types of frame sway are shown in Fig. 7-18. In both cases, the lines of corrective force are shown. The places where the frame should be held are clearly labeled, and arrows also indicate where heat should be applied.

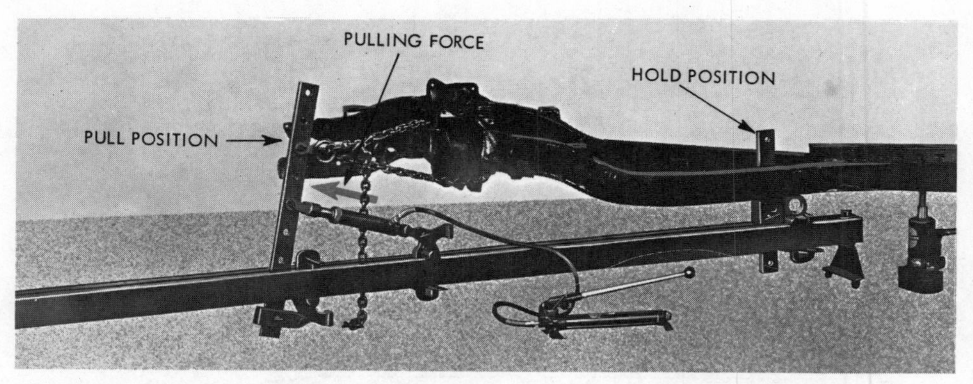

Fig. 7-17. The portable body and frame aligner is correcting an hour-glass type frame side rail for sway caused by a front end collision. A chain is wrapped around the rail of point P and a tool bar is placed against the tube of H position to provide a diagonal corrective force. (John Bean Corp.)

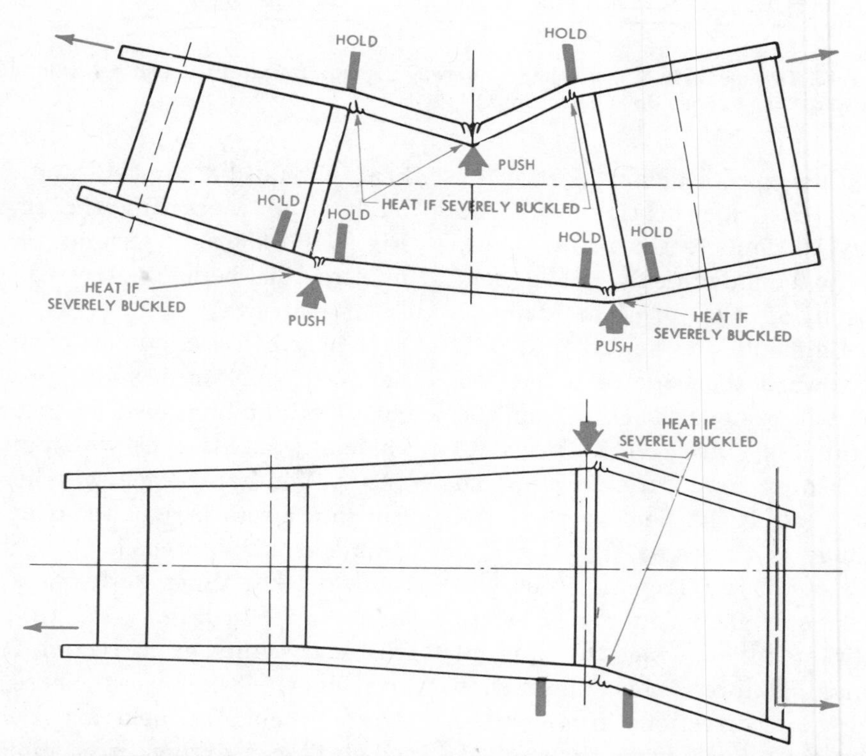

Fig. 7-18. Top: sway from collision in center; Bottom: sway from rear end collision. (John Bean Corp.)

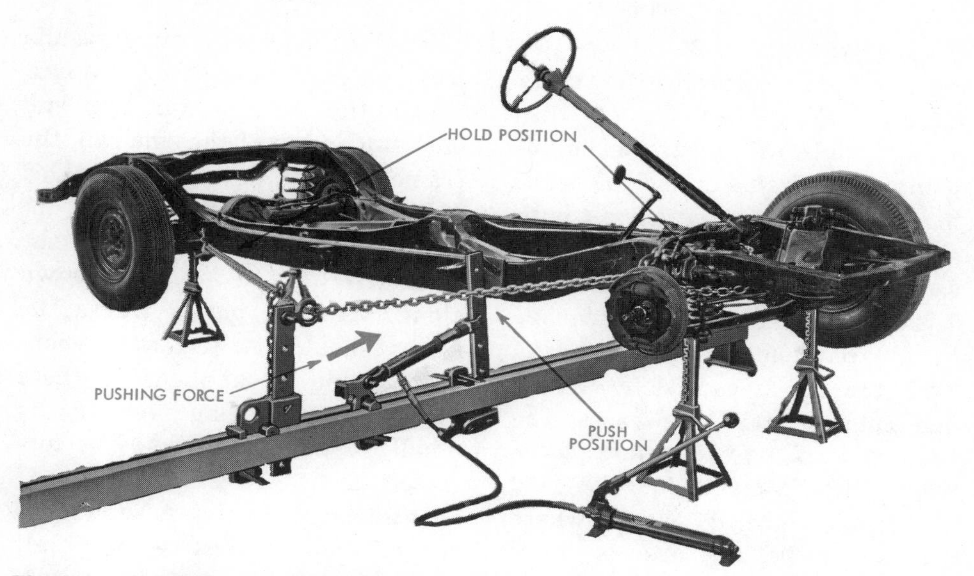

Fig. 7-19. The body and frame aligner in the process of correcting vehicle side sway. This method of alignment is often referred to as the bow string method. Push is applied against only one frame side rail and the vehicle body transmits the force of this push to the other rail.

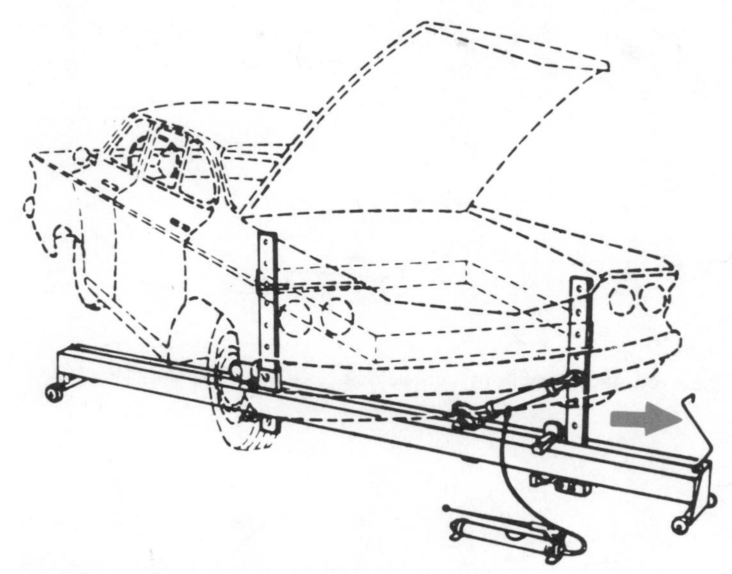

Fig. 7-20. The body and frame aligner correcting a unitized body for sway caused by a rear end collision. Notice that the diagonal push is exerted from inside the car, eliminating the need for outer sheet metal removal. (John Bean Corp.)

Figs. 7-19 and 7-20 show two frames being corrected for sway damage.

Sag. Side rail sag is misalignment of the frame due to the bending downward of either or both side rails. Two different types of sag are shown in Figs. 7-21 and 7-22. In Fig. 7-21, the sag is caused by a front end collision. In Fig. 7-22, the sag is caused by a rear end collision. In both cases, the lines of corrective force and places where the frame should be held are clearly labeled. Places where heat should be used are also indicated. Fig. 7-23 shows a sagged frame being corrected.

Mashed or Buckled Frame. A mashed or buckled frame is more seriously damaged than either a swayed or sagged frame. A mashed or buckled frame results from an extremely severe impact. In addition to side rail sag and buckling on top of the side rail, the frame is bent down and buckled underneath the side rail.

In both Figs. 7-24 and 7-25, the corrective lines of force are shown along with the places where the frame should be held and where heat should be applied. In these instances, the damage nearest the middle of the frame should be corrected first.

Diamond Frame. A diamond-shaped frame comes as the result of a low impact at one corner, sufficient to push the cross members out of being at right angle to the side rail.

Such damage is shown in Fig. 7-26, and the way in which the

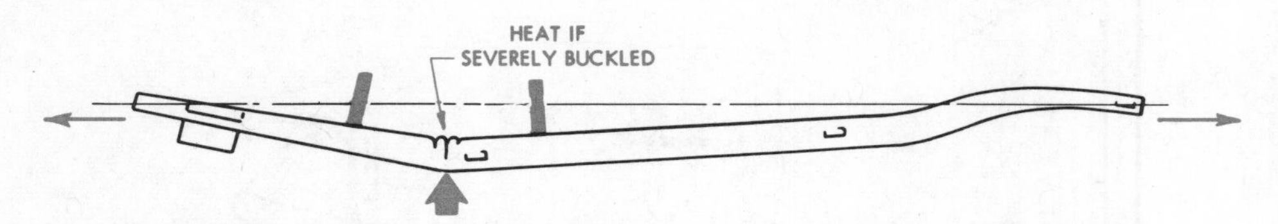

Fig. 7-21. Side rail sag from front end collision. (Bear Mfg. Co.)

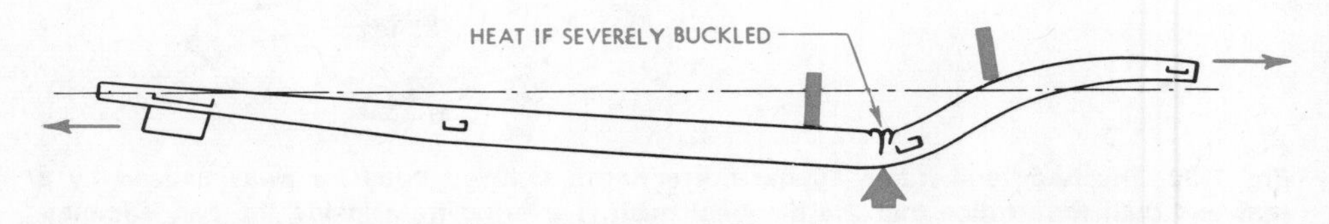

Fig. 7-22. Side rail sag from rear end collision. (Bear Mfg. Co.)

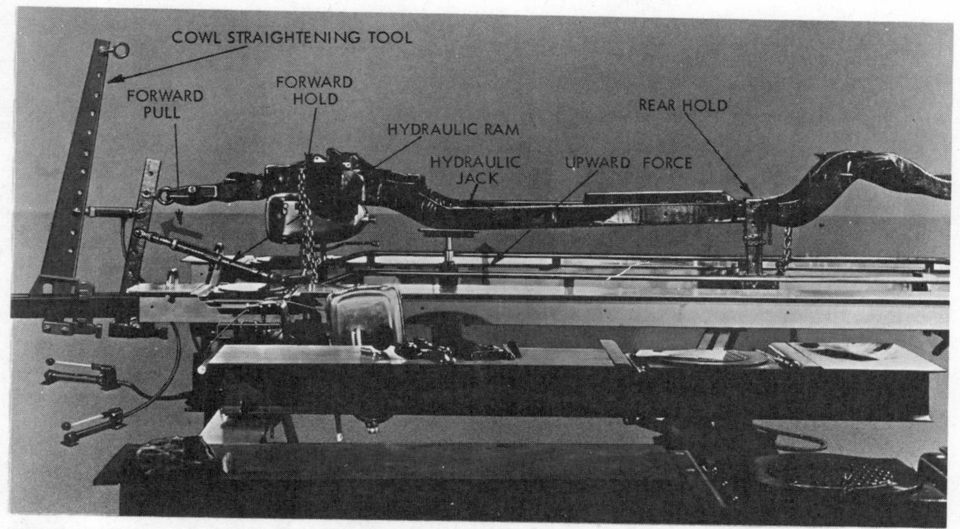

Fig. 7-23. The frame straightener and body press is correcting a sagged frame side rail. Note the various hookups for applying the correcting force plus the body upright tool for correcting damage in the cowl area of the body. Also note the position of the forward and rear holds (John Bean Corp.)

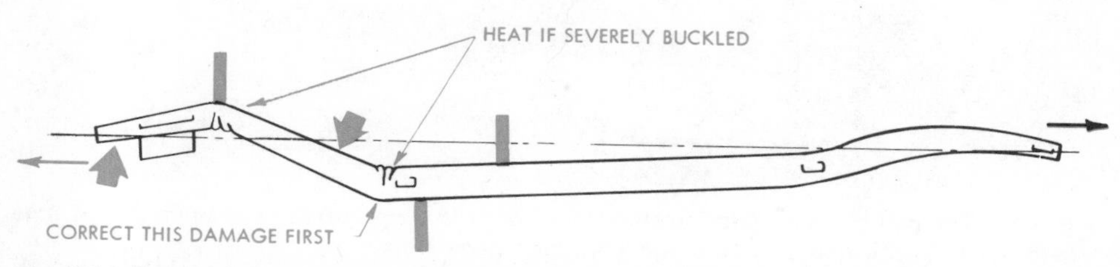

Fig. 7-24. Frame mashed and buckled from front end collision showing most likely points of frame buckling. (Bear Mfg. Co.)

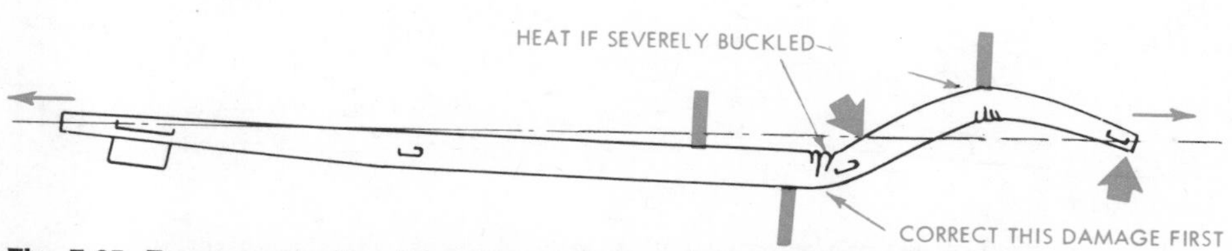

Fig. 7-25. Frame mashed and buckled from rear end collision. (Bear Mfg. Co.)

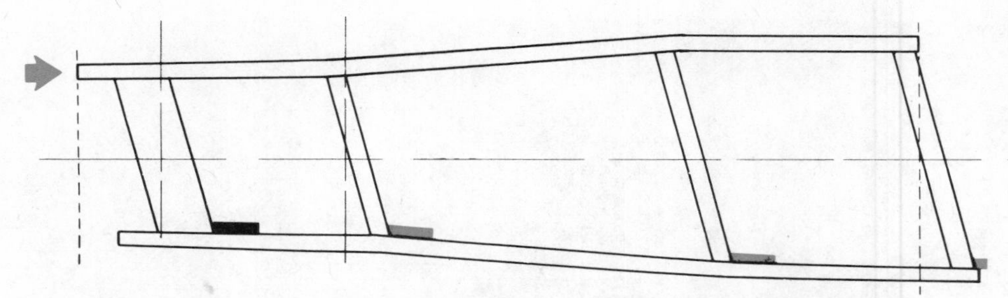

Fig. 7-26. Diamond frame as it develops from a strong corner impact. (Bear Mfg. Co.)

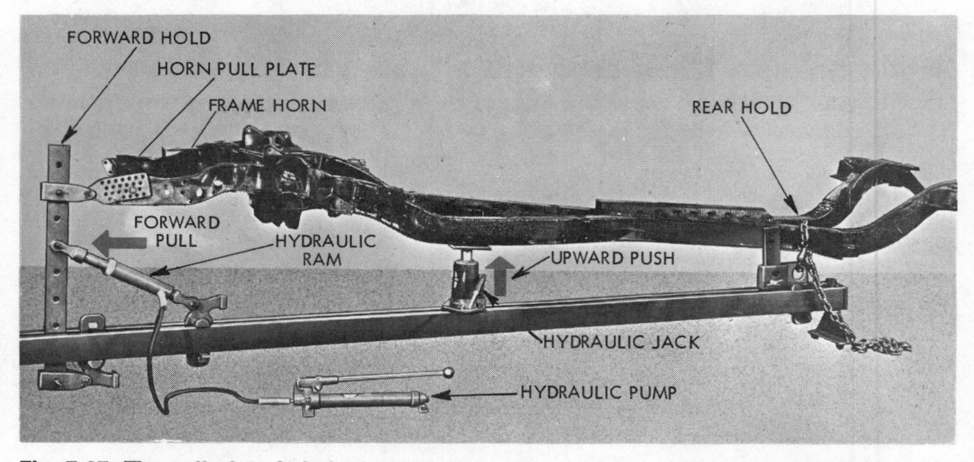

Fig. 7-27. The pull plate is bolted to the frame horn to help correct this hour-glass frame which has both sag and diamond damage. (John Bean Corp.)

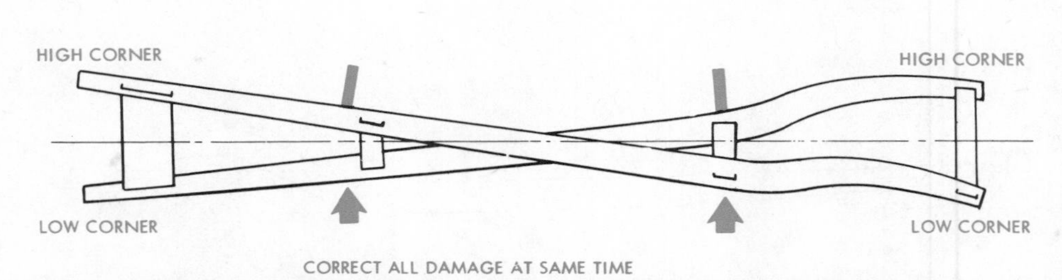

Fig. 7-28. Twisted frame represents a complex type of damage. (Bear Mfg. Co.)

damage should be corrected is indicated by arrows showing where corrective force should be applied and where the frame should be held. Fig. 7-27 shows a frame being corrected by a frame and body aligner.

Twisted Frame. Hold the frame down at the two points indicated in Fig. 7-28. If you have four separate jacks, pressure can be applied at the four points indicated at the same time. If you have only one jack, you will have to move the jack a number of times. If the damage is severe, the cross member flanges at the side members may be twisted. Apply heat at these points as the pressure is applied. Fig. 7-29 shows a twisted frame being corrected.

Holder. If you are working with a frame straightening machine such as shown in Fig. 7-29, the method of holding is obvious since almost every possible requirement has been anticipated in the design. If you must improvise setups, several things are possible.

Eyebolts in the Floor. Some shops have been very successful in holding frames down by running a chain through the eye of an eye-

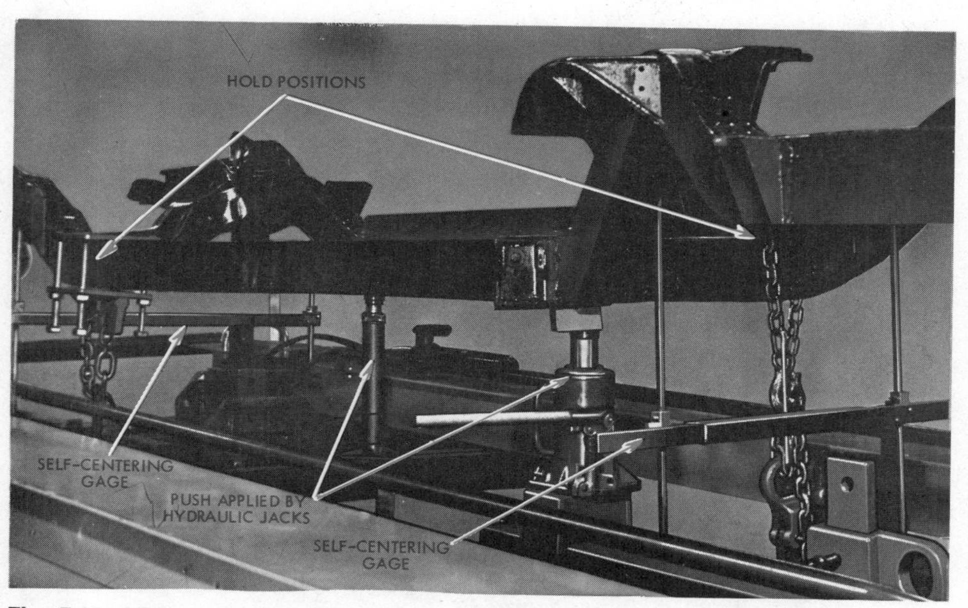

Fig. 7-29. When correcting this twisted truck frame with the frame straightener and body aligner, chains are used to hold the carriage beams at the hold position while the hydraulic jacks apply a pushing force. The hydraulic jacks are used to lift the frame until all the self-centering gages are in a parallel alignment. Usually the frame must be corrected past the misalignment, and in the opposite direction of the damage, in order to bring the frame to the correct position. (John Bean Corp.)

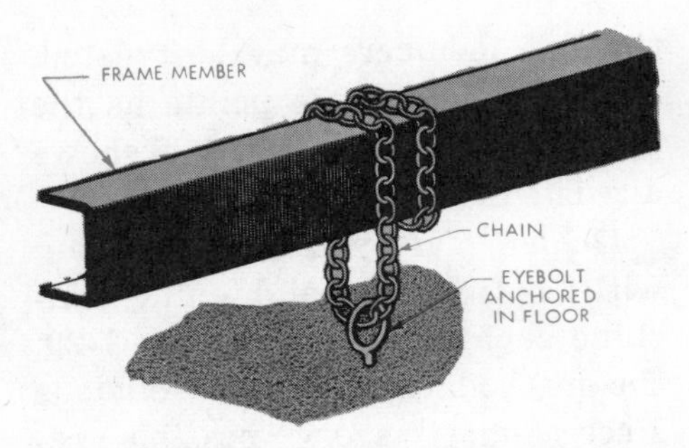

Fig. 7-30. Eyebolt and chain used to hold down frame.

bolt and over the frame, Fig. 7-30. The eyebolt must be firmly anchored into the floor. Any number of eyebolts can be used.

An I-beam, chains, and blocks can be used not only to hold the frame down, but can be used to hold the frame when straightening it in a horizontal plane as well. The I-beam also provides a base for the jacks with which the corrective force is applied. How this is accomplished is shown in Fig. 7-31.

The pressure required for straightening frames can be applied with the same hydraulic jacks used for correcting body damage. However, as a rule, larger heavier-duty jacks are used for straightening truck frames. Assistance to the jacks, of course, is afforded by the use of the heating torch.

Remember that all of these jacks are very powerful. Spread the force exerted by the jack by means of a suitable head on the jack or by means of a block, Fig. 7-31. This is particularly important when you are working on comparatively light passenger car frames.

Some types of frame damage may permit pushing from one portion of the frame to another. In these cases, don't lose sight of the fact that the *pressure is being delivered to both ends of the jack,* otherwise you may be doing new damage while correcting the old.

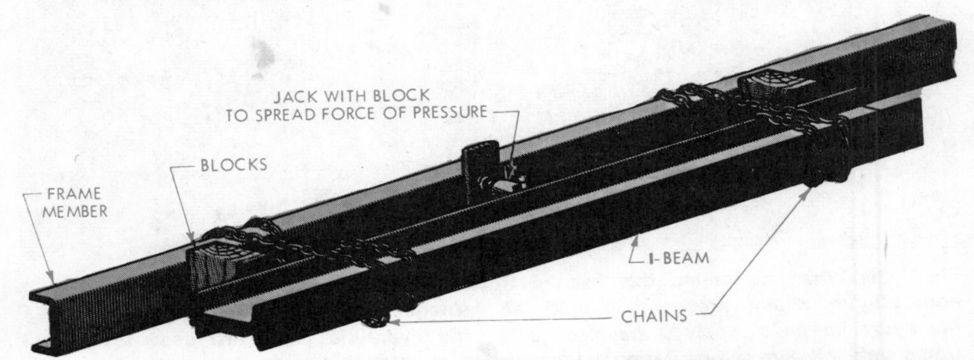

Fig. 7-31. Use of I-beam to hold and to provide a base from which pressure is applied. (Bear Mfg. Co.)

Reinforcement

Reinforcements are added to frames when there is doubt that the frame will withstand the strains to which it will be subjected. A typical example of when a frame reinforcement is needed is when a dump truck frame has sagged and then been straightened. A sagged dump truck frame is illustrated in Fig. 7-32. Sometimes new trucks have their side members reinforced so that sag will not occur.

Most of the strain on a frame is vertical. For this reason, the reinforcement added would be positioned so that it will resist vertical stress. Reinforcements can be made from angle iron, flat plates, channels, or any type of section which will fit the contour of the frame in the area needing reinforcements. Reinforcements can be either welded or riveted into place, or they can be fastened by both welds and rivets.

In the example shown in Fig. 7-32, either a flat plate can be welded and riveted to each side member across the area needing reinforcement, or else a channel section which will fit inside the frame can be used. The type of reinforcement used depends on whether or not it can be installed without interfering with other members of the frame or working parts of the chassis.

Reinforcements can be made from any stock thickness which may seem desirable, depending on the use for which the vehicle is intended. The reinforcement should extend a considerable distance along the frame beyond the area being reinforced.

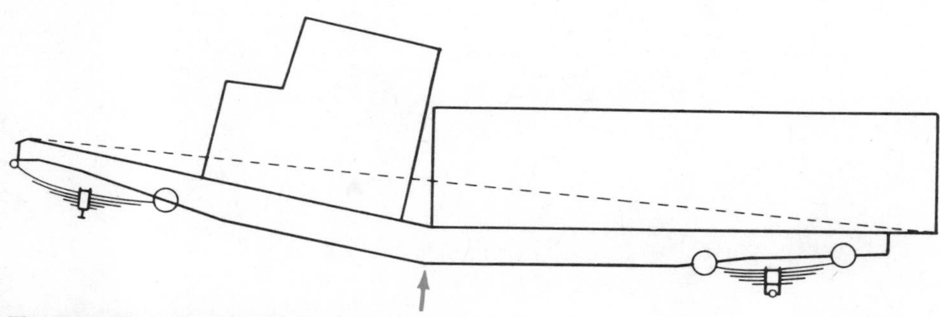

Fig. 7-32. Sagged dump truck frame.

Checking On Your Knowledge

The following questions give you the opportunity to check up on yourself. If you have read the chapter carefully, you should be able to answer the questions. If you have any difficulty, read the chapter over once more so that you have the information well in mind before you go on with your reading.

1. What is the most common method for fastening frame members together?
2. Can frame misalignment have a bearing on anything other than body alignment?
3. What is meant by the term "dog tracking"?
4. When a new frame member is installed in place of a member which was bolted in place, how should the new member be fastened?
5. Why are hot rivets generally used for frame riveting?
6. What is the minimum equipment with which you can check frame alignment?
7. When checking the alignment of the center section of a frame, why is it a good idea to loosen the frame-to-body bolts if the frame does not rest squarely on the work horses?
8. What do most passenger automobile frames have in common at the center section?
9. What damage might occur if an attempt is made to straighten a severely bumped frame without the use of heat?
10. What color should a folded frame member be when it is at the proper temperature to be straightened?
11. In general, can the same hydraulic tools be used to apply pressure for frame straightening and for body straightening?
12. Reinforcements are usually positioned to resist stress in what direction?
13. How are frame reinforcements usually fastened in place?
14. Are frames sometimes reinforced before damage has occurred?

An Approach to Collision Jobs

Chapter

8

This chapter, in a very real sense, can be called a summation of everything you have learned about collision work thus far. The explanations given will enable you to correctly apply the technical skills to actual jobs.

However, there is much more to collision work than the mastery of skills. You must be able to apply these skills and the knowledge you have acquired profitably and economically. The reasons why you should study the collision damage before you start corrective operations, and the kind of things you should look for and note, are re-emphasized in the first section.

While a number of separate discussions of measuring have appeared in the preceding chapters, the next section gives you additional detailed information on how to make body measurements. Several sequences of damage correction are presented in the following sections so you can see the value of applying corrective measures in their proper sequence. Another section explains how to evaluate the separate considerations involved in deciding whether a panel or part should be repaired or replaced. The next section gives the same type of treatment to the question of filling panels with solder or straightening them. The final section of this chapter brings together all of the technical information you have learned and shows you how to apply it in estimating the cost for a repair in advance.

Extent of Damage

The ultimate success of any collision repair job depends on the accuracy of the analysis of what is damaged, and how the damage occurred. This principle is true whether you are working on a conventional body and frame or on a car of unit construction.

There is a definite five-step procedure to follow in correcting collision damage. This procedure is as follows:

1. Determine the extent of the damage.
2. Familiarize yourself with the construction of the vehicle.
3. Decide upon a plan for correction after careful study of the damage.
4. Perform the actual collision repair in progressive steps.
5. Check the work frequently until damage is corrected.

In collision work, as we have stressed so often, the corrective forces must be applied in a manner directly opposite to and in the reverse order of the forces which caused the damage. When a damaged car or truck is brought to you for repair, determine all you can about the way in which the damage occurred. In addition to providing the order of procedure for correcting body and frame damage, your inquiries may reveal a number of things which will have a bearing on where you should look for hidden damage.

The front and rear suspensions, the entire power train (transmission, drive shaft, rear axle, etc.), brakes, steering mechanism, the power plant (engine and related parts), and the electrical system all are subject to damage in a collision. By finding out wherever possible just how the damage occurred, you will know precisely where to look or check for parts needing repair or replacement. Always include a check of wheel alignment on every collision job of any consequence. Look for damage to the radiator, cracked cylinder block or transmission case, bent axle housings, broken engine supports, etc.

While the straightening of body panels and fenders represents the field in which the greatest volume of collision work is done, collision damage occurs on mechanical parts of the vehicle as well. The repair of mechanical parts is an important part of the repair of collision damage. When you are finished repairing a vehicle damaged in a collision or one that has turned over, it must run well, it must steer well, and the brakes and all of the electrical units must be in operating condition. Although the correction of mechanical difficulties caused by the collision involves other skills and techniques than are practiced by the collision expert, he cannot ignore them and must provide for their correction.

Make free use of your measuring facilities when you are studying the damage to a car. Sometimes a panel can be knocked out of line without actually distorting any visible part of it. When this occurs and you fail to make the necessary measurements, it is easy to miss the fact that it is not in its proper location. This will not be brought to light until you attempt to align it with the surrounding panels after they have been straightened. It is better to make too many measurements and find that most everything you have checked is in alignment than to make too few and find that nothing fits after you have straightened all of the bent parts or panels.

Where you cannot find out just what happened by asking someone, you will find, with a little practice and close attention to what you see, that you can usually reconstruct the sequence in which the series of events occurred.

Consider a car which has rolled over. As the car moves along the highway, something occurs causing it to swerve into a deep ditch and turn over. First of all, the forward motion of the car would cause backward strain of the roof panel when it hit the ground. With the car turning over as well as traveling forward, hitting the ground will cause sideward strain as well. As the car rolls over onto its top, the impact causes downward strain of the whole top. When the car is righted, the top appears to be pushed back, to one side, and down.

Each of these damages occurred in the order just given. It is necessary to correct them in the reverse order. Studying the damage permits you to reconstruct the sequence of events which caused the damage, thereby providing the proper order in which the damage should be corrected. Always correct first the damage which occurred last.

Body Measurements

The basic principles of measurements as used in collision work were presented in Chapter 1. Further examples of measuring have been presented in most of the other chapters as well. The purpose of this section is not to repeat what has been covered before, but to emphasize some of the things already said and to provide some additional or more detailed instructions.

The measurement of frames and unit construction underbodies was completely covered in Chapter 7. For this reason, this discussion will deal primarily with body measurements.

Body measurements are made in the same way in both unit construction cars, and in vehicles that have a conventional frame. Checking body measurements is done mostly by a system of diagonal comparisons commonly called X-checking. The most widely used method of making these measurements is by use of a body alignment gage, called a *body tram gage* (Chapter 7). Bodies are measured first to determine the location and extent of the damage before correction, and secondly, during the correction, to determine when alignment has been restored. In both cases, the system and principles of the measurements are the same.

In body measuring, the body is divided into sections. The area from the front door forward is the front section. The area from the front door to the rear door is the center section. The area from the rear door to the trunk compartment is the rear section. The trunk compartment is considered as a separate section.

Sometimes the damage is not confined to a single section. This makes it necessary to check from one section to another to find out just where misalignment really lies. All of these measurements are explained in this section.

Checking Individual Sections. Fig. 8-1 shows how the diagonals are set up for checking the alignment of the front section. A convenient point *A* is located at or near the base of the right-front hinge pillar. The tram gage is extended to reach from that point diagonally across to point *B* located near the top of the left-front hinge pillar. The length of the gage is locked at the length of the distance from *A* to *B*, Fig. 8-1. All dimensions are measured from *inside corners*.

It is absolutely essential that point *C* be in exactly the same relative position on the left side of the car body as point *A* on the right side. Likewise, points *B* and

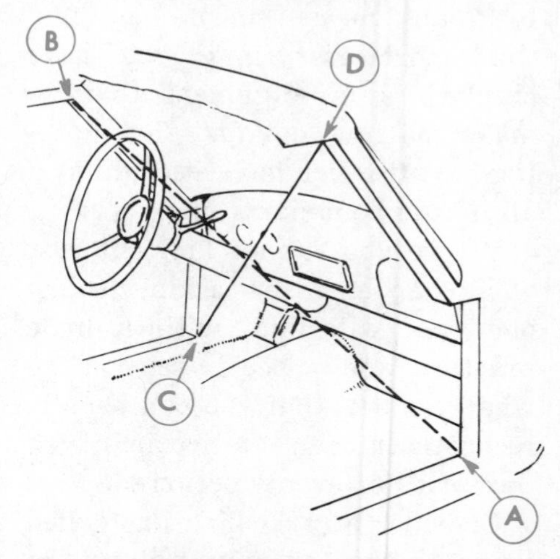

Fig. 8-1. Diagonals for checking front section.

D must be in the same relative positions toward the top of the left and right front hinge pillars.

The tram gage is then placed at point *C* and along the diagonal toward point *D*. If the length of the diagonal *C* to *D* exactly coincides with the length of the gage, that is, if it is the same length as the diagonal *A* to *B*, then the front section is in alignment. However, if the tram gage should not reach from point *C* to point *D*, as in Fig. 8-2, then it is obvious that the front section slants toward the right side. If, as in Fig. 8-3, the gage projects from point *C* to beyond point *D*, instead of to the inside corner, then the front section slants to the left. Depending upon the extent of the damage, this procedure should be followed in X-checking each section of the car body individually.

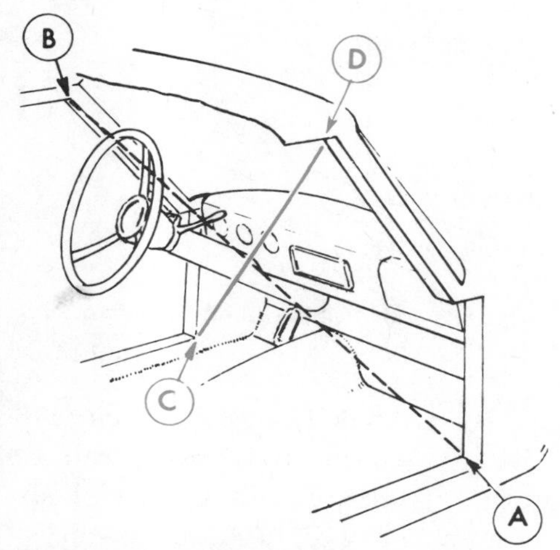

Fig. 8-2. Front section out of alignment slanting to the right.

To assure accuracy in actual practice, points *A*, *B*, *C*, and *D* should be established before any X-checking is done. Generally, points *A* and *C* can be most conveniently located at the corner formed by the juncture of the right and left front hinge pillars with the body sills. Here the fishtail construction at the end of the gage comes into practical use since it permits the gage to be lodged against the corner.

The easiest and most accurate way to establish points *B* and *D*

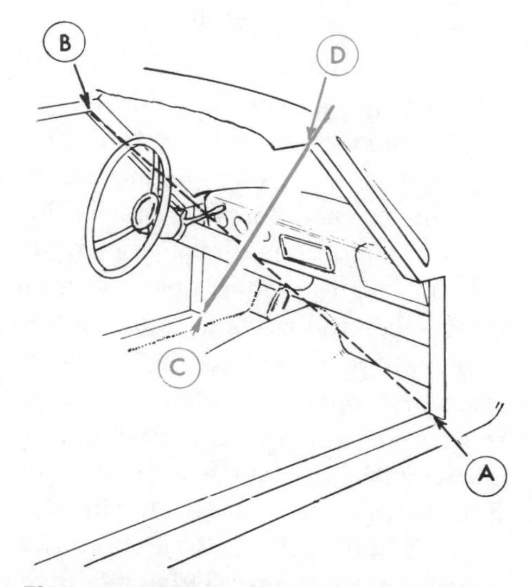

Fig. 8-3. Front section out of alignment slanting to the left.

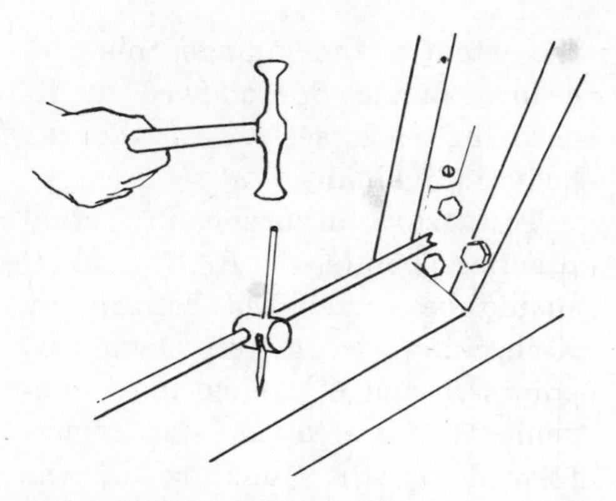

Fig. 8-4. Establishing point on sill.

is to set and lock the scriber about 4″ in from the end of the gage. Place that end of the gage against the front hinge pillar so that the scriber indicates a point on the body sill about 4″ in back of the pillar, Fig. 8-4. Use a light blow from a hammer to mark this point with the scriber. Repeat this procedure on the opposite body sill. starting again from the pillar.

The next step is to extend the gage straight up from the point you have just marked until the end of the gage is about even with the top of the door opening and the scriber indicates a point on the front hinge pillar about 4″ down from the opening. Lock the gage in this position and mark the upper point with the scriber, Fig. 8-5. Follow this procedure on the opposite pillar, but do not change the length of the gage. This will give you points *B* and *D*.

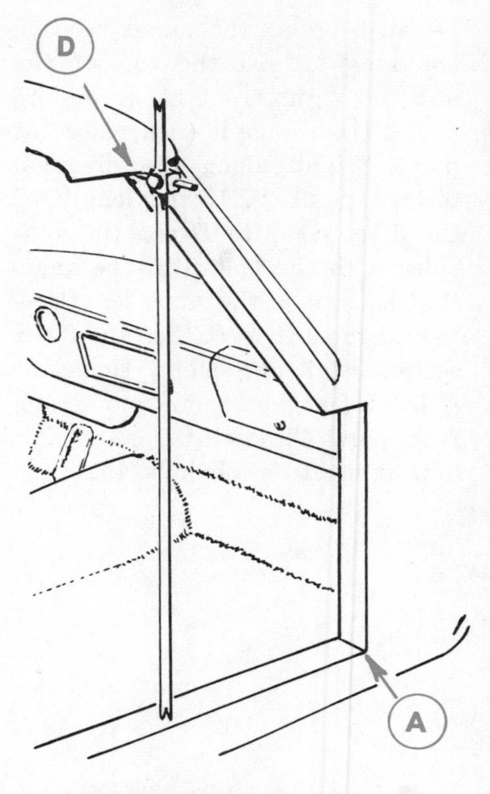

Fig. 8-5. Establishing point on pillar.

By similar procedure, you will be able accurately to establish other points within the car body which you will need for X-checking the various sections. However, this X-checking only determines alignment of individual sections.

Comparative Alignment Checking. In addition to checking the individual sections of the body, it must be determined whether or not all sections are in complete alignment with each other. That is, the front

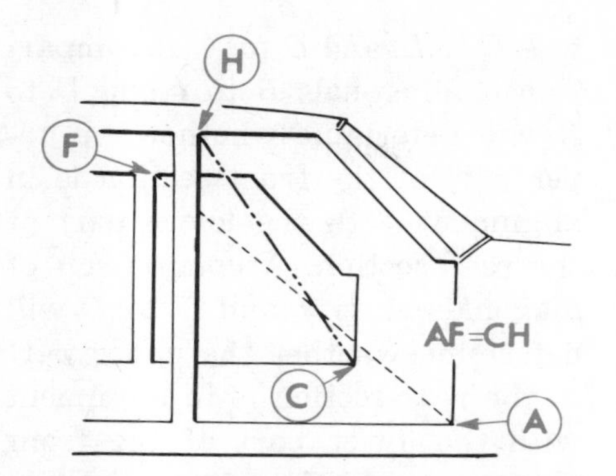

Fig. 8-6. Checking alignment of front to center section.

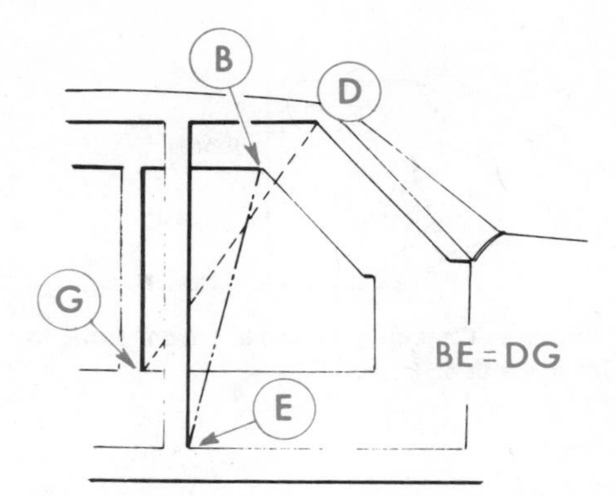

Fig. 8-7. Checking alignment of center to front section.

section must be in alignment with the center section, the center section must be in alignment with the rear section, and the rear section must be in alignment with the front section. Occasionally, the trunk compartment must also be checked for alignment with the rear and center sections.

In checking the alignment of one section with another, the two sections are thought of as forming a cube or boxlike area. The diagonals are always run from one corner to the opposite corner so that they pass through the center of the cube or box. Just as in X-checking individual sections, the opposite diagonals are compared with each other and must exactly coincide in length. Otherwise, the two sections are not in alignment. How to check the front with the center section for alignment is shown in Figs. 8-6 and 8-7.

In Fig. 8-6, the diagonal *A* to *F* is compared with its opposite diagonal, *C* to *H*. If the two diagonals coincide, if *A* to *F* is the same distance as *C* to *H*, then the lower part of the front section is in alignment with the upper part of the center section.

In Fig. 8-7, the diagonal, *B* to *E* is compared with its opposite diagonal, *D* to *G*. If the two diagonals coincide, if *B* to *E* is the same distance as *D* to *G*, then the upper part of the front section is in alignment with the lower portion of the center section. If all the diagonals of the boxlike area formed by the two sections are checked and found to be equal, the front and center sections are in alignment.

Fig. 8-8 shows the diagonal measurements used to check the

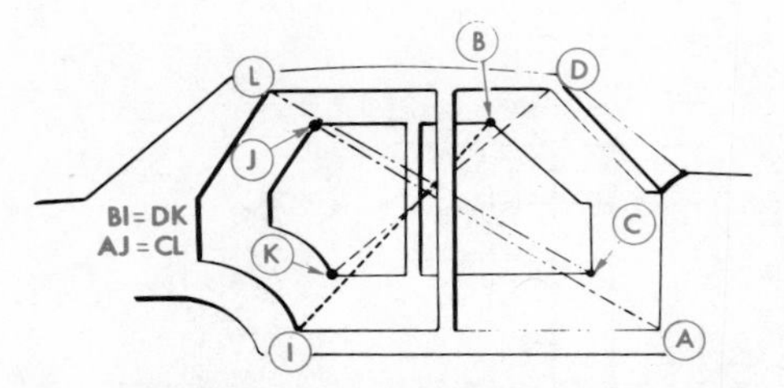

Fig. 8-8. Checking alignment from front to rear section.

alignment of the front section in relationship to the rear section.

First, points *A, B, D,* and *C* and *I, J, K,* and *L* are established. This establishes the diagonals *A* to *J*, *B* to *I*, *C* to *L*, and *D* to *K*. A comparison of diagonals *B* to *I* and *D* to *K* will determine whether the upper part of the front section is in alignment with the lower part of the rear section. A comparison of diagonals *A* to *J* and *C* to *L* will determine whether the upper part of the rear section is in alignment with the lower part of the front section. Any difference in the two sets of diagonals indicates misalignment. The length of the diagonals involved will indicate which way the body is slanting. You can then apply corrective measures.

Typical Repairs

Top or Roof Panel

A damaged all-metal top is shown in Fig. 8-9. In this collision, the damage created backward strain on the lower portion of the lower crown section of the top. It caused a locking of the upper part of the quarter panel against the inner construction.

Fig. 8-9. Damaged metal top.

The first operation here is to push out the quarter panel upper portion. This is done with a power tool setup as shown in Fig. 8-10. A quarter panel molding spoon is used in conjunction with a remote-controlled jack.

Fig. 8-10. Pushing out upper portion of lower quarter panel.

You can see from the illustration that before any repair operations could be performed, it was necessary to remove the interior trim. Pushing the quarter panel inner construction back into place relieves somewhat the backward strain, and the next operation can be performed.

In Fig. 8-11, the side of the metal top is being pushed out by means of a top rail spoon which is being used with a remote-control jack. Pushing out the top in this manner relieves the downward strain, and the final straightening operations can be performed.

Another tool is shown in Fig. 8-12 in use for a further pushing operation on the top. This is a corner and header panel spoon, and it too is used with a remote-control jack. This represents the final operation performed with power tools, and only the hand operations remain to finish the job.

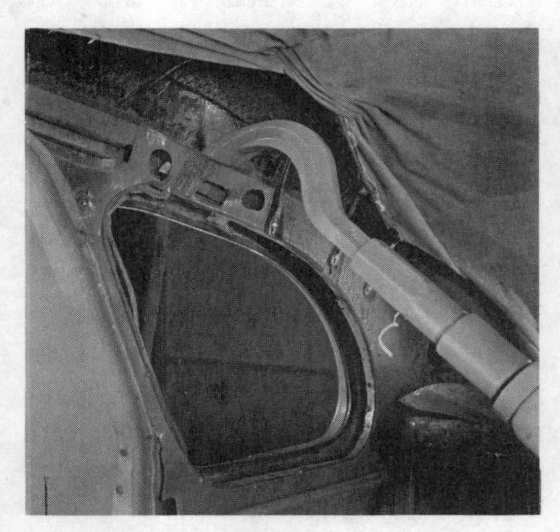

Fig. 8-11. Pushing out side of metal top.

Fig. 8-12. Final power tool operation in pushing out side of metal top.

The first hand operation is to raise all of the low spots. This is done by using a pick tool of the proper shape for reaching this particular damage, and a metal bumping hammer, Fig. 8-13. A body file and holder, shown in use in Fig. 8-14, are used to reveal low spots by line filing. The final finished job, which has been properly ground with a disk grinder, is shown in Fig. 8-15 ready for the refinishing operation.

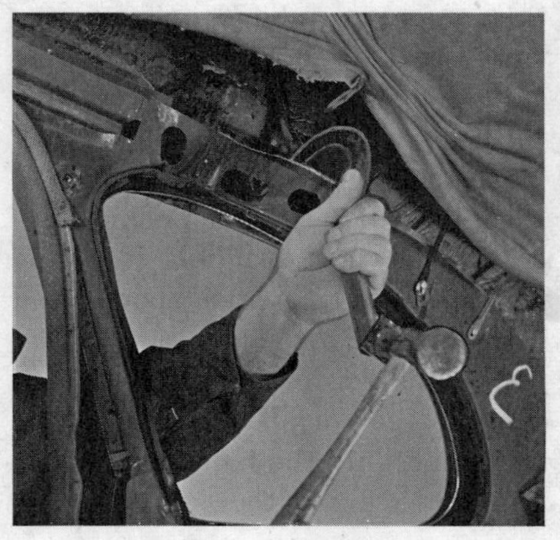

Fig. 8-13. Raising low spots with hammer and pick tool.

Fig. 8-14. Line filing with body file and holder.

Fig. 8-15. Completed job ready for the refinishing operation.

Front Quarter Panel

In this next sequence of operations, you will be shown the method of straightening damage which has occurred in the left front quarter panel area. This is one of the most critical areas in the entire body. It is also one of the most difficult to straighten because of the complex construction.

Repair to this area can be made easier if you remember to study the damage carefully, then determine a way in which to proceed with the correction. Check your progress with tram gages and alignment gages while the corrections are being made.

Fig. 8-16 shows the left front

Fig. 8-16. Badly torn and buckled left front wheelhouse inner panel. (Blackhawk Mfg. Co.)

Fig. 8-17. Portable frame aligner and jack in place to pull wheelhouse panel down and out. (Blackhawk Mfg. Co.)

wheelhouse inner panel assembly badly torn and buckled. The cowl was driven back on the left-hand side and the front frame member was badly kinked behind the rear engine mount. Note how the left front wheel has been driven back against the wheelhouse.

The first pull is made on the wheelhouse inner panel with a frame aligner, Fig. 8-17. A small jack is placed to exert an upward push against the sagged area while the frame aligner pulls the wheelhouse panel down and out. For heavy pulls, the pull plate may sometimes have to be welded to the frame member to avoid tearing the metal of the panel.

Next, the jack and frame aligner are placed to make a diagonal pull to swing the bottom of the wheelhouse inner panel into line, as is shown in Fig. 8-18.

In Fig. 8-19, the top of the wheelhouse inner panel is being pulled out. Notice the effective method of anchoring the chain to the panel by the use of a pry bar. With the setup shown, the pry bar presses against the reinforced panel section for a heavy pull.

An underbody clamp anchors the frame aligner to the car, Fig. 8-20. Because the car has a unitized body, the clamp must be fas-

Fig. 8-18. Placing the jack and frame aligner to make a diagonal pull. (Blackhawk Mfg Co.)

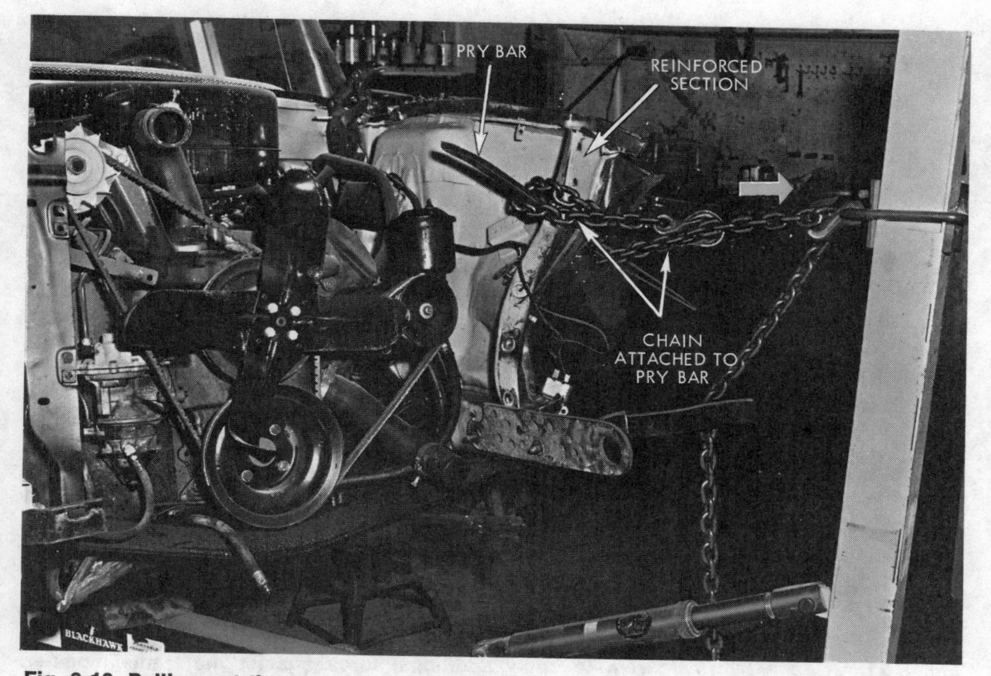

Fig. 8-19. Pulling out the top of the wheelhouse inner panel. (Blackhawk Mfg. Co.)

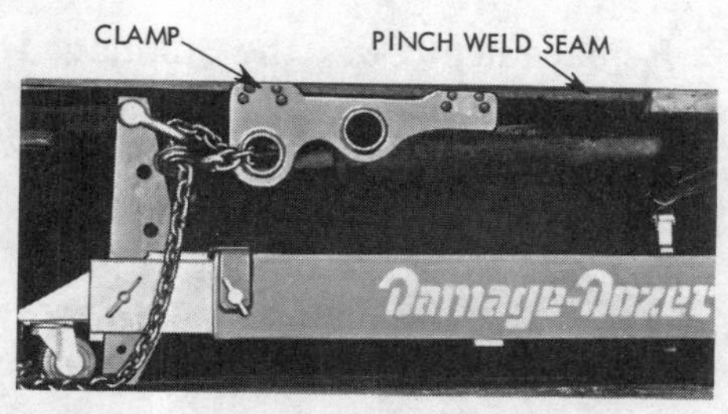

Fig. 8-20. An underbody clamp fastened to a pinch weld seam. (Blackhawk Mfg. Co.)

tened to the pinch weld seam beneath the rocker panel.

In order to straighten the buckled bottom of the wheelhouse inner panel, a hydraulic ram, Fig. 8-21, exerts force while tension is applied with the frame aligner.

Roughing out means restoring panels to approximate shape and dimension even though they may later be replaced. If panels are not roughed out before any cutting is done, adjacent structures to which the panels are welded may retain their damaged contours after cutting. If this occurs, the replacement panels will not fit and it is a losing battle trying to obtain a proper joint.

For instance, when a wheelhouse inner panel is badly buckled, the cowl is usually damaged.

Fig. 8-21. Using a hydraulic ram to apply additional force against the frame member. (Blackhawk Mfg. Co.)

If the wheelhouse panel is cut loose from the cowl before a pull is exerted on it, the cowl will remain buckled and distorted. Then it will be extremely difficult to straighten the cowl area so that the replacement panel can be welded to it. Therefore, always work the damaged panels back to shape and dimension before attempting any cutting operations.

Up to this point in the repair, all of the work has been roughing out. More than one pull has been made and the frame aligner and hydraulic jack have both been used to apply force.

Replacement of the damaged wheelhouse panel is considered more economical than repair, therefore the panel is removed, Fig. 8-22. Note the damaged areas of the cowl, and the buckling in the frame member just behind the engine mount.

After the wheelhouse panel is removed, the cowl is no longer reinforced and the remaining buckling can be straightened with the help of a hydraulic ram, Fig. 8-23. The repair is not attempted until after the reinforcing parts are removed. This reduces the strain on the sheet metal.

Fig. 8-22. The wheelhouse panel is removed from the car. (Blackhawk Mfg. Co.)

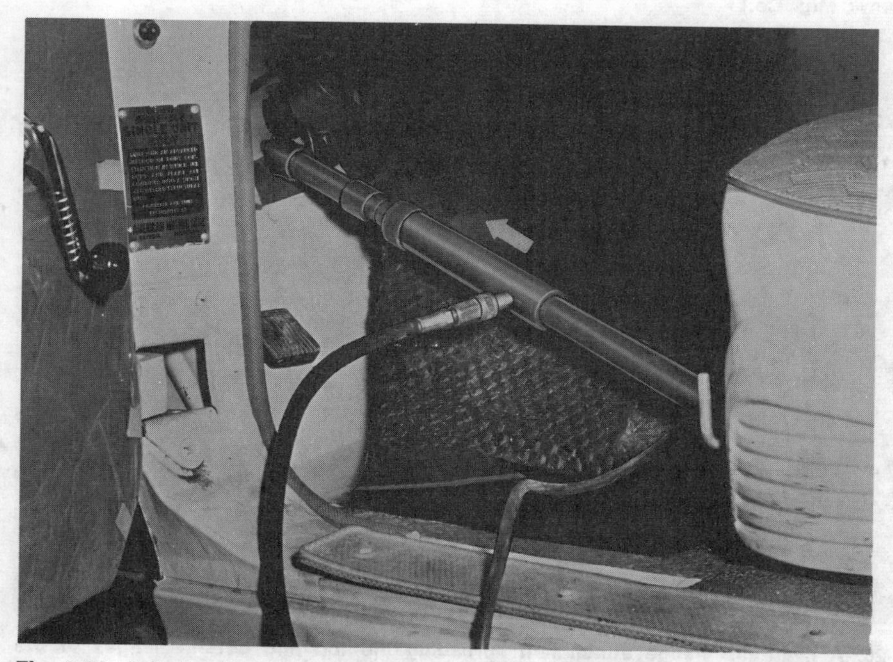

Fig. 8-23. A hydraulic ram removing buckles in the cowl. (Blackhawk Mfg. Co.)

Fig. 8-24. Using a hydraulic ram to pull the frame member back into its proper position. (Blackhawk Mfg. Co.)

Fig. 8-25. A hydraulic wedge attachment spreading the top and bottom flanges of the frame member. (Blackhawk Mfg. Co.)

In order to swing the frame member back into its proper position, a hydraulic ram setup is used, Fig. 8-24. While the pull is maintained, the buckle in the frame member is pounded out.

Because the replacement wheelhouse panel nests inside an opening in the frame member, and because the opening collapsed during the collision, a hydraulic wedge attachment is used to spread the top and bottom flanges in the frame member, Fig. 8-25. Structural sections like the frame member must be restored to a near equivalent of original condition.

Next, the replacement panel is fitted in place and checked to see that all joining surfaces fit properly, Fig. 8-26. Careful measuring and proper pulling have made the replacement panel a close fit. This emphasizes the importance of checking with alignment gages and tram gages as the pulls are made.

A friction jack is used as shown in Fig. 8-27 to pull the new replacement panel back into place against the cowl. One hook is fastened to the panel, while a strap is used to fasten the other end of the jack to the cowl.

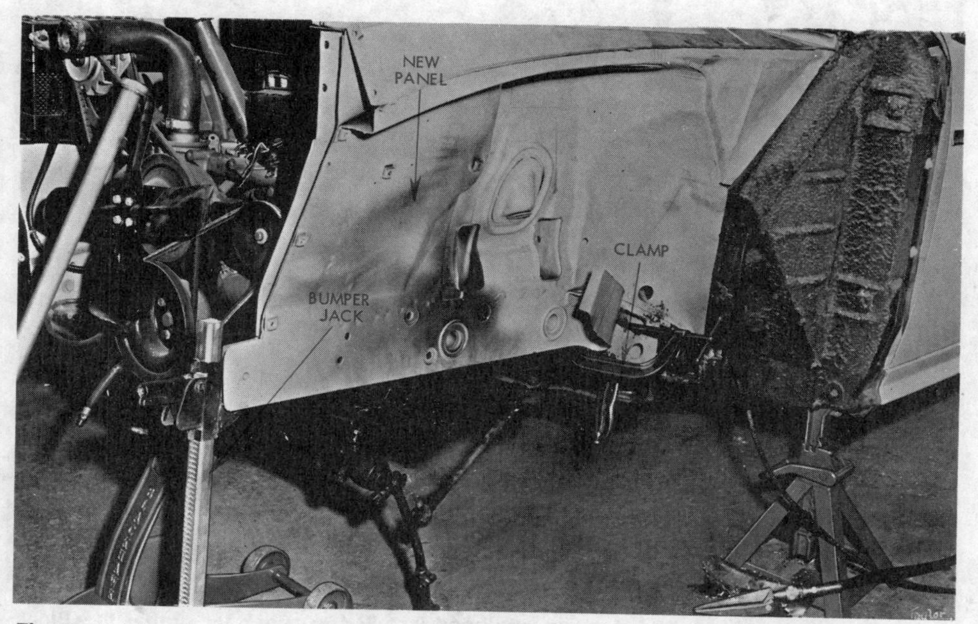

Fig. 8-26. The replacement wheelhouse panel fitted into place. (Blackhawk Mfg. Co.)

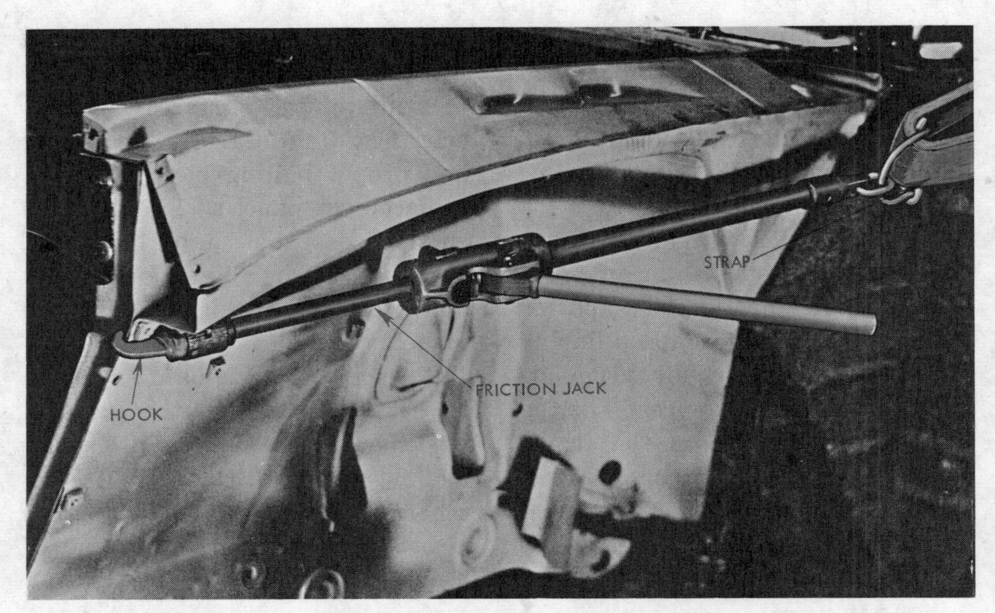

Fig. 8-27. Using a friction jack to pull the replacement panel into position against the cowl. (Blackhawk Mfg. Co.)

Fig. 8-28. New panel clamped in place with hood installed to check for proper fit. (Blackhawk Mfg. Co.)

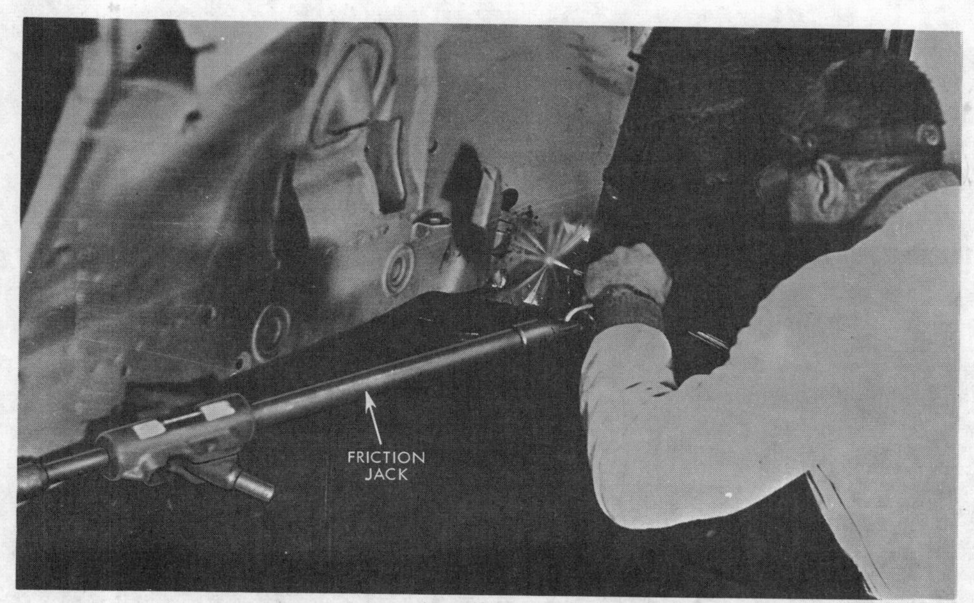

Fig. 8-29. Welding the new panel to the body. (Blackhawk Mfg. Co.)

Fig. 8-30. Installed panel and hood. (Blackhawk Mfg. Co.)

In Fig. 8-28, the new panel has been clamped in place and the hood has been installed to check for proper fit. Note the position of the bumper jack and the friction jack. While the new panel is properly supported and clamped, it is gas welded to the body, Fig. 8-29.

Fig. 8-30 shows the new panel and hood installed. The next step involves installing and fitting the fender, suspension, and radiator.

Fig. 8-31. Car with fender fitted and ready for paint. (Blackhawk Mfg. Co.)

Fig. 8-32. Completed repair job. (Blackhawk Mfg. Co.)

In Fig. 8-31, the fender has been fitted and only the painting and mechanical work remain to be done. Fig. 8-32 shows the finished job after painting.

One factor that does not show in the preceding illustrations is the time spent in checking the damage and then deciding how to proceed. There is no substitute for planning the body repair job before doing the actual work.

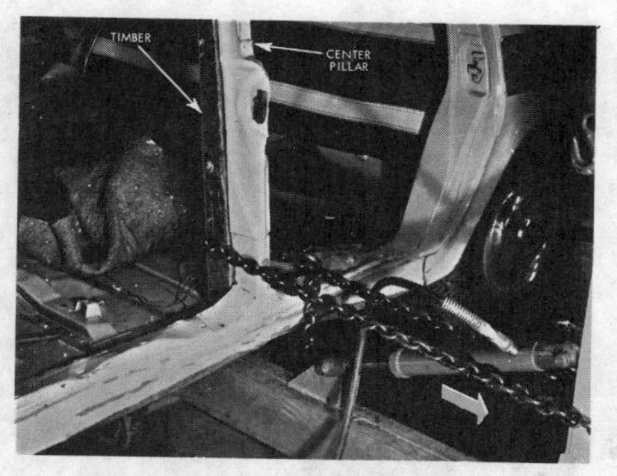

Fig. 8-34. Frame aligner pulling against timber to straighten pillar. (Blackhawk Mfg. Co.)

Side Panel Repair

Fig. 8-33 shows a car which has been hit in the left center pillar. The pillar is pushed in and the box sill in the area of the rocker panel is distorted.

First, the doors are removed so they can be straightened or replaced. Then the center pillar is pulled back to the proper position with a frame aligner. A timber is positioned as in Fig. 8-34 to prevent crushing the metal at the chain attachment point and to help remove bends in the pillar.

To anchor the frame aligner without injuring the body, a 4 × 6 timber is placed across the door opening on the opposite side of the car as shown in Fig. 8-35. Notice

Fig. 8-33. Car with damaged side. (Blackhawk Mfg. Co.)

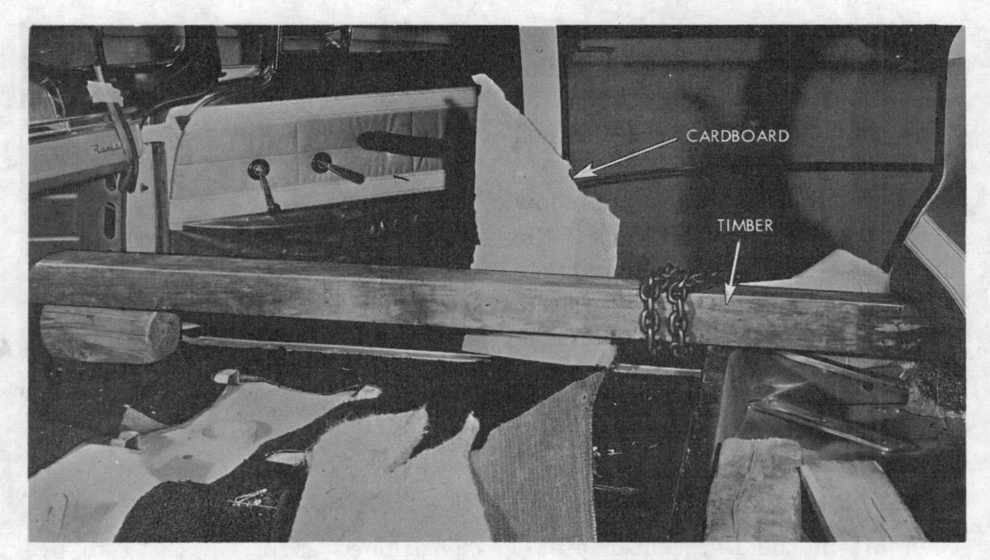

Fig. 8-35. Timber being used to anchor frame aligner. (Blackhawk Mfg. Co.)

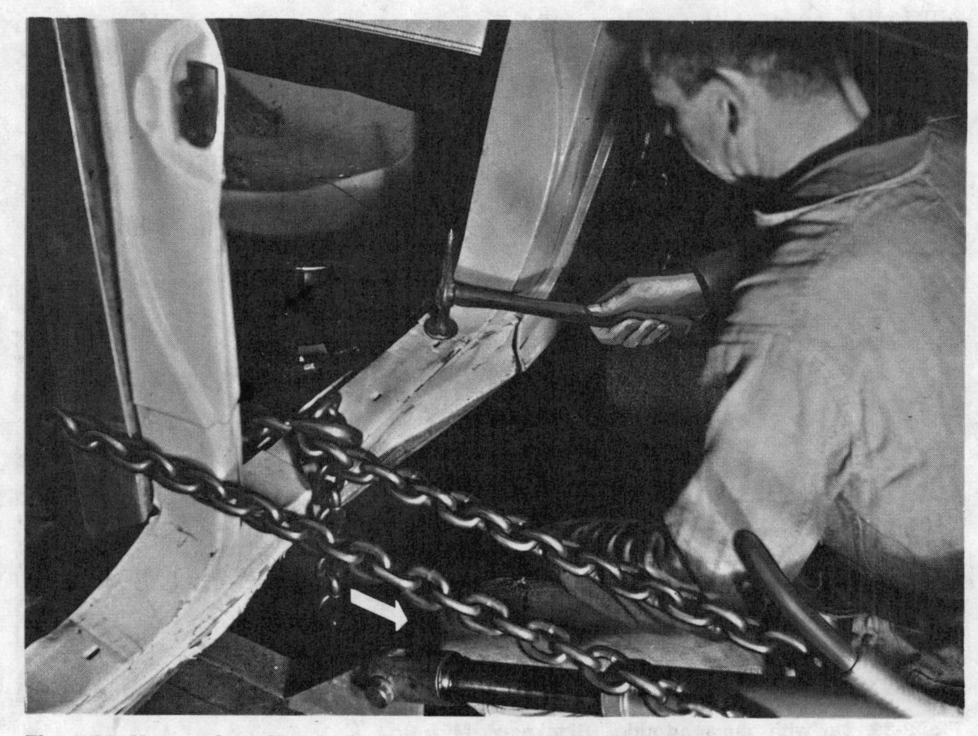

Fig. 8-36. Hammering sill area back into shape. (Blackhawk Mfg. Co.)

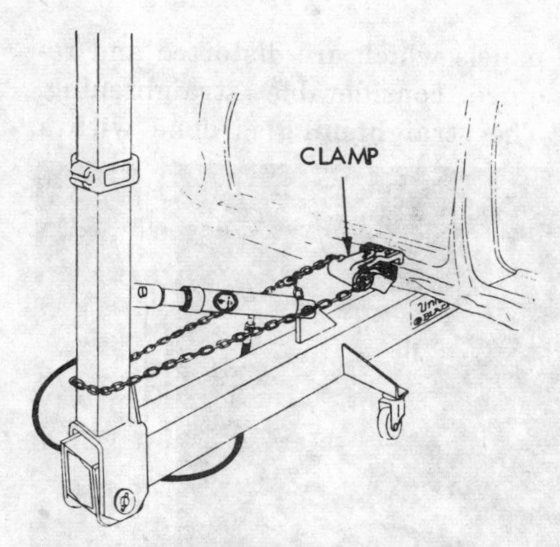

Fig. 8-37. Using clamp to pull out front door sill area when the sill is twisted or badly bent. (Blackhawk Mfg. Co.)

that the front trim is removed and a sheet of cardboard is used to protect the trim on the center pillar.

After the pillar is pulled out to its original position, the sill area is worked back into approximate shape by hammering as in Fig. 8-36. The hammering is done while pull is maintained by the frame aligner.

To pull out the sill area under the front and rear doors, openings are cut in the rocker panels so that a clamp can be attached, Fig. 8-37. The sill areas are then pulled out—first the front, and then the rear.

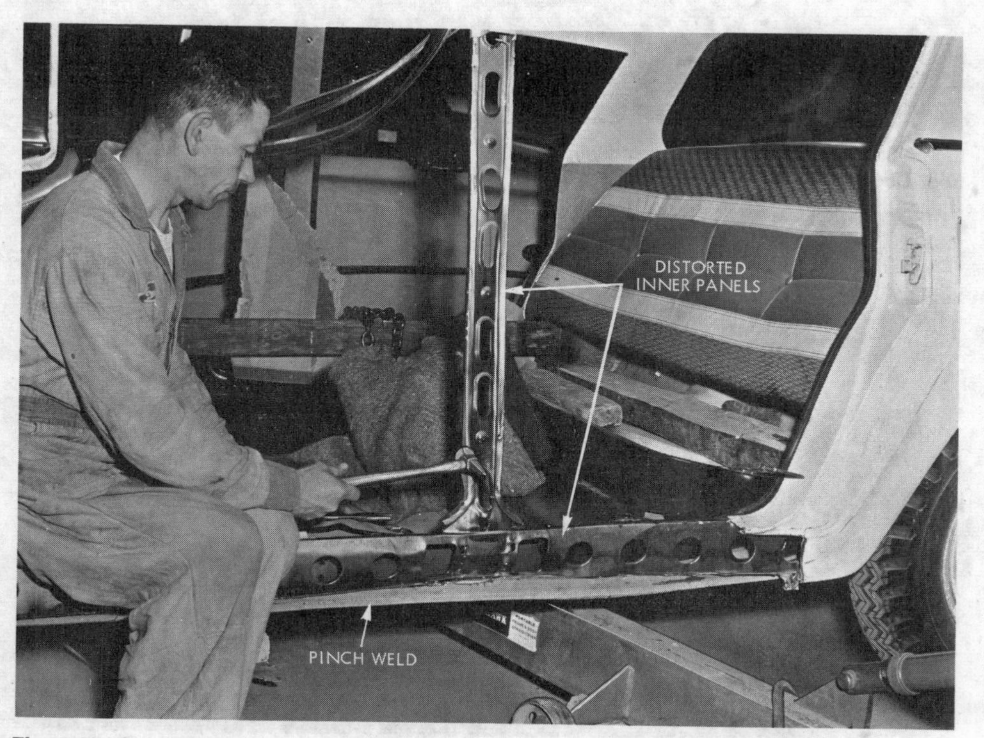

Fig. 8-38. Straightening distorted inner reinforcing panels. (Blackhawk Mfg. Co.)

After the side is roughed out, the outer panels are cut off to gain access to the inner reinforcing panels which are distorted and require considerable straightening. The straightening is done with a

Fig. 8-39. Replacement doors and sill panels in place to determine door fit. (Blackhawk Mfg. Co.)

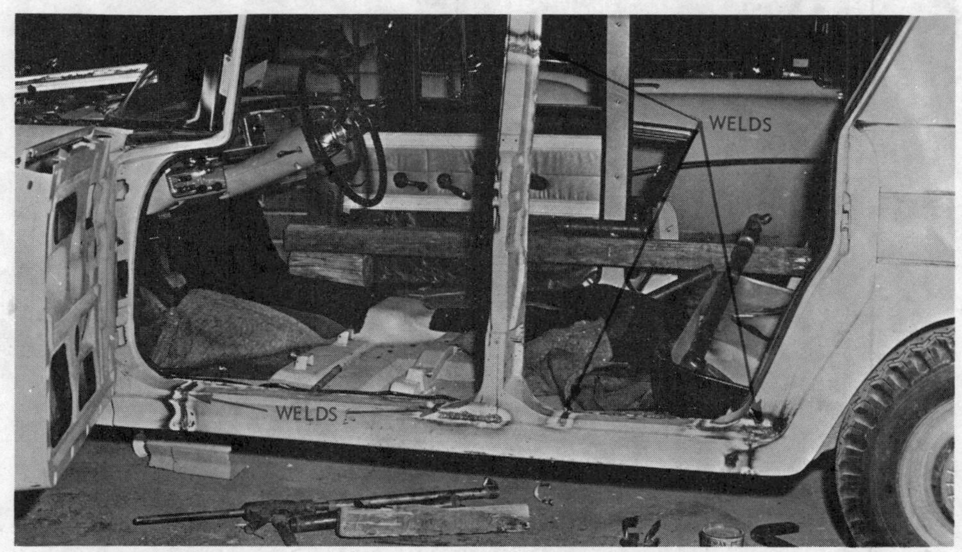

Fig. 8-40. Replacement panels welded in place. (Blackhawk Mfg. Co.)

hammer and a common pry bar, Fig. 8-38. The pry bar is used to reach behind the horizontal reinforcing panel. The pinch weld joining the sections at the bottom of the sill area is also straightened out by hammering after the reinforcing panel is straightened.

In the next step, the replacement doors and sill panels are set in place to determine door fit, Fig. 8-39. In order to obtain the proper door opening, a friction jack is used to hold the sill panels while they are spot welded in place.

Fig. 8-40 shows the replacement panels welded in place and the repairs substantially complete. The remainder of the repair will consist of hanging the doors, adding trim, and finishing.

Rear End Repair

The car in Fig. 8-41 has been struck in the rear center. Both rear quarter panels are buckled out as shown, and the complete rear end has dropped. The rear cross member is crushed and the rear glass is pulled out of place.

Fig. 8-42 shows the separation

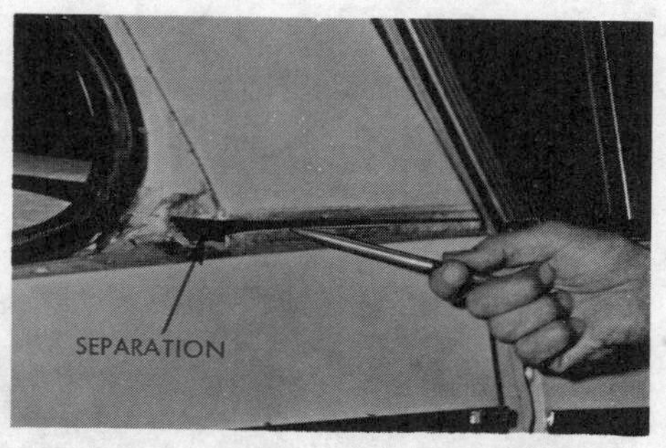

Fig. 8-42. Roof and quarter panel separated by collision. (Blackhawk Mfg. Co.)

Fig. 8-41. Car with rear collision damage. (Blackhawk Mfg. Co.)

of the roof and quarter panels which is exactly the type of damage for which you must be on the alert. Sometimes it may be difficult to detect and a comparison must be made with another car of the same make and model.

The rear wheelhouse inner panel has buckled and the trunk floor pan has bulged up as shown in Fig. 8-43. This distortion occurred on both sides.

To correct the damage, a chain pull plate is attached from the body to a frame aligner Fig. 8-44. The anchor post of the frame aligner is butted against the engine rear support member. A steel plate is used to spread the load on the engine rear support member to prevent damaging it. The car is then lowered onto stands, and an upward pull is made on the left side of the car. While the metal is under tension, a sledge is used to reduce the buckles in the trunk floor pan and the rear wheelhouse inner panel.

Fig. 8-45 shows the severe buckles in the frame member at the

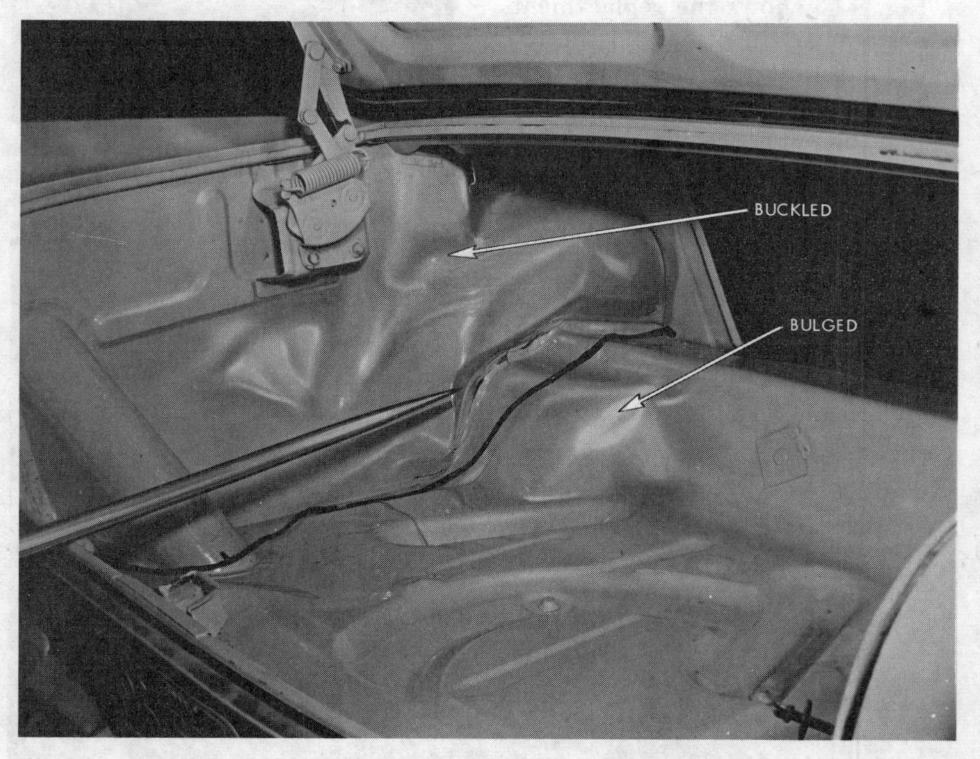

Fig. 8-43. Buckled wheelhouse inner panel and bulged trunk floor pan. (Blackhawk Mfg. Co.)

Fig. 8-44. Correcting left-side rear end damage with the frame aligner. (Blackhawk Mfg. Co.)

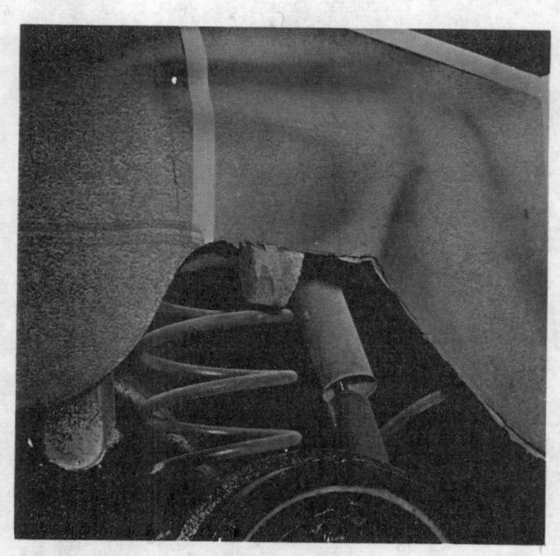

Fig. 8-45. Buckled rear wheelhouse inner panel. (Blackhawk Mfg. Co.)

right rear wheelhouse inner panel. In order to straighten the dropped right rear end and remove the buckles, the frame aligner is set up as shown in Fig. 8-46. The rear cross member is then pulled out. At this point, rough-out work is complete. The proper fit of doors, rear deck cover, and rear glass is checked and adjusted. The job is then ready for finishing.

Fig. 8-47 shows the method used to hold down the area adjacent to the buckling by cutting holes through the wheelhouse panel.

Fig. 8-46. Correcting right-side rear end damage with frame aligner. (Blackhawk Mfg. Co.)

Fig. 8-47. Method of holding down area adjacent to buckled section. (Blackhawk Mfg. Co.)

After the area is straightened, the holes are closed and brazed shut.

When repairing unitized bodies, the collision man makes extensive use of underbody clamps for holding and pulling. In Fig. 8-48 an eight-way clamp is shown. The holes in the clamp are positioned to direct the chain pull toward the center of the clamp jaws to help prevent tearing the pinch weld.

Fig. 8-48. An eight-way underbody clamp for holding or pulling on pinch weld.

In summing up this repair, notice that the job consisted not just of one operation, such as pulling, but of a combination of pulling, hammering, and the use of hydraulic force. Also notice that some thought was given to how to pull and what steps were taken to assist the pull.

Always follow the basic steps of collision damage repair: locate the damage; plan the work; rough out the work; and check the work.

Fender Repair

The first operation in the straightening of this damaged fender is performed with a fender beading tool and a roughing hammer, Fig. 8-49. In this operation, the fender beading tool is hooked over the edge of the fender that is bent up and under. The roughing hammer is then used on the hammer pad of the beading tool. Hammering will bring the edge of the fender back down where it belongs. The roughing hammer is used for this operation because it is heavy enough to provide the impact necessary to reverse the kink in the fender.

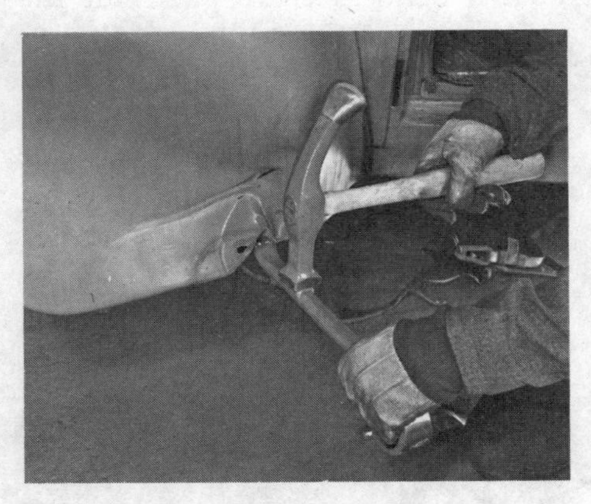

Fig. 8-49. Hooking down edge of fender with beading tool and hammer.

Fig. 8-50 shows all of the tools which will be used for the bumping operations necessary to straighten this fender. In this illustration, the

Fig. 8-50. Collision tools used for correcting fender damage.

toggle action spreader is shown inserted behind the fender skirt, ready for use.

The toggle action spreader is shown being used to push out the skirt area of the fender in Fig. 8-51. This portion of the fender is an unsupported area, and it was buckled in by the initial impact of the damaging force. For this pushing operation, the spreader is inserted between the fender skirt and the mudguard which is behind the fender skirt, Fig. 8-52. This mudguard is attached to the frame and to the bottom of the fender skirt at the bottom edge. This pushing operation will remove most of the damage from the skirt area.

The balance of the operations required to completely remove the damage are performed with hand tools. It is necessary to have the skirt area of the fender restored to normal before the lower edge and fender bead can be restored. The finishing operation on the buckled skirt area is done with a surfacing

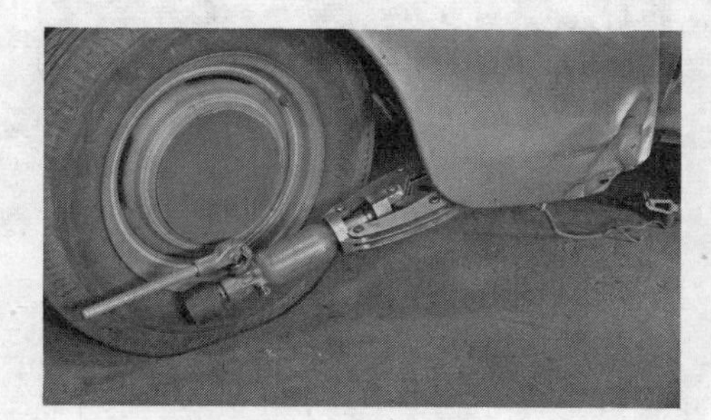

Fig. 8-51. Pushing out fender skirt with toggle action spreader.

Fig. 8-52. Spreader inserted between fender skirt and mud guard.

spoon and a bumping hammer. Spring hammering will bring this surface back to its original contour.

Notice in the illustration of spring hammering that the collision man is wearing gloves. When a bumping hammer is used directly against a spoon or dolly, one's hands may sting from the impact of the hammer on the dolly. Wearing gloves will prevent this from becoming annoying.

The final finish hammering is done with a fender hammer and a high crown dolly, Fig. 8-53. The high crown area above the front end of the running board is finished in this manner. Fig. 8-54 shows the high crown dolly which is used with the fender hammer.

Fig. 8-54. High crown dolly used with fender hammer.

This same hammer and dolly are used to reshape the flange on the fender.

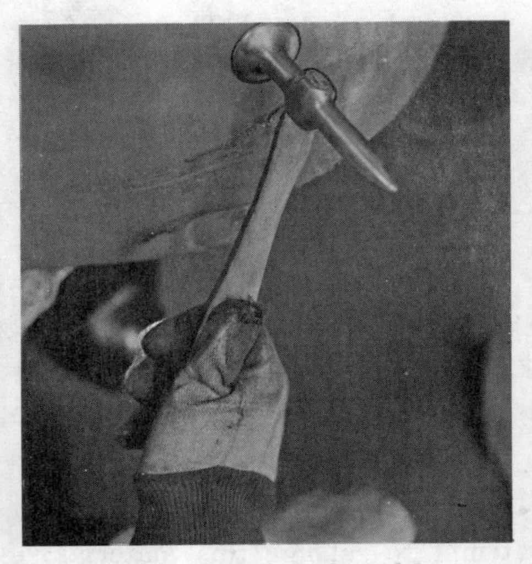

Fig. 8-53. Finish hammering high crown area of fender.

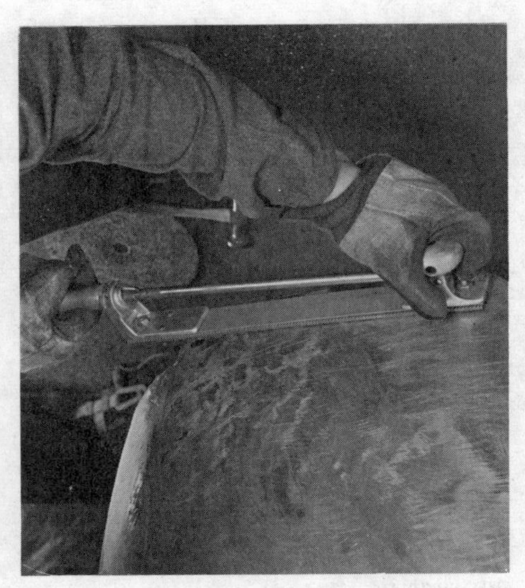

Fig. 8-55. Filing fender skirt.

The low spots are brought up after the fender has been restored to its normal contour. Any low spots which cannot be removed for one reason or another are then filled with solder. The solder is filed smooth with a body file, Fig. 8-55, at the same time the entire fender area is filed to prepare it for sanding. The entire area is then sanded with a disk grinder and the job is ready for the paint shop.

Replacement Versus Repair

It is probably true that an ingenious collision man can repair anything that has been damaged in a collision. However, attempts to repair parts and panels that obviously should be replaced prove nothing except your poor judgment. As you gain experience in collision work, you will find that you are able at a glance to estimate the time required to do a particular job and can make your decision on the spot as to whether a particular part or panel will be replaced.

You can do this only if you are familiar with the prices you will have to pay for the parts involved. Several independent companies have available complete body panel and parts lists, indexed with prices. Every progressive body shop should have a set of them for its own use.

On unit construction cars, replacement of panels is more common because the construction is of such a nature that damage is more localized. Shock is absorbed in the contacting panel.

The following parts and materials are almost always replaced rather than repaired. Bright metal parts are repaired when or wherever a compromise in quality is acceptable. Due to their intricate design and to the nature of the material from which they are made, bright metal parts do not lend themselves to straightening or welding. Even in those cases where a satisfactory job of straightening is performed, the parts generally have to be replated. The cost of replating is often greater than the cost of a new part.

Interior trim panels generally can be cleaned and repaired satisfactorily to permit their re-use. Cardboard backing can be replaced, or in some instances stiffened by gluing an additional cardboard reinforcement to them.

Body deadening material is replaced. Padding used for sound deadening usually tears apart as you attempt to remove it. An attempt to salvage this material is generally a waste of time, making it more costly than new material.

In collision work, you will have two extremes of quality that you will have to observe. Some variations in these extremes of quality will always be necessary. These two considerations depend upon whether you are working on used cars or on a vehicle where an insurance company will be paying for the damage on a client's car.

Used Cars. If you are working for a new or used car dealer, you will have the problem of restoring used cars to a salable condition. Some compromise in quality is necessary in these cases. Your goal is to determine quickly what you can do to restore the appearance of the vehicle to an acceptable standard with the amount of money the dealer is able to spend on it. In these cases, a good many compromises from the ideal are necessary. Particularly when working on older cars, the extra cost involved in striving for perfection is not justified since these costs will have to be added to the selling price.

Privately owned automobiles which have become damaged and for which the owner must pay the repair charges, fall approximately in this same category. Here again, you must compare the benefits to be derived from perfection with what you can accomplish with a minimum of time and material. You will often find that these owners welcome your suggestions for the more economical job and will become one of the best advertisers for your shop and practices.

Still another consideration arises in conjunction with jobs which are to be paid for by an insurance company and where the owner feels that he has every right to have his car restored to a like-new condition. On these jobs, you may encounter rusted-out fenders which do not lend themselves to repair. Where a minor damage to a fender tears it loose from the body due to the fact that the fender has rusted through, you may be required to improvise repairs which, while they may fall far short of restoring the vehicle to a like-new condition, will be satisfactory to both the owner and to the insurance company.

Quality Repairs. Where insurance pays the damage or where an uninsured owner of a new car or nearly new car requires correction of collision damage, the quality of your work must be such that when you have finished, there is no indication of the damage having occurred.

This does not necessarily mean that if the fender is damaged it must be replaced with a new one, though many owners will probably insist on this. As a matter of fact, you will find that if, in bidding for this work you consistently include the cost of replacement parts, the insurance company will send its business elsewhere. For this reason, you will have to be diplomatic with the owner of a shiny new car which has become damaged through no fault of his own and who insists on a new fender or a new door or whatever part happens to be damaged. If the kind of damage lends itself to repair, then you will have to repair it.

If a more economical, yet equally satisfactory job can be done by repairing, don't argue with the owner. In the early stages of negotiations, submit your bid to the insurance company in a way that calls for repairing of the damage rather than replacement.

Your attitude in this instance is not to pass the burden of responsibility on to the insurance company. Instead, you must protect them, since the company, rather than the owner of the vehicle, is your customer. In other words, minimize the damage to the owner. Indicate to him that the particular part is easily repaired and that replacement of the door or fender, or whatever the part happens to be, probably would not be as satisfactory as the mere pushing out and painting of the damaged part. You will find that you can appease the owner satisfactorily without getting into trouble with the insurance company.

The uninsured new car owner is a little different. He is more apt to welcome your suggestion of repair rather than replacement, particularly when you can assure him that there will be no question of the quality. Sometimes you will find that the new or nearly new car owner will feel that the repaired part will not match the rest of the car. In these cases you can point out to him that a new fender or door will have to be refinished in your shop just as would any repaired part. After all, it is the paint that a person sees. Whether the part is replaced or repaired, the paint is the same and is applied by the same people.

Each of these cases may require a slightly different handling. For the most part, however, you will find that you can sell repair rather than replacement.

This discussion presumes that the repair can be performed more economically than the part involved can be replaced. The relationship of these two costs will vary among different shops. The car dealership doing collision work on the make of car it sells has a price advantage in obtaining new fenders, doors, panels, etc., that is not enjoyed by the independent collision shop. For this reason, the dealership can often replace a part more economically than it can repair it. The same damage in an independent shop might be repaired more economically than it could be replaced due to the shorter discount the independent shop might receive on the part involved.

In arriving at a conclusion as to whether a particular part should be replaced or repaired, don't lose sight of installation time. Installation time can be considerable as, in the case of a door, for example, for all of the door hardware, glass, and interior trim must be transferred from one door to the other. In the case of the front fender, you may have additional problems of grille and hood alignment when you have installed the part. All of these considerations must be a part of your evaluation as to whether to repair or replace.

Cost. In most cases, the cost of the part installed as compared with the cost of the repair will be the determining factor as to which course you will follow. As mentioned in the discussion involving used cars, something less than perfection is generally acceptable in older automobiles. Often you will be working on fenders which have had innumerable previous repairs. When you start to work on them, you will find that they have been so filled with solder that you cannot make an economical repair.

If the points favoring repair outweigh the points favoring replacement by only a small margin, it might be a good idea to determine whether or not the particular part has been filled with solder. If you find that it has been, recommend replacement rather than repair of that particular part.

When you are working on a car where the owner of the vehicle is personally paying the cost, it may be well to place yourself in his position. Again, if you are working on a used car, put yourself in the place of the person who would buy a car of that particular age group. A person who is driving an older car, or the person who buys a car of that type on the used car lot, probably does so for economic reasons. An extra thirty or forty dollars spent on the restoring of collision damage might amount to a hardship for this person. In most cases, a person in this group would rather have some slight imperfection in the car than to spend the extra money. On the other hand, the owner of a shiny new car generally has just paid, or contracted to pay, a substantial amount of money for the car, and he doesn't want to be reminded of the damage in any way by the appearance of the car after you have repaired it. In these cases, you will have to work for perfection.

Obviously, there are a number of intermediate steps between these extremes. It is important that you recognize these differences in the problem, and match your recommendations to suit the vehicle wherever possible.

The Quality Habit. Throughout this volume, the instructions given have been toward achieving the skill and knowledge necessary to restore damaged parts to a like-new condition. This like-new condition refers not only to appearance, but to function as well. As a craftsman, you will have pride in your workmanship, and even in those cases where sacrifice of quality is indicated as being acceptable, you will want to do just a little more than enough to make the job acceptable. This is good experience for you, and it is good practice because it keeps you in the quality habit.

Time of Repairs. Time is always a factor in repairing collision jobs. However, after the first shock at seeing his automobile seriously damaged in a collision, the average vehicle owner becomes reconciled to the fact that he is going to be deprived of its use for a few days. It is not unusual for the vehicle to set for a number of days before clearance is received from the insurance company to proceed with the work. When the OK to proceed is received, the owner is still quite anxious to get the car. If you let the situation get out of your control, he may demand some unreasonable delivery time. About the only satisfactory way you can meet this situation is to propose some alternate method of repair at either an increased cost or at some sacrifice of quality.

Usually in an instance of this kind where, due to the owner's insistence that the car must be delivered more quickly, you point out to him that to do so would represent a sacrifice in quality or an increase in cost to him, the owner will change his mind and permit you to proceed as you originally planned.

In considering the question of repair versus replacement, don't be misled into believing that the replacement of a part always is more quickly effected than the repair of the part. This, in many cases, is not true. Replacement of a particular part often entails work over and above the work required to repair the part.

Filling Versus Straightening

The question of whether to straighten out a sunken area or attempt to fill the depression with solder often arises. In general, there are not many times when it is more economical to use body solder to fill a depression than to straighten it.

If you lack equipment to get in behind inner construction satisfactorily, it may be necessary to fill with solder. Bring the surface up as far as you can by whatever means are available, even though you cannot bring it all the way up. This will reduce the amount of solder you will have to use. At any place where a low spot exists, you should consider filling the low spot with solder if the area is not extensive. This is particularly true if getting behind the damage involves a lot of work.

If there is a possibility that you can make a satisfactory repair of collision damage by straightening it without marring the paint, you can afford to remove a lot of parts for the cost of repainting. Soldering, of course, necessitates repainting the area involved.

Solder filling has an important part in collision work, and the advisability of filling with solder must be considered on jobs that lend themselves to this method. Since solder is expensive, you may find that the cost of solder and the time to apply it is more than the cost of bumping out the damage.

In cases of minor damage to a door, either of the quarter panels, or to a rocker panel sill, it is sometimes more economical to fill the depressed area with solder. Repairing of damage in these areas usually involves the removal of interior trim and sometimes some of the exterior trim. The labor involved in removing and installing the trim so that you could gain access to the damage from the inside to push it out, sometimes is greater than the cost of filling with solder. This sometimes is particularly true if the panel is to be repainted.

In damage of this type, it is sometimes possible to weld a piece of welding rod to the center of the lowest portion of the damage area. By pulling on the welding rod, you may be able to draw out the depressed panel, Fig. 8-56.

In some instances, you may have to drill a hole in the inner construction to gain access to the back of the damaged area. In other instances, you may have to drill a

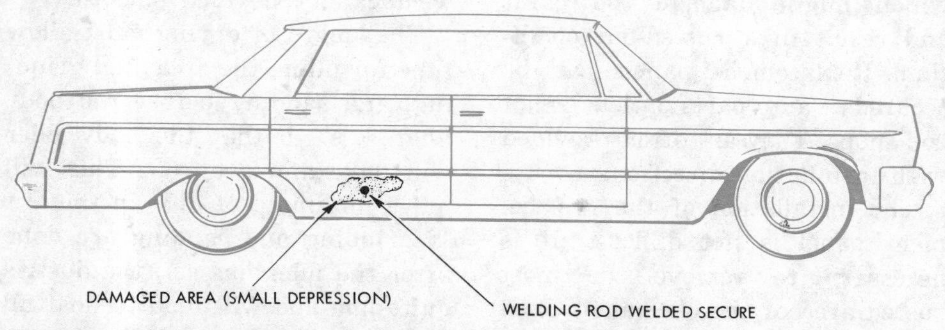

Fig. 8-56. Welding rod attached to panel to pull out damaged area.

hole in the outer panel to work through. Later you will have to fill the hole. If you are merely pulling the panel out so as to reduce the amount of solder required, filling the hole will be no problem since a small hole is easily filled with solder as a part of the building up of the contour.

Low Cost, Short Duration Repairs

Sometimes, it is desirable to make improvements in the appearance of a car, even though the resale value may be rather low. However, if the car is in good mechanical condition, it is probably a wise investment if the repairs can be made at a nominal cost.

Replacement Panels. Low cost, fiber glass panels are available for most cars. These fiber glass panels are for replacing rocker panels, splash shields, and lower back panels. These areas of a car body are the most susceptible to rust and damage from road debris which might damage the paint and result in a rusted-out condition. Replacement panels can be secured at auto parts outlets or hot rod shops. They are often provided with installation directions.

The installation of the replacement panel is not difficult. It is necessary to remove the most rusted area of the old panel. Then fit the new panel in place and drill the required holes through the old and the new panel. Then secure the new panel to the old with sheet metal screws. The panel can then be sanded and finished to match the color of the car.

Body Filling. Another very acceptable and low cost method of repair is to use a plastic body filler. Chapter 10 gives detailed instructions on plastic filler systems. Plastic body filler usually comes in cans. It is mixed with a drying agent or thinner to give it the proper drying time for the desired job. Plastic body filler can be used to build up areas of a body that putties will not fill. Such areas include:

1. Sections of metal that cannot be worked.
2. Sections that cannot be restored to original contour.
3. Holes or tears in the edges of doors, fenders, or quarter panels.
4. Sections weakened by rust or rusted out altogether.
5. Welded sections where the weld cannot be filed smooth.

The length of drying must allow time for filling the area, and grinding, and sanding before the body filler sets, so that the body filler will flake and drop off. This will put a minimum of dust in the air. If grinding and sanding are done after the filler has set, the dust is quite fine and will tend to float all over the shop.

When a hole or tear in the metal is mended, it should be backed up with a fiber glass screen or cloth. Thoroughly clean the back of the panel at least two inches around the hole to be mended. Saturate the screen or cloth with a plastic body filler and then place it over the hole from the back of the panel overlapping the metal in the cleaned area. After it has set, the hole can be filled a little higher than the panel to allow for sanding before finishing the metal flush with the panel.

When a rusty area is reinforced, it should be done in the same way with the fabric extending at least two inches onto firm metal. If plastic filler is anchored on metal softened or weakened by rust, the metal is likely to pull out, taking the plastic with it.

If lead is selected as a body filler, the following steps should be followed:

1. Tin the areas to be leaded, using acid core, liquid, or paste solder.
2. When applying the lead, use a wide flame to melt the bar and concentrate the flame on the lead. If the flame is held on the metal, it may wrinkle.
3. A wooden paddle should be used to smooth out the lead. Beeswax or a similar lubricant should be used on the paddle to keep the lead from sticking to it.
4. Grind and sand smooth.
5. Neutralize the leaded area with a solution of equal parts of alcohol, ammonia and water. Then treat the entire area, including all bare metal, with rust inhibitor and metal conditioner.

Estimating

In collision work, estimating is the selling part of the operation. Most collision jobs are paid for by an insurance company. Insurance companies generally require at least two estimates, and with all other things being equal, the shop that submits the lowest estimate will get the work.

In collision work, all estimates are considered firm. In other words, while a vehicle owner may not regard an estimate as a commitment to do the work involved for the amount of money shown, to the insurance company it is a firm pledge. If you hedge on your estimates, you will soon find that you will not secure future business from the insurance companies.

Actually, the estimate for repairing collision damage is a bid or proposal indicating the amount of money for which you will do the job. Your estimate should be detailed so that the insurance company can determine from the estimate just what it is you propose to do to the vehicle.

The estimate must include the cost of the parts, labor, material, the shop overhead, and the shop profit. Parts and labor should be included at their list price. That is, the catalog price for the parts without discount and the selling rate or retail rate for labor in your shop should be quoted.

Most collision shops consider insurance companies as valuable customers to whom they are willing to give a discount on parts. The usual practice is to show the parts at full list price, but to include an additional entry, "discount on parts—20 per cent" (or whatever discount is being allowed). They then show the amount of the discount in dollars and deduct it from the total amount of the estimate. The difference is shown as net cost. The amount of discount you can allow on parts is controlled by the amount which you receive in purchasing them. Don't give away all of your parts discount.

The cost of labor that you indicate on your estimate is based on the retail labor rate that has been established for your shop. A discussion of how a retail rate is established is presented in this section. This retail rate is multiplied by the number of hours and fractions thereof required to do the job. The number of hours required can be based on a flat rate schedule or based on the amount of time you estimate the jobs will take without regard to any published figures. These alternate methods are also discussed in this section.

The Retail Rate. The retail rate is the amount in dollars and cents that you charge to your customers for labor. This amount must include the actual cost of the labor; the cost of overhead, including such items as supervision, depreciation on equipment, supplies; and a profit for the shop.

The actual cost of the labor is the amount of money paid to the collision man. In the event some unskilled labor is used, this time should be charged for at the retail rate for the unskilled labor.

The retail rate generally is established by multiplying the wages received by the collision man by two and one-half. This means that the collision man is receiving as compensation 40 per cent of the retail rate. This is a lower percentage than is paid in some parts of the country for automobile repair mechanics. However, the amount of supplies used in collision work makes it necessary that a larger amount be apportioned to overhead than in the automotive repair department.

In some sections, where a working agreement between labor and management calls for the collision man receiving 50 per cent of the retail charge, the cost of supplies (solder, welding rod, gas, etc.) are listed separately on the estimate and are not considered as a part of the overhead.

From the foregoing, you can see that it is an easy matter to establish a retail labor rate for any community.

The cost of making estimates where you lose the job to some other shop, and the cost of supervision, rent, heat, light, electric power, welding gas, welding rod, solder, flux, and dozens of other items, make up the overhead of the shop. Overhead represents between 40 and 50 percent of the retail rate. The remaining 10 to 20 percent make up the shop profit, without which no business can long continue.

The Flat Rate. Most collision shops prepare their estimates from a flat rate time schedule as published by the automobile manufacturer or some flat rate service. In preparing these flat rates, the time allowance generally is quite liberal. The time shown is sufficient to permit the below-average collision man to do the job. The flat rate, however, generally does not take into account variations that exist in damage to a particular part. In using a flat rate manual to establish your estimate, there is a tendency for the estimate to be high unless you deliberately make allowances for those parts of the job that can be corrected simultaneously.

Estimate Based on Time and Material. As you gain experience in collision work, you will be able to determine quickly just how you will go about correcting a particular collision job. A car that is pushed in for its entire length often can be pushed back in shape almost as a single operation by using a number of power jacks. If your competition is adhering to a flat rate price and if you are truly skilled and make an accurate estimate of the number of hours the job will take, you will find that in most cases your estimate will be the low one. This will be particularly true on the easy jobs. This means that you will be getting a large percentage of the easy, high-profit jobs. Your competitor, using a cut-and-dried flat rate for estimating, will be getting the tough, low-profit jobs that you lose.

Much has been written on collision work estimating. If there were but one or two things that you could learn, and from these become an infallible estimator of collision costs, these things would be listed at this point. However, this whole volume is filled with the things which are factors in estimating collision work. For example, the factor of quality, discussed in conjunction with used cars, is an important consideration for which the flat rate does not generally make allowances. How well you can evaluate the advisability of replacing a part as compared to repairing it as discussed elsewhere in this chapter is also an important consideration, as is the question of filling versus straightening. The amount of hardware and trim which you must remove to begin the job is an important cost consideration also.

Regardless of whether you are figuring your estimates on a flat rate or on a time and material basis, the automobile body and frame must be considered by sections in order to locate and determine the extent of the damage.

Checking On Your Knowledge

The following questions give you the opportunity to check up on yourself. If you have read the chapter carefully, you should be able to answer the questions. If you have any difficulty, read the chapter over once more so that you have the information well in mind before you go on with your reading.

1. Why should a study of collision damage be made before any attempt is made to straighten it?
2. In what direction must the corrective forces be applied in collision work?
3. How is it possible to determine sometimes just how a collision occurred without questioning someone as to the particulars?
4. When should the damage which occurred last be corrected?
5. What name is given to the system of diagonal comparison used for checking body alignment?
6. What piece of measuring equipment is most usually used for making body measurements?
7. Why is it necessary to make measurements at various stages in the correction of collision damage?
8. When a body is divided into sections for measurement, is the trunk compartment considered as part of the rear section?
9. Why is it sometimes necessary to check the alignment of one body section with another body section?
10. When the alignment of two sections is checked, what shape are the two sections considered as forming?
11. What are the principal considerations involved in determining whether to replace a part or repair it?
12. Is it usually best to repair or replace bright metal parts when they are damaged?
13. Is it usually possible to re-use interior trim panels after a collision repair?
14. When reconditioning used cars, is it always possible to do a high quality job?

Refinishing Practices

Chapter

9

The straightening of damaged automobile bodies and their repainting, two widely different crafts, are generally associated with each other. In smaller shops particularly, a single body shop man is often a combination collision man and painter. Even in shops where there is no overlapping between the body shop and the paint shop, each must be familiar with the techniques of the other.

Chapter 4 explains how the body shop prepares metal for the painter. Painters are sometimes required to repaint jobs on which a metal finisher has not worked, making it necessary for the painter to perform some metal finishing steps. A metal finisher who appreciates just how far the painter can go in filling up scratches is less liable to turn out work that cannot be properly refinished. Likewise, a painter who appreciates some of the problems confronting the metal finisher will not make unreasonable demands upon the body shop.

Painting is largely a matter of skill developed through practice, plus a thorough knowledge of painting materials. Skill can only be acquired through directed practice. This chapter will guide you in acquiring painting skill. The paint industry is constantly improving its products through continuing research and as a painter you must keep your knowledge of materials up to date.

This chapter, plus some practice, should equip you to work on used car appearance reconditioning or price refinishing. The experience you need for the custom-shop quality jobs that sell for a high price is acquired only through a lot of painting experience, with a constant striving for perfection on each job. As no previous knowledge of the subject is assumed, it is recommended that each section be studied, and that the exercises be performed in the order presented.

Finishing Materials

The major materials in refinishing are usually considered as the finish materials, the material that results in a color being put on the surface. In reality there are many more materials that have a critical

BUICK & SPECIAL
to 1956 ... 6
1957 ... 3
1958-1962 ... 7
1963-1965-1971 ... 5, 7, or 9

CADILLAC
to 1956 ... 6
1957-1962 ... 7
1963-1965 ... 9
1971 ... 7

CHEVROLET
to 1956 ... 6
1957-1958 ... 3
1959-1962 ... 7
1963-1964 ... 5
1964 Chevelle ... 7
1965 Chevelle & Chev.-1971 ... 7

CHEVY II
1962 ... 6
1963-1964 ... 5
1965 ... 6
1971 ... 7

CORVAIR
1960-1965 ... 4

CHRYSLER
1952-1955 ... 7
1956 ... 12
1957-1958 ... 10
1959 ... 6
1960-1964 ... 1
1965-1971 ... 7

IMPERIAL
1952-1955 ... 7
1956 ... 12
1957-1961 ... 10
1962-1963 ... 7
1964-1965 ... 1
1971 ... 7

DE SOTA
1952-1956 ... 7
1957-1959 ... 6, 3, or 13
1960-1961 ... 1

DODGE
1956-1959 ... 6
1960-1961 ... 6, 10, or 7
1962 ... 6, 10 or 11
1963-1965 ... 11 or 1
1965-Model 880 ... 7
1971 7

LANCER
1961-1962 ... 11

FORD
1953-1961 ... 1

FORD FAIRLANE
1962-1965 ... 2

FORD GALAXIE
1962 ... 1
1963-1965-1971 ... 2

FALCON
1960-1965 ... 2

THUNDERBIRD
1955-1957 ... 6
1958-1962 ... 1
1963-1965-1971 ... 2

WILLYS ... 6

LINCOLN & CONTINENTAL
1955-1962 ... 1
1963-1965-1971 ... 2

MERCURY
1953-1962 ... 1
1963-1965-1971 ... 2

COMET & METEOR
1960-1965-1971 ... 2

NASH & RAMBLER
1953-1957 ... 6 or 3
1958-1959 ... 6
1960-1965 ... 1 or 2

OLDSMOBILE & F-85
to 1956 ... 6
1957-1958 ... 3
1959-1962 ... 7
1963-1965-1971 ... 5 or 9

PLYMOUTH
1958-1959 ... 7
1960-1961 ... 10 or 7
1962-1965 ... 6, 10 or 11
1971 ... 7

VALIANT
1960-1965 ... 7 or 11

PONTIAC & TEMPEST
to 1957 ... 6
1958-1962 ... 7
1963-1965-1971 ... 5 or 9

STUDEBAKER
Lark or Avanti ... 8

Where to find Paint Identification Plates

The 1906 Model "G" Limousine by Studebaker

THE LISTINGS ON PAGE 338 ARE RELATED TO THE NUMBERED PANELS INDICATED BELOW

1. LEFT FRONT BODY PILLAR
2. REAR FACE OF LEFT FRONT DOOR
3. CENTER OF FIRE WALL UNDER HOOD
4. LEFT SIDE REAR ENGINE COMPARTMENT
5. RIGHT SIDE OF UPPER SHROUD, UNDER HOOD
6. LEFT SIDE OF FIRE WALL UNDER HOOD
7. RIGHT SIDE OF FIRE WALL UNDER HOOD
8. STICKER ON UNDER-SIDE OF GLOVE BOX
9. LEFT SIDE OF UPPER SHROUD, UNDER HOOD
10. RIGHT SIDE OF RADIATOR YOKE UNDER HOOD
11. LEFT FRONT FENDER SHIELD UNDER HOOD
12. LEFT SIDE OF STONE SHIELD UNDER HOOD
13. RIGHT SIDE OF STONE SHIELD UNDER HOOD

LOCATION OF PLATES SHOWN ON DIAGRAM ARE APPROXIMATE

Fig. 9-1. Paint data location. (Rinshed-Mason Co.)

bearing on just how good the finish or color coat looks. These are the thinners, solvents, reducers, primers, sealers, etc., that are applied as undercoats to properly prepare the surface for the color coats.

Later in this chapter recommended systems are listed to show

TABLE 9-1 LOCATION OF COLOR CODE ON FOREIGN CARS

Make of Car	Location
Alfa Romeo	3 digit "AR" number stencilled under trunk lid on '68-'70. Earlier models no number. No number on "Spyder" model.
Aston Martin	No color code number on car.
Austin-BMC	No color code number on car.
BMW	Color name on I. D. plate inside rear front fender, starting with 1968 models.
Citroen	3 digit "AC" number on round brass tag on plate on rear front fire wall.
Datsun	3 digit number on fire wall I. D. tag on 1967 and later models.
Dodge Colt	No number on car.
Ford Capri	Capri color code on I. D. plate on top of engine side apron panel.
Ford Cortina	2 digit letters on patent plate under hood inside rear front fender. '69 model has 2 letters and 1 number (i.e. B5P).
Fiat	3 digit number on 600 model rear fire wall, right front fire wall all other models.
Honda	No color code on car.
Jaguar	No color code on car.
Mazda	No paint number on car.
Mercedes	3 digit DB number on plate inside left front door post or on plate near hood lock.
Opel Kadette	'68 model 3 numbers under lock lower deck panel. '69-'70 model 2 letters on body plate.
Peugeot	4 digit number on right front fender under hood.
Plymouth Cricket	2 or 3 number digit stamped on chassis I. D. plate on fire wall.
Porsche	4 digit number on left front door post; first 2 numbers indicate color number.

TABLE 9-1 LOCATION OF COLOR CODE ON FOREIGN CARS (CONT'D)

Renault	3 digit number stencilled on wall in rear of luggage compartment or on battery compartment.
Rolls Royce	No color code number on car.
Rootes (Chrysler)	2 or 3 digit number stamped on chassis I. D. plate on fire wall.
Rover	No number on car.
Simca	No paint number on car until 68. Name now under hood stencilled inside right front fender.
Saab	Numerical letter on fire wall.
Subaru	No paint number on car.
Toyota	3 digit number on left side fire wall to 1969. 1970 has no paint code number on car.
Triumph	2 digit number on I. D. plate of fire wall or I. D. plate on left hand post under hood.
Volvo	2 digit number on left side fire wall. (Plate shows chassis color and trim number in that sequence.)
Volkswagen-Audi	Number on tag behind spare tire all models. 1970 models tag on panel left side of spare tire.

you which materials should be used, and the sequence of applications required for matching the original surface of the unit on which you are working.

Original Finishes. In the years prior to 1955, baked enamel was the standard finish on all automobiles. Then a transition started to super enamels which evolved into "Acrylic Enamels and from Nitrocellulose Lacquers to Acrylic Lacquers." Since 1965 the original finish for each major manufacturer is as follows:

Chrysler Corporation	Acrylic Enamel
Ford Motor Company	Acrylic Enamel
American Motors	Acrylic Enamel
General Motors Corporation	Acrylic Lacquer

During the transition from the older type finishes to the newer, each model year had the type of paint clearly identified on the vehicle Patent Plate. Necessary information for interpreting the Patent Plate data is made readily available to all refinishing shops by both the car manufacturers and paint and refinishing materials manufacturers. Patent Plates are not all located in the same place on vehicles. For the location on older models, which you may encounter in restoration projects, the location is shown in a very unique way in Fig. 9-1.

The method of refinishing that you will use depends on the identification of the material used for the original finish. Therefore proper identification of the original finish is of the utmost importance to a good paint job.

Patent Plate location information on late model cars is readily available from paint manufactuers. For foreign cars, see Table 9-1.

Equipment

Some of the materials with which you will be working can be explosive under certain conditions, and almost all of them are flammable. Before you make your final decisions about the selection of paint shop equipment it is recommended that you obtain a copy of the National Fire Protection Association booklet, *Standards for Spray Finishing Using Flammable Materials.*

Spray Booth or Paint Room

Where local ordinances permit it, and where no fire hazard exists, small spot repairs of lacquer can be accomplished without either a spray booth or drying oven. On the other hand, it is extremely important to recognize that almost all paint materials, including acrylics, lacquers, enamels, thinners, solvents, primers, etc., are potential fire hazards. Paint fires burn violently and get out of control very quickly. Vapors from evaporating thinners can quickly spread throughout an enclosed area and be ignited by sparking motors, light fixtures, switches, cigarettes, welding torches, etc. Good spray painters observe the following common sense rules of safety.

The Painter's Seven Rules Of Safety.

1. Provide a good ventilation system to remove fumes.
2. Display NO SMOKING and CAUTION signs in and around the spray areas.
3. Keep fire extinguishers and fire fighting equipment in handy spots.
4. Never drive a car in or out of a spray booth—push it by hand.
5. Comply with safety codes on electrical equipment; never use makeshift electrical set-ups.
6. Regularly check all electrically driven equipment; be sure

ground wires are intact to avoid static electricity.

7. Keep the area, including the floors, clean. Avoid fire from spontaneous combustion by disposing of dirty rags and papers daily, preferably just before quitting time.

The time will come when you will plan a complete refinish job. You will need a spray booth which meets National Fire Protection Association Standards and a drying oven. Fig. 9-2 shows a schematic of a paint spray booth with a drying chamber.

With this particular unit, an operational pressurized air replacement unit is also shown. Air replacement is a critical problem. When any type of power exhaust is in operation in a building, the exhausted air must be replaced, otherwise an air starved condition may be set up in the shop, and outside air will seep into the building from every door and window. In a body shop, the incoming air should be moisture and dust free, therefore it is filtered. In cold climates it must also be heated.

Spray Gun

Most automotive paint shops use the kind of spray gun shown in Fig. 9-3. This gun has a cup that holds the paint. A trigger on the gun allows compressed air to blow through the gun and out of the nozzle. Paint is drawn up into the center of this air stream and out of the nozzle. To flatten this paint-and-air stream, two additional streams of air are directed at its sides through two *horn holes*.

Some guns are provided with several additional air jets that help to break up the more viscous (sticky) materials, such as super and acrylic enamels, Fig. 9-4, top.

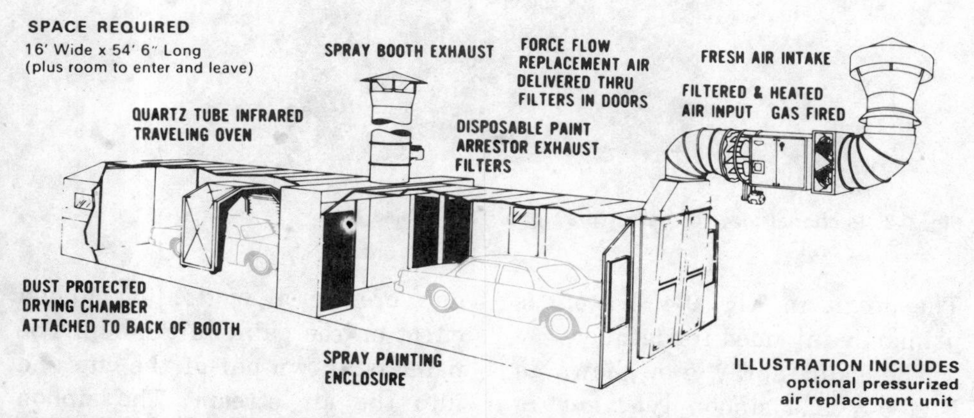

Fig. 9-2. Spray paint booth with drying chamber. (Rotunda Equipment, Ford Motor Co.)

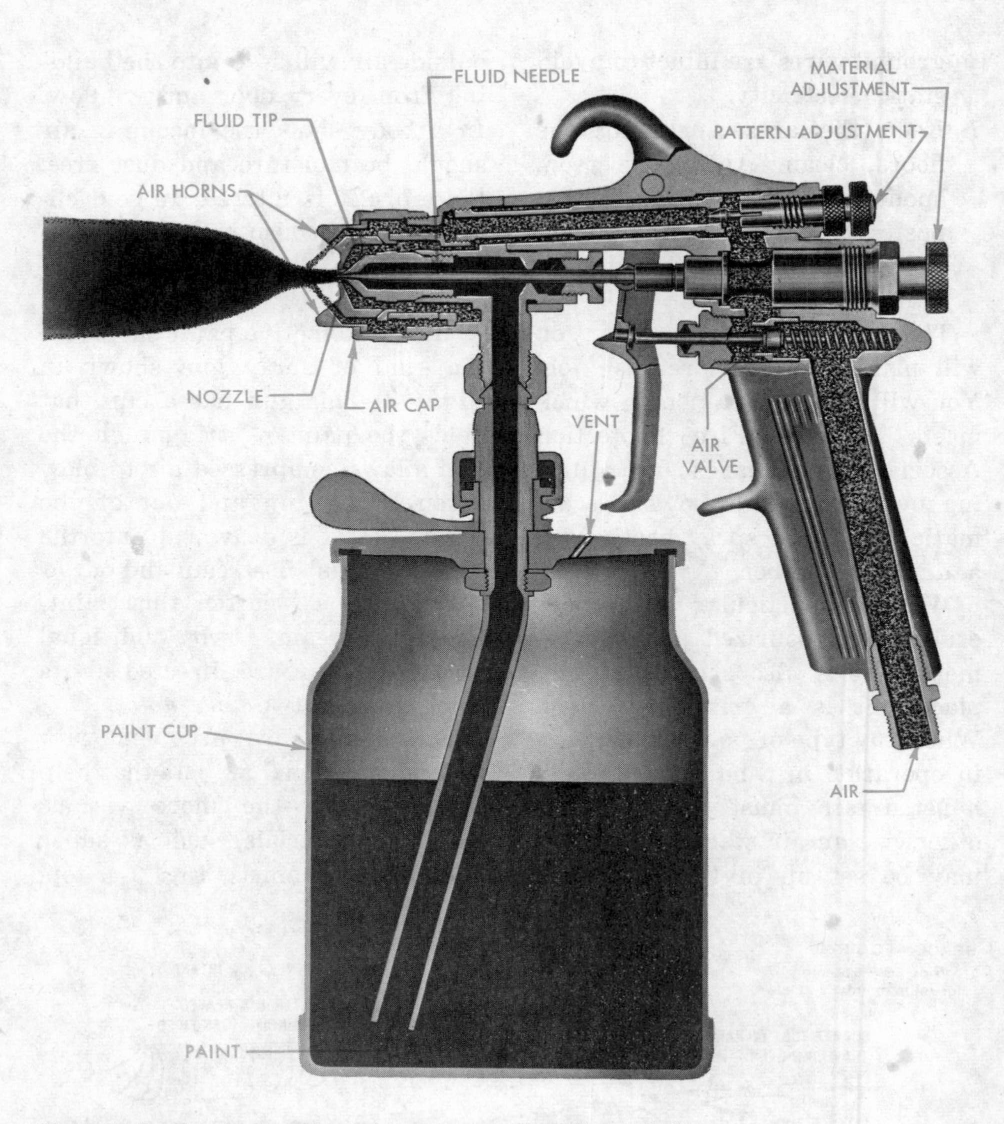

Fig. 9-3. Sectional view of paint spray gun. (De Vilbiss Co.)

The nozzle in Fig. 9-4, bottom is primarily intended for lacquers.

The paint spray gun shown in Fig. 9-3 is a siphon type gun in which the air velocity through the gun creates a suction or siphon effect on the paint in the cup. The paint is drawn out of the cup and into the air stream. The siphon type of gun is the most commonly

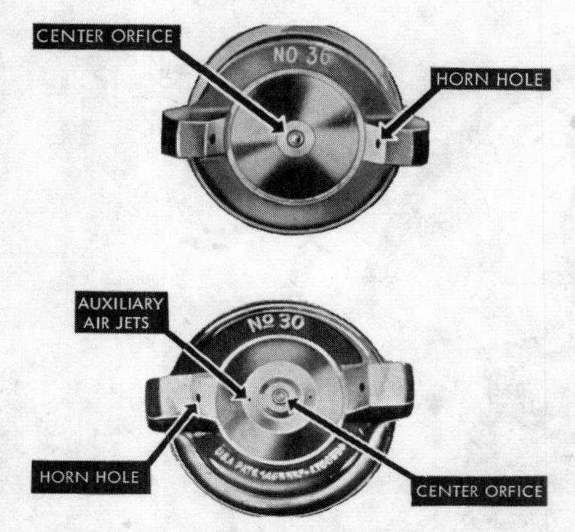

Fig. 9-4. Spray gun for super and acrylic enamels; spray gun for lacquers.

used in spray paint shops because it is the least expensive. It does not, however, compare favorably with the controlled-pressure spray guns used in car manufacturers' paint operations.

One gun which does compare favorably to production plant spray guns is the remote-cup gun, Fig. 9-5. With this gun, the paint is delivered from a remote cup, under pressure, to the spray gun itself. An air supply, fed to the gun, controls the spray pattern and is not required to siphon paint from the paint cup; therefore less actual air pressure is required. The arrangement provides more even pressures than with the siphon type of gun.

The remote-cup gun is easier to handle because the operator does not lift the cup and the paint supply. The gun can be used in a horizontal or an upside-down position, Fig. 9-5, with no danger of dripping paint from the cup vent.

In any shop which does a large amount of paint work, remote-cup gun installation should be considered because of the advantages of controlled-pressure spraying.

Air Pressure System. A spray gun uses approximately nine cubic feet of air per minute. Air compressor capacity usually averages about four cubic feet of air per minute for each one horsepower of the compressor motor. Thus, two spray guns in simultaneous use require a five horsepower (20 cubic feet per minute) air compressor.

If the compressor lacks the capacity to keep the required quantity of compressed air flowing to the spray gun, the additional air needed must come from the reserve tank. As you use more air than the compressor is supplying, the pressure in the tank and the pressure at the gun are gradually reduced. *A change of pressure while you are applying paint can cause considerable trouble.* This will be particularly true later, as you spray color containing metal particles. Metallic paints are very popular but difficult to apply uniformly unless the air pressure to the spray gun remains constant.

Another cause of pressure loss is air-line resistance. Both the air

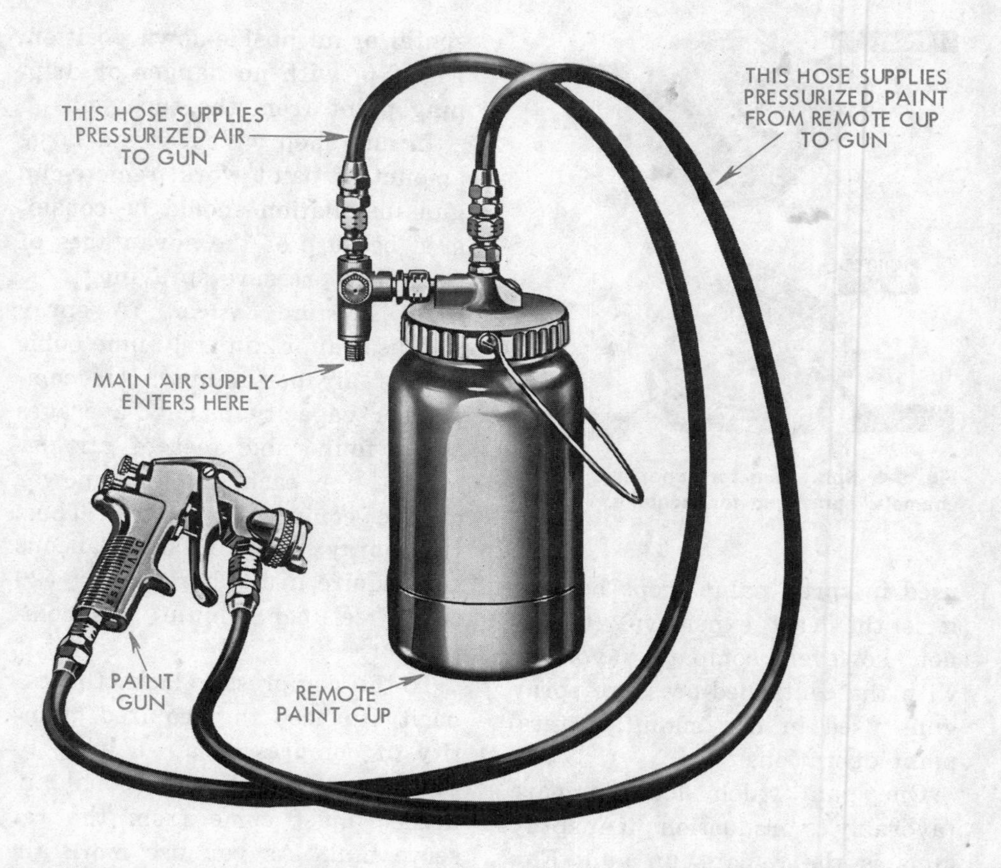

Fig. 9-5. Remote-cup paint spray gun (top); spraying rocker panel with gun in upside-down position (bottom). (DeVilbiss Co.)

lines and the air hose running to the spray gun must be of adequate size; otherwise, the pressure at the gun will drop as soon as you start to paint. This will result in more paint coming out of the nozzle during the first instant you pull the trigger than during the rest of the stroke. Any variation in pressure will cause trouble with almost any kind of paint, and will make a good job with metallic paints almost impossible.

Some shops make the mistake of using hose designed for use with grease guns instead of air hose designed for use with paint spray guns. To avoid excessive line loss, the hose carrying air to your spray gun should have a $\frac{5}{16}''$ diameter passage to handle the volume of air required.

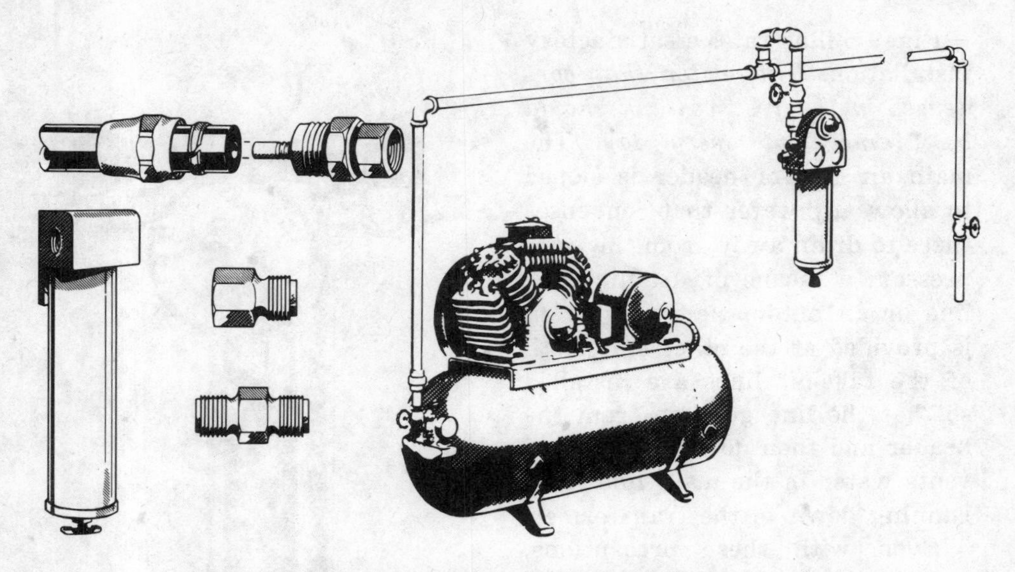

MINIMUM PIPE SIZE RECOMMENDATIONS

COMPRESSING OUTFIT		MAIN AIR LINE PIPE	
Size	CFM*	Length	Size
1 1/2 and 2 H P	6 to 9	Over 50 ft	3/4"
3 and 5 H P	12 to 20	Up to 200 ft	3/4" 1"
5 to 10 H P	20 to 40	Up to 100 ft Over 100 to 200 ft Over 200 ft	3/4" 1" 1 1/4"
10 to 15 H P	40 to 60	Up to 100 ft Over 100 to 200 ft Over 200 ft	1" 1 1/4" 1 1/2"

* cu. ft./min.

Fig. 9-6. Typical compressor, air transformer, and spray gun installation. (De Vilbiss Co.)

The entire air system must be installed so as to be self draining. The moisture in the air condenses when the air is released from under pressure or is cooled. If this water gets into your paint, or on the surface you are painting, it will spoil the job.

Fig. 9-6 illustrates a satisfactory installation. *The water that condenses in the reserve tank should be drained out every day.* The main air line or header is sloped to allow any water that condenses there to drain away from the compressor; a means of draining the line or an automatic water drain is provided at the other end. Both of the take-off lines are installed so that the line goes up from the header and then down, which prevents water in the main line from running down to the transformer.

Even with these precautions, some water can condense in the line running down from the main air line or header. A pressure regulator called an *air transformer* must be used to insure a flow of clean, dry air at the correct pressures. A typical air transformer is illustrated in Fig. 9-7. *It is extremely important to use exactly the pressure specified by the paint manufacturer.* In general, a pressure of 50 psi at the transformer is required for lacquer material and 60 psi at the transformer for synthetic enamels.

To use the spray gun, connect the air hose and spray gun to the transformer. Shut off the material adjustment on the spray gun. Hold the spray gun trigger all the way back (wide open) and adjust the air transformer to the desired pressure.

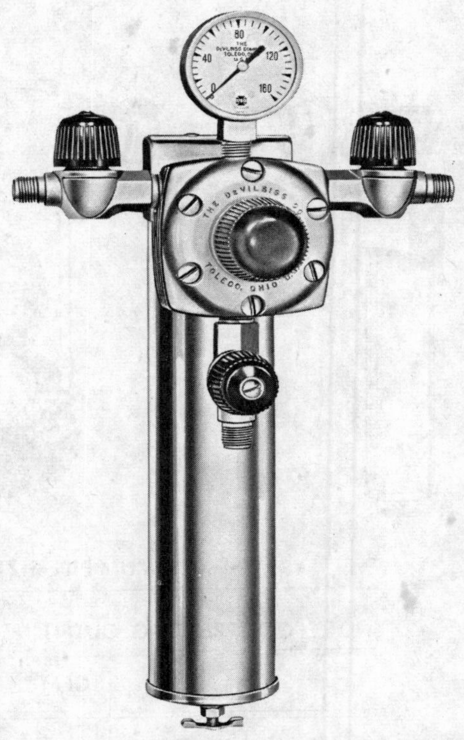

Fig. 9-7. Air transformer with automatic drain to remove air line moisture and to prevent accumulated moisture from entering the lacquer or enamel. (De Vilbiss Co.)

Excessive air pressure wastes thinners when spraying lacquer. Insufficient air pressure will not supply enough volume or velocity of air to properly atomize the more viscous synthetic enamels.

Checking Line Drop. To determine the drop in air pressure between the air transformer and the spray gun, it is necessary to install a T-fitting and a pressure gage between the air hose and the spray gun, Fig. 9-8.

Fig. 9-8. T and gage to check pressure at the gun. (De Vilbiss Co.)

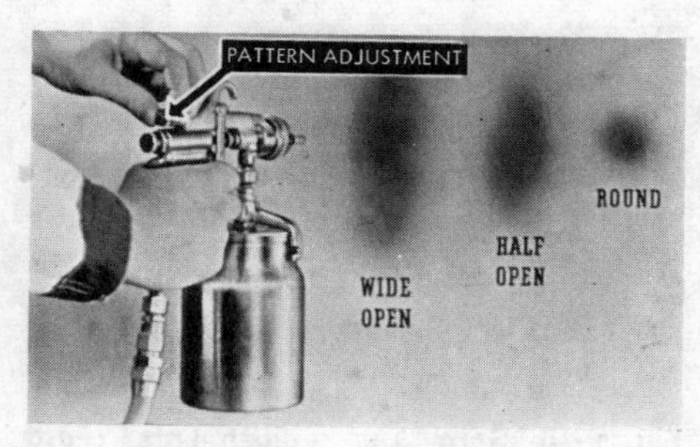

Fig. 9-9. Setting the pattern adjustment. (Ford Motor Co.)

Hold the gun wide open again and compare the pressure reading at the gun to the regulated pressure reading at the transformer. The difference in these two readings is the pressure loss in the hose running from the transformer to the spray gun. You will find that it is impossible to do good paint work if you have excessive pressure drop at the gun. However, if some compromise in quality is acceptable, or if you possess enough skill to overcome this handicap, you may wish to readjust the pressure at the regulator to raise the pressure at the gun to the recommended reading.

Adjusting Spray Gun. With the air pressure adjusted, the material adjustment shut off, and the gun cup filled with properly strained and reduced primer-surfacer, you are ready to adjust the spray gun.

First, you must establish the correct spray pattern and the correct material adjustment. To accomplish this, you hang a piece of paper on the wall with masking tape. This paper is used to test your adjustments. It can also be used for practicing with the spray gun until you get the feel of the gun and acquire enough skill to start working on an automobile.

Secondly, position yourself in front of this paper so that your feet are 15″ to 20″ apart, and you can hold the spray gun comfortably with the head directly in front of you and about 8″ away from the paper. Now, hold the spray gun trigger open and turn the material adjustment out, i.e., counterclockwise, until paint starts to appear on the paper. Fig. 9-9 shows a range of patterns that are possible.

Material Adjustment. Paint spray guns are provided with a *material adjustment* and a *pattern adjustment*. The material adjustment, Fig. 9-10, shows adjustments which

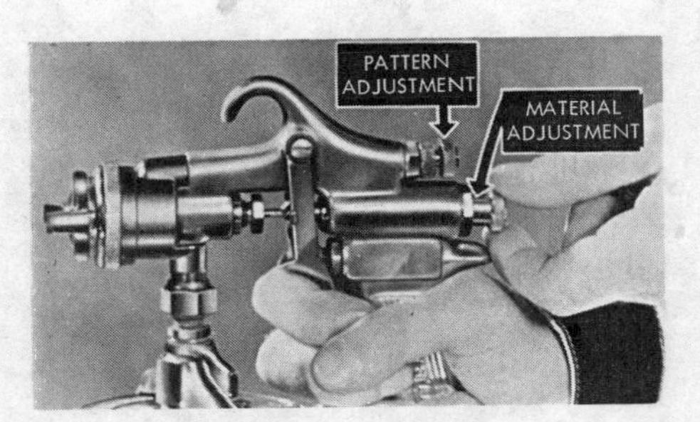

Fig. 9-10. Spray gun adjustments. (Ford Motor Co.)

control the amount of paint that will flow out of the nozzle. In learning to use a spray gun, turn this adjustment all the way to the right (clockwise) to completely shut off the paint. Then, as you start to use the gun, turn the adjustment to the left (counterclockwise) to increase the amount of paint until you have it set to the amount of paint you can handle. You will be able to handle more paint with experience.

At the beginning, if you cut the material adjustment down, you will be less apt to spoil a job that you may have spent hours in preparing for paint. With experience, you will be able to handle the gun with the material adjustment all the way open for some materials.

Pattern Adjustment. The pattern adjustment controls the air to the horn holes. Fig. 9-9 shows that the shape of the stream of paint and air from the gun can be adjusted. Except for making spot repairs or painting narrow surfaces, the pattern is set wide open.

As a beginner, you will probably find it better to start with the pattern adjustment half open. If the pattern coming from the gun is horizontal rather than vertical, loosen the air cap collar on the spray gun head (Fig. 9-3) and turn the horns so that they are horizontal instead of vertical. This will turn the spray pattern 90°.

If the paint pattern looks like those illustrated in Fig. 9-11, upper left, your spray gun is dirty. Thoroughly clean the gun head and nozzle. Don't attempt to paint with an imperfect pattern. If the paint pattern is heavy in the center as shown in Fig. 9-11, upper right, either the material in the gun needs further reduction (add more thinner or reducer), or higher air pressure is required.

If the spray pattern looks like the one illustrated in Fig. 9-11, lower left, the air pressure is too high for the consistency of the material in the gun; reduce the air pressure. When correct gun adjustments, proper air pressures, clean gun, properly mixed paint, and the correct distance between the gun and the surface are employed, a perfect pattern as in Fig. 9-11, lower right can be obtained.

Spraying Exercise. You are now ready to use the spray gun. Without pulling the trigger, practice moving the gun across the paper, holding or maintaining the distance

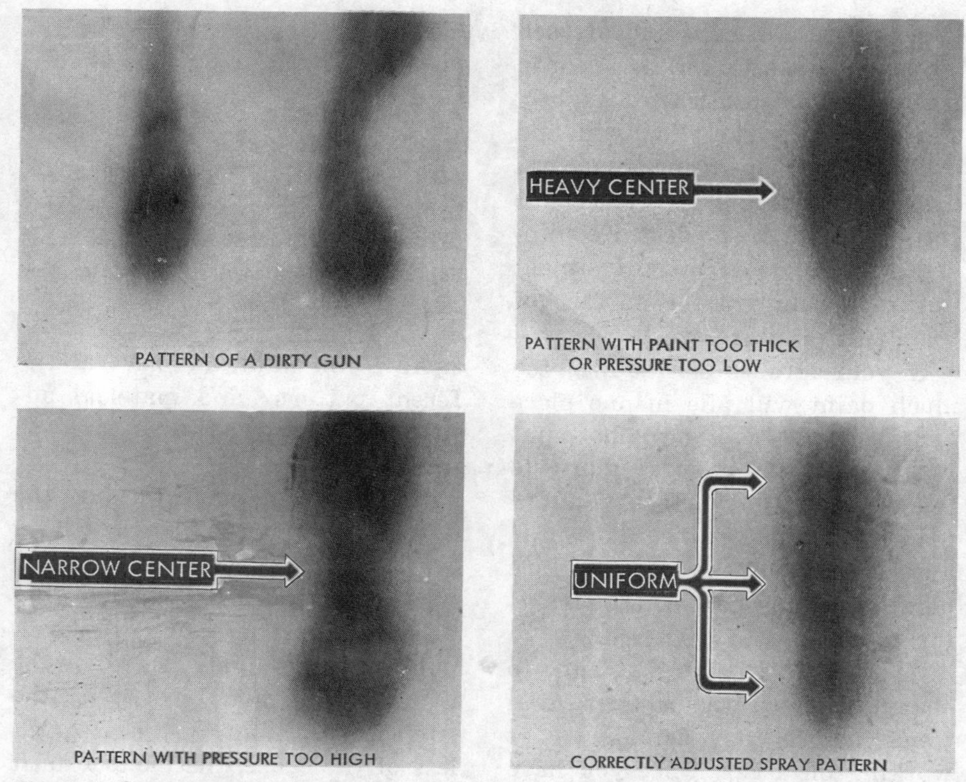

Fig. 9-11. Spray-patterns. (Ford Motor Co.) Pattern of dirty spray gun. Pattern with paint too thick or pressure too low. Pattern with pressure too high. Correctly adjusted spray pattern.

between the gun head and the paper. You will find that this is easier to do if your head, shoulders, arm, and the spray gun all move together. Try to confine movement to your waist, hips, and legs.

Once you have developed the ability to make a stroke about 16″ or 18″ long while maintaining the correct distance between the gun and the paper, close the material adjustment. Then, pulling and releasing the trigger each stroke, again practice the stroke.

CAUTION: Remember that the trigger must never be opened when the gun is not in motion.

This means that the trigger is not pulled until the gun is already in motion at the beginning of each stroke. Likewise, the trigger is released just before the end of each stroke. Keeping this in mind, open the material adjustment slightly and start to spray. You will find that the half open spray pattern previously set will be the easiest for you to handle at first. Keep increasing the material adjustment until the paint on the surface of the paper appears wet.

If your strokes slow down, too much paint will pile in one place and the paint will sag. The paint will also sag if the spray gun gets too close to the surface you are painting. If you get the gun too far away from the surface you are painting at any part of the stroke, the material may go on dry.

You will probably want to change your practice paper several times before you actually start working on a car. Once you have mastered the technique of the correct stroke and proper timing in triggering the gun, start to cover the surface of the paper with overlapping strokes, attempting to apply a uniform thickness of paint. You may have to make a number of trials before you get the kind of surface you want, and several different patterns and material adjustments may be necessary as well.

Fig. 9-12. Orange peel. (Ford Motor Co.)

If the paint appears like the *orange peel* pattern shown in Fig. 9-12, the cause is usually one or a combination of the following things: improper air pressures, paint not thoroughly mixed, or the incorrect distance between the surface and the spray gun. Regardless of the cause, the trouble must be corrected before you start working on the car.

Once you feel that you have mastered the handling of the spray gun and its adjustments, you should be ready to apply primer-surfacer to a car fender or body panel.

Methods

In painting a fender or panel, as a painter, you must inspect the metal finish first, making sure the metal finisher has prepared the fender for you. Go over the entire repair with No. 360 grit metal cloth to remove any burrs raised by the grinder. Your fingers will feel any irregularities in the metal through the cloth as you work.

Masking. All parts of the car not being painted should be masked at this time. Masking merely means the covering of surfaces with masking tape to protect them from unwanted paint.

Masking tape is waterproof paper gummed on one side. It comes in rolls of various widths from 1/4" to 2" wide. Care must be used not to have the tape cover anything that you do want painted. When you are going to be sanding near chrome parts, it is a good practice to mask the chrome so as not to scratch it during the sanding.

This fender was *spot repaired.* However, as a beginner you should learn by painting an entire fender or panel rather than attempt the more difficult spot repair at this time. In painting the entire fender on this particular car, you might remove the bumper bar rather than mask it. On late model cars this involves too much work, so you should mask the bumper. The rest of the car would also be masked with masking tape and paper.

Fig. 9-13 shows a *apron taper* that will apply about half of the width of the masking tape to paper. Such a device saves considerable time. An equally satisfactory job can be done by putting masking tape on the edge of wrapping paper or newspaper. Lay the paper on a clean, flat surface and apply the masking tape so that half of its width is on the paper.

Fig. 9-13. Applying masking tape with apron taper from roll. (Minnesota Mining and Mfg. Co.)

If you are painting a fender or body panel, all other parts of the car within a foot of where you will be applying paint should be masked, Fig. 9-14. It may be wise to mask everything with 18" of where the new paint will be applied if the painter is a beginner.

Sanding. To repaint all of a fender, all of the old paint should be wet-sanded with No. 320 grit waterproof paper, either on a rubber block such as used for featheredging, or with a felt pad. Use a wet sponge to keep the surface wet during the sanding. While sanding, always keep your strokes going in the same direction. The strokes may vary from 6" to 12" in length. Use a stroke length that seems to come natural to you.

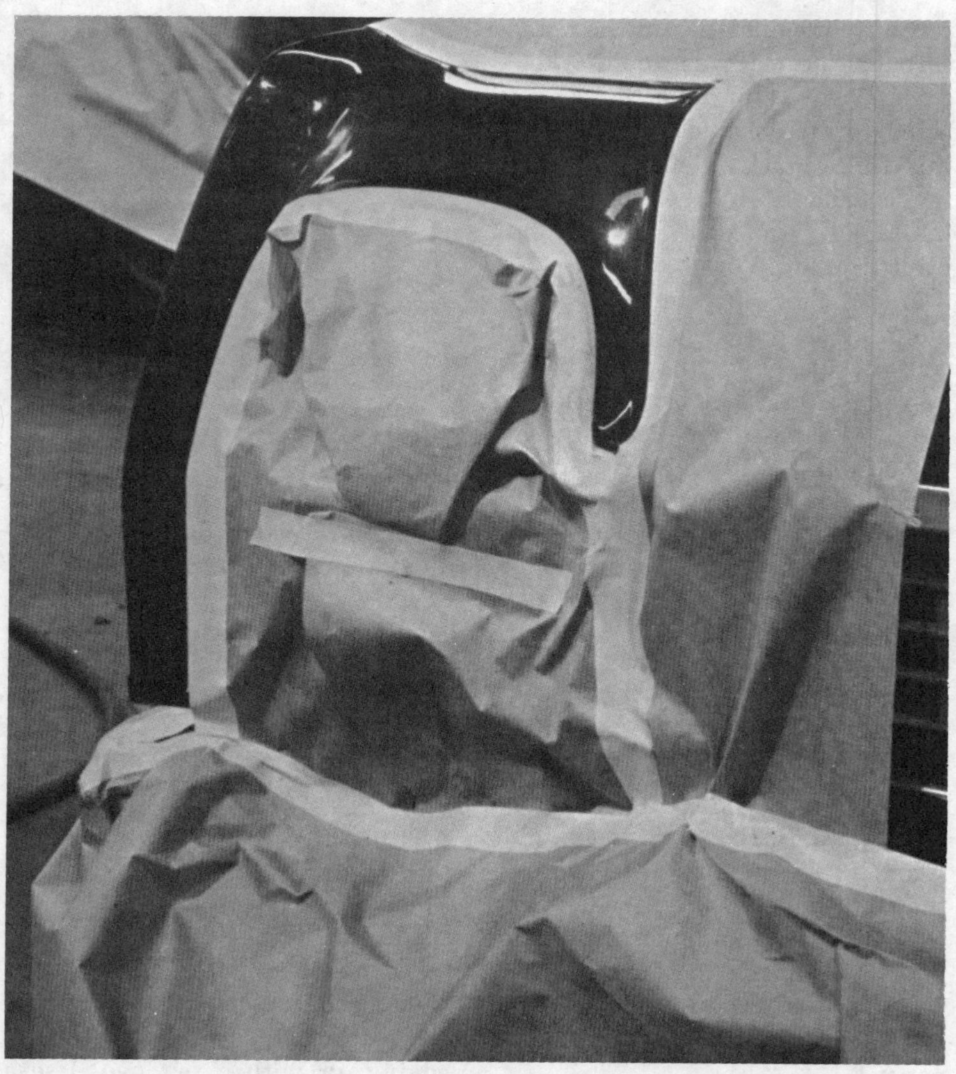

Fig. 9-14. Using paper to mask around headlight, grille and front bumper. (Minnesota Mining and Mfg. Co.)

The purpose of this sanding is to obtain a smooth surface that will provide *tooth* for the new paint. Stop sanding when the surface is smooth. Check your progress frequently by pulling the edge of a *squeegee* over the wet surface. The squeegee will remove the water from the smooth surface; any pits or depressions in the paint will remain wet, and thus will become apparent. The squeegee used by a sander works like the squeegees used for cleaning windows. It wipes the water off of the surface. This squeegee, however, is merely a rubber block about 1/4″ thick, 1/2″ wide, and 2 1/2″ long. If, however, you are not painting the whole fender or panel, then the next step is that of featheredging.

Featheredging. Featheredging is the gradual tapering of the old finish so that the old paint and the bare metal form an uninterrupted smooth surface. Properly featheredged, each layer of the old finish will be approximately 1/4″ wide at the narrowest point. Care in this operation is essential to prevent trouble from an uneven or ridged surface later on.

Block sanding is essential in featheredging. It can be done either by machine or by hand for the intermediate featheredging step. Fig. 9-15 shows a panel in the intermediate stage of featheredging. This step is accomplished with No. 240 A-grit waterproof silicone carbide paper used wet for block sanding. The three areas worked are shown in the inset in Fig. 9-15. These are the bare metal, the old primer, and the old paint.

Some painters will prefer to use a dry sanding method with a machine sander. In this case, No. 180 A-grit silicone carbide stearated paper can be used with a machine to produce results similar to wet sanding by hand. Electrical tools should not be used on wet surfaces for safety reasons.

Final featheredging is usually done by block sanding, wet, using No. 320 grit waterproof silicone carbide finishing paper. Some prefer to do the featheredging by block machine dry sanding as shown in Fig. 9-16. When this is done, No. 240 grit silicon carbide stearated paper is used. With any featheredging method, the sanded area should extend several inches beyond the edge of the paint into the old finish. This will improve the adhesion of the new paint, preventing failure by peeling.

After featheredging is completed, a good commercial cleaner should be used to clean the entire area thoroughly. This will remove any particles left from sanding, as well as oil, film or dirt that can cause problems later.

Putty Glazing. If you encounter deep pits that do not go down to bare metal, it is not necessary to sand them out. These pits can be filled with *glazing putty,* which is packaged in both cans and tubes. Glazing putty packaged in tubes is better for use in small shops because it will keep longer.

Only a small amount of putty is pressed into the pit with a putty knife. The surplus is then scraped

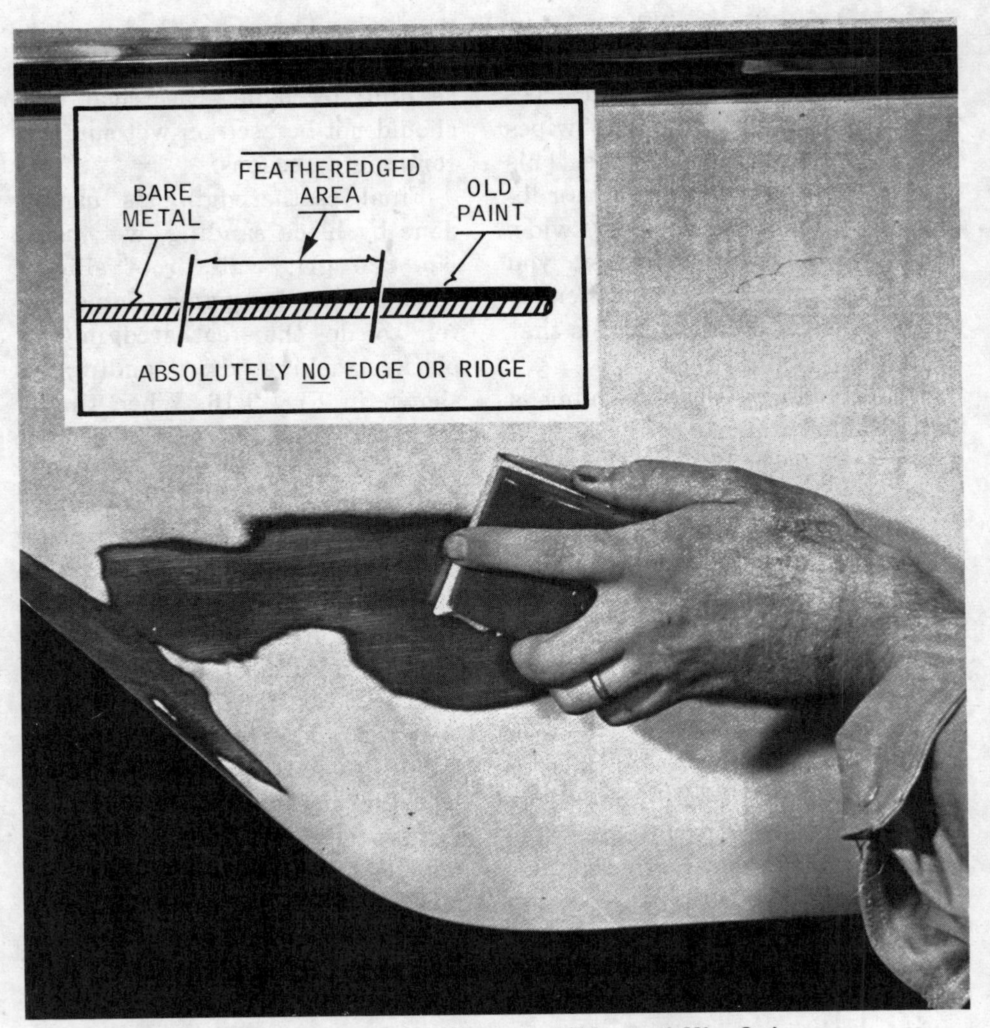

Fig. 9-15. Intermediate featheredging. (Minnesota Mining and Mfg. Co.)

off, but *do not scrape off too much.* Leave enough so that there will be something to sand after it dries.

Cleaning. When all of the surface to be repainted, including any putty-glazed spots, has been sanded, the entire surface must be cleaned. Wet sanding leaves a mud-like accumulation on the surface. This mud and all traces of water must be removed. Wipe the surface clean and, with a *duster gun,* use compressed air to blow out any water or mud that may have lodged in crevices or behind decorative trim.

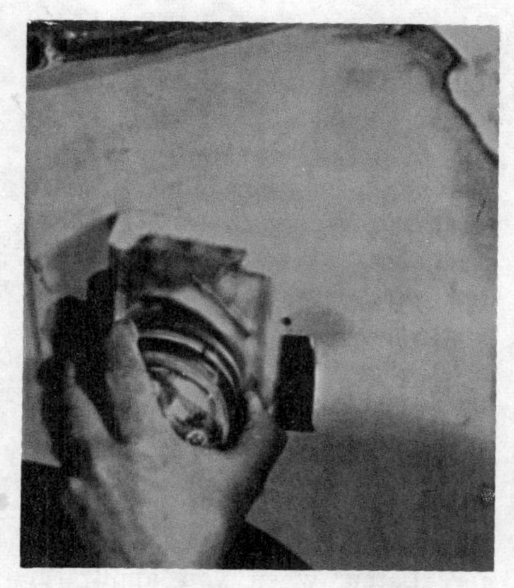

Fig. 9-16. Final featheredging. (Minnesota Mining and Mfg. Co.)

Small areas or particles of wax, or other protective coatings that were on the surface, are apt to remain even after sanding; all traces of these materials must be removed. Removal of these particles is accomplished by wiping the surface with a clean cloth dipped in a special solvent designed for this purpose. All major automotive paint companies sell solvents, under various trade names, for dissolving these protective agents. These materials will make the surface *chemically clean,* a prime requisite of a good paint job.

CAUTION: Avoid touching the

Fig. 9-17. Surface must be chemically clean. (Paul Lawrence Dunbar Vocational High School, Chicago, Illinois)

surfaces with your hands from this point on. The small amount of natural oils in the skin can affect the final paint job.

In spot repairs, *dewax* at least 12″ beyond the spot to be repaired Fig. 9-17.

Foundation Coats. Two different foundation coats are used under the final color or finish coat. The first coat material is called the *primer*. It functions as an adherent to bare metal. The second foundation coat material is called the *surfacer*. Several coats of surfacer are used to build up the surface. This is necessary to provide enough thickness to permit sanding without cutting through the primer to bare metal.

In most retail paint shops a combination *primer-surfacer* is in general use. All bare metal must be covered with either a coat of primer and several coats of surfacer or with several coats of primer-surfacer. At first it is better to start with a primer-surfacer rather than to use the two different materials.

But note that the finish coat controls the type of undercoats to be used. Although the final results look very similar, paint manufacturer's recommendations should never be ignored with respect to their outline of systems for various materials. You should always check very carefully to be sure that acrylic lacquer undercoating materials are used when applying *acrylic lacquers*. The same holds true of *acrylic enamels*.

In addition, products of one paint manufacturer should never be mixed with or used in conjunction with products manufactured by another.

For your first attempt at spraying a panel, it may be advisable to use an *enamel* primer-surfacer. While it will require a longer drying period, it has the advantage of not being soluble in lacquer thinner. Later, when you apply the color coat, the new color coat can be washed off with thinner without damaging the primer-surfacer coat should you make a mistake or have an accident.

Primer-Surfacer. If the color coat is to be put on the same day, use lacquer primer-surfacer. Stir the material you use in the can until it is thoroughly mixed. Use a metal stirrer with square corners that will reach and stir up the material in the corners of the can.

Using a clean can for mixing, follow the manufacturer's directions and reduce the material to the specified consistency. When using lacquer primer-surfacer, pour the specified amount of lacquer thinner into the mixing can. If you are using synthetic enamel primer-surfacer, add the specified amount of synthetic *enamel re-*

ducer. Wipe the stirrer clean, and thoroughly mix the primer-surfacer with the thinner or reducer. Strain the reduced and thoroughly mixed primer-surfacer directly into the spray gun cup.

During your practice exercises, you were applying paint to a flat piece of paper and the strokes made were straight. However, since practically no surface on an automotive vehicle is flat, to maintain the proper distance between the spray gun and a curved surface, it is necessary that the spray gun strokes conform to the contour of the surface you are painting.

Fig. 9-18 shows a student getting ready to paint a fender. You will note that he is establishing the distance between the spray gun and the surface to be painted with his left hand. With the little finger and thumb extended, the hand is used as a gage to establish that distance.

Fig. 9-19 shows what the correct stroke should be for the fender previously discussed. Practice making such a stroke without pulling the trigger. It may be helpful if you can have someone looking down from above to tell you how well you are following the contour

Fig. 9-18. Gun held at proper distance. (Paul Lawrence Dunbar Vocational High School, Chicago, Illinois)

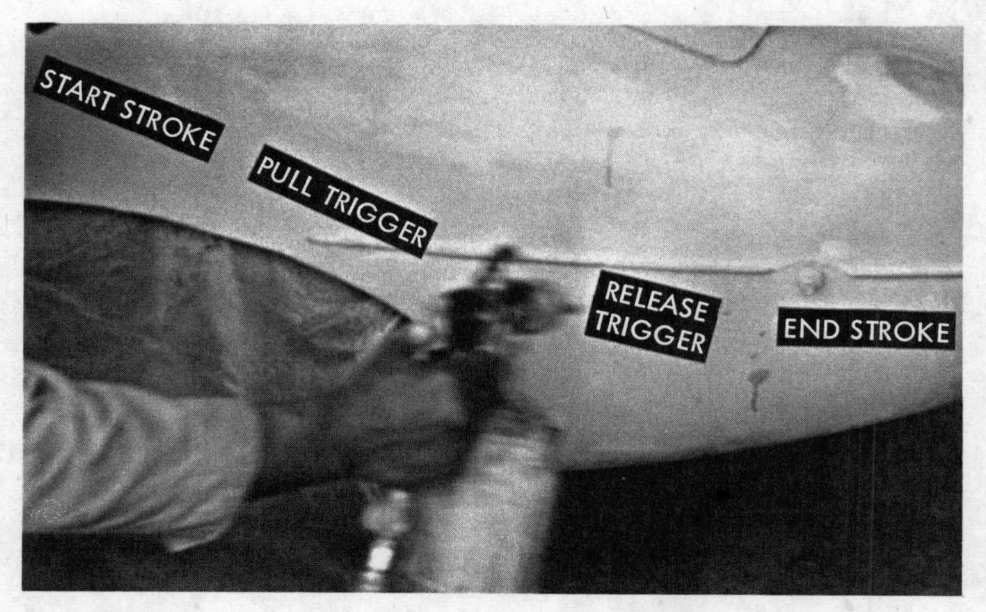

Fig. 9-19. Stroke curved to match contour. (Paul Lawrence Dunbar Vocational High School, Chicago, Illinois)

of the surface and if you are maintaining the proper distance between the spray gun and the car.

Now wipe the surface clean and again practice the stoke illustrated in Fig. 9-20. When you feel you have mastered it, start pulling the spray gun trigger after the stroke is under way and releasing the trigger before stopping the movement of the gun, as in Fig. 9-19. After the first stroke, raise the gun slightly and put on a second, overlapping stroke; continue until you have covered the entire surface to be painted. Remember, strokes should be made with the whole body. Space the feet wide apart and shift your weight from one foot to the other as you make each stroke. Confine your movement to your waist, hips, and legs. This will permit your head, shoulders, arm, and spray gun to move together as a unit. *Avoid using your wrist.* Use of your wrist during the stroke will turn the spray gun away from right angles to the surface, and excessive spray dust will be blown on areas that you do not want to paint.

If you make a mistake or if the paint sags or runs, it can be removed with lacquer thinner, and you can start over. Small imperfections are not serious, however all of the bare metal must be covered. Several coats are required to pro-

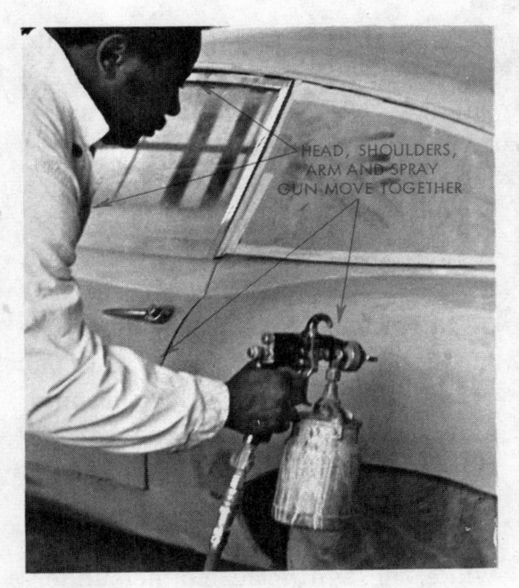

Fig. 9-20. Correct stance for spray gun stroke. (Paul Lawrence Dunbar Vocational High School, Chicago, Illinois)

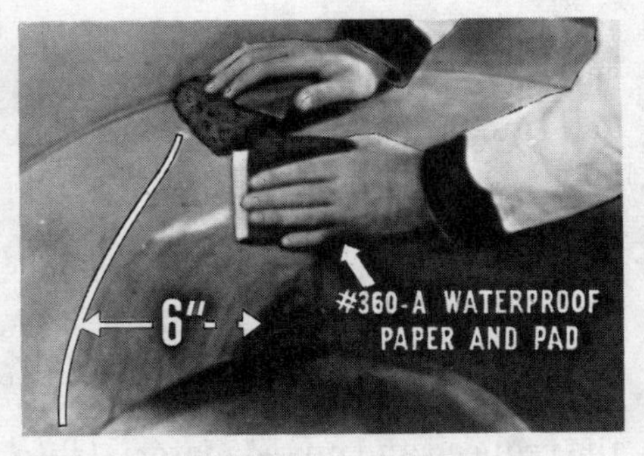

Fig. 9-21. Sand beyond surfaced area. (Ford Motor Co.)

vide enough thickness to permit sanding later. It may be advisable to spray a small amount of primer-surfacer over any portions of the fender that may have been putty glazed.

Preparing for Color Coat. If you are using acrylic enamel primer-surfacer, allow it to dry overnight; if you are using an acrylic lacquer primer-surfacer, allow it to dry from 30 to 60 minutes. In either case, when the primer-surfacer is thoroughly dry, wet-sand it with No. 360 A-grit waterproof paper, using a pad and water to level off and remove all orange peel from the surface.

If you are working on a spot repair during the sanding, Fig. 9-21, sand beyond the resurfaced area at least 6". Slightly scuffing or roughening the old finish provides adhesion or tooth where the color coat is to be tapered off.

After sanding, the surface again must be cleaned. All traces of sanding mud and water must be removed. Wipe clean and blow off the surface. Then, just before you are ready to spray on the color coat, wipe the entire area to be sprayed with a *tack rag* to remove all dust and lint.

Tack Rag: A tack rag is a rag treated with a varnish containing excessive oils that resist drying Such a treated rag will pick up dust and lint from the surface Tack rags can be purchased from all automotive paint supply houses, or you can, in an emergency, make one yourself by spraying a piece of muslin with synthetic enamel.

Applying Lacquer Color Coat. Thoroughly clean your spray gun and gun cup. Pour a clean can about one-quarter full of lacquer color that has been thoroughly stirred. Add the specified amount of lacquer thinner. Making sure your stirrer is clean, thoroughly mix the thinner and lacquer. Strain the reduced and mixed material into the gun cup and install it on the gun. You are now ready to apply color to the fender. For your first experience in applying color, confine yourself to lacquer rather than synthetic enamel.

You will find that lacquer is easier to apply and therefore a better instructive medium for you at this time. Using the same techniques that were discussed for the application of primer-surfacer to the fender, spray the entire fender or body panel with horizontal strokes of the spray gun.

As soon as you have covered the surface with the strokes in one direction, go over it again with strokes in the opposite direction. If the first time you use horizontal strokes (vertical pattern), the next time turn the air horns on the spray head so as to provide a horizontal pattern and then go over the surface again with overlapping vertical strokes. Be sure, during both of these coats, that you maintain the distance between the spray gun nozzle and the surface being painted, and that your gun at all times is at right angles to the surface. Make sure that the speed of each stroke is uniform throughout the stroke.

If you used a synthetic enamel primer-surfacer for the foundation coats, and if you have an accident or make a mistake in applying the lacquer color, wash the color coat off with a lacquer thinner and, after it is dry, make another attempt. As shown in Fig. 9-22, the paint you have just put on is entirely soluble in lacquer thinner while the synthetic enamel undercoat is not. The new paint can be washed right off without damaging the undercoat.

In Fig. 9-22 the paint has sagged below the gasoline tank filler. Whenever this occurs, it is better to wash off the paint and start over. This is not accomplished as easily if you used a lacquer primer-

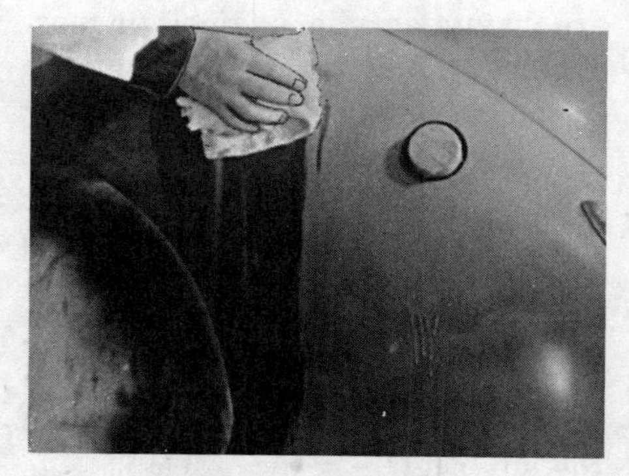

Fig. 9-22. Removing lacquer just applied. (Ford Motor Co.)

surfacer. In this case, the thinner used to remove the color coat also will remove the primer-surfacer and you will find yourself wiping the surface back to bare metal. If this should happen, you must reapply and sand the primer-surfacer coat.

Finishing the Job. When the lacquer color coat is thoroughly dry, all traces of orange peel or any slight imperfections can be removed with No. 600 grit wet or dry sandpaper and water.

Again clean and dry the surface and apply a mist coat of clear lacquer thinner. Clean all traces of color from the spray gun cup and head and put a small amount of thinner in the cup. To apply a mist coat, hold the gun nozzle about 12″ away from the surface. As soon as the paint appears wet, stop the mist coat. Too much thinner will soften the color coat and may cause it to run.

The purpose of the mist coat is to remove the minute scratches caused by the sanding. Lacquer is soluble in thinner; so, if you hold the gun too close, the thinner will go on wet, and its velocity will be great enough to damage the paint.

After the job is thoroughly dry again, carefully remove the masking tape and paper and go over the new surface with a liquid polish. If the new paint on the fender or panel makes the rest of the car look dull, recommend that the balance of the car be compounded and polished, or that wax or one of the other protective materials be applied to the entire car.

Spot Repairs

Weathering tends to lighten colors and reduce gloss. Extreme weathering imparts a chalklike appearance to the finish. For these reasons, it is usually advisable to repaint an entire fender or body panel rather than to make a spot repair.

Spot repairs however can be made on either a lacquer or synthetic enamel finish. Such spot repairs are usually made with lacquer or acrylic lacquer, regardless of the original finish.

First the oxidized paint must be removed from the entire fender or panel. This is best accomplished with rubbing compound. Rubbing compound is an abrasive that is applied to a rag or a polishing wheel for the purpose of grinding or rubbing off this unwanted material. Rubbing compounds come in *fine* and *coarse grits*. Until you have gained experience in the use of rubbing compound, it is best to confine yourself to fine compounds. Similar materials are used in preparing cars for wax or other surface protection.

You will occasionally see cars on which the finish has been compounded through the color so that the undercoating or foundation coats are visible. Such exposed surfacer can be recovered with a color coat by means of a spot repair. Whether the original finish was lacquer or synthetic enamel, the spot repair is always made with lacquer.

The entire fender or panel involved is first compounded to restore the original color.

Color Choice. It is impractical to try to tint or blend colors so that they match the aged paint on the balance of the fender or panel. Rather, the spot repair is made with the original color blended into the old finish by the technique explained in this section.

Place a color chip of what you believe to be the original color on the fender or panel, and wet both surfaces, Fig. 9-23. The water on the old paint will give it gloss so that it will have approximately the same luster as the color chip. While wet, it is easy to determine whether or not the color chip is the same color as the original finish.

In making spot repairs, always use the original color. If the original color was synthetic enamel, use the same color in lacquer.

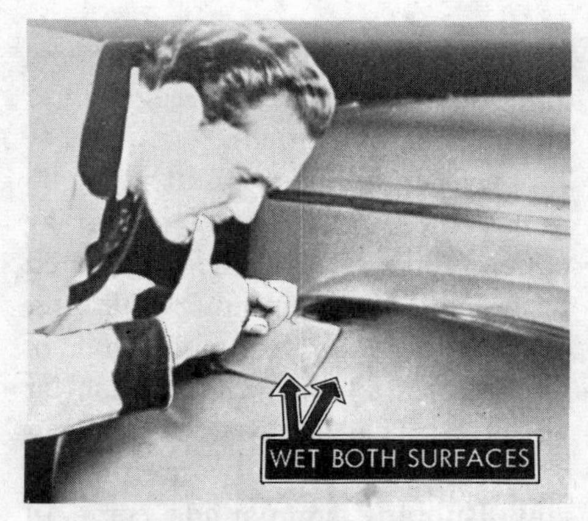

Fig. 9-23. Wetting old surface for comparison with color chip. (Ford Motor Co.)

Surface Preparation. The old surface must be prepared for the color coat in the manner explained in the preceding section. If the paint has worn through to bare metal, primer-surfacer must be applied and sanded smooth.

In addition to sanding the actual spot to be repaired, sand or scuff the old paint from 6″ to 10″ in all directions from the spot. This scuffed or roughened area beyond the surfacer is used to taper the paint, so that there will be no definite point at which the new color coat ends. This is accomplished as illustrated in Fig. 9-24. Hold the gun far enough away from the job that the material momentarily goes

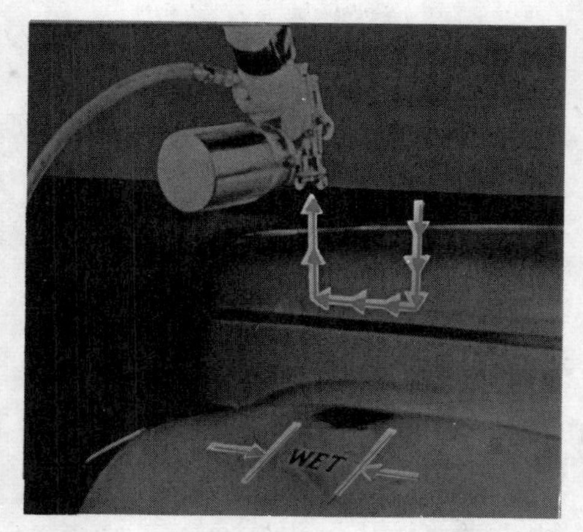

Fig. 9-24. Movement of spray gun to blend in a spot. (Ford Motor Co.)

on dry. Immediately move the gun toward the job to normal spraying distance and make a stroke across the area, pulling the gun away from the job at the end of a stroke.

The marked-off areas in Fig. 9-25 show just how the color coat goes on. In the area where primer-surfacer was exposed, the paint must go on wet. Immediately adjacent to this wet area the lacquer goes on dry; beyond this, less dust and beyond that, nothing. This tapers off the amount of color so that if a difference in color exists between the old and new paint, it will not be marked by a distinct line between the two colors.

After the lacquer color coat has been applied, clean the spray gun, and put lacquer thinner in the cup. The lacquer thinner will be applied to the surface in the form of a mist with insufficient velocity to displace any of the previously applied paint. This mist of lacquer thinner (without any color) will dissolve whatever color went on in the form of dust. The wet lacquer dust will level out and fill the small scratches in the scuffed area, forming a good bond.

Since the dust was tapered off

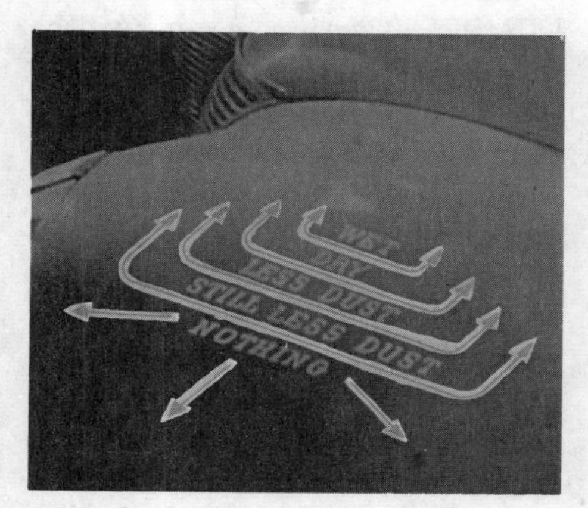

Fig. 9-25. Stages in spot repair. (Ford Motor Co.)

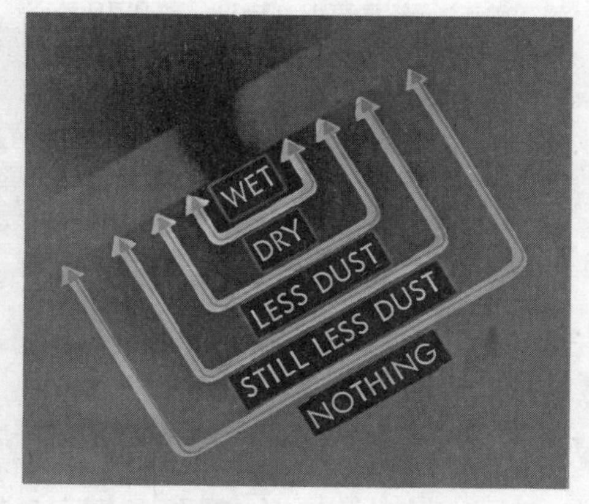

Fig. 9-26. Application of paint in blending. (Ford Motor Co.)

to nothing, Fig. 9-25, a blend of the old color without a joint of any kind will result. To illustrate this method of color blending, Fig. 9-26 shows the blending of two different colors.

A piece of masking tape was placed over a portion of the surface to be spot repaired. After blending in the manner outlined in the preceding instructions, the masking tape was removed. Notice that there is no line of demarcation between the two colors except where the tape was removed. This is a severe example in which an almost black gray was blended onto a white surface. You will never be required to blend such extreme differences in color.

After the spot repair has dried, compound the entire fender, or panel, including the new paint. Go over the entire surface with a liquid polish or apply a paint protecting material if it is desired.

Complete Paint Job

After you have acquired enough experience with refinishing single fenders or panels, and have learned how to handle the gun on spot repairs, you can start working on complete paint jobs. In painting a complete car, you do the same things you have previously learned, but on a larger scale.

Masking. Fig. 9-27 shows how a rear door and headlining of a car could be masked to keep paint off of them when the edges of the door and the hinge pillar are painted.

Fig. 9-28 shows the windshield, side windows, wipers, antenna and door handle masked. In this case, the side windows are masked with a single width of 15″ masking paper. On the windshield, two 15″ widths are overlapped. The wipers, antenna and door handle are simply covered with tape of the appropriate width.

Fig. 9-29 shows the use of narrow masking tapes in the masking of trim mouldings and decorative lettering. Tapes come in widths from 1/8″ to 3″. In this case, the 1/8″ tape is being used to mask the lettering. (Fig. 9-14 earlier shows the method used for headlights, grille and front bumper.)

Wheel discs which cover both the wheel and the wheel covers and which are taped to the tires are available.

Proper masking is not difficult. It does not have to look especially neat. The only thing to remember is to *provide a shield for every area*

Fig. 9-27. Masked rear door edge and hinge pillar.

Fig. 9-28. Masking of upper body. (Minnesota Mining and Mfg. Co.)

Fig. 9-29. Masking moldings and decorative lettering. (Minnesota Mining and Mfg. Co.)

on which you do not want paint.

Much time and considerable difficulty can be saved if you mask trim and decorative moldings instead of removing and replacing them. It is difficult to achieve proper alignment if you remove them and replace them, and moulding clips are often stubborn, especially if they are rusty.

Water Sand. Water sand the entire car until smooth, using No. 320 grit waterproof paper on a rubber block, Fig. 9-30. Check your progress with a squeegee, Fig. 9-31. If you encounter scratches, pits, or bare metal, you will have to putty glaze, featheredge, or resurface them.

Putty Glaze. Unless putty glaze is completely dry all the way

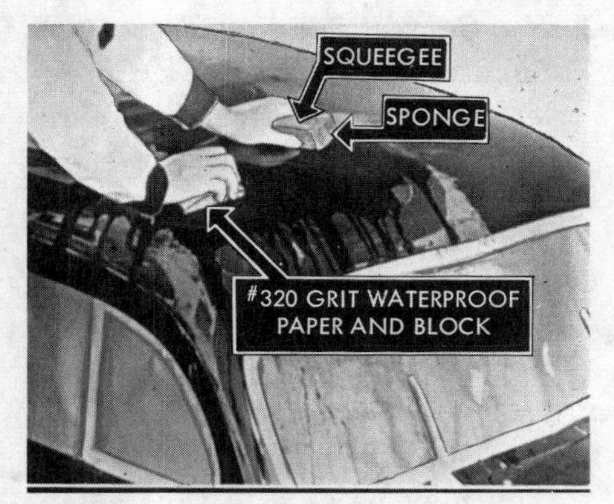

Fig. 9-30. Water sanding with water proof paper. (Ford Motor Co.)

Fig. 9-31. Checking progress with a squeegee. (Ford Motor Co.)

through, it will sink after the sanding. This will result in a slight depression on the finished surface. It is a good plan to do whatever putty glazing has to be done as soon as practical. Stone marks and any small pits in the paint should be filled with glazing putty when the pit does not go all the way down to the bare metal.

Featheredge. Featheredge the paint in any areas where the bare metal is exposed, using No. 240 grit waterproof paper and water. Featheredge scratches or pits that go down to the metal. Fig. 9-32 shows a special head for a portable grinder that reduces the labor of featheredging.

Resurface Bare Metal. Apply two coats of primer-surfacer to all bare metal, and cover all spots that have been featheredged or putty glazed. When the surfacer is completely dry (one hour for lacquer; overnight for synthetic enamel primer-surfacer), water sand it with No. 320 grit waterproof paper on a rubber block.

Clean and Dewax. Remove all moisture and dust, being espe-

Fig. 9-32. Machine featheredging. (Paul Lawrence Dunbar Vocational High School, Chicago, Illinois)

cially particular at crevices, corners, and seams. Render the entire surface chemically clean with solvent to remove wax or other protective material.

Paint Preparation. Pour the paint into a clean can and reduce as specified in manufacturer's directions. Before reducing the paint, be sure that it is well mixed by stirring vigorously and thoroughly with a square stirrer, as recommended previously.

Use lacquer thinner for lacquer color coat. Use synthetic enamel reducer for synthetic enamel.

Reducers and thinners are rated as *slow, medium,* and *fast,* to permit matching the material to the spraying temperature. Use a slower thinner than normal for your first complete paint jobs. Be sure your gun is clean, and strain the material directly into the gun cup.

Apply Color Coat. Successful painters follow eight basic rules. How well you have observed these instructions will have a direct bearing on the quality of the color coat you are about to apply.

Eight Auto Painting Rules:

1. *Clean the Surface.* Never cut corners in the surface preparation. Wash with water; remove wax, silicone, oil and grease with a solvent cleaner; and etch bare metal with a phosphate cleaner. These are musts.
2. *Use Correct Sanding Technique.* Sand scratches will be no problem. Use the proper grit papers. Equally important is the sanding technique. Bearing down on the paper only introduces sand scratches. Light pressure on the paper, allowing the paper to do the work, is the correct way.
3. *Use Top Quality Thinners.* You cannot economize on thinners. You may be able to save a few cents on a gallon of cheap thinner, but you will spend dollars in terms of time and effort to make up for its shortcomings.
4. *Use the Correct Amount of Thinner.* Never under-reduce paint. Use the reduction specified on the directions for each product. And again, use a top quality thinner. Never try to increase film build by cutting back on the amount of thinner.
5. *Stir Thoroughly.* Regardless of the paint manufacturer or the kind of paint it is, acrylic, lacquer, enamel, or undercoat, stir the paint thoroughly.
6. *Use Low Atomizing Pressure.* Do not be wasteful and cause yourself work by blowing paint all over the shop, High air pressures often result in such serious problems as overspray, poor adhesion, porosity, poor gloss, or poor flow and blushing as well as added air cost (from over worked compressors) and

wasted paint. When properly reduced, paint can be perfectly atomized at low pressures. 40-45 psi is a good range for most purposes. Follow paint manufacturers' directions.

7. *Use Correct Painting Procedure.* Keep the spray gun perpendicular to the work. Follow the contour of the panel, maintaining a distance of 6″ to 8″ from the surface. The spray pattern should be 5″ to 6″ wide. Watch the timing between coats, especially when using an air-dry enamel material. Delay in applying the second coat can seriously upset the correct drying process, and with some types of materials it will lead to lifting or wrinkling, resulting in additional work to correct the problems.

8. *Maintain Good Ventilation.* See that plenty of fresh air is available in the spray area, especially during the drying stage. Air should be in the temperature range of 65°-95°F. Acrylics, lacquers and enamels gen-

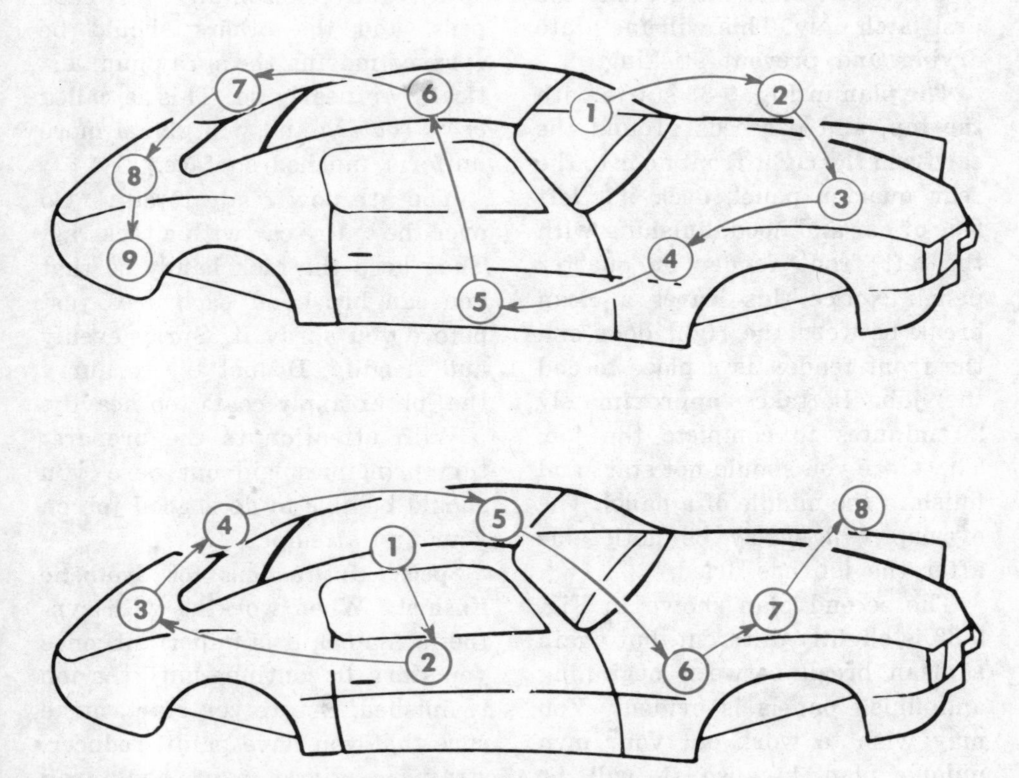

Fig. 9-33. Complete paint job plans: two methods. (Rinshed-Mason Co.)

erally require approximately 16 hours to completely air dry. Forced drying of course, depends on the equipment available. Never allow the finish to air dry in a small closed room or spray booth.

Systematic Paint Plan. For complete paint jobs, several plans or systems can be used. Two recommended plans or systems are shown in Fig. 9-33. Whichever plan you use, remember to first paint the hidden edges: door jams, trunk lids, hood edges, etc. Leave them slightly ajar. Close the doors to the first latch only. This will facilitate drying and prevent sticking.

The plan in Fig. 9-33 starts with the top, and proceeds around the car from the right front door to the rear quarter panel, deck lid, left side of car and hood, finishing with the left front fender or quarter panel. Notice this leaves a clean break between the right door and the front fender as a place to end the job. It takes approximately 20 minutes to complete the job. Therefore you should not start and finish in the middle of a panel. The overlap will surely be noticeable after the job has dried.

The second plan shown in Fig. 9-33 is slightly different, but again a clean break between beginning and finish panels is evident. You may wish to work out your own unique plan because it will be more comfortable to you. But always remember to have a natural, clean break between beginning and finish panels.

Do not attempt too large an area at one time. Move the spray gun through a comfortable swing. Allow about a 50% overlap with each pass. Most refinish acrylics and lacquers, including undercoats, require the application of 3 to 6 medium wet coats. Half of this number should be sprayed at right angles to the other coats. One coat should be sprayed moving the spray gun horizontally for each pass, and the others should be sprayed moving the spray gun vertically or nearly so. This is called *cross coating* and will give a more uniform finished surface.

You are now ready to start. Go over the entire car with a tack rag. Then keep the tack handy so that you can brush off each area just before you spray it. Spray evenly and steadily. Do not try to hurry the job or apply coats too heavily.

With attention to the preparation principles laid out here, you should be able to do a good job on your first attempt.

Special Instructions for Synthetic Enamel. When working with synthetic enamel, it is important, once you start, to continue until the job is finished. Before you start, make sure that you have paint, reducer, strainer, stirrer, and tack rag handy. You can't afford to lose time looking for things. If the enamel sets, you will probably have to compound the overspray. Lacquer thinner will dissolve the overspray and fuse it with the first paint you applied only if you put the lacquer thinner mist coat on within 20 minutes of the time the job is started. Use lacquer thinner because synthetic enamel reducer will not dissolve the overspray.

Remove Masks and Touch Up Paint. While synthetic enamel dries dust free in as little as 30 minutes, it remains soft for some time, so the masks must not be removed until the enamel is hard. If the paint is air dried, it should set overnight to harden. If the paint is oven dried, allow the car to set at least an hour after it has cooled down to room temperature before removing the masking.

If the car was painted with lacquer, the masks can be removed in one hour after painting is completed.

Once you have removed the masks, inspect the entire car for areas where small particles of paint may have been pulled off by the masking tape. Touch up these spots, as well as any others that you may find, with a stripping brush. Carefully check all door and deck lid edges.

Follow Up Procedures. For cars that have been painted with synthetic enamel, clean up and polish the entire car, using a liquid polish. For a more expensive job, the finish may be compounded to reduce orange peel and remove the shine. *This should not be done, however, before the new paint has aged at least two weeks.*

For cars painted with lacquer, while painting a car with lacquer will usually cost more for materials than synthetic enamel, lacquer has the advantage of producing a perfectly smooth finish with some additional work. This smooth finish is accomplished by sanding the new paint with No. 600 grit paper to remove all orange peel. A mist coat of lacquer thinner is then sprayed over the completed job, dissolving the scratches and producing a smooth finish. An even smoother finish is accomplished by compounding after the mist coat has thoroughly dried.

Checking On Your Knowledge

The following questions give you the opportunity to check up on yourself. If you have read the chapter carefully, you should be able to answer the questions. If you have any difficulty, read the chapter over once more so that you have the information well in mind before you go on with your reading.

1. Why should an automotive painter have some knowledge of metal finishing?
2. What are two basic differences in lacquers and synthetic enamels?
3. How do you keep the spray-gun hose from rubbing on the new paint?
4. What is the purpose of featheredging? What kind of paper is used? What grit number?
5. How does the water help you when sanding old paint?
6. What grit paper is used for sanding the old paint?
7. What does the squeegee show you?
8. What is putty glazing?
9. How is the surface to be painted rendered chemically clean?
10. What is the function of the primer-surfacer?
11. How is the paint-and-air stream from a spray gun flattened?
12. What two adjustments are provided on a spray gun?
13. Ordinarily, what kind of primer-surfacer would be used as a foundation for a lacquer finish coat?
14. Why should a stirrer have square corners?
15. How much air does a paint spray gun use?
16. What is the purpose of the air transformer?
17. Which requires the greater air pressure, synthetic enamel or lacquer?
18. How is pressure line drop checked?
19. What things are required for a perfect paint pattern?
20. What must be happening when you pull the spray gun trigger?
21. The spray gun trigger is released before what phase of the full spray operation?
22. Why must you avoid using your wrist at either end of the paint stroke?
23. How long should lacquer primer-surfacer dry before you attempt to sand it?
24. What grit paper can be used to remove orange peel from lacquer finish coats?
25. What is a mist coat?
26. What is ¼″ wide masking tape used for?
27. Why must putty glaze be completely dry before sanding?
28. How long should you wait before removing the masks from a car that has just had the paint baked on?

Adhesives, Coatings and Sealers

Chapter 10

The increasing sophistication of the motoring public has been responsible for many innovations, especially those that contribute to the comfort and convenience of owning cars and of driving them. While most of these developments have been mechanical, such as air conditioning, speed control, and climate control, not much has been said of an equally large number of improvements made in the manufacture of car bodies.

Most of the body construction improvements have been aimed at providing a quieter ride and tighter sealing to enhance heater and air conditioner performances, and to provide better ventilation generally. Styling trends have had their effect on the construction techniques used.

The end result of all this activity is the development of new products and new techniques to provide suitable service in body shops. The most notable change in body construction is the marked increase in the use of adhesives and sealers.

It might be well to take a look at some of the major reasons why automotive engineers are saying that we are in the *Adhesive Era*. Following are specific advantages an adhesive can offer compared to mechanical fastening devices:

1. Join dissimilar materials to obtain the advantages of both materials.
2. Provide insulation to prevent electrical (hi-metallic) and galvanic corrosion by acting as a barrier between the surfaces.

3. Seal as well as bond.
4. Distribute stresses evenly over a wider area, which permits the use of lighter gage materials.
5. Provide dimensional stability by cross bonding (as in plywood).
6. Maintain integrity of the bonded materials by eliminating holes; is not affected by detempering or crystallizing metals introduced through welding or brazing.
7. Provide smooth contours to contribute to improved styling.
8. Impart flexibility to the joint to increase vibration resistence and fatigue life.
9. Can be much faster and less expensive than mechanical fastening due to the low equipment costs and ease of automation.

Now, lets take a look at what this means to you as a body man. You must become familiar with the materials now available to you, and with how to use them to your advantage. You must also acquire a vocabulary that will enable you to remain knowledgeable concerning adhesives, coatings and sealers in the future, as new developments and techniques occur.

This chapter is designed to give you a complete working knowledge of these various materials. It also deals with specific repair instructions so that you can use them. Because of the low cost of the materials involved, you will probably be able to practice on your own car and thereby improve its appearance and structural soundness. You have an opportunity to learn and at the same time increase the value of your car.

Plastic Filler Systems

Starting with what you already know, we will define *adhesives* and *elastomers* as those substances *which hold things together* and those *which resist the effort to pull them apart*. Some of these substances you have used already, the starch pastes and gums which make the surfaces of two sheets of paper stick together, the glue applied to wood or fibre surfaces to hold them together, and the rubber cements used on paper or plastic surfaces that are not too similar in construction. Rubber cements also hold different kinds of materials together.

Rubber is an elastomer. Although it will stretch, as an elastomer it resists the effort so hard that it will return to its original position time after time. Rubber is also sticky. Like glue adhesive, it will hold things together. Thus *adhesion* and *elastomeric qualities* often seem found in the same material, so that some people will call all adhesives elastomers even though some have less of one of these qualities than the other. Rubber, for instance, is a good adhesive, but it is the finest elastomer we know.

Plastic systems may be developed that have the same qualities of *adhesion* and *elastomeric resistance* to being pulled apart as rubber adhesion systems. Some of these plastics are *wet systems* like rubber cement, which is a latex base in a solvent, or they may be *dry systems* that adhere without being wet.

Another kind of adhesive system is represented by *mastic cements,* which are rather like gums or plastics, but with *filler* added to give them body or thickness. When glues, plastics, and rubber adhesives are too thin and fail to fill holes and roughnesses in the surfaces being glued together, a *filler* may be added to thicken them. Fillers, *thickeners,* and other chemicals are thus used to modify the characteristics of an adhesive.

Bases and Solvents. Any material from which an adhesive can be made is called a *base* (an adhesive base). Dry glue is a base, uncured rubber (latex) is a base, dry plastics may be bases. Any material that puts them in solution or in a liquid state is usually called a *solvent.* Thus water is a solvent for glue, alcohol is a solvent for plastic, and liquid naphtha is a solvent for rubber.

Solvents may also be used for *wetting agents,* wetting the surfaces to which an adhesive will be applied, or wetting a dry base material so that it will adhere. Solvents which dissolve an adhesive until it can be applied are called *vehicles;* they carry the adhesive to where it is to be deposited. Paint vehicles are solvents, and a solvent may be a paint vehicle. Acetone, mineral oil, and many other hydrocarbons are used as solvents.

For those wet systems of adhesives that are too thick, a solvent thinner may be used to make them more dilute or to make them more soluble, as well as to put them in solution. When solvents are used on dried adhesives, or bases, the solvents cause the adhesives to *become plastic,* or more *viscous* (the amount the liquid will flow). When an adhesive is just right for application it may be *tacky,* like glue beginning to gel or set.

The rate at which adhesives reach a final cured state is partly dependent on the kind of adhesive. For instance, rubber cement always stays tacky, and never really sets into a solid. Some of the solvent is held inside the adhesive, bound up in the spaces between the molecules of the rubber.

Other adhesives set hard. Many plastics are this way. Whether the solvent evaporates or stays in the adhesive as a gel (like jello), the molecules of the plastic lock all the solvent and plastic into a hard substance which we would normally consider a *solid*. But plastic solids will have some rubber-like qualities, they remain somewhat elastic, or *elastomeric*.

Glues and mastics tend to *set* hard, and once set, lose most of their elastic qualities and then hold materials together mostly by surface attraction and by extending into the little holes in the surfaces of the materials it causes to adhere together.

Adhesives will set faster and cure harder or tougher (the elastic quality) if certain chemicals are added. These may be *catalysts*, which are chemicals that affect the actions of other chemicals without being affected by the chemical action themselves, or they may be *activators*, which are chemicals that start a reaction, like the setting of an adhesive. Other chemicals, called *accelerators*, will speed up the setting or the long term curing of an adhesive.

The difference between a *gel*, a *set* and a *cure* is either a matter of time or a matter of more than one chemical process. Some adhesives gel easily, that is, they become tacky enough that nothing will easily pull the adhering surfaces apart. Then they set harder and harder as time goes on. Sometimes this causes them to lose their elastic qualities so that all old adhesives must be cleaned from surfaces that must be joined again.

Other adhesives go through another chemical reaction, such as the cross-linking of plastic molecules, which binds them into tougher and longer lasting adhesives. A cured strip of plastic may be like one huge molecule (a collection of molecules) the entire length of a seam three feet long! Thus, setting and curing may be different processes or may refer to a difference in the length of time a process goes on.

Bonding Surfaces. Two surfaces, or two pieces of metal, plastic, wood or any solid, that must be mated together, may be joined by an adhesive. In welding we learned to put two like pieces of metal together; in brazing we learned to put two different metals together; with adhesives we can put almost any kind of unlike materials together.

With adhesives we can bond or cause to stick together such different materials as a plastic vinyl cover on a metal car top. We can apply an acrylic plastic panel to a metal (sheet steel) door. Glass cloth can be made to stick to rusted fenders, and holes may be filled with plastic-and-metal fillers containing ground metal that can be filed and finished with acrylic plastic paint.

Adhesives may be stronger than bonding two surfaces together by riveting, brazing, or welding. The reason that adhesives may be so strong is that they adhere by three different processes of attraction, sometimes all working together:

(1) filling holes in surfaces to be bound together.
(2) molecular attraction by a stronger force than that which makes air stay with the earth and not fly off in space.
(3) chemical attraction where one surface loses atoms to the other surface and the atoms of both materials fuse into those of the other.

Bonding as a Process. When two pieces of different material, or of the same material, are bound together, we say they are *bonded.* Bond is like bind, so that you can bond materials together if you can bind them. But bond means more, for as the chemist uses the idea, if a chemical bond can be made to exist between two materials in a chemical reaction, he finds that they have much greater strength to resist being pulled apart than if they are merely glued together.

Surface Conditions. Surfaces are nothing more than the faces of two things which are to be joined together. Obviously, the flatter the surfaces, or the more they fit together, the better the joint will be. Such surfaces may be called *bonding surfaces, contacting surfaces, joining surfaces, faying surfaces,* or *mating surfaces.*

The greater difference between any two surfaces to be bonded, the harder it is to bind them together. Also, the greater the space between them, the stronger the adhesive has to be, for its body will be the real material between two widely separated joining surfaces. A *filled adhesive* may have to be used.

If you will fit a curved surface to a straight surface, you will see the problem, Fig. 10-1. The straight surfaces in Fig. 10-1 will easily mate and can be strongly bonded by the adhesive. The curved surface in the same figure will more easily be separated from its mating surface even though the same bonding agent is used.

Again from metals we take the idea of slowly stretching apart under two forces pulling from opposite directions. We say the metal has a *yield point* or a *yield value,* which is the strength of the metal to resist forces pulling it apart. A bar of 1″ carbon steel has a yield strength of 40-60,000 pounds; it

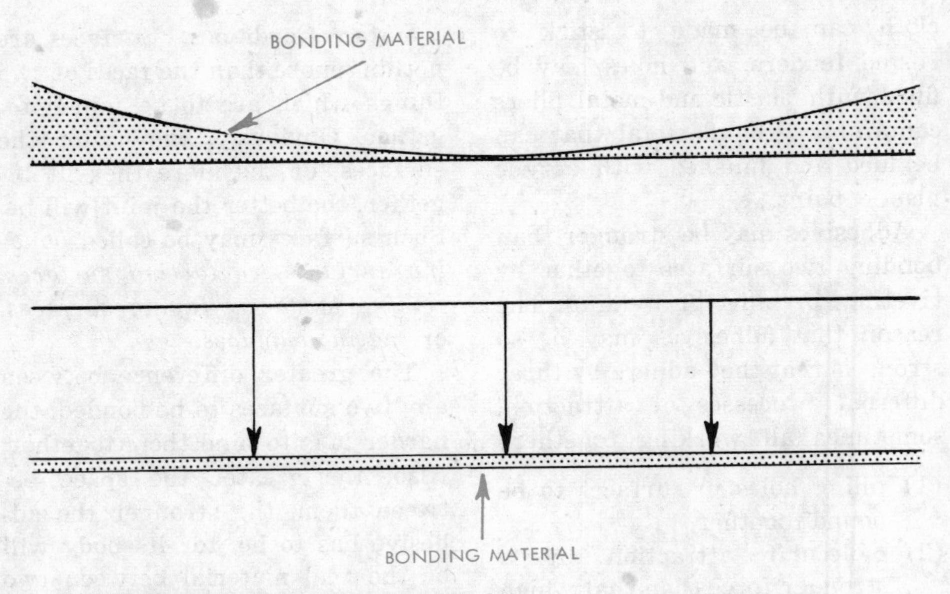

Fig. 10-1. Fitting surfaces together with adhesives.

will pull apart under that much force.

If the forces causing a steel rod to break apart are applied sideways instead of at opposite ends, the metal will fail much sooner. This is what is done in a *shear test*, the metal rod is literally cut in two by sideways pressure. The principle is expressed in Fig. 10-2. The *shear strength* of any material is its ability to withstand a sideways pressure or motion.

It is extremely likely that plastics, sealers and adhesive coatings, as we know them now, will be used extensively in automotive collision work during the foresee-

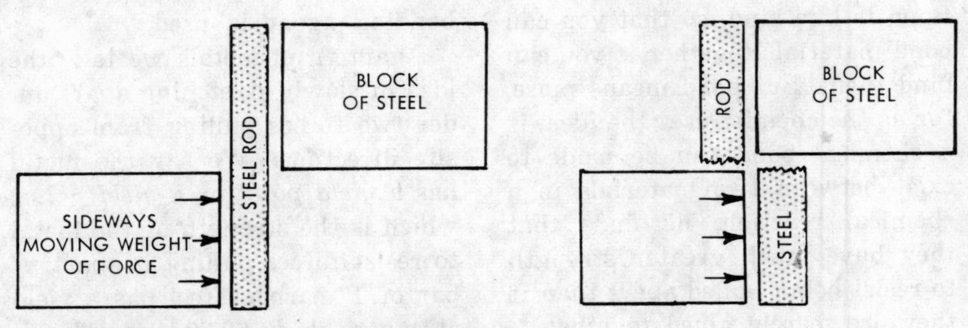

Fig. 10-2. Shearing forces shown before and after.

able future. What is more likely, is the development of new products which will make these materials an even more basic part of the everyday tools used in collision repair. For that reason, we are including at the end of this chapter a glossary of terms that will enable you to understand the language.

You will not understand each of these terms at first reading. It is unlikely that you will need all this vocabulary at any given time in your career. However, it is here, and it will serve as a complete and authoritative reference for your future convenience.

The definitions are set up alphabetically for ease of reference. You will find that the directions on materials you will be using will make free use of these terms. Therefore you should make an effort to understand as many as you can. See pages 406-414 for definitions.

Applying Plastic Fillers

Plastic fillers are an invaluable aid in repairing body damages in areas where inner construction does not allow you to completely bump out damage. It can also be used when a surface is damaged or torn so badly in a small area that an entire panel would have to be replaced at high cost.

Applying and Finishing Fillers. If you follow the simple instructions outlined here, you can do a very good job with plastic fillers in a very short time.

Filler must be applied to an absolutely clean surface. All the old paint must be removed first. This is accomplished using No. 24 grit, type D open coat disc, as shown in Fig. 10-3.

After grinding, clean the surface thoroughly with a good solvent or cleaner to remove any film of dirt, oil, wax or grease.

The filler you are using may come in a can or a tube. Filler should be mixed on a non-porous surface such as a piece of clean glass or metal. Mixing pads are also available for this purpose.

If you are using filler from a can, place the filler on the mixing pad. For an amount of filler the size of a golf ball, use either 8 drops of liquid hardener, or ½″ to ¾″ of cream hardener from a tube.

Use a wide putty knife to draw the filler out to about 1/16″ thick film. Use a side-to-side, wavy motion as you draw the filler out.

Push the filler into a pile. Do not fold it over, as this traps air and can result in pinholing as it dries. Repeat these mixing steps at least

Fig. 10-3. Achieving a clean, even surface (Minnesota Mining and Mfg. Co.)

five times to remove any air and to be sure the hardener is thoroughly mixed into the filler.

Apply the filler to the surface being worked, as shown in Fig. 10-4. Do not put the filler on in blobs and do not fold it over. Draw it out slowly and evenly, and smooth it as much as you can while it remains easy to work. Do not at-

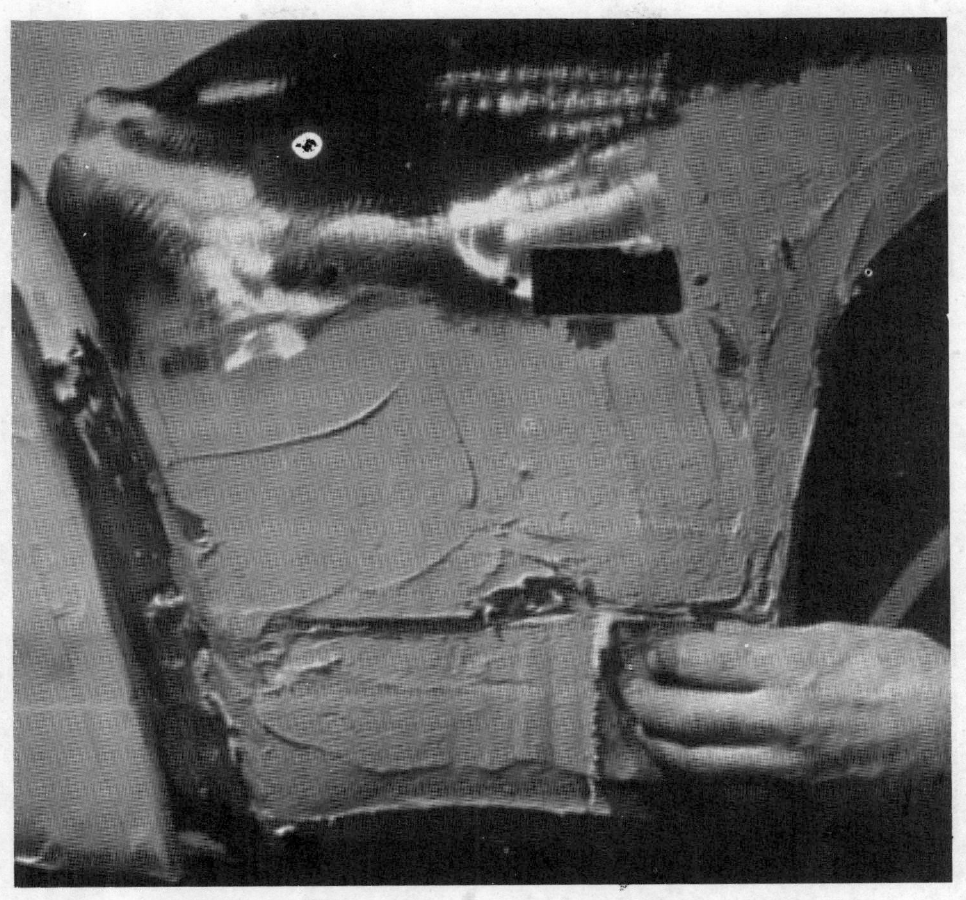

Fig. 10-4. Applying plastic filler in thin layers. (Minnesota Mining and Mfg. Co.)

tempt to work it too long, as it begins to cure immediately after it is applied.

The filler is ready for sanding after curing approximately 30 minutes at 70°F. In colder weather, allow a longer curing period. See Plastic Filler Curing Techniques following.

Level the filler nearly to the contour desired by using a No. 24 grit type D open coat disc as shown in Fig. 10-5. This is the first step in the shaping and contouring for the finished job. Therefore you should not cut too deeply.

You may use an 8″ open coat paper disc on a sponge back-up pad, as shown in Fig. 10-5, or you may use 2¾″ x 17½″ paper strips on hand tools. In some shops, air files are used for this operation.

Fig. 10-5. Shaping and contouring the finish of the plastic filler.

The intermediate finishing operations are accomplished using No. 36 or No. 40 grit, open coat aluminum oxide paper discs or strips. The final step in finishing the plastic filler is done with No. 80 grit, aluminum oxide stearated paper discs, sheets or strips. Discs should not be used for this operation until you have achieved a certain amount of skill in shaping contours with a disc grinder. Fig. 10-6 shows a power sander being used for the finish sanding operation. The problem most frequently encountered in finishing filler is that you cut too deep. It must not be ground or sanded lower than the surrounding surface. This can be prevented by using a tool that bridges the depressed area, as shown in the inset in Fig. 10-6.

After the surface is contoured, proceed as you normally would in

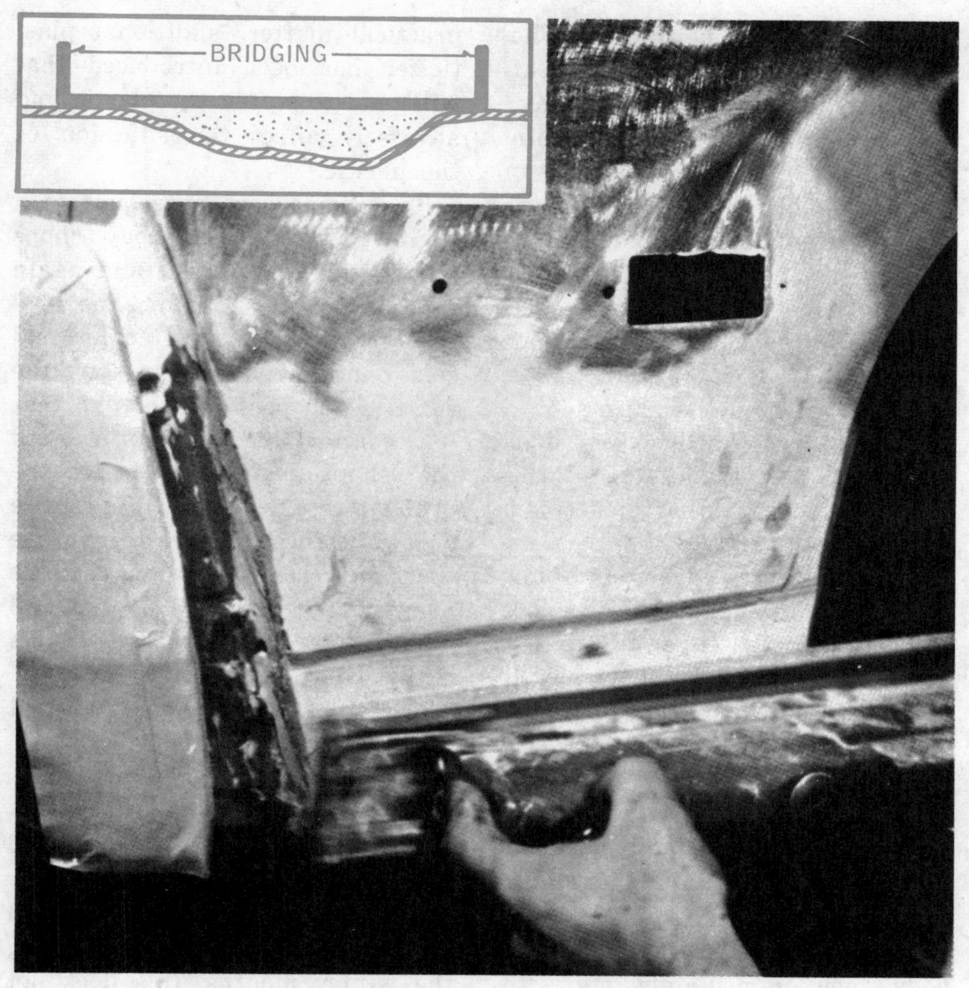

Fig. 10-6. Final finishing of plastic filler. (Minnesota Mining and Mfg. Co.)

refinishing the surface with the proper undercoats for the type of finish being applied: lacquer, enamel or acrylic.

Curing Techniques. Plastic filler is affected by temperature. Cream hardening plastic is affected more than that cured with liquid hardener. As the temperature goes down, the cure time goes up.

In the process of curing, chemical reaction causes heat to develop within the patch itself. This heat helps in the curing of the patch. For this reason, the center of the patch, where it is thicker, will cure faster than the perimeter. The sheet metal tends to draw the heat from the patch, and on a cold day, with cold sheet metal, the thin edges of the patch cure slowly.

Because of this slow curing, peeling often takes place on plastic that is apparently cured. The test procedure at the shop level is to scratch the plastic with your fingernail. If it shows white, it is ready to be filed, perhaps.

Invariably the body man scratches it in the center of the patch where it is the thickest; it will show white; he will proceed to file, and peel the edges. The only problem is that the material has not cured on the edge, due to the heat loss through the sheet metal.

Therefore, when the complaint of improper featheredging, peeling of the edges, comes in, you can be sure that it is a case of the material just being filed a bit too soon and not having had an opportunity to thoroughly cure.

As soon as cold weather comes, body men immediately start to add additional catalyst to the patch. This tends to speed up the setting of the plastic somewhat, but very little, and it only speeds up the gel; it does not affect the rest of the cure cycle (namely, sand time, file time).

Because additional catalyst has been introduced, additional gas has been introduced, and as a very practical matter, additional plasticizer has been introduced that will tend to soften the plastic and adversely affect the adhesion of the plastic.

The increase in cure time is a common problem in body shops during the fall months and again in the spring. During the fall months the shop gets colder and colder until it is time to start the furnace and heat the shop so that it is comfortable to work in. With the shop properly heated, the problem resolves itself. It is a little of two things. Body men realize that they have to allow a little more curing time in the fall months, and secondly, when it gets really cold, they heat the shop. The rest of the winter is without further curing problems.

In the spring, the reverse happens. Over the winter body rebuilders have gradually increased the catalyst beyond what they should have in an attempt to speed up the cure of the plastic. During the winter months, this does not cause them any great difficulty. The material (catalyst) simply is not used up; it lays dormant in the patch, uncured and unused.

When warm weather comes, they add the same amount of catalyst that they have been accustomed to add in the winter time and because there is so much catalyst it causes a vast amount of gas, create pinholing problems. In addition there are new adhesion problems in that all that plasticizer in the hardener starts to react adversely against the plastic filler itself.

Again in the spring, the material peels on the edges and there are too many pinholes. By the time the body man realizes what has caused this, the temperature is more consistently warm, they cut back on their catalyst and have no difficulty during the summer months.

Dries Too Slowly. The cure of plastic filler is caused by temperature. All plastic when cured with liquid hardener gels in 3½ to 4 minutes. All cream hardener gels in 4½ to 7 minutes. (All material is tested at 70°F.) A temperature of 50°F will slow down the cure cycle by as much as 50%.

Therefore, the 4 minute cure now becomes a 6 minute cure, and so on down the line as the temperature decreases. In field applications a cure that runs from 4 to 10 minutes should be considered permissable.

Optimum curing is obtained by using the prescribed dosage of hardener, and not more than 15% more than this. Therefore, if directions on the can say "to an amount the size of a golf ball, add 6 drops" —it is permissable to add 7 to 8 drops. You will speed up the cure somewhat by doing this. However, if you add 12 drops, you will have doubled the dosage and this will tend to slow down the cure. A small amount of additional hardener will speed it up; too much additional hardener will slow it down. With cream hardener, the same thing applies.

With plastic fillers, the material cured with liquid hardener cures more rapidly than that cured with cream.

Cures Too Rapidly. On an extremely hot day, if the material is applied to the hot sheet metal of a car, it will cure very rapidly. This will cause excessive gas and will cause very much pinholing. Plastic filler should not be applied to hot sheet metal. The car should be brought into the shade before application of the plastic, otherwise the hot metal will cause gassing.

Troubles with Plastic Filler

The most common complaint of the trade is *pinholing*. This is a much maligned term. A pinhole is really a fine tunnel-like hole in the plastic filler that shows up when the material is sanded, which must be filled in with spot putty for a smooth finish coat. Pinholing is caused by air or gas in the plastic filler. Any air or gas entrapped when the material is applied leaves voids behind it when it is cured, and of course, pinholes result when it is sanded.

Procedure to Eliminate Pinholes. Cut down the use of the hardener that is used . . . this is the principal cause of most pinholing. The hardener turns from a liquid or paste to a gas in the cure cycle. This gas expands rapidly, making voids in the plastic, and the result is pinholing. By cutting down the amount of the hardener, you cut down the amount of gas, thereby cutting down the number of pinholes.

Work the plastic back and forth on the patch until it begins to gel. There will always be a certain number of pinholes in plastic filler. If the body man will continue to work the plastic back and forth with a squeegee until such time as it starts to harden he will work out most of the entrapped air and eliminate most of the pinholes.

Pinholes Under Paint. We are often confronted with the problem of pinholes, and upon investigation find that this is not the case at all, but the paint itself has minute nodules on it.

Further investigation will disclose that the plastic does have minor voids on the surface, and over these voids are bumps or pinholes referred to by the complaint. This is the problem of bleed-through in one of its forms. This is caused by the solvents in the finish eating through and burning holes in the plastic.

Bleed-Through. As mentioned above in pinholing, *bleed-through* takes several forms. Bleed-through can be blushing of the paint, discoloration of the paint, and little pinholing of the plastic and bumping of the paint. The cause of this is almost invariably acrylic finishes. You do not run into this situation with normal enamels. Acrylics use a very volatile thinner. This thinner is also a solvent for styrene, a part of the chemical structure of plastic filler.

The Procedure When Using Acrylics. The primer should be allowed to dry thoroughly. The first coat of acrylic should be laid on wet, but allowed to flash off before the second coat is applied. This generally takes about ten minutes.

If a flash off period is allowed between coats, and it usually takes about three coats to cover, you will not have a bleed-through problem. However, if you lay one coat on top of the next with a flash-off between coats, the trapped solvents in the first coat will penetrate inward through the primer and into the plastic. Therefore, to eliminate the problem of blushing and surface pinholing, allow the primer to thoroughly dry and wait long enough for the acrylic to act as a sealer. *Paint manufacturers do not recommend a dust coat of acrylic as it spoils the smoothness.*

Peeling. Peeling occurs very rarely, and is attributable to one of the following problems. If the metal is not properly prepared and rust remains, the plastic will eventually be forced off. If a surface preparation such as metal prep, silicone wash, or common solvent wash-downs leave a film, there will not be a good bondable surface. If excessive quantities of hardener are used the plastic will soften after it has cured, and it will lift.

Cracking. Generally there is no explanation for plastic cracking. Plastic will withstand terrific impact and a great amount of flexing before cracking. It is almost impossible to determine the cause of cracking of plastic filler because it never seems to happen in the same body shop twice.

Dust and Water Proofing

All automobile manufacturers make every possible effort to properly seal their car bodies at the time of manufacture. In fact the sealing of bodies to protect the interior of the car has been a never ending problem. Manufacturers have generally been very successful in this respect. Even so, as a body man you will be called on to correct water leaks and dust leaks.

Leaks may be caused by displaced panels due to an accident. These are generally the easiest to repair, because the extent of the damage that has been corrected will serve as a guide to the areas you should explore. However, leaks may occur from the normal stress and movement of panels over a period of time or several thousand miles of operation. These are the hard-to-locate types of leaks. Figs. 10-7, 10-8 and 10-9 show some of the hundreds of sealed joints in a car body.

Several factors contribute to the occurence of water or dust leaks. As an automobile travels along the highway, a partial vacuum is created behind every rear surface. If a window or ventilater is opened in the upper area of the car, the movement of the car will draw out the air in the passenger compartment, creating a vacuum in the body.

When a vacuum exists for any reason air will rush in, through even the smallest openings, to replace the air drawn out by the vacuum. This air can come in through a lock pillar, a hole in the cowl, around a windshield or door weatherstrip, or in a hundred places that you might never con-

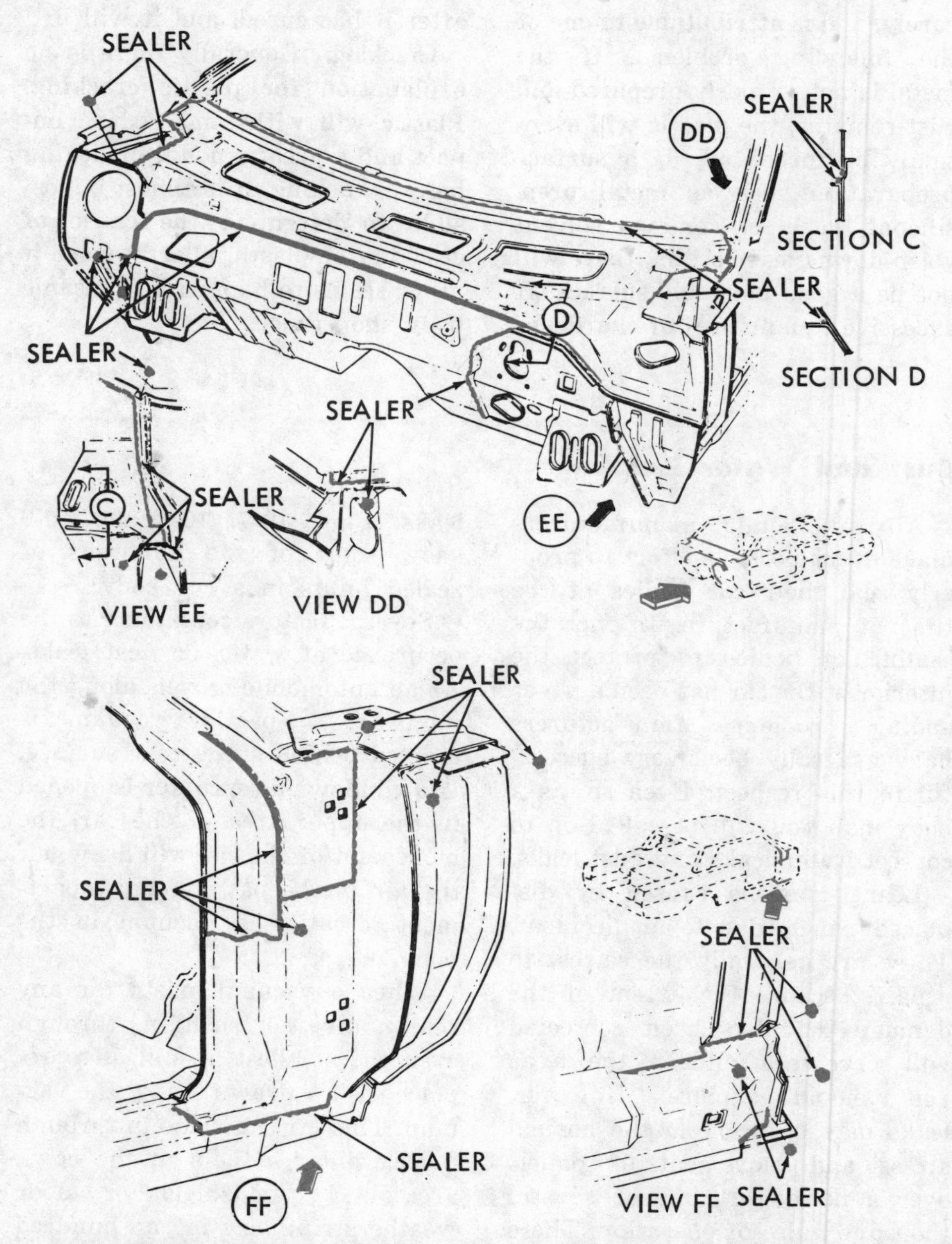

Fig. 10-7. Dash panel and side cowel sealer locations indicated for filling after body straightening. (Ford Motor Co.)

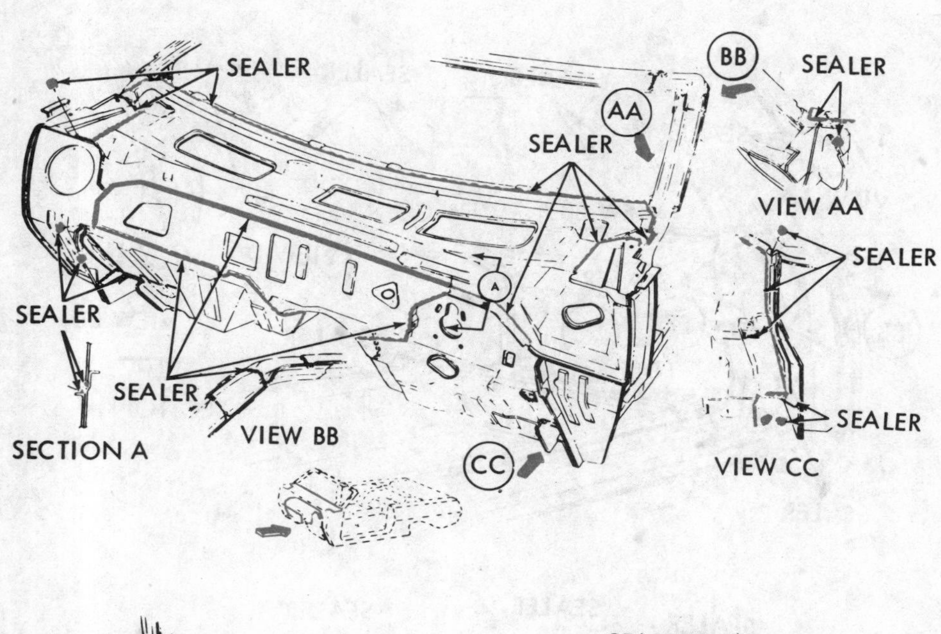

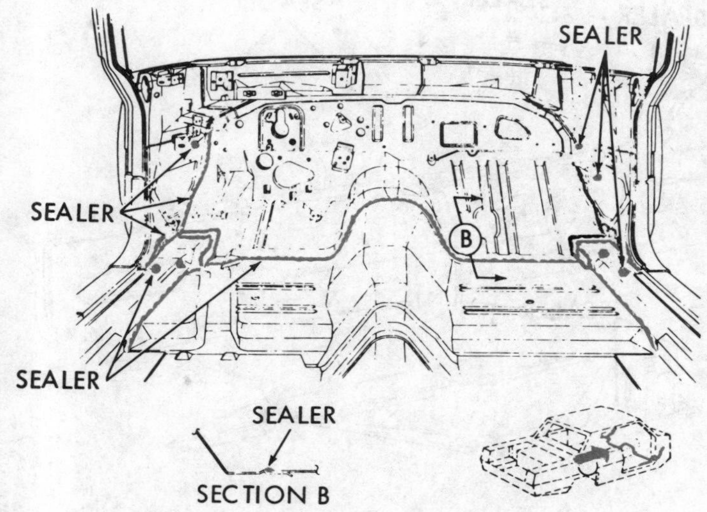

Fig. 10-7 (continued)

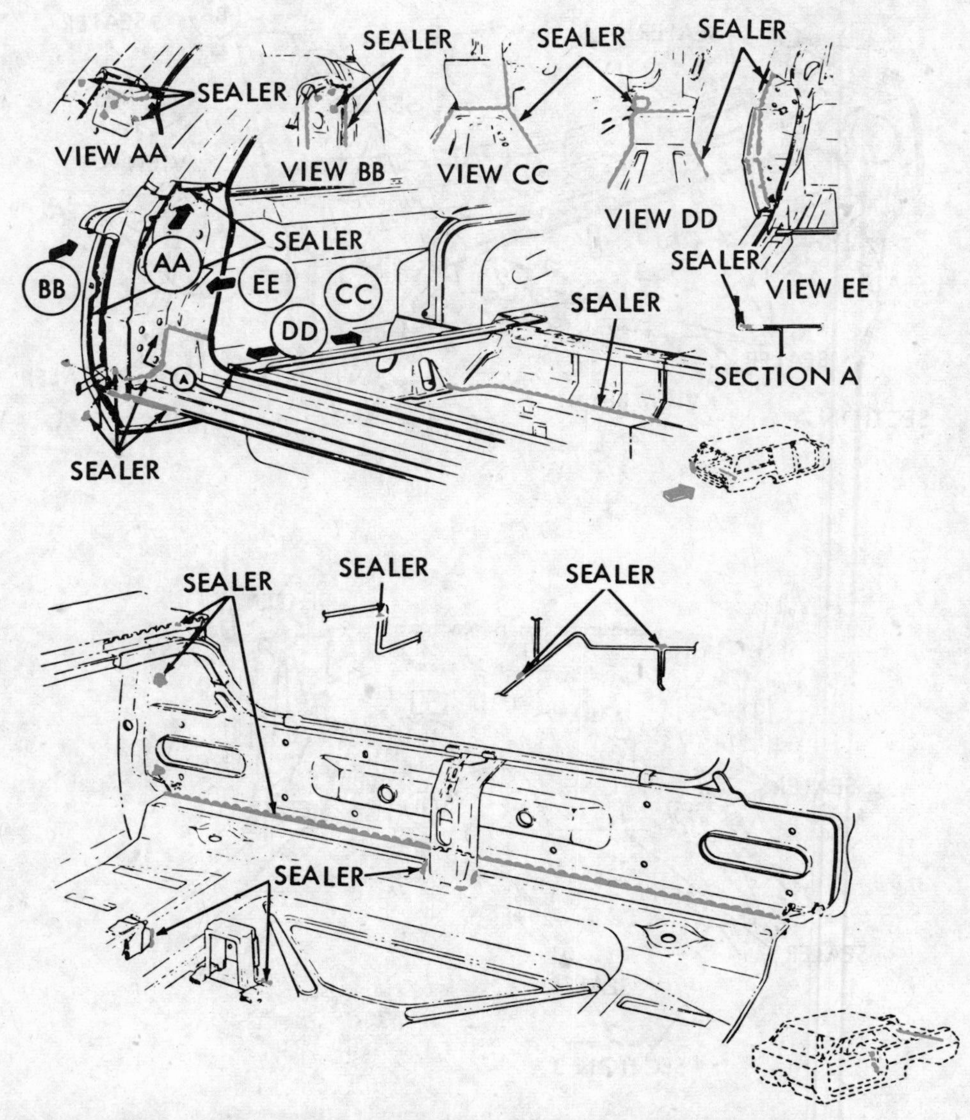

Fig. 10-8. Body rear and underbody sealer locations to be checked to prevent dust entry or water penetration. (Ford Motor Co.)

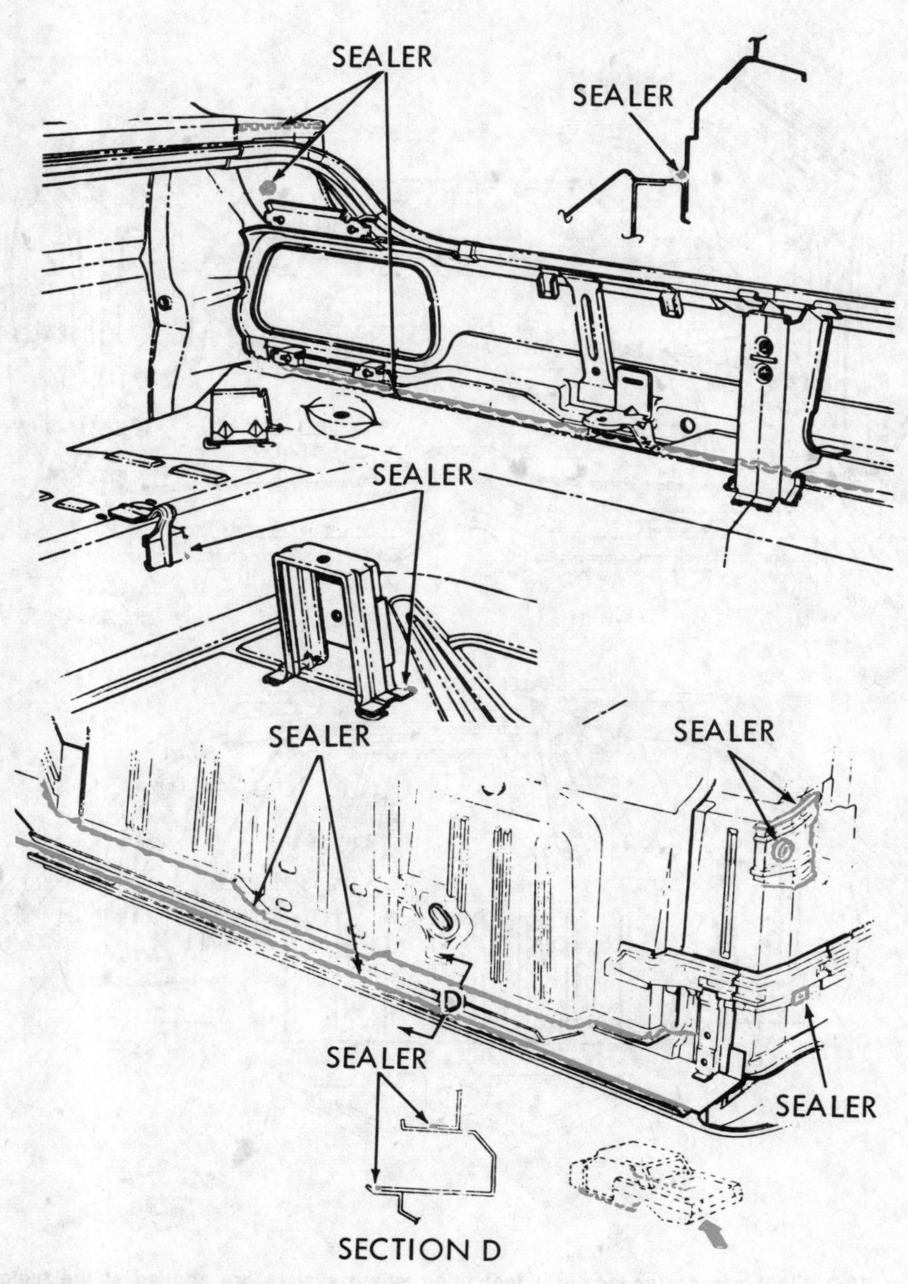

Fig. 10-8 (continued)

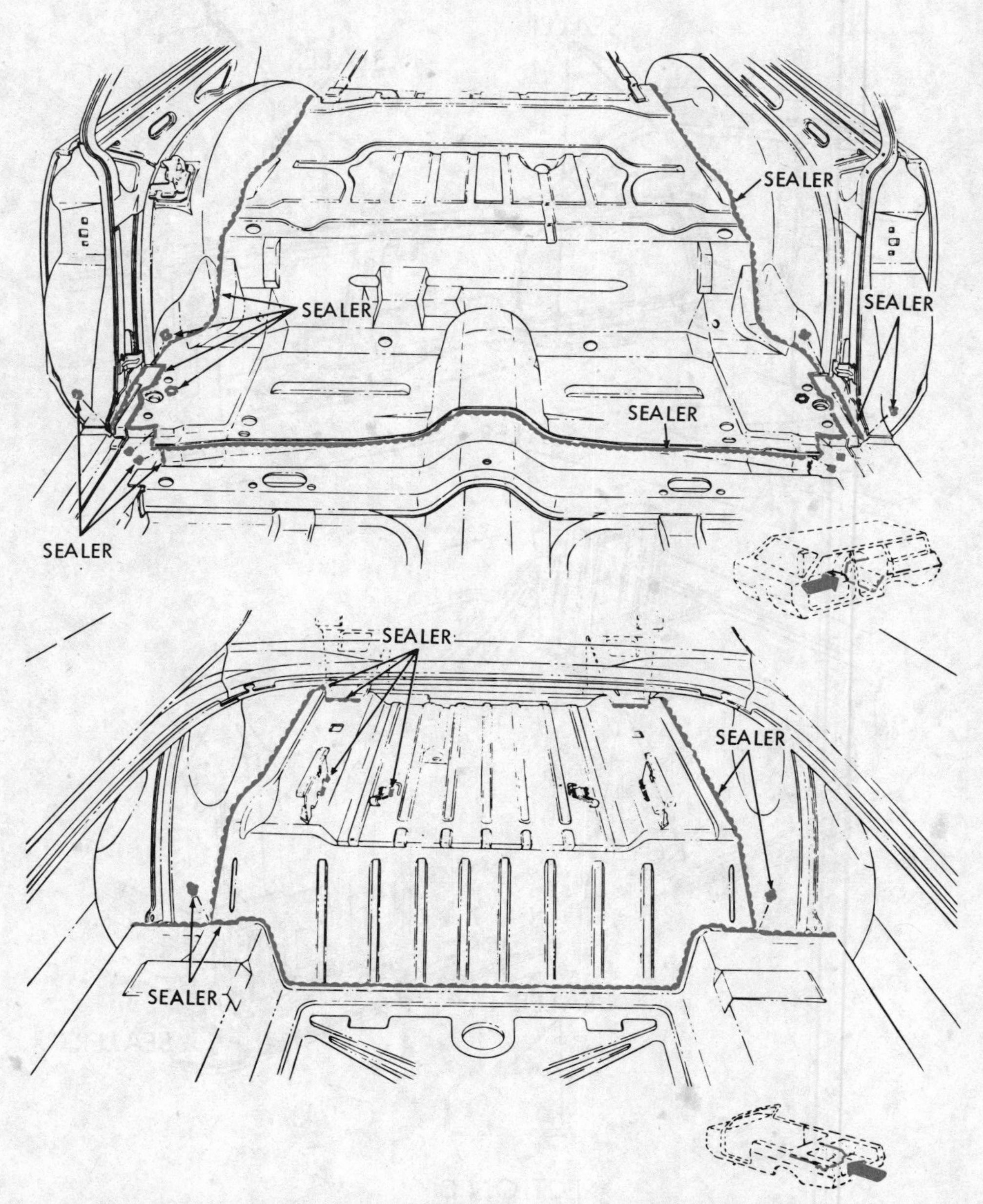

Fig. 10-9. Floor pan sealer locations indicating where sealers are applied at the factory. (Ford Motor Co.)

sider as possible points of leakage.

If this incoming air is dust laden, dust will be carried into the car. Objectionable odors can be drawn in either from the outside or from the engine compartment through openings for wiring, tubing or control mechanisms that are not properly sealed.

It must also be remembered that water can enter any opening that will permit the entry of dust. Unlike dust leaks, which occur mainly when a car is in motion, water leaks can occur with the car standing still. The area most susceptible to these kinds of leaks are the door and window weatherstrips and the bonds between the windshield and rear window and the body.

Considerations are so similar in correcting either dust or water leaks that the procedures used are the same. It might be well to remember that dust leaks usually occur around the underbody, the cowl or around door openings. Holes are provided in the floor pan and cowl for the control pedals and various other items that must be connected between the instrument panel and the engine compartment. Seals are placed around these openings so that dust cannot enter. If these seals become worn, it is necessary to replace them.

Weatherstriping around the doors, and especially along the bottom of doors, may become worn or displaced by an improperly fitting door. If this happens, it will be necessary to either re-ce-

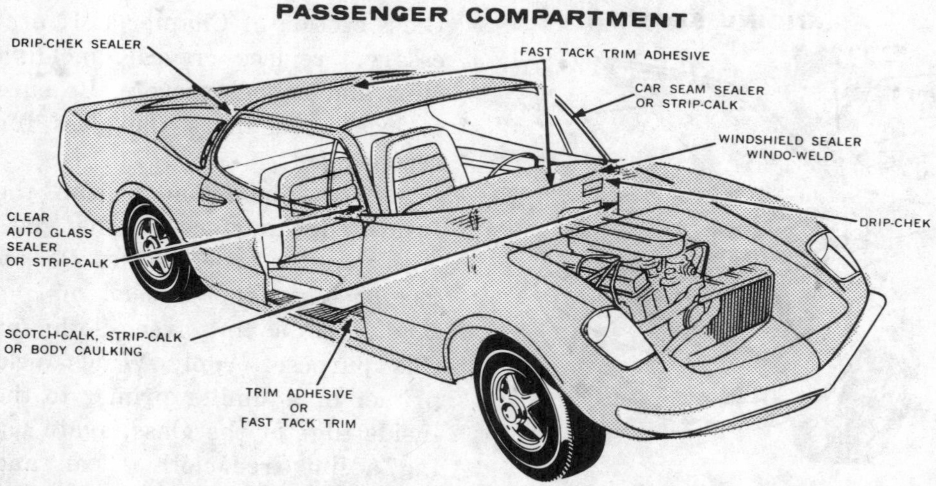

Fig. 10-10. Passenger compartment showing possible points of water or dust entry. (Minnesota Mining and Mfg. Co.)

ment the old weatherstrip in place, shimming behind it if necessary, or replace it with a new one.

Leak Correction Procedures. It would be impossible to give a procedure for correcting every leak possible. However, some of the more likely points of water or dust leaks are covered here.

For this exercise, the car has been divided into three major areas. Each of these areas is illustrated, showing possible points of leakage and suggesting the type of sealant or adhesive that is best suited to correcting that particular problem. Fig. 10-10 shows the passenger compartment, or central car body. Fig. 10-11 shows the engine compartment and Fig. 10-12 shows the trunk compartment.

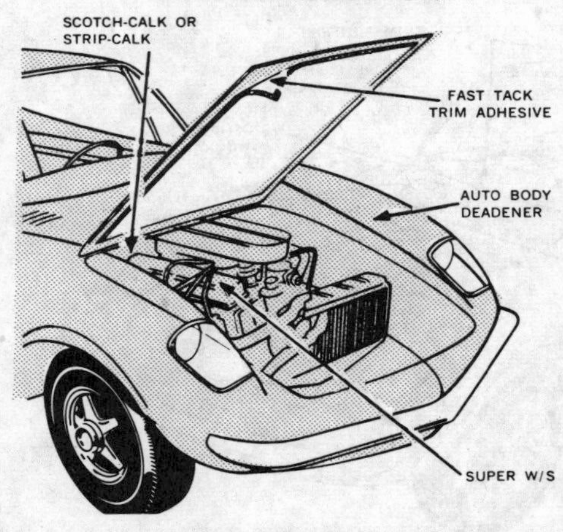

Fig. 10-11. Engine compartment showing possible points of dust and water entry. (Minnesota Mining and Mfg. Co.)

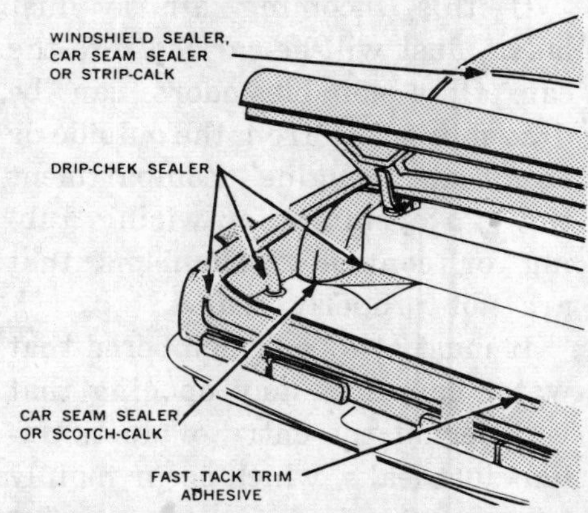

Fig. 10-12. Trunk compartment showing possible points of dust and water entry. (Minnesota Mining and Mfg. Co.)

Sealing Windshields and Rear Windows

Remove windshield or rear window according to manufacturer's directions, or see Installing Glass section of Chapter 1. If necessary, replace reveal molding clips and rubber spacers. Be sure to locate and mark the glass for replacement.

Surface Preparation. Clean the inside edge surface of the glass with naphtha type solvent. *Do not use gasoline or kerosene of any kind.* Use a lint free cloth for this purpose. Apply Winds-Weld primer or a similar primer to the inside edge of the glass, again using a lint free cloth. Clean and prime the pinchweld flange in the same manner. Wipe off any spilled

7. Replace pad patches by cementing pad to roof panel with nitrile vinyl trim adhesive.

Installation of Padded Vinyl Roofs

1. Completely mask off area of roof panel which is not covered by fabric cover. Extend tape over windshield upper reveal molding so cement will not contact paint or adhesive caulking material.
2. Where possible, install new cover at room temperature (approximately 72 degrees), to permit easier fitting and removing of wrinkles from new cover assembly.

NOTE: Where a new cover is installed at temperatures below 72 degrees, fabricated pliers will aid in removing wrinkles, Fig. 10-14.

3. Determine the center line of the roof panel by marking center points on windshield and back window opening with tape or equivalent.
4. Lay the cover on the roof panel and fold cover lengthwise, precisely on center. Mark the center at front and rear of cover.
5. Remove the cover from the roof panel and lay the cover with lining side upward on a clean flat surface.
6. Apply nitrile type vinyl trim adhesive to that part of the lining side of the cover that will contact the metal portion of the roof panel. Cement should be applied so it overlaps the pad approximately 1″.

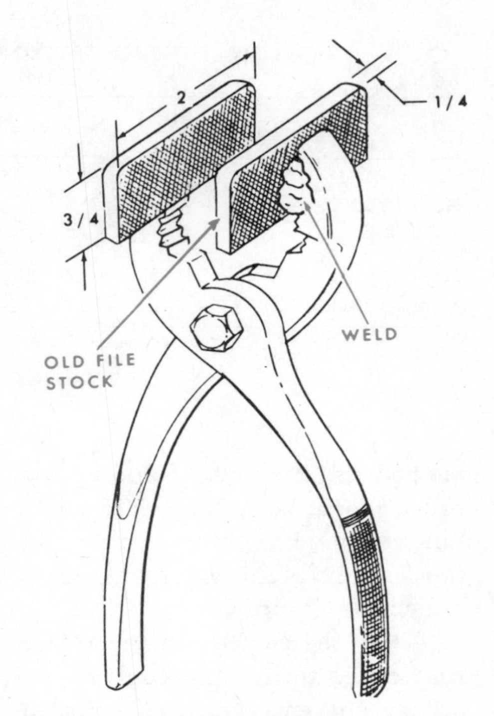

Fig. 10-14. Fabric roof cover pliers. (Fisher Body Div., General Motors Corp.)

NOTE: It is recommended that the vinyl trim adhesive be applied with a spray gun. As an alternate method, a brush or roller may be used. If the spray method is used, a spray gun with a pressure cup and a specific tip and air cap should be used, shown in Table 10-1.

The recommended air pressures are:

Air Line Pressure—50 lbs

Cup Pressure—2 to 4 lbs

Permalastic or 3M Vinyl Trim Adhesive purchased in the field is of spraying consistency. If rolling

TABLE 10-1 TIPS FOR SPRAYING VINYL TRIM ADHESIVE

	De Vilbiss		Binks	
GUN MODEL	MBC-510	JGA-502	62	18
1 QT PRESSURE	KB-519	KB-519	80-256	80-210
AIR CAP	24	24	66 PG	66 PG
FLUID TIP	E	E	66	66
FLUID NEEDLE	E	E	365	65

method is used, a mohair type roller should be utilized. Make certain cement is applied evenly and there are no highlights from excess cement build-up.

7. Allow the cement on the fabric roof cover to dry thoroughly.

8. Lay the cover on the dry roof panel and align to correspond with centerline of roof panel. Determine proper material overhang at back window openings (approximately 2″ overhang at seam area at back window).

9. Cut relief notches in cover at all weld-on studs and angle cuts as required in corners of back window opening. Apply cement to back window opening and cement cover in opening. In the event a reveal molding clip cannot be removed, trim the cover around the clip and cement the cover down behind the clip, Fig. 10-13.

10. Be sure that the edge of back glass is protected, and install drive nails at seam locations, as low in the opening as possible.

11. Apply cement to one side of exposed roof panel where cover is attached; make certain cement overlaps pad approximately 1″, and cement the cover to cement covered areas. Relief notches must be cut in cover at weld-on studs on roof panel, Fig. 10-13.

12. Repeat above step on opposite half of roof panel.

13. Install drive nails across top and down sides of back window openings approximately 3″ apart and two in each upper corner, as in Fig. 10-13.

14. Carefully install drive nails as low as possible above each reveal molding clip that could not be removed. When installing drive nails it is best to first use an awl or similar tool to initiate a hole in metal. Strike drive nails only hard enough to seat them. Installation of drive nails should also be as low as pos-

sible in back window opening.
15. Apply cement to roof extension areas overlapping pad by 1″ and below back window opening.
16. Cement the cover below back window opening, and then roof extension area, right and left sides. Note that you cement the cover on roof extension areas by pulling cover down and rearward. When operation is completed, fabric cover should be free of all winkles and draws in this area.
17. Position roof panel molding retainers over weld-on studs and install retaining clips.
18. Trim fabric cover in a line along retainers. *Do not damage paint finish.* At front corners, raise cemented edge of cover and, using scissors or sharp knife, cut a radius so roof panel moldings will cover the cut edge. Re-cement the fabric cover to the roof panel. Remove masking tape from roof panel, Fig. 10-13.
19. Trim the material along the belt line at roof extension area and below the back window, along the rear end belt molding area. If it is necessary to trim material from outer edge of fabric cover around back window openings, raise cemented edge and cut as required.
20. Apply a film coat of silicone sealant (such as Dow Corning Automotive Sealant, General Electric RVP Sealant) to the edges of cover in back window opening, at belt area and at edges under roof panel moldings. Make certain that around all the reveal molding clips that were not removed, the edge of the material is also sealed, Fig. 10-13.
21. Remove all previously installed protective covering from back glass and body.
22. Install all previously removed moldings and assemblies. Minor creases and fold marks will normally disappear after the cover assembly has been on for a little while.

Wood Grain Transfers

Many Station Wagon models have wood grain transfers on the sides and door panels. These repairs or replacements do not require special skills or knowledge. The procedures given here will apply to all such surfaces.

Pressure Sensitive Wood Grain Transfer Repair

It is not necessary to replace the vinyl wood grain transfer because of blisters, air bubbles, chips or scratches.

To repair blisters or air bubbles, pierce the bubble or blister with a pin. Work the trapped air out of the bubble and press the transfer firmly against the sheet metal. It may be necessary to preheat the metal to soften the adhesive.

For chips or scratches, use touch-up paint to repair the damaged areas. Wood grain transfer touch-up paints are available in several colors to match various shades of wood graining.

Pressure Sensitive Wood Grain Transfer Replacement

1. Remove the wood grain plastic trim rail(s) or moldings.
2. Clean the surface to be sure it is free of dirt, oil, wax or other foreign material. Use a clean rag, paper towel or sponge wet with silicone wax remover. Be sure the flanges, corners and depressions are clean to assure maximum transfer adhesion.
3. Repair the panel by metal finishing, if required.
4. If the original grained transfer has been damaged, scratched or cut, or partially removed during metal finishing, the damaged area should be sanded smooth and the original transfer film featheredged with 320-grit or finer sandpaper.
5. Putty the damaged area with spot putty on a squeegee or a flexible glazing knife to build up the surface to the level of the original film. This should be done only on a small area. If the damaged area is large, apply primer with a spray gun to build up the surface to the level of the original film.
6. Allow the primer or spot putty to dry thoroughly. Then, sand the primer and the entire grained panel with 320-grit or finer sandpaper. Repeat step 5 if necessary.
7. If the repair is being made to a door, trim the existing transfer film from the leading and trailing edges of the panel. Sand the edges of the panel and the inner surface of the flanges. Use the same procedure for the trailing edge of the fender and leading edge of the quarter panel.
8. Prepare a wetting solution by mixing one ounce of liquid detergent or soap solution (Car Wash) in a pail of warm water.
9. Cut the repair transfer to the desired size, using care to align the wood grain with the surrounding panels.
10. Place the transfer face down on a clean bench or other suitable flat surface and pull the paper backing off the transfer film. Be careful not to stretch or tear the transfer film.

11. Apply the wetting solution liberally to the tacky side of the transfer and to the panel being repaired with a rag or sponge. It is extremely important that the vehicle panel surface, the transfer film and the wetting solution all be at a moderate temperature above 65 degrees F, when performing this operation. Live steam, hot water or an electrically heated air blower may be used to soften the repair transfer film to make it conform to the vehicle panel and to aid in bending the transfer around the panel edges.
12. Position the transfer film on the panel. The presence of the wetting solution will help to prevent the pressure sensitive adhesive from sticking to the panel. This permits moving the transfer film to align the simulated caulk lines or wood grain pattern with the adjacent panels.
13. Smooth the transfer film on the panel with a rag or sponge wet with the wetting solution to remove large air pockets.
14. Squeegee the transfer film on the panel, working from the high point of the contour line on the panel. This will remove the wetting solution from between the transfer film and the panel and allow the adhesive on the film to stick to the panel. Remove any air or water bubbles as necessary by pricking them with a pin, and squeegee the film flat again.
15. Wrap the transfer film around the edges of the door, the quarter panels, and the trailing edge of the front fender. Apply to the edges and press the transfer film firmly against the flange, and squeegee.
16. Wipe the surface dry with a clean soft cloth and install the grain plastic trim rails or mouldings over the wood grain transfer.

GLOSSARY OF ADHESIVES, COATING, AND SEALERS TO FOLLOW

Adhesives Coatings and Sealers
(A Glossary)

A

accelerate: To accelerate an adhesive is to speed up a chemical reaction or a curing process. For example, you can speed up the drying time of an adhesive or sealer by increasing the temperature. Also, by adding a chemical curing agent, or accelerator, to a base compound.

accelerator: A material added to an adhesive to speed up its cure or to chemically convert the whole mass to a solid. Accelerators differ from catalysts in that they are a part of the chemical reaction and lose their chemical identity as a result.

acetone: A fast drying solvent used in some rapid drying adhesives, such as nitrile rubber, or vinyl resin-based types.

activate: To change an adhesive film from a dry or inactive state to a useful, sticky state.

adhere: To bond or to cause two surfaces to stick together.

adherend: Each surface that is to adhere to another is called an adherend.

adhesion: The force which causes two surfaces to adhere, the sticking together of surfaces in contact with each other.

adhesive: Any substance used to form a bond between two materials is an adhesive. An adhesive must bond both mating surfaces through *specific adhesion* (molecular attraction), through *mechanical anchoring* (by flowing into holes in porous surfaces), or through *fusion* (partial solution of both surfaces in the adhesive or its solvent vehicle). Various descriptive adjectives are used with the term adhesive to indicate types, such as:

1. *physical form*—liquid adhesive, film adhesive, etc.
2. *composition*—resin adhesive, rubber adhesive, silicone based, mastic, etc.
3. *end use*—metal-to-metal adhesive, plastic adhesive, rubber adhesive, etc.
4. *application*—sprayable adhesive, hot melt adhesive, etc.

aging: The cracking, checking, or general deterioration produced by exposure of an adhesive, coating or sealer to the weather or some other given set of conditions for a length of time.

air drying adhesives: Adhesives that can be dried at room temperature without the use of heat. This type of adhesive consists of solid particles dissolved or dispersed in a liquid. When the liquid evaporates, it leaves the dry adhesive film. Most elastomer based adhesives are of this type.

application: The act of applying adhesives. For adhesives and coatings the principal methods of application are: brushing, spraying, dipping, stenciling, flowing, stamp-padding, roll coating, knife coating, squeegeeing, or troweling with spatula or notched trowel. For sealers: spatula, caulking gun, flow gun, pressure extrusion units and spray gun.

B

base: The major ingredient, other than pigments and filler, that make up the non-volatile portion of an adhesive, coating, or sealing compound.

bleeding: The separation of components of a dried adhesive, coating or sealer film, resulting in an oil-like stain on the surfaces to be bonded, or on finishes.

body: A term used in describing the thickness or consistency (viscosity) of an adhesive, coating or sealer.

bond: The grip exerted by one material on another. *Noun:* The attachment between two surfaces that have been joined. *Verb:* To joint materials together with adhesives. To cause them to adhere.

bonding range: The time during which a satisfactory bond can be made. It is usually expressed in two numbers, the first number being the time in minutes one must wait after applying adhesive before trying to bond the surfaces, and the latter number being the longest drying period within which satisfactory bonds can be made, usually ten to thirty minutes after applying the adhesive.

bond strength: The force or strength necessary to break a bond between two adhering surfaces or materials.

butyl rubber: A synthetic rubber used as a base for one type of adhesive. It has poor resistance to petroleum oils and gasoline but excellent resistence to vegetable and mineral oils; to such solvents as acetone, alcohol, phenol, and ethylene glycol; and excellent resistence to water and gas absorbtion and sunlight.

C

catalyst: A chemical which modifies a chemical reaction between other chemicals but is not itself used up in the process.

chemical curing: The setting or curing of an adhesive, coating or sealer, brought about by the addition of heat, a catalyst, or an accelerator.

coat: Single coat means to apply one layer of material on a surface. Double coat means to apply two coats of adhesive, coating, or sealer to a surface. In spraying, it means to spray first a single coat with vertical strokes and then a second coat across with horizontal strokes, or vice versa.

consistency: The stiffness, or fluid quality of an adhesive coating or sealer compound.

contacting surfaces: Any two surfaces to be brought together and bonded.

coverage: The area over which a quantity of adhesive, coating or sealer can be applied at a specific thickness, usually expressed in terms of square feet per gallon.

creep: The change of an adhesive or sealer under constant pressure or load, following its first slip from its original position (elastic deformation). Creep at room temperature is sometimes called cold flow.

cure: To change the properties of an adhesive by chemical action. Usually accomplished by the action of heat, pressure, and catylists, alone or in combination.

curing time: The time required to effect a cure.

D

de-laminate: To split a layered or laminated material into its separate layers. Sometimes used to describe failure of an adherend in bond strength testing.

drying time: The time required for a solvent to evaporate after an adhesive film has been spread over the two surfaces to be bonded.

E

elasticity: The property of an adhesive or sealer which enables it to recover its original shape and size when deforming forces are removed. It is the ability to change size or shape repeatedly without breaking the molecular bonds that cause an object to hold its shape.

elastomer: A classification of rubberlike substances used in the formulation of adhesives, coatings and sealers without reference to their composition. Also classed as an elastic material that can be stretched repeatedly to at least twice its original length and, upon sudden release of stress, to return with equal force to its approximate original length.

epoxy adhesives: Adhesives which offer a combination of high room temperature strength with good load bearing properties. These adhesives have exceptional adhesion to metal surfaces.

F

faying surface: The inner mating or contacting surfaces of a joint; common area of two surfaces that are bonded together with an adhesive.

film, adhesive: A thin layer of dried adhesive. Also describes a class of adhesives provided in dry film form with or without reinforcing fabric and which are cured by means of heat and pressure.

G

glue: Originally, a hard, sticky gelatin obtained from hides, tendons, cartilage, bones and other connective tissues of animals. Also, an adhesive prepared from these substances by application of water and heat. It is chemically known as collagen.

gr-s: Is used as an adhesive base. GR-S has about the same resistance to solvents and chemicals as natural rubber, but its water resistance is much better.

H

heat curing adhesives: Adhesives that require a definite period of time above room temperature to develop full bond strength. They can be of one or two part composition. The term is usually applied to those adhesives that require 180°F or above to effect a cure.

heat reactivate: To soften a dried thermoplastic adhesive film to a sticky stage by application of heat Used as a method of bond.

holiday: A void or hole in an adhesive or coating film, whether microscopic or normally visible.

I

inorganic: Not organic, i.e. composed of matter other than animal or vegetable. In technical terms, any substance that is not a carbon compound (with the possible exception of the oxides and sulfide of carbon).

J

joint: The location at which two adherends are held together by an adhesive.

K

ketone: Organic solvents commonly used in nitrile adhesives and vinyl coatings.

L

lamination: The process of bonding two or more layers or plies of material together with an adhesive.

lifting: Softening and penetration of an adhesive film by the solvents or plasticizing oils of another film, which result in raising, wrinkling and loss of adhesion.

M

mastic: Any heavy-bodied adhesive of such a consistency that it must be applied by notched trowel, gob or by buttering methods.

misting: The fog sometimes produced during adhesive, coating or sealer spray application is usually caused by excessive atomizing pressure. Most common when spraying water-dispersed products of very thin consistency or slow drying materials such as diluted house paint.

N

neoprene rubber: Is used as an adhesive base. Commonly used where oil and gasoline resistance is required. Resistance also to swelling action of pure aromatic chemicals, and to fuels.

nitrile rubber: Also known as Buna-N rubbers, these adhesives have high strength, excellent aging properties and good chemical resistance, including resistance to both aliphatic and aromatic solvents and to most plasticizers which cause bond failure of other adhesives. Nitrile has excellent resistance to petroleum oils and gasolines, to mineral and vegetable oils, but poor resistance to oxygenated solvents like acetone. It has good heat resistance and is the most commonly used adhesive material in applications exposed to hot oils.

O

oil (drying): Any oil that hardens in the presence of air and sunlight.

oil (non-drying): Any oil that does not have the ability to take up oxygen from the air to change it from a liquid to a solid state. Mineral oils are non-drying oils; so are a few vegetable oils.

oil (semi-drying): Those oils which are only partially hardened or are changed into a sticky mass when exposed to air and sunlight. The chief semi-drying oils used in paint, varnish and lacquers are soybean oil, corn oil and cottonseed oil.

P

peelback: A method of separating a bond of two flexible materials or a flexible and a rigid material that have been bonded with an adhesive. The flexible material is pulled from the mating surface at a 90 or 180 degree angle to the plane in which it is adhered. The stress is concentrated along the line of immediate separation. Strengths are expressed in pounds per inch width (piw).

plasticize: To soften an adhesive, coating or sealer, generally by the addition of high boiling liquids or plasticizers.

plasticizer: A liquid or solid chemical added to a compound to impart softness or flexibility. Some plasticizers have an undesirable tendency to migrate from the parent material into nearby surfaces which are receptive. When they migrate into adhesive films, for instance, they generally cause loss of strength or complete failure of the bond.

polysulfide: Synthetic rubber compounds used in adhesives, coatings and sealers. When cured, they are almost unaffected by aliphatic or aromatic solvents; and retain flexibility and shock resistance at low temperature. Flow characteristics, odor and high relative cost limit their use as adhesives to very specialized applications. High performance sealers of this base are widely used for aircraft and marine requirements.

pot life: The rating in hours of the time interval following the addition of accelerator before a chemically curing adhesive or sealer will become too thick to pass viscosity (consistency) requirements. Closely related to working life.

pressure sensitive adhesive: Type of adhesive that retains its tack or stickiness even after complete release of the solvent.

R

reactivate: To restore the tackiness of a completely dried adhesive. Reactivated adhesives are useful in that the adhering surfaces may be coated with adhesive and the surfaces mated again after short term exposure. Reactivated bonds set almost immediately.

reactivation, heat: To restore the tackiness of the adhesive with heat, and then to bond under pressure.

reactivation, solvent: To restore the surface tackiness in a dry adhesive film with a suitable solvent.

reclaimed rubber: Reprocessed rubber (tires, inner tubes, rubber novelties), either synthetic or natural, used as an adhesive base. Because of characteristic advantages of low cost, good physical properties, wide tack range, tolerance of surface preparation and high wet strength, these are the most widely used of the rubber based adhesives.

resilience: Capability of a sealer or coating to return to its original size and shape after deformation.

S

sealer: Any material used to fill cracks and pinholes in a metal surface to be painted, applied before the base coat or as a base coat primer-sealer.

setting time: The time required for a adhesive, sealer or coating to approach maximum strength and firmness as it dries or sets.

shear test: A method of separating two adhesive bonded materials by forcing (either by compression or tension) the mating faces to slide over each other. The force exerted in distributed over the entire bonded area at the same time. Strengths are recorded in pounds per square inch (psi).

shelf life: The length of time a packaged adhesive, coating or sealer can be stored under specified temperature conditions and remain suitable for use.

silicone adhesives: Adhesive compounds of this base have remarkable stability through a wide temperature range. Chief limitations in present use are their high temperature cure, sensitivity to fuels, and relatively high cost. Outstanding high temperature (above 300°F) and low temperature (−100°F) performance have been reported. Highly resistant to oxidation, to ozone, and to corona radiations. Very good dielectric properties.

skinning (1): When adhesives and sealers contain fast drying solvents, there is a tendency for the applied film to dry rapidly at the surface which slows down the evaporation of the solvent that remains in the film. This condition can lead to blistering, checking or cracking, particularly if the film is exposed to temperatures near or above the boiling point of the solvent.

skinning (2): Many coatings, particularly oxidizing types, have a tendency to skin over when left exposed to the air in an open vessel or in a partially filled container. Later when the material is forced through a spray gun, the air breaks the skin into a number of particles which appear on the work as specks. This condition can be overcome by straining the coating and by taking care to store it in completely filled containers.

softening point: The temperature at which a known load will cause the bond failure of a one-square inch sample of cloth bonded to steel (sheer bond). Since softening under heat is progressive, increasing with temperature, it is rarely stated that a product is hard or soft at a certain temperature. The preferred method is to report what weight per square inch area it can support without failure.

solids: Non-volatile ingredients in an adhesive, coating or sealer. Same as solids content.

solvent: Any liquid which will dissolve another substance. The solvent power of a liquid is specific; that is, it will dissolve some substances but no others. Solvents are often of a volatile nature and do not remain in a set or cured adhesive, coating, or sealer film. Their main purpose in adhesives, coatings, or sealers is to convert the solid portion into a more fluid state so that it can be easily applied.

solvent resistance: Ability of an

adhesive, coating or sealer to withstand total immersion in a given solution without losing its original properties.

stability: Property which allows an adhesive, coating or sealer compound to be stored under specific conditions without loss of its original properties.

surfaces: The faces of materials to be joined by an adhesive, or covered by a coating, or sealed by a sealer.

synthetic rubber: Any rubber which is manufactured by a chemical process as distinguished from natural rubber obtained from trees. Typical examples of chemical rubbers are GR-S, butyl, neoprene, nitrile and polysulfide rubbers.

T

tack: The sticky quality of an adhesive film, either while wet or after the film has set. Technically it is the pull resistance (measured in dynes) exerted by a material completely adhering to two surfaces being pulled apart.

tackiness: The stickiness of the adhesive film while in the stage of drying.

tensile strength: The resistance which an adhesive film remains tacky.

tack range: The time during of a film to distortion or rupture when it is exposed to forces exerted in opposite directions (measured in psi).

toxicity: A term referring to the physiological effect of absorbing a poisonous substance into the system, either through the skin, through mucous membranes or into respiratory system. When describing their toxic effect, solvents are usually classified as having high, medium or low toxicity, depending upon whether a solvent vapor concentration of less than 100, 100 to 400 or over 400 parts per million respectively is the maximum amount permissible in the air for safe or healthful working conditions.

U

under cure: Degree of cure less than optimum. May be evidenced by tackiness, softness, off-color or inferior physical properties of an adhesive.

V

vehicle: The liquid portion of an adhesive, coating or sealer compound consisting of the binder and volatile thinners.

viscosity: Comparative fluidity or stiffness of liquid adhesives, coatings and sealers.

vulcanization: The setting of rubber into a solid material by use of moderate heat and sulfur or a sulfur compound.

W

wetting: The ability of an adhesive, coating or sealer compound to wet or adhere to a surface immediately on contact even when the film is extremely thin.

Y

yield value (1): Minimum force which must be applied to an adhesive, coating or sealer to start the molecules of the adhesive flowing over one another, ending eventually in bond failure.

yield value (2): The amount (gallonage) that a given adhesive, coating or sealer formula will yield in actual production.

Checking On Your Knowledge

The following questions give you the opportunity to check up on yourself. If you have read the chapter carefully, you should be able to answer the questions. If you have any difficulty, read the chapter over once more so that you have the information well in mind before you go on with your reading.

1. Can adhesives be used to join dissimilar materials?
2. Can rubber compounds be used as adhesives and elastomers?
3. Are plastic adhesives capable of being used for both adhesion and elastomeric resistance?
4. What is a base compound?
5. When surfaces have been bonded, what does that mean?
6. What does a solvent do?
7. Name three processes which adhesives may offer toward achieving a strong bond?
8. Will adhesives be used less or more in the future?
9. Where are plastic fillers used in auto repair?
10. On what kinds of surfaces are fillers mixed?
11. Are plastic fillers slowed or speeded up by dropping temperatures?
12. Is it possible to use too much catalyst in the summer?
13. What causes pinholing?
14. What is bleed-through?
15. How long would you wait after applying a coating of acrylic before you apply the second coat?
16. Is it true that water will enter a car body only when it is in motion?
17. What are the three areas of a car body likely to need leak correction?
18. When a vinyl roof is applied to a car, must a covering be used between the vinyl and the bare metal?
19. Is old vinyl roofing removed before a new one is applied?
20. At what temperature are vinyl covers installed?
21. Are wood grain transfers strictly for the specialist, or can a regular refinisher apply them?

Index

Numerals in **bold type** refer to illustrations

Q

R